SIMMS

INTEGRATED

MATHEMATICS

A Modeling Approach Using Technology

Level 2, Third Edition

 KENDALL/HUNT PUBLISHING COMPANY
4050 Westmark Drive   Dubuque, Iowa 52002

CONTRIBUTORS

Masha Albrecht ▪ *Glenn Allinger* ▪ *Byron Anderson* ▪ *Staci Auck* ▪ *Shirley Bagwell* ▪ *Cliff Bara* ▪ *Gary Bauer* ▪ *Jack Beal* ▪ *Patricia Bean* ▪ *Glenn Blake* ▪ *Kyle Boyce* ▪ *Monty Brekke* ▪ *Ruth Brocklebank* ▪ *Lee Brown* ▪ *Maurice Burke* ▪ *Clay Burkett* ▪ *Randy Carspecken* ▪ *John Carter* ▪ *William Chalgren* ▪ *Terri Dahl* ▪ *Ted Drieth* ▪ *Wendy Driscoll* ▪ *Bonnie Eichenberger* ▪ *Todd Fife* ▪ *Jerry Fisher* ▪ *John Freal* ▪ *John Gebhart* ▪ *Kimberley Girard* ▪ *Janet Higgins* ▪ *James Hirstein* ▪ *Sherry Horyna* ▪ *Jeffrey Hostetter* ▪ *Alexander Johnson* ▪ *Danny Jones* ▪ *Russ Killingsworth* ▪ *John Knudson-Martin* ▪ *Robbie Korin* ▪ *Pam Koterba* ▪ *Janet Kuchenbrod* ▪ *Phillip Lieske* ▪ *Satinee Lightbourne* ▪ *Fred Longhart* ▪ *Karen Longhart* ▪ *Johnny W. Lott* ▪ *Franklin Lund* ▪ *Mike Lundin* ▪ *Joy Lustgraaf* ▪ *Mark Lutz* ▪ *Peggy Lynn* ▪ *Douglas Mack* ▪ *Pat Mauch* ▪ *Patty Mazurek* ▪ *Anne Merrifield* ▪ *Mary Ann Miller* ▪ *Susan Moore* ▪ *Mindy Obert* ▪ *Laurie Paladichuk* ▪ *Roger Patterson* ▪ *Arthur Perleberg* ▪ *Margaret Plouvier* ▪ *Dean Preble* ▪ *Darlene Pugh* ▪ *Peter Rasmussen* ▪ *Howard Reinhardt* ▪ *Kate Riley* ▪ *Todd Robbins* ▪ *Dick Sander* ▪ *Lisa Schlange* ▪ *Verne Schlepp* ▪ *Lisa Scott* ▪ *Dick Seitz* ▪ *Mike Sinclair* ▪ *Ed Sisolak* ▪ *Tim Skinner* ▪ *David Stabio* ▪ *Paul Swenson* ▪ *Thomas Teegarden* ▪ *David Thiel* ▪ *Otis Thompson* ▪ *Michael Trudnowski* ▪ *Deanna Turley* ▪ *Karen Umbaugh* ▪ *Sharon Walen* ▪ *Anne Watkins* ▪ *Marcia Weinhold* ▪ *Daniel West* ▪ *Teri Willard* ▪ *James Williamson* ▪ *Lisa Wood* ▪ *Mike Wood* ▪ *Steve Yockim*

SERIES EDITOR

Terry A. Souhrada

TECHNICAL EDITOR

Peter W. Fong

This material is based upon work supported by the National Science Foundation under Cooperative Agreement No. OSR 9150055. Any opinions, findings, conclusions or recommendations expressed in this material are those of the author(s) and do not necessarily reflect the views of the National Science Foundation.

Cover Credits:
  © JupiterImages Corporation: top left skier and top right snowflake
  © Corbis: bottom left skiers and bottom right snow

ISBN 0-7575-2031-6

Contents

Preface

In recent years, many voices have called for the reform of mathematics education. The concerns cited include international test scores in mathematics, the retention of students in mathematical and scientific career paths, and the production of mathematically literate adults. Attempts to identify the root causes of these concerns have targeted not only the methods used to instruct and assess students, but also the nature of the mathematics that students learn and the manner in which they are expected to learn.

The Systemic Initiative for Montana Mathematics and Science (SIMMS) began as a five-year, cooperative enterprise of the state of Montana and the National Science Foundation. Funded through the Montana Council of Teachers of Mathematics, and led by mathematics and science teachers from around the state, SIMMS had an ambitious list of objectives, including redesigning the 9–12 mathematics curriculum using an integrated, interdisciplinary approach for *all* students; incorporating the use of technology in all facets and at all levels of mathematics and science; and developing and publishing curriculum and assessment materials for grades 9–16.

With additional funding from the National Science Foundation and the support of teachers, students, and the Kendall/Hunt Publishing Company, these curricular objectives have continued for more than a decade.

What Is Integrated Mathematics?

An integrated mathematics program "consists of topics chosen from a wide variety of mathematical fields . . . . [It] emphasizes the relationships among topics within mathematics as well as between mathematics and other disciplines" (Beal, et al., 1992; Lott and Reeves, 1991).

In its 2000 document, *Principles and Standards for School Mathematics*, the National Council of Teachers of Mathematics addressed curricular reform with these recommendations:

> Mathematics comprises different topical strands, such as algebra and geometry, but the strands are highly interconnected. The interconnection should be displayed prominently in the curriculum and in instructional materials and lessons. A coherent curriculum effectively organizes and integrates important mathematical ideas so that students can see how the ideas build on, or connect with, other ideas, thus enabling them to develop new understandings and skills . . . .
>
> Big ideas encountered in a variety of contexts should be established carefully, with important elements such as terminology, definitions, notation, concepts, and skills emerging in the process . . . .
>
> In addition, the curriculum should offer experiences that allow students to see that mathematics has powerful uses in modeling and predicting real-world phenomena. (pp. 15–16)

SIMMS *Integrated Mathematics* offers this coherent curriculum, built around big ideas in a variety of contexts, while providing experiences that allow students to model and predict phenomena.

In order to create innovative and accessible materials, a diverse group of more than 80 secondary teachers of mathematics and science, mathematicians, and mathematics educators contributed their skills as writers and reviewers. The SIMMS *Integrated Mathematics* curriculum is expressly designed for use in heterogeneous classrooms, and seeks to encourage the participation of underrepresented groups in mathematics.

Each academic year of SIMMS *Integrated Mathematics* includes algebra, geometry, probability, statistics, and discrete mathematics. Essential mathematical concepts are explored more than once, each time at a slightly higher level—in different settings and in different years—to help students build both vital connections and critical competencies. Students investigate mathematics in the context of crucial social and environmental issues—such as population growth, oil spills, and earthquake damage—along with other real-world topics including map-making, business inventory, digital animation, and automobile insurance.

Technology in the Classroom

SIMMS *Integrated Mathematics* focuses on the future needs of mathematically literate adults. Because of this commitment, the use of technology is a fundamental part of curriculum.

In *Principles and Standards for School Mathematics,* the Council noted that "Technology is essential in teaching and learning mathematics; it influences the mathematics that is taught and enhances students' learning" (p. 24). Nearly all current research on the appropriate use of technology in the classroom indicates that students using technology become better problem solvers, without suffering a decline in their more traditional skills.

SIMMS *Integrated Mathematics* works best when students have access to a word processor, spreadsheet, graphing utility, geometry utility, statistics package, and computer algebra system. (Many reasonably priced graphing calculators now include all of these features, with the exception of word processing.)

Student Performance

During the development of SIMMS *Integrated Mathematics,* researchers conducted periodic assessments of student performances in pilot schools. After the publication of the first edition, a four-year longitudinal case study was completed. In these studies, two basic measures—a selection of open-ended mathematical tasks and the PSAT—were administered to experimental and control populations.

On the test of open-ended tasks, technology was made available to both groups. In a comparative analysis, SIMMS *Integrated Mathematics* students were more likely to provide justification for their solutions and made more and better use of graphs, charts, and diagrams. They also demonstrated a greater variety of problem-solving strategies and were more willing to attempt difficult problems.

For the PSAT, technology was not allowed for either group. Student mathematics scores indicated no significant differences in achievement. In other words, although SIMMS *Integrated Mathematics* students were denied access to the technology typically available for classroom work, their performance on the PSAT matched that of their peers.

A summary of the pilot study, as well as a larger National Science Foundation study involving students in selected U.S. cities, is now in print (Senk and Thompson, 2003).

A Look to the Future

Once again in *Principles and Standards for School Mathematics,* the Council argues that:

> When students can connect mathematical ideas, their understanding is deeper and more lasting. They can see mathematical connections in the rich interplay among mathematical topics, in contexts that relate mathematics to other subjects, and in their own interests and experience. Through instruction that emphasizes the interrelatedness of mathematical ideas, students not only learn mathematics, they also learn about the utility of mathematics. (p. 64)

This deep and lasting understanding is what all teachers desire for their students. The third edition of SIMMS *Integrated Mathematics* builds on reform middle-school curricula, and is designed to replace all currently offered secondary mathematics courses, with the possible exception of Advanced Placement Calculus.

—Johnny W. Lott, former co-director of The SIMMS Project and past president of the National Council of Teachers of Mathematics

References

Beal, J., D. Dolan, J. Lott and J. Smith. *Integrated Mathematics: Definitions, Issues, and Implications; Report and Executive Summary.* ERIC Clearinghouse for Science, Mathematics, and Environmental Education. The Ohio State University, Columbus, OH: ED 34701, January 1990, 115 pp.

Lott, J., and A. Reeves. "The Integrated Mathematics Project." *Mathematics Teacher* 84 (April 1991): 334–35.

National Council of Teachers of Mathematics. *Curriculum and Evaluation Standards for School Mathematics.* Reston, VA; NCTM, 1989.

———. *Principles and Standards for School Mathematics.* Reston, VA: NCTM, 2000.

Senk, S., and D. Thompson (eds.). *Standards-Based School Mathematics Curricula: What Are They? What Do Students Learn?* Mahwah, NJ: Lawrence Erlbaum Associates, 2003.

The SIMMS Project. *Monograph I: Philosophies.* Missoula, MT: The Montana Council of Teachers of Mathematics, 1993.

Souhrada, T. "Secondary school mathematics in transition: A comparative study of mathematics curricula and student results." *Dissertation Abstracts International* 62.4 (October 2001): 1355A.

Introduction

When the first edition of SIMMS *Integrated Mathematics: A Modeling Approach Using Technology* was published more than a decade ago, it provided an innovative approach to teaching and learning high school mathematics. The third edition maintains this standard while representing a significant revision of previous versions.

SIMMS *Integrated Mathematics* now includes four levels, offering a comprehensive alternative to traditional secondary mathematics courses. Each year-long level contains 15 modules. All modules are divided into activities, typically including an exploration, a discussion, warm-up problems, a set of homework assignments, and a research project.

Assessment materials—including alternative assessments that emphasize writing and logical argument—are an integral part of the curriculum. Each activity includes one or more suggested assessment items, identified in the Teacher Edition, while each module closes with an open-ended summary assessment. A more traditional assessment, for use at the teacher's discretion, appears in the Teacher Resources, along with short quizzes and review problems, as well as blackline masters for classroom handouts.

Level 1: A First-Year Course

Level 1 concentrates on the knowledge and understanding that students need to become mathematically literate citizens, while providing the necessary foundation for those who wish to pursue careers involving mathematics and science. Each module presents the relevant mathematics in an applied context. These contexts include human nutrition, the properties of reflected light, population growth, structural physiology, and topographic maps, among others. Mathematical content includes data collection, presentation and interpretation; linear, quadratic, and exponential functions; probability; trigonometric ratios; and an introduction to graph theory.

Level 2: A Second-Year Course

Level 2 continues to build on the mathematics that students need to become mathematically literate citizens. While retaining an emphasis on the presentation and interpretation of data, Level 2 also introduces such topics as matrix operations, elementary polynomials, combinatorics, statistics, and fair division. Students investigate traditional geometry, including proof, within the context of home building. They explore transformational geometry through cartoon animation. Other contexts include genetics, business inventory, radioactive decay, and carnival games.

Level 3: A Third-Year Course

This level continues to build mathematical understanding and logical reasoning, based on the first two years of work. Students expand their knowledge of data analysis, algebraic functions, geometric proof, probability, and graph theory. Contexts include map coloring, logarithmic scales, navigation, and quality control, among others. Specific mathematical topics include trigonometric functions, the normal curve, spherical geometry, parametric equations, basic topology, and an introduction to limits.

Level 4: A Fourth-Year Course

For some students, this course represents the end of a high-school mathematical career. For others, this course represents a stepping-stone to advanced placement courses. Because of these different needs, this course is both mathematically and contextually challenging and engaging. Students explore complex numbers, conic sections, hypothesis testing, finite geometry, mathematical induction, and derivatives. Applied contexts include cartography, automobile insurance, and compound interest, among others.

The Student Edition

The third edition of SIMMS *Integrated Mathematics* contains all of the basic elements found in previous editions, along with some new features. For example, each activity now offers an additional problem set, designed to hone mathematical skills before students encounter more complicated assignments. Several individual modules were substantially revised, presenting fresh approaches to geometric proof, hypothesis testing, compositions of functions, and other topics.

Explorations

Nearly all activities contain at least one exploration, giving students a hands-on opportunity to develop their own understandings of mathematical concepts. To facilitate the exchange of ideas and strategies, explorations are designed for work in a variety of instructional formats, including small groups.

Discussions

Discussions give students a structured forum for sharing insights and communicating mathematical ideas, and give teachers a setting for assessing comprehension and reinforcing essential concepts.

Mathematics Notes

Mathematics Notes formally summarize the mathematics students are expected to understand and apply. Each typically includes a definition or explanation, a description of the appropriate notation, and an example or graph.

Warm-Ups

These problem sets—a new feature in the third edition—are designed to review essential mathematical skills and vocabulary before students proceed to the Assignment. Warm-up problems typically do not invoke a real-world context.

Assignments

As in previous editions, most assignment problems present mathematics in applied contexts. Some extend previously learned concepts to other mathematical settings. Students are encouraged to justify their solutions and describe their reasoning.

Research Projects

Many modules contain a Research Project, offering students an opportunity for further study of contemporary or historical mathematics.

Summary Assessment

Summary Assessments typically ask students to demonstrate their problem-solving skills in the same context used in the module. They are often project-oriented and suitable for collaborative work.

Module Summary

At the end of every module, a Module Summary repeats the important mathematics from each activity.

Glossary

The Glossary offers an alphabetical list of definitions for all of the terms and concepts in an entire level (also included in the Teacher Edition).

Selected References

This list provides a helpful compilation of print and other resources for the entire level (also included in the Teacher Edition).

The Teacher Edition

To facilitate the implementation of the curriculum, the Teacher Edition contains the following features, several of which have been newly incorporated in this revision.

Overview/Objectives/Prerequisites

Each module begins with a brief overview of its contents, outlined activity by activity. This overview is followed by a list of teaching objectives, each identified by the activity number (in parentheses), and a list of prerequisite skills and knowledge.

Planning Guide

The planning guide displays the materials and technology needed for the entire module in a single table. It also provides an estimated timeline for the module, assuming approximately 50-minute class periods.

For added convenience, necessary materials and technology also are listed at the beginning of each activity.

Student Outcomes

This new feature appears near the beginning of each activity. It briefly describes the mathematics that students should gain from each exploration and discussion.

Warm-Ups, Assignments, and Assessment Items

Warm-Ups and Assignments appear at the end of each activity. Warm-Ups allow students to practice individual mathematical skills before tackling more complicated problems or real-world applications.

Each Assignment is separated into two sections. The problems in the first section cover all the essential mathematics in the activity. The second section provides optional problems—often presented in different contexts—for additional homework or enrichment.

Suggested assessment items are identified in the Teacher Edition by an asterisk preceding the problem number. These items give teachers an opportunity to conduct formative assessments during each activity.

Sample Responses

Appropriate responses are given for each Exploration, Discussion, Warm-Up, Assignment, and assessment item. When correct answers may vary, sample responses offer one or more reasonable solutions with corresponding justifications.

Teacher Notes

Teacher Notes offer practical teaching tips from experienced teachers. These notes appear throughout the Teacher Edition, providing advice on classroom management, alternate materials, possible extensions, calculator programs, and other topics.

Teacher Resources

A Teacher Resources CD provides more tools and flexibility for classroom implementation, including Flashbacks, Periodic Assessments, Module Assessments, and blackline masters. When these materials are available, the Teacher Edition displays the following icon.

Flashbacks

These brief problem sets provide a review of the prerequisite skills for each activity.

Periodic Assessments

To assist in ongoing, formative assessment, these short quizzes cover the mathematical content in two or three activities.

Module Assessment

This typically provides a more traditional alternative to the Summary Assessment in the Student Edition. Like Flashbacks and Periodic Assessments, the Module Assessment is designed for use at the teacher's discretion.

Templates

Templates are provided for use as blackline masters for classroom handouts or visual aids. When required, the Teacher Edition includes instructions for their distribution during specific explorations or assignments.

Professional Development

SIMMS Integrated Mathematics was written, reviewed, and piloted by a diverse group of secondary teachers. Many of these teachers are knowledgeable and experienced consultants, available to help schools plan appropriate inservice programs. Please contact Kendall/Hunt Publishing Company for more information.

Marvelous Matrices

module 1

Overview

In this module, students explore matrices as tools for storing, organizing, and analyzing data. The operations of matrix addition, scalar multiplication, and matrix multiplication are introduced within a business context.

Activity 1:   Students are introduced to requirement graphs and matrices as ways to organize data.

Activity 2:   Students are introduced to addition and scalar multiplication of matrices.

Activity 3:   Students are introduced to matrix multiplication.

Objectives

In this module, students will:

* organize and interpret data using requirement graphs (1)
* organize and interpret data using matrices (1, 2)
* determine the dimensions of a matrix (1)
* interpret the meaning of elements within a matrix (1, 2, 3)
* identify two or more matrices that are equal (2)
* add and subtract matrices (2)
* multiply a matrix by a scalar (2)
* multiply two matrices (3).

Prerequisites

For this module, students should know:

* how to use tree diagrams
* how to interpret data tables
* how to calculate the mean of a data set
* how to interpret subscripted variables.

 Flashbacks, for use at your discretion, appear in the Teacher Resources for this module. These brief problem sets provide a review of some prerequisite skills for each activity.

Planning Guide

Activity	Materials	Technology	Time Line
Activity **1**	■ none	■ matrix manipulator	2 days
Activity **2**	■ none	■ matrix manipulator	3 days
Activity **3**	■ none	■ matrix manipulator	3 days
Assessment Activities	■ none	■ matrix manipulator	3 days **Total: 11 days**

Introduction

The use of matrices for inventory control is based on ideas from management science, specifically Leontief input-output models.

This activity defines matrices, simple components, composite products, requirement graphs, and total requirement matrices. Students explore matrices as a tool for storing and interpreting data.

Materials List

■ none

Technology

■ matrix manipulator (optional)

Student Outcomes

After completing the following exploration and discussion, students should be able to:

✳ create a requirement graph

✳ interpret a requirement graph in terms of its components

✳ create a matrix

✳ interpret data within a matrix.

Exploration

This exploration demonstrates the usefulness of requirement graphs and requirement matrices for data storage.

a. Sample requirement graph:

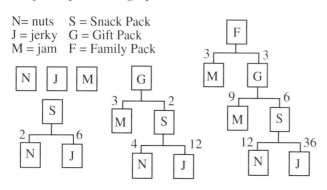

N = nuts   S = Snack Pack
J = jerky   G = Gift Pack
M = jam   F = Family Pack

Introduction

Welcome to the Age of Information. Office workers and company presidents, homeowners and rent payers, consumers and manufacturers—all are bombarded daily by mountains of data. Somehow, some way, you have to make sensible decisions based on that information. Those decisions range from simple day-to-day choices to those with major personal or financial impact.

A typical business manager juggles information such as monthly sales, production costs, company inventory, and employee productivity. A **matrix** is one mathematical tool used to organize the information needed to make good decisions. In this module, you look at how a small business grapples with the same problems that confront corporate giants such as General Motors and Motorola.

ACTIVITY 1

Family Snack, a branch of the Family Corporation, sells nuts, beef jerky, and jam. These three products are sold separately, as shown in Figure 1-1, and in assortment packages. Because they cannot be divided into smaller products, these three items are considered **simple components.**

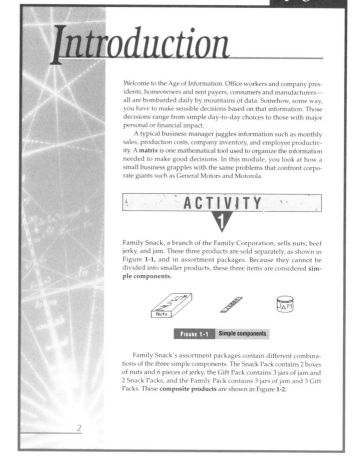

FIGURE 1-1   Simple components.

Family Snack's assortment packages contain different combinations of the three simple components. The Snack Pack contains 2 boxes of nuts and 6 pieces of jerky, the Gift Pack contains 3 jars of jam and 2 Snack Packs, and the Family Pack contains 3 jars of jam and 3 Gift Packs. These **composite products** are shown in Figure 1-2.

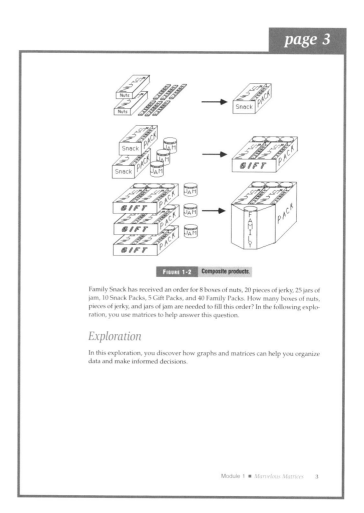

FIGURE 1-2   Composite products.

Family Snack has received an order for 8 boxes of nuts, 20 pieces of jerky, 25 jars of jam, 10 Snack Packs, 5 Gift Packs, and 40 Family Packs. How many boxes of nuts, pieces of jerky, and jars of jam are needed to fill this order? In the following exploration, you use matrices to help answer this question.

Exploration

In this exploration, you discover how graphs and matrices can help you organize data and make informed decisions.

business note

One way to represent a company's product line is with a **requirement graph**. A requirement graph is a tree diagram that shows each product's components at each level of its assembly. A complete requirement graph has simple components at the end of each branch.

For example, consider a company that sells mathematics supplies. This company's simple components are graph paper, rulers, compasses, and protractors. It also sells two composite products: the Euclid Set and the Complete Set. The Euclid Set contains 10 rulers and 5 compasses. The Complete Set contains 2 Euclid Sets, 10 packs of graph paper, and 10 protractors.

A requirement graph for this product line is shown in Figure **1-3**.

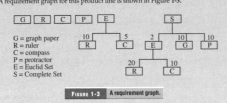

G = graph paper
R = ruler
C = compass
P = protractor
E = Euclid Set
S = Complete Set

FIGURE 1-3   A requirement graph.

a. Draw a requirement graph for Family Snack's product line (see Figures **1-1** and **1-2**).

b. Use the requirement graph from Part **a** to complete Steps **1–5**.

1. Describe the Snack Pack in terms of its simple components.
2. Describe the Gift Pack in terms of its simple components and composite products.
3. Describe the Gift Pack in terms of its simple components only.
4. Describe the Family Pack in terms of its simple components and composite products.
5. Describe the Family Pack in terms of its simple components only.

b. 1. A Snack Pack consists of 2 packages of nuts and 6 pieces of jerky.

2. In terms of its simple components and composite products, a Gift Pack consists of 2 Snack Packs and 3 jars of jam.

3. In terms of its simple components only, a Gift Pack consists of 4 packages of nuts, 12 pieces of jerky, and 3 jars of jam.

4. In terms of its simple components and composite products, a Family Pack consists of 3 Gift Packs and 3 jars of jam.

5. In terms of its simple components only, a Family Pack consists of 12 packages of nuts, 36 pieces of jerky, and 12 jars of jam.

c. A total requirement matrix for this product line is shown below.

$$
\mathbf{R} = \begin{array}{c} \\ N \\ J \\ M \\ S \\ G \\ F \end{array} \begin{array}{c} \begin{array}{cccccc} N & J & M & S & G & F \end{array} \\ \left[\begin{array}{cccccc} 1 & 0 & 0 & 2 & 4 & 12 \\ 0 & 1 & 0 & 6 & 12 & 36 \\ 0 & 0 & 1 & 0 & 3 & 12 \\ 0 & 0 & 0 & 1 & 2 & 6 \\ 0 & 0 & 0 & 0 & 1 & 3 \\ 0 & 0 & 0 & 0 & 0 & 1 \end{array}\right] \end{array}
$$

mathematics note

A **matrix** (plural **matrices** or **matrixes**) is a rectangular arrangement of rows and columns used to organize information. A matrix of *i* rows and *j* columns has **dimensions** $i \times j$ (read "i by j"). Matrices are named using bold, uppercase letters or descriptive words. Each item in a matrix is an **element**.

A company can use a requirement graph to create a **total requirement matrix**. In a total requirement matrix, each item sold is represented in a column heading, while each simple component or composite product is represented in a row heading. Each element indicates the number of that simple component or composite product required to produce the corresponding item sold.

For example, the matrix **T** shown below is a total requirement matrix for the product line described by the requirement graph in Figure 1-3. In this matrix, G represents graph paper, R represents ruler, C represents compass, P represents protractor, E represents Euclid Set, and S represents Complete Set. In matrix **T**, the values 10, 20, 10 in the S column represent the total number of simple components required for a Complete Set. This total includes the simple components for the two Euclid sets that are part of a Complete Set.

$$
\mathbf{T} = \begin{array}{c} \\ G \\ R \\ C \\ P \\ E \\ S \end{array} \begin{array}{c} \begin{array}{cccccc} G & R & C & P & E & S \end{array} \\ \left[\begin{array}{cccccc} 1 & 0 & 0 & 0 & 0 & 10 \\ 0 & 1 & 0 & 0 & 10 & 20 \\ 0 & 0 & 1 & 0 & 5 & 10 \\ 0 & 0 & 0 & 1 & 0 & 10 \\ 0 & 0 & 0 & 0 & 1 & 2 \\ 0 & 0 & 0 & 0 & 0 & 1 \end{array}\right] \end{array}
$$

Matrix **T** has 6 rows and 6 columns, so its dimensions are 6×6. The element in the third row, fifth column indicates that there are 5 compasses in each Euclid Set.

c. Use the requirement graph from Part **a** to create a total requirement matrix **R** for Family Snack's product line.

Discussion

a. In this case, it means that there are 5 compasses in a Euclid Set.

b. 1. The elements along the diagonal represent the number of a given product contained in the product itself, which is always 1.

   2. An element of 0 indicates that a given product contains none of a specific simple component or composite product.

c. Each element in the requirement matrix can be calculated by adding the numbers in the appropriate product tree which correspond with a particular item. In the product tree for a Family Pack, for example, the two boxes that represent jam are accompanied by the numbers 9 and 3. The sum of these numbers (12) is the element in row M of column F of matrix **R**. This indicates that there are 12 jars of jam in a Family Pack.

d. In the requirement matrix **R,** the elements in the rows that correspond with nuts, jerky, and jam represent the numbers of these simple components contained in each item. The desired quantity of each simple component can be found by multiplying each of these elements (shown in bold in the following equations) by the number of the corresponding item in the order, then finding the resulting sum.

$$N = 8 \bullet \mathbf{1} + 20 \bullet \mathbf{0} + 25 \bullet \mathbf{0} + 10 \bullet \mathbf{2} + 5 \bullet \mathbf{4} + 40 \bullet \mathbf{12} = 528$$

$$J = 8 \bullet \mathbf{0} + 20 \bullet \mathbf{1} + 25 \bullet \mathbf{0} + 10 \bullet \mathbf{6} + 5 \bullet \mathbf{12} + 40 \bullet \mathbf{36} = 1580$$

$$M = 8 \bullet \mathbf{0} + 20 \bullet \mathbf{0} + 25 \bullet \mathbf{1} + 10 \bullet \mathbf{0} + 5 \bullet \mathbf{3} + 40 \bullet \mathbf{12} = 520$$

Family Snack needs 528 packages of nuts, 1580 pieces of jerky, and 520 jars of jam to fill the order.

Warm-Up

1. a. 3×2
   b. 2×2
   c. 2×4
   d. 3×3
   e. 1×2
   f. 3×1

2. Answers will vary. Sample response:

$$\begin{bmatrix} -5 & -1 \\ 0 & 2 \\ 3 & 7 \end{bmatrix}$$

3. 15 elements

Assignment

Problems suitable for use as assessment items are identified by an asterisk (*).

1.1 Using the method described in Part **d** of the discussion, Family Snack needs 140 packages of nuts, 420

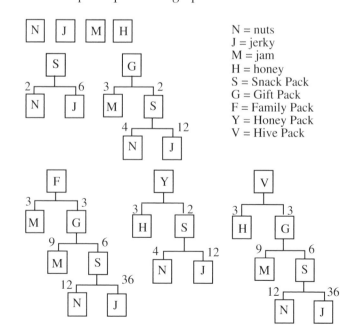

pieces of jerky, and 108 jars of jam to fill the entire order. In the calculations below, the matrix elements are shown in bold.

$$N = 20 \bullet \mathbf{1} + 60 \bullet \mathbf{0} + 48 \bullet \mathbf{0} + 24 \bullet \mathbf{2} + 12 \bullet \mathbf{4} + 2 \bullet \mathbf{12} = 140$$

$$J = 20 \bullet \mathbf{0} + 60 \bullet \mathbf{1} + 48 \bullet \mathbf{0} + 24 \bullet \mathbf{6} + 12 \bullet \mathbf{12} + 2 \bullet \mathbf{36} = 420$$

$$M = 20 \bullet \mathbf{0} + 60 \bullet \mathbf{0} + 48 \bullet \mathbf{1} + 24 \bullet \mathbf{0} + 12 \bullet \mathbf{3} + 2 \bullet \mathbf{12} = 108$$

* **1.2** **a.** Sample requirement graph:

N = nuts
J = jerky
M = jam
H = honey
S = Snack Pack
G = Gift Pack
F = Family Pack
Y = Honey Pack
V = Hive Pack

b. Create a total requirement matrix for this product line that includes the new products.

c. Determine the number of jars of jam in one Hive Pack.

1.3 The owners of Sammie's Spreadables sell a variety of cracker spreads. The requirement matrix for the company's product line is shown below.

$$S = \begin{array}{c} \\ \text{shrimp} \\ \text{lobster} \\ \text{spinach} \\ \text{Six-Pack} \\ \text{Ten-Pack} \end{array} \begin{array}{ccccc} \text{shrimp} & \text{lobster} & \text{spinach} & \text{Six-Pack} & \text{Ten-Pack} \\ \begin{bmatrix} 1 & 0 & 0 & 2 & 3 \\ 0 & 1 & 0 & 2 & 3 \\ 0 & 0 & 1 & 2 & 4 \\ 0 & 0 & 0 & 1 & 1 \\ 0 & 0 & 0 & 0 & 1 \end{bmatrix} \end{array}$$

a. Create a requirement graph that corresponds with matrix **S**.

b. How can you identify the simple components in matrix **S**?

c. Sammie's Spreadables has received an order for 8 Ten-Packs. Describe how you could use matrix **S** to determine the number of each simple component needed to fill the order.

* * * * *

1.4 The Holiday Hands Company sells packages of cheese and meat products. There are six items in their product line: cheddar cheese logs, cheese-and-bacon logs, summer sausage logs, Snack Packs, Hand-Out Packs, and Pig-Out Packs. The Snack Pack contains two cheddar cheese logs and three summer sausage logs. The Hand-Out Pack contains three cheddar cheese logs and two cheese-and-bacon logs. The Pig-Out Pack contains one Snack Pack and two Hand-Out Packs.

a. Create a requirement graph for Holiday Hands' product line.

b. Create a total requirement matrix for Holiday Hands' product line.

c. Determine the number of summer sausage logs in one Pig-Out Pack.

d. Determine the number of cheddar cheese logs in one Pig-Out Pack.

b. A total requirement matrix for this product line is shown below.

$$\begin{array}{c} \\ N \\ J \\ M \\ H \\ S \\ G \\ F \\ Y \\ V \end{array} \begin{array}{ccccccccc} N & J & M & H & S & G & F & Y & V \\ \begin{bmatrix} 1 & 0 & 0 & 0 & 2 & 4 & 12 & 4 & 12 \\ 0 & 1 & 0 & 0 & 6 & 12 & 36 & 12 & 36 \\ 0 & 0 & 1 & 0 & 0 & 3 & 12 & 0 & 9 \\ 0 & 0 & 0 & 1 & 0 & 0 & 0 & 3 & 3 \\ 0 & 0 & 0 & 0 & 1 & 2 & 6 & 2 & 6 \\ 0 & 0 & 0 & 0 & 0 & 1 & 3 & 0 & 3 \\ 0 & 0 & 0 & 0 & 0 & 0 & 1 & 0 & 0 \\ 0 & 0 & 0 & 0 & 0 & 0 & 0 & 1 & 0 \\ 0 & 0 & 0 & 0 & 0 & 0 & 0 & 0 & 1 \end{bmatrix} \end{array}$$

c. There are 9 jars of jam in one Hive Pack.

* **1.3 a.** Sample requirement graph:

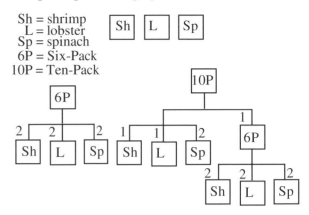

Sh = shrimp
L = lobster
Sp = spinach
6P = Six-Pack
10P = Ten-Pack

b. In a column for a simple component, the element 1 occurs once; the rest of the elements in the column are 0.

c. Sample response: Read the number of simple components in the Ten-Pack column. This tells how many of each are required for each Ten-Pack. Multiply these numbers by 8. You would need 24 shrimp spreads, 24 lobster spreads, and 32 spinach spreads.

✳ ✳ ✳ ✳ ✳

* **1.4 a.** Sample requirement graph:

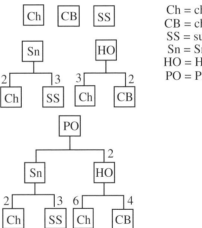

Ch = cheddar cheese log
CB = cheese and bacon log
SS = summer sausage
Sn = Snack Pack
HO = Hand-Out Pack
PO = Pig-Out Pack

b. The corresponding total requirement matrix is shown below.

$$\begin{array}{c} \\ Ch \\ CB \\ SS \\ Sn \\ HO \\ PO \end{array} \begin{array}{cccccc} Ch & CB & SS & Sn & HO & PO \\ \begin{bmatrix} 1 & 0 & 0 & 2 & 3 & 8 \\ 0 & 1 & 0 & 0 & 2 & 4 \\ 0 & 0 & 1 & 3 & 0 & 3 \\ 0 & 0 & 0 & 1 & 0 & 1 \\ 0 & 0 & 0 & 0 & 1 & 2 \\ 0 & 0 & 0 & 0 & 0 & 1 \end{bmatrix} \end{array}$$

c. There are 3 summer sausage logs in one Pig-Out Pack.

d. There are 8 cheddar cheese logs in one Pig-Out Pack.

1.5 a. Sample requirement graph:

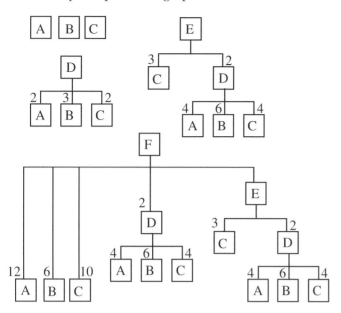

b. Sample response: The simple components in matrix **T** are A, B, and C. In a column for a simple component, the element 1 occurs once; the rest of the elements in the column are 0.

c. Sample response: Read the number of simple components (As, Bs, and Cs) in the F column. This tells how many of each are required for each F. Multiply these numbers by 10. You would need 200 As, 180 Bs, and 210 Cs.

* 1.6 a. Sample requirement graph:

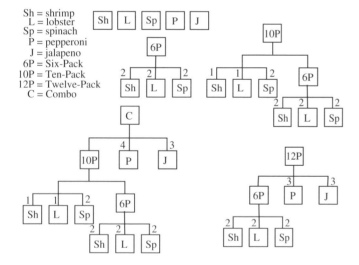

1.5 Use the requirement matrix shown below to complete Parts **a–c**.

$$
\mathbf{T} = \begin{array}{c c} & \begin{array}{c c c c c c} A & B & C & D & E & F \end{array} \\ \begin{array}{c} A \\ B \\ C \\ D \\ E \\ F \end{array} & \left[\begin{array}{c c c c c c} 1 & 0 & 0 & 2 & 4 & 20 \\ 0 & 1 & 0 & 3 & 6 & 18 \\ 0 & 0 & 1 & 2 & 7 & 21 \\ 0 & 0 & 0 & 1 & 2 & 4 \\ 0 & 0 & 0 & 0 & 1 & 1 \\ 0 & 0 & 0 & 0 & 0 & 1 \end{array} \right] \end{array}
$$

a. Create a requirement graph that corresponds with this requirement matrix.

b. Identify the simple components in matrix **T** and describe how you recognized them.

c. Describe how you could use the total requirement matrix to determine the amount of each simple component needed to fill an order for 10 pieces of item F.

1.6 In addition to those described in Problem **1.3**, Sammie's Spreadables has added four more items to its product line. These include a pepperoni spread, a jalapeño spread, a Twelve-Pack, and a Combo Pack. The Twelve-Pack contains a Six-Pack, 3 pepperoni spreads, and 3 jalapeño spreads. The Combo Pack contains a Ten-Pack, 4 pepperoni spreads, and 3 jalapeño spreads.

a. Create a total requirement graph for Sammie's expanded product line.

b. Create a total requirement matrix for Sammie's expanded product line.

c. Determine the number of spinach spreads in one Combo Pack.

ACTIVITY 2

In Activity **1**, you used requirement graphs and requirement matrices to represent Family Snack's product line. In this activity, you use matrices to organize and analyze other types of data.

Exploration

Family Snack employs three salespeople: Keyes, Zhang, and Troy. In September, Keyes sold 8 packages of nuts, 12 packages of jerky, 0 jars of jam, 16 Snack Packs, 28 Gift Packs, and 8 Family Packs.

b. The corresponding total requirement matrix is shown below.

$$
\begin{array}{c c} & \begin{array}{c c c c c c c c c} Sh & L & Sp & P & J & 6P & 10P & 12P & C \end{array} \\ \begin{array}{c} Sh \\ L \\ Sp \\ P \\ J \\ 6P \\ 10P \\ 12P \\ C \end{array} & \left[\begin{array}{c c c c c c c c c} 1 & 0 & 0 & 0 & 0 & 2 & 3 & 2 & 3 \\ 0 & 1 & 0 & 0 & 0 & 2 & 3 & 2 & 3 \\ 0 & 0 & 1 & 0 & 0 & 2 & 4 & 2 & 4 \\ 0 & 0 & 0 & 1 & 0 & 0 & 0 & 3 & 4 \\ 0 & 0 & 0 & 0 & 1 & 0 & 0 & 3 & 3 \\ 0 & 0 & 0 & 0 & 0 & 1 & 1 & 1 & 1 \\ 0 & 0 & 0 & 0 & 0 & 0 & 1 & 0 & 1 \\ 0 & 0 & 0 & 0 & 0 & 0 & 0 & 1 & 0 \\ 0 & 0 & 0 & 0 & 0 & 0 & 0 & 0 & 1 \end{array} \right] \end{array}
$$

c. There are 4 spinach spreads in one Combo Pack.

In the same month, Zhang sold 12 packages of nuts, 4 packages of jerky, 24 jars of jam, 8 Snack Packs, 24 Gift Packs, and 12 Family Packs.

Troy's September sales included 12 packages of nuts, 0 packages of jerky, 12 jars of jam, 12 Snack Packs, 36 Gift Packs, and 4 Family Packs.

a. Use a matrix to organize this information in each of the following ways. Record the dimensions of each matrix.

   1. Designate each row by a salesperson's name and each column by a product name.

   2. Designate each row by a product name and each column by a salesperson's name.

mathematics note

Two matrices are **equal** if they have the same dimensions and if corresponding elements are equal.

For example, consider matrices **A** and **B** below.

$$A = \begin{bmatrix} 1 & 4 \\ 3 & 2 \\ 7 & 6 \end{bmatrix} \qquad B = \begin{bmatrix} 1 & 4 \\ 3 & 2 \\ 7 & 6 \end{bmatrix}$$

These matrices are equal because the dimensions of both are 3×2 and because the element in row 1, column 1 of matrix **A** is the same as the element in row 1, column 1 of matrix **B**; the element in row 1, column 2 of matrix **A** is the same as the element in row 1, column 2 of matrix **B**; the element in row 2, column 1 of matrix **A** is the same as the element in row 2, column 1 of matrix **B**; and so on.

b. Are the matrices created in Part **a** equal? Explain your response.

c. In October, Keyes sold 8 packages of nuts, 4 packages of jerky, 24 jars of jam, 12 Snack Packs, 8 Gift Packs, and 36 Family Packs.

In the same month, Zhang sold 16 packages of nuts, 8 packages of jerky, 28 jars of jam, 16 Snack Packs, 20 Gift Packs, and 32 Family Packs.

Troy's October sales included 8 packages of nuts, 12 packages of jerky, 4 jars of jam, 16 Snack Packs, 8 Gift Packs, and 0 Family Packs.

Select one of the matrices that you created in Part **a** for September's sales. Using the dimensions of this matrix, create the corresponding matrix for October's sales.

Module 1 ■ *Marvelous Matrices*   9

ACTIVITY 2

In this activity, students are introduced to matrix addition and scalar multiplication in the context of inventory control.

teacher note

A brief assessment of the mathematical content in Activities **1** and **2**, for use at your discretion, appears in the Teacher Resources for this module.

Materials List

■ none

Technology

■ matrix manipulator (optional)

Student Outcomes

After completing the following exploration and discussion, students should be able to:

✳ create a matrix given a related set of data

✳ add or subtract two matrices

✳ multiply a matrix by a scalar

✳ use technology to manipulate matrices

✳ determine the arithmetic mean of corresponding elements from two or more matrices

✳ determine if the sum of two matrices cannot be found

✳ justify that matrix addition is commutative.

Exploration

a. 1. The dimensions of this matrix are 3×6.

$$S = \begin{array}{c} \\ K \\ Z \\ T \end{array} \begin{array}{cccccc} N & J & M & S & G & F \\ \begin{bmatrix} 8 & 12 & 0 & 16 & 28 & 8 \\ 12 & 4 & 24 & 8 & 24 & 12 \\ 12 & 0 & 12 & 12 & 36 & 4 \end{bmatrix} \end{array}$$

  2. The dimensions of this matrix are 6×3.

$$R = \begin{array}{c} \\ N \\ J \\ M \\ S \\ G \\ F \end{array} \begin{array}{ccc} K & Z & T \\ \begin{bmatrix} 8 & 12 & 12 \\ 12 & 4 & 0 \\ 0 & 24 & 12 \\ 16 & 8 & 12 \\ 28 & 24 & 36 \\ 8 & 12 & 4 \end{bmatrix} \end{array}$$

b. Although they illustrate the same information, the matrices created in Part **a** are not equal because they have different dimensions.

c. Sample 3×6 matrix:

$$O = \begin{array}{c} \\ K \\ Z \\ T \end{array} \begin{array}{cccccc} N & J & M & S & G & F \\ \begin{bmatrix} 8 & 4 & 24 & 12 & 8 & 36 \\ 16 & 8 & 28 & 16 & 20 & 32 \\ 8 & 12 & 4 & 16 & 8 & 0 \end{bmatrix} \end{array}$$

d. 1. The matrix **T** below shows the total of the corresponding elements in matrices **S** and **O**.

$$\mathbf{T} = \begin{array}{c} \\ \text{K} \\ \text{Z} \\ \text{T} \end{array} \begin{array}{cccccc} \text{N} & \text{J} & \text{M} & \text{S} & \text{G} & \text{F} \\ \left[\begin{array}{cccccc} 16 & 16 & 24 & 28 & 36 & 44 \\ 28 & 12 & 52 & 24 & 44 & 44 \\ 20 & 12 & 16 & 28 & 44 & 4 \end{array}\right] \end{array}$$

2. The matrix **D** below shows the differences between the corresponding elements in matrices **O** and **S**.

$$\mathbf{D} = \begin{array}{c} \\ \text{K} \\ \text{Z} \\ \text{T} \end{array} \begin{array}{cccccc} \text{N} & \text{J} & \text{M} & \text{S} & \text{G} & \text{F} \\ \left[\begin{array}{cccccc} 0 & -8 & 24 & -4 & -20 & 28 \\ 4 & 4 & 4 & 8 & -4 & 20 \\ -4 & 12 & -8 & 4 & -28 & -4 \end{array}\right] \end{array}$$

e. The matrix **N** shows the product of each element in matrix **O** multiplied by 2.

$$\mathbf{N} = \begin{array}{c} \\ \text{K} \\ \text{Z} \\ \text{T} \end{array} \begin{array}{cccccc} \text{N} & \text{J} & \text{M} & \text{S} & \text{G} & \text{F} \\ \left[\begin{array}{cccccc} 16 & 8 & 48 & 24 & 16 & 72 \\ 32 & 16 & 56 & 32 & 40 & 64 \\ 16 & 24 & 8 & 32 & 16 & 0 \end{array}\right] \end{array}$$

f. 1. This matrix can be determined by matrix addition.

$$\mathbf{N+O} = \begin{array}{c} \\ \text{K} \\ \text{Z} \\ \text{T} \end{array} \begin{array}{cccccc} \text{N} & \text{J} & \text{M} & \text{S} & \text{G} & \text{F} \\ \left[\begin{array}{cccccc} 24 & 12 & 72 & 36 & 24 & 108 \\ 48 & 24 & 84 & 48 & 60 & 96 \\ 24 & 36 & 12 & 48 & 24 & 0 \end{array}\right] \end{array}$$

2. This matrix can be determined by matrix subtraction.

$$\mathbf{N-S} = \begin{array}{c} \\ \text{K} \\ \text{Z} \\ \text{T} \end{array} \begin{array}{cccccc} \text{N} & \text{J} & \text{M} & \text{S} & \text{G} & \text{F} \\ \left[\begin{array}{cccccc} 8 & -4 & 48 & 8 & -12 & 64 \\ 20 & 12 & 32 & 24 & 16 & 52 \\ 4 & 24 & -4 & 20 & -20 & -4 \end{array}\right] \end{array}$$

3. This matrix can be determined by matrix addition.

$$\mathbf{S+O+N} = \begin{array}{c} \\ \text{K} \\ \text{Z} \\ \text{T} \end{array} \begin{array}{cccccc} \text{N} & \text{J} & \text{M} & \text{S} & \text{G} & \text{F} \\ \left[\begin{array}{cccccc} 32 & 24 & 72 & 52 & 52 & 116 \\ 60 & 28 & 108 & 56 & 84 & 108 \\ 36 & 36 & 24 & 60 & 60 & 4 \end{array}\right] \end{array}$$

---

d. 1. Create a matrix that displays the total number of each product sold by each salesperson during September and October.

2. Create a matrix that shows the change in the sales of each product by each salesperson from September to October.

e. As the holiday season approaches, the company expects November sales to be twice that of the previous month. Create a matrix that shows the predicted sales of each product for each salesperson.

mathematics Note

Matrix addition can be performed on two matrices with the same dimensions by adding the corresponding elements of each matrix. For example, the addition of two 2×3 matrices is shown below.

$$\begin{bmatrix} 1 & 2 & 3 \\ -3 & 4 & 5 \end{bmatrix} + \begin{bmatrix} 7 & -8 & 9 \\ 10 & 11 & -2 \end{bmatrix} = \begin{bmatrix} (1+7) & (2-8) & (3+9) \\ (-3+10) & (4+11) & (5-2) \end{bmatrix} = \begin{bmatrix} 8 & -6 & 12 \\ 7 & 15 & 3 \end{bmatrix}$$

Matrix subtraction can be performed in a similar manner. For example, the following equation shows the subtraction of one 2×2 from another.

$$\begin{bmatrix} 1 & -2 \\ -3 & 4 \end{bmatrix} - \begin{bmatrix} 0 & 1 \\ 2 & -5 \end{bmatrix} = \begin{bmatrix} (1-0) & (-2-1) \\ (-3-2) & (4-(-5)) \end{bmatrix} = \begin{bmatrix} 1 & -3 \\ -5 & 9 \end{bmatrix}$$

In **scalar multiplication**, each element of a matrix is multiplied by a constant, or scalar. The multiplication of a matrix **M** by a scalar k is denoted by $k \bullet \mathbf{M}$.

For example, consider the matrix **M** below.

$$\mathbf{M} = \begin{bmatrix} 5 & 4 \\ -2 & 8 \\ 0 & -1 \end{bmatrix}$$

Multiplying **M** by the scalar 5 produces the following result.

$$5 \bullet \mathbf{M} = 5 \bullet \begin{bmatrix} 5 & 4 \\ -2 & 8 \\ 0 & -1 \end{bmatrix} = \begin{bmatrix} 5(5) & 5(4) \\ 5(-2) & 5(8) \\ 5(0) & 5(-1) \end{bmatrix} = \begin{bmatrix} 25 & 20 \\ -10 & 40 \\ 0 & -5 \end{bmatrix}$$

---

f. Use technology to complete Steps **1–3** below. Assume that November sales are represented by the matrix you created in Part **e**.

1. Determine a matrix that displays the total sales of each product by each salesperson during October and November.

2. Determine a matrix that shows the change in the sales of each product by each salesperson between September and November.

3. Determine a matrix that shows total sales of each product by each salesperson for September, October, and November.

g. The arithmetic mean of two numbers can be found by dividing their sum by 2 or multiplying their sum by 1/2. Use scalar multiplication to complete Steps **1** and **2** below.

1. Determine a matrix that shows mean sales of each product by each salesperson during September and October.

2. Determine a matrix that shows mean sales of each product by each salesperson during September, October, and November.

Discussion

a. In Part **a** of the exploration, you created two matrices that represent the same information. Each matrix is the **transpose** of the other. The transpose of matrix **A** is denoted by $\mathbf{A}^\mathsf{T}$ or $\mathbf{A}'$.

Describe how you would determine the transpose of a given matrix.

b. Describe how you determined the mean sales for all three months in Part **g** of the exploration.

c. Do you think that any two matrices **A** and **B** can be added together? Explain your response.

d. When matrices are added, subtracted, or multiplied by a scalar, what are the dimensions of the resulting matrix? Why does this occur?

e. Do you think that matrix addition is commutative? In other words, does $\mathbf{A} + \mathbf{B} = \mathbf{B} + \mathbf{A}$, where **A** and **B** are matrices? Justify your response.

Warm-Up

1. In Parts a–g below, perform the indicated operation(s), if possible. If an operation is not possible, explain why.

a. $\begin{bmatrix} 5 & 9 \\ -1 & 4 \end{bmatrix} + \begin{bmatrix} -3 & 3 \\ 1 & 5 \end{bmatrix}$

b. $\begin{bmatrix} 2 & 4 \\ -2 & 3 \end{bmatrix} + \begin{bmatrix} 4 & -3 & 6 \\ 2 & 8 & -2 \end{bmatrix}$

c. $\pi \bullet \begin{bmatrix} 5 & 7 \\ 11 & -4 \\ 3 & 0 \end{bmatrix}$

d. $4 \bullet \begin{bmatrix} 2 & 6 & -9 \\ 3 & 7 & 11 \end{bmatrix} - \begin{bmatrix} 8 & 15 & 2 \\ -5 & 6 & 0 \end{bmatrix}$

e. $\begin{bmatrix} 3 & 4 \\ 1 & -7 \end{bmatrix} + \begin{bmatrix} 0 & 0 \\ 0 & 0 \end{bmatrix}$

f. $\begin{bmatrix} r & 2s \\ p & -q \end{bmatrix} + \begin{bmatrix} r & s \\ m & n \end{bmatrix}$

g. $a \bullet \begin{bmatrix} r & s \\ m & n \end{bmatrix}$

Assignment

2.1 To promote the company's products, Family Snack's business manager plans to visit six U.S. cities. In the matrix below, each element represents the distance in kilometers between two of these cities.

	Miami	New York	Chicago	Kansas City	Seattle	Los Angeles
Miami	0	1747	1901	1986	4374	3742
New York	1747	0	1141	1755	3853	3922
Chicago	1901	1141	0	662	2779	2792
Kansas City	1986	1755	662	0	2410	2170
Seattle	4374	3853	2779	2410	0	1534
Los Angeles	3742	3922	2792	2170	1534	0

a. What does the element in row 4, column 5 represent?

b. The element 2779 appears twice in this matrix. Describe both of its positions and identify what each represents.

c. What do the zeros indicate in this matrix?

---

g. 1. This matrix can be determined as follows.

$$\frac{1}{2}(\mathbf{S} + \mathbf{O}) = \begin{array}{c} \\ K \\ Z \\ T \end{array} \begin{bmatrix} \begin{array}{cccccc} N & J & M & S & G & F \end{array} \\ 8 & 8 & 12 & 14 & 18 & 22 \\ 14 & 6 & 26 & 12 & 22 & 22 \\ 10 & 6 & 8 & 14 & 22 & 2 \end{bmatrix}$$

2. This matrix can be determined as shown below.

$$\frac{1}{3}(\mathbf{S} + \mathbf{O} + \mathbf{N}) = \begin{array}{c} \\ K \\ Z \\ T \end{array} \begin{bmatrix} \begin{array}{cccccc} N & J & M & S & G & F \end{array} \\ 10\frac{2}{3} & 8 & 24 & 17\frac{1}{3} & 17\frac{1}{3} & 38\frac{2}{3} \\ 20 & 9\frac{1}{3} & 36 & 18\frac{2}{3} & 28 & 36 \\ 12 & 12 & 8 & 20 & 20 & 1\frac{1}{3} \end{bmatrix}$$

Discussion

a. Sample response: The *n*th row of the original matrix becomes the *n*th column of the transpose, while the *n*th column of the original matrix becomes the *n*th row of the transpose. In other words, all the rows are turned into columns, and vice versa.

b. Sample response: The mean sales matrix was found by adding the matrices for September, October, and November, then multiplying the result by the scalar 1/3.

c. Sample response: No. Only matrices with the same dimensions can be added together.

d. Sample response: The dimensions of the resulting matrix are the same as the dimensions of the original matrix (or matrices). Scalar multiplication does not change the dimensions of the resulting matrix.

e. Sample response: Yes. Matrix addition involves adding corresponding elements of matrices with the same dimensions. Because order does not matter when adding two real numbers, matrix addition is commutative.

Warm-Up

1. a. $\begin{bmatrix} 5 & 9 \\ -1 & 4 \end{bmatrix} + \begin{bmatrix} -3 & 3 \\ 1 & 5 \end{bmatrix} = \begin{bmatrix} 2 & 12 \\ 0 & 9 \end{bmatrix}$

b. Addition is not possible because the matrices do not have the same dimensions.

c. $\pi \bullet \begin{bmatrix} 5 & 7 \\ 11 & -4 \\ 3 & 0 \end{bmatrix} = \begin{bmatrix} 5\pi & 7\pi \\ 11\pi & -4\pi \\ 3\pi & 0\pi \end{bmatrix} \approx \begin{bmatrix} 15.7 & 22.0 \\ 34.6 & -12.6 \\ 9.4 & 0 \end{bmatrix}$

d. $4 \bullet \begin{bmatrix} 2 & 6 & -9 \\ 3 & 7 & 11 \end{bmatrix} - \begin{bmatrix} 8 & 15 & 2 \\ -5 & 6 & 0 \end{bmatrix} = \begin{bmatrix} 0 & 9 & -38 \\ 17 & 22 & 44 \end{bmatrix}$

e. $\begin{bmatrix} 3 & 4 \\ 1 & -7 \end{bmatrix} + \begin{bmatrix} 0 & 0 \\ 0 & 0 \end{bmatrix} = \begin{bmatrix} 3 & 4 \\ 1 & -7 \end{bmatrix}$

f. $\begin{bmatrix} 2r & 3s \\ p + r & -q + n \end{bmatrix}$

g. $\begin{bmatrix} ar & as \\ am & an \end{bmatrix}$

Assignment

Problems suitable for use as assessment items are identified by an asterisk (*).

2.1 a. The element in row 4, column 5 represents the distance from Kansas City to Seattle.

b. In row 5, column 3, 2779 represents the distance from Seattle to Chicago. In row 3, column 5, 2779 represents the distance from Chicago to Seattle.

c. The zeros represent the distance from a city to itself.

2.2 **a.** Sample matrix:

$$
\mathbf{T} = \begin{array}{c} \\ E_1 \\ E_2 \\ E_3 \\ E_4 \end{array} \begin{array}{cccc} T_1 & T_2 & T_3 & T_4 \\ \left[\begin{array}{cccc} 8 & 7 & 4 & 10 \\ 10 & 4 & 5 & 8.5 \\ 6 & 3.5 & 4 & 9 \\ 8 & 6.5 & 8 & 6 \end{array}\right] \end{array}
$$

b. The following assignment requires a minimum of 6 hr to complete all four tasks: Assign task 3 to employee 1, task 2 to employee 2, task 1 to employee 3, and task 4 to employee 4.

c. There is no other set of assignments that completes the day's tasks in 6 hr. To complete all the tasks in 6 hr, employee 4 must do task 4 (because all the other tasks take this employee more than 6 hr). Likewise, employee 1 must do task 3. Employee 2 must do task 2 or task 1, because tasks 2 and 4 are already taken. Task 1 requires more than 6 hr for employee 2 to complete, so employee 2 must do Task 2. This leaves employee 3 with task 1.

* 2.3 **a.** The dimensions of matrix **I** are 3×4.

b. This element (22) represents the inventory of large, red sweat pants.

c. The new inventory is shown in matrix **A** below.

$$
\mathbf{A} = \begin{array}{c} \\ B \\ R \\ Y \end{array} \begin{array}{cccc} S & M & L & XL \\ \left[\begin{array}{cccc} 31 & 45 & 44 & 28 \\ 32 & 47 & 42 & 30 \\ 29 & 35 & 38 & 32 \end{array}\right] \end{array}
$$

d. Using scalar multiplication:

$$
3 \cdot \mathbf{I} = \begin{array}{c} \\ B \\ R \\ Y \end{array} \begin{array}{cccc} S & M & L & XL \\ \left[\begin{array}{cccc} 33 & 75 & 72 & 24 \\ 36 & 81 & 66 & 30 \\ 27 & 45 & 54 & 36 \end{array}\right] \end{array}
$$

e. The sum of the following matrix and matrix **I** is matrix **A**.

$$
\begin{array}{c} \\ B \\ R \\ Y \end{array} \begin{array}{cccc} S & M & L & XL \\ \left[\begin{array}{cccc} 20 & 20 & 20 & 20 \\ 20 & 20 & 20 & 20 \\ 20 & 20 & 20 & 20 \end{array}\right] \end{array}
$$

2.2 Each of Family Snack's four production employees is capable of performing the following daily tasks:

Task 1: Making and packaging jam.
Task 2: Roasting and packaging nuts.
Task 3: Preparing and packaging jerky.
Task 4: Filling and delivering orders.

Because their skill levels differ from task to task, the time necessary for each employee to complete each task varies as described below.

Employee 1 can do task 1 in 8 hr, task 2 in 7 hr, task 3 in 4 hr, and task 4 in 10 hr.

Employee 2 can do task 1 in 10 hr, task 2 in 4 hr, task 3 in 5 hr, and task 4 in 8.5 hr.

Employee 3 can do task 1 in 6 hr, task 2 in 3.5 hr, task 3 in 4 hr, and task 4 in 9 hr.

Employee 4 can do task 1 in 8 hr, task 2 in 6.5 hr, task 3 in 8 hr, and task 4 in 6 hr.

a. Create a matrix to organize this data. Designate each employee by a row heading.

b. Assign one task to each employee so that all the tasks are completed in the least amount of time. (Assume that all tasks can be performed simultaneously.)

c. Is there more than one possible response to Part b? If so, describe another solution.

2.3 A Family Corporation sportswear outlet, Family Funwear, sells sweat pants in three colors—blue, red, and yellow—and four sizes: S, M, L, and XL. The number of each item in their current inventory is shown in matrix **I** below.

$$
\mathbf{I} = \begin{array}{c} \\ \text{blue} \\ \text{red} \\ \text{yellow} \end{array} \begin{array}{cccc} S & M & L & XL \\ \left[\begin{array}{cccc} 11 & 25 & 24 & 8 \\ 12 & 27 & 22 & 10 \\ 9 & 15 & 18 & 12 \end{array}\right] \end{array}
$$

a. What are the dimensions of matrix **I**?

b. What does the element in row 2, column 3 represent?

c. After receiving a new shipment of sweat pants, the store's stock of each item increases by 20. Create a matrix to represent this new inventory.

d. In preparation for an upcoming sale, the manager triples the store's original inventory. Create a matrix to represent this new inventory.

e. Create a matrix that, when added to matrix **I**, results in the matrix for Part c.

2.4 Family Funwear plans to add four different styles of knitted sweaters to its clothing line. To accomplish this goal, the company has purchased four knitting machines and has hired four new workers. During some initial trials, the company gathered the following production data:

> In one day, worker 1 can produce 3 of style A, 6 of style B, 7 of style C, or 4 of style D.
>
> Worker 2 can produce 4 of style A, 5 of style B, 5 of style C, or 6 of style D.
>
> Worker 3 can produce 6 of style A, 3 of style B, 4 of style C, or 4 of style D.
>
> Worker 4 can produce 5 of style A, 5 of style B, 3 of style C, or 6 of style D.

a. Create a matrix to organize this data. Designate each worker by a row heading.

b. To produce the maximum number of sweaters each day, which worker should knit each style? Justify your response.

c. What is the maximum number of sweaters that the four workers can produce in one day?

d. Is there more than one possible response to Part **b**? If so, describe another solution.

* * * * *

2.5 Family Bicycles, another division of the Family Corporation, builds and sells three types of bicycles: mountain bikes, touring bikes, and cross-country bikes. Each type is sold in three different frame sizes: 43 cm, 48 cm, and 54 cm.

In the 43-cm frame size, Family Bicycles has 112 mountain bikes, 117 touring bikes, and 111 cross-country bikes in stock. In the 48-cm frame size, they have 190 mountain bikes, 122 touring bikes, and 92 cross-country bikes. In the 54-cm frame size, they have 101 mountain bikes, 216 touring bikes, and 132 cross-country bikes.

a. Create a matrix to represent the company's entire stock of bicycles. Designate each frame size by a row heading.

b. The company's marketing department predicts that sales of each style and size of bicycle will increase by 20% next month.

2.4 a. Sample matrix:

$$
\begin{array}{c}
\\ W_1 \\ W_2 \\ W_3 \\ W_4
\end{array}
\begin{array}{cccc}
A & B & C & D \\
\left[\begin{array}{cccc}
3 & 6 & 7 & 4 \\
4 & 5 & 5 & 6 \\
6 & 3 & 4 & 4 \\
5 & 5 & 3 & 6
\end{array}\right]
\end{array}
$$

b. Answers may vary. Sample response: Worker 1 should knit style C because this is the maximum number of sweaters that can be knitted by any worker. Similarly, worker 2 should knit style D; worker 3 should knit style A; and worker 4 should knit style B. This arrangement allows the production of 24 sweaters per day.

c. The maximum number of sweaters possible is 24.

d. There is more than one possible response. Assigning worker 1 to style C; worker 2 to style B; worker 3 to style A; and worker 4 to style D also results in the production of 24 sweaters per day.

✳ ✳ ✳ ✳ ✳

* 2.5 a. Sample matrix:

$$
\mathbf{U} =
\begin{array}{c}
\\ 43 \\ 48 \\ 54
\end{array}
\begin{array}{ccc}
MT & TR & CC \\
\left[\begin{array}{ccc}
112 & 117 & 111 \\
190 & 122 & 92 \\
101 & 216 & 132
\end{array}\right]
\end{array}
$$

b. 1. Answers may vary. Sample response: Because sales are predicted to increase by 20%, the numbers of bicycles needed will be approximately equal to the entries in 1.2 • **U**. After performing this scalar multiplication, you can use nearby integers to estimate next month's sales.

2. The elements in the following matrix correspond to the numbers of bicycles that are needed to meet next month's sales.

$$1.2 \bullet \mathbf{U} \approx \begin{array}{c} \\ 43 \\ 48 \\ 54 \end{array} \begin{array}{ccc} MT & TR & CC \\ \begin{bmatrix} 135 & 141 & 134 \\ 228 & 147 & 111 \\ 122 & 260 & 159 \end{bmatrix} \end{array}$$

* 2.6 a. The number of mountain bikes in stock on December 1 was $5 + 17 + 13 = 35$.

b. The number of 48-cm bikes in stock was $17 + 9 = 26$.

c. The total number of bicycles in stock was $5 + 17 + 13 + 11 + 9 + 18 = 73$.

d. Through matrix subtraction, the number of bicycles sold during December can be represented as follows:

$$\mathbf{I_1} - \mathbf{I_{31}} = \begin{array}{c} \\ mountain \\ touring \end{array} \begin{array}{ccc} 43 & 48 & 54 \\ \begin{bmatrix} 2 & 6 & 8 \\ 5 & 9 & 8 \end{bmatrix} \end{array}$$

e. The 48-cm touring bike was the best-selling bike in December.

f. Eight of the 54-cm mountain bikes sold during the month.

g. The 48-cm touring bike is the only model that needs to be reordered.

2.7 a. 1. Because matrices **C** and **N** have the same dimensions, they can be added to create matrix **T**. Matrix **T** represents the total inventory after next week.

2. This matrix addition is shown below.

$$\mathbf{T} = \mathbf{C} + \mathbf{N} = \begin{array}{c} \\ white \\ red \\ blue \\ green \end{array} \begin{array}{ccc} MT & TR & CC \\ \begin{bmatrix} 106 & 112 & 73 \\ 133 & 135 & 93 \\ 82 & 137 & 40 \\ 116 & 101 & 149 \end{bmatrix} \end{array}$$

b. To determine the numbers of bicycles required, students should perform the following matrix subtraction:

$$\mathbf{S} - \mathbf{T} = \begin{array}{c} \\ white \\ red \\ blue \\ green \end{array} \begin{array}{ccc} MT & TR & CC \\ \begin{bmatrix} 10 & 20 & 14 \\ 12 & 12 & 10 \\ 12 & 15 & 14 \\ 14 & 16 & 9 \end{bmatrix} \end{array}$$

1. Describe how to create a matrix that displays the number of each bicycle that must be in stock to meet next month's sales.

2. If the current inventory represents just enough stock to supply this month's orders, how many of each bicycle should be stocked next month? Explain your response.

2.6 One of the stores that sells Family Bicycles handles only mountain bikes and touring bikes. The inventory matrices $\mathbf{I_1}$ and $\mathbf{I_{31}}$ show the number of bicycles in stock at the beginning of sales on December 1 and at the close of sales on December 31, respectively:

$$\mathbf{I_1} = \begin{array}{c} \\ mountain \\ touring \end{array} \begin{array}{ccc} 43 & 48 & 54 \\ \begin{bmatrix} 5 & 17 & 13 \\ 11 & 9 & 18 \end{bmatrix} \end{array} \quad \mathbf{I_{31}} = \begin{array}{c} \\ mountain \\ touring \end{array} \begin{array}{ccc} 43 & 48 & 54 \\ \begin{bmatrix} 3 & 11 & 5 \\ 6 & 0 & 10 \end{bmatrix} \end{array}$$

Assuming the shop did not receive any new bicycles during December, complete Parts **a–g** below.

a. How many mountain bikes did the store have in stock on December 1?

b. How many 48-cm bikes were in stock at the start of the month?

c. What was the total number of bicycles in stock on December 1?

d. Write a 2 × 3 matrix that represents the number of bicycles sold during December. Explain how you determined the elements in this matrix.

e. Which individual model and size sold best during the month?

f. How many 54-cm mountain bikes were sold during December?

g. At the end of the month, the store manager orders more of each model and size for which no more than one-third of the initial inventory remains. Which bicycle(s) should be reordered?

2.7 Family Bicycle offers four different frame colors: white, red, blue, and green. Its current inventory of mountain, touring, and cross-country bicycles is represented in matrix **C** below.

$$\mathbf{C} = \begin{array}{c} \\ white \\ red \\ blue \\ green \end{array} \begin{array}{ccc} MT & TR & CC \\ \begin{bmatrix} 100 & 100 & 67 \\ 121 & 135 & 89 \\ 82 & 125 & 34 \\ 100 & 95 & 145 \end{bmatrix} \end{array}$$

Next week, the company will add the bicycles represented in matrix **N** to its inventory.

$$\mathbf{N} = \begin{array}{c} \\ white \\ red \\ blue \\ green \end{array} \begin{array}{ccc} MT & TR & CC \\ \begin{bmatrix} 6 & 12 & 6 \\ 12 & 0 & 4 \\ 0 & 12 & 6 \\ 16 & 6 & 4 \end{bmatrix} \end{array}$$

a. 1. Describe how matrix addition can be used to determine a matrix that represents the company's total inventory after next week.

2. Write the matrix that represents the company's total inventory after next week.

b. The matrix **S** represents the inventory that the company must have in stock before the summer sales begin. How many more bicycles should the company produce to reach this goal?

$$\mathbf{S} = \begin{array}{c} \\ white \\ red \\ blue \\ green \end{array} \begin{array}{ccc} MT & TR & CC \\ \begin{bmatrix} 116 & 132 & 87 \\ 145 & 147 & 103 \\ 94 & 152 & 54 \\ 130 & 117 & 158 \end{bmatrix} \end{array}$$

ACTIVITY 3

All businesses record information on profit and loss. One way to organize and analyze this information is with matrices. In this activity, you explore how Family Snack uses matrices to keep track of its profits.

Exploration 1

Family Snack's employees earn a commission on every sale. As part of the company's bookkeeping procedures, the business manager monitors both the weekly sales and the weekly commissions of each salesperson. The matrix **W** below shows one week's sales of cases of Snack Packs, Gift Packs, and Family Packs by Keyes and Zhang.

$$\mathbf{W} = \begin{array}{c} \\ K \\ Z \end{array}\begin{array}{c} S \quad G \quad F \\ \left[\begin{array}{ccc} 4 & 7 & 2 \\ 2 & 6 & 3 \end{array}\right] \end{array}$$

The company sells Snack Packs for $45.00 per case, Gift Packs for $70.00 per case, and Family Packs for $95.00 per case. This information can be represented in a **column matrix**, as shown below. Each element in the matrix $\mathbf{M_P}$ represents the price per case of a particular item.

$$\mathbf{M_P} = \begin{array}{c} \\ S \\ G \\ F \end{array}\begin{array}{c} Price \\ \left[\begin{array}{c} 45.00 \\ 70.00 \\ 95.00 \end{array}\right] \end{array}$$

a. 1. Determine the value of the sales made by each employee in matrix **W**.

2. Describe how you determined the values in Step **1**.

ACTIVITY 3

In this activity, students are introduced to matrix multiplication.

teacher note

A brief assessment of the mathematical content in Activity **3**, for use at your discretion, appears in the Teacher Resources for this module.

Materials List

■ none

Technology

■ matrix manipulator

Student Outcomes

After completing the following explorations and discussions, students should be able to:

✴ multiply matrices by hand

✴ determine the dimensions of the product matrix in a matrix multiplication

✴ interpret the data in a product matrix

✴ use technology to multiply matrices, specifically ones with larger dimensions

✴ recognize matrices that cannot be multiplied

✴ show why matrix multiplication is not commutative.

teacher note

In Exploration **1**, students are expected to find product matrices by hand. In Exploration **2**, students use technology to multiply matrices.

As students observe in Part **d** of Exploration **1**, matrix multiplication does not always lead to a meaningful product in a real-world context. For help in interpreting the results of matrix multiplication, students should examine the row and column headings. In this case, the column headings of the matrix on the left must be the same—and in the same order—as the row headings of the matrix on the right.

Exploration 1

a. 1. Keyes made $860 in sales, while Zhang made $795 in sales.

2. Sample response: To determine the value of the sales made by each person, you must multiply the number of cases of each item sold by the selling price of that item, then add these products. **Note:** Some students might recognize that each row in the sales matrix **W** can be multiplied by the column matrix $\mathbf{M_P}$, as shown below.

$$\mathbf{W \bullet M_P} = \begin{array}{c} \\ K \\ Z \end{array}\begin{array}{c} Sales \\ \left[\begin{array}{c} 860.00 \\ 795.00 \end{array}\right] \end{array}$$

b. 1. Sample matrix:

Com.

$$\mathbf{M_C} = \begin{array}{c} S \\ G \\ F \end{array}\begin{bmatrix} 2.25 \\ 4.20 \\ 7.20 \end{bmatrix}$$

2. The matrix below illustrates the product $\mathbf{W} \bullet \mathbf{M_C}$.

Com.

$$\mathbf{W} \bullet \mathbf{M_C} = \begin{array}{c} K \\ Z \end{array}\begin{bmatrix} 52.80 \\ 51.30 \end{bmatrix}$$

c. 1. The product matrix is shown below.

Sales   Com.

$$\mathbf{W} \bullet \mathbf{M} = \begin{array}{c} K \\ Z \end{array}\begin{bmatrix} 860.00 & 52.80 \\ 795.00 & 51.30 \end{bmatrix}$$

2. The dimensions of the matrix are 2×2.

3. The information in the matrix represents the total value of the sales and commissions for each salesperson.

d. 1. The product matrix is shown below.

$$\mathbf{M} \bullet \mathbf{W} = \begin{array}{c} S \\ G \\ F \end{array}\begin{bmatrix} 184.5 & 328.5 & 96.75 \\ 288.4 & 515.2 & 152.6 \\ 394.4 & 708.2 & 211.6 \end{bmatrix}$$

2. The dimensions of the matrix are 3×3.

3. Sample response: The information in the matrix has no meaning in this context. For example, the entry 184.5 represents the sum of the sales made by Keyes and the commission earned by Zhang on Snack Packs. This information is not of any use to the company.

Discussion 1

a. Answers will vary, depending on the methods students used in Part **a**. Sample response: Matrix multiplication is the better method because it is more orderly, especially when the numbers of elements in the matrices grow larger.

b. The number of columns in matrix **A** must equal the number of rows in matrix **B**.

c. Sample response: The operation $\mathbf{W} \bullet \mathbf{M}$ is more efficient because it is a one-step process that includes all of the information in one place.

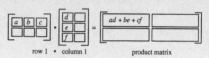

mathematics note

When a matrix **P** with dimensions $k \times m$ is multiplied by a matrix **Q** with dimensions $m \times n$, the dimensions of the **product matrix P • Q** are $k \times n$. The number of columns in the first matrix must equal the number of rows in the second matrix.

To obtain the product matrix, row 1 of the first matrix is "multiplied" with column 1 of the second matrix, as shown in Figure **1-4**. This process is repeated until each row of the first matrix has been multiplied with each column of the second matrix.

row 1 • column 1   product matrix

FIGURE 1-4   Multiplying row 1 by column 1.

When row 1 of the first matrix is multiplied with column 1 of the second matrix, the sum of the products is placed in row 1, column 1 of the product matrix. In general, when row i of the first matrix is multiplied with column j of a second matrix, the sum of the products is placed in row i, column j of the product matrix.

For example, the equation below shows a 2×3 matrix **P** multiplied with a 3×2 matrix **Q**. The dimensions of the product matrix **P • Q** are 2×2.

$$\begin{bmatrix} 2 & 6 & 9 \\ 1 & 3 & 4 \end{bmatrix} \bullet \begin{bmatrix} 2 & 7 \\ 5 & 8 \\ 9 & 0 \end{bmatrix} = \begin{bmatrix} 2\bullet2+6\bullet5+9\bullet9 & 2\bullet7+6\bullet8+9\bullet0 \\ 1\bullet2+3\bullet5+4\bullet9 & 1\bullet7+3\bullet8+4\bullet0 \end{bmatrix} = \begin{bmatrix} 115 & 62 \\ 53 & 31 \end{bmatrix}$$

b. The commission earned for selling a case of Snack Packs is $2.25, for a case of Gift Packs is $4.20, and for a case of Family Packs $7.20.

1. Write a column matrix $\mathbf{M_c}$ to represent the commission earned by selling a case of each product.

2. Use matrix multiplication to determine the commission earned by each salesperson for the sales shown in matrix **W**.

c. In Parts **a** and **b**, you used two different column matrices to represent Family Snack's selling prices and commissions. As shown below, these two matrices could also be combined into a single 3×2 matrix.

Price   Com.

$$\mathbf{M} = \begin{array}{c} S \\ G \\ F \end{array}\begin{bmatrix} 45.00 & 2.25 \\ 70.00 & 4.20 \\ 95.00 & 7.20 \end{bmatrix}$$

1. Use the process described in the mathematics note to find the product $\mathbf{W} \bullet \mathbf{M}$.

2. Record the dimensions of the product matrix.

3. Describe the information contained in the product matrix.

d. 1. Use the process described in the mathematics note to find the product $\mathbf{W} \bullet \mathbf{M}$.

2. Record the dimensions of the product matrix.

3. Describe the information contained in the product matrix.

Discussion 1

a. Compare the methods you used to determine the values in Parts **a** and **b** of the exploration. Which appears to be the better method and why?

b. If the product matrix $\mathbf{A} \bullet \mathbf{B}$ exists, what must be true about the number of columns in matrix **A** and the number of rows in matrix **B**?

c. What advantages are there to performing the operation $\mathbf{W} \bullet \mathbf{M}$ instead of the operations $\mathbf{W} \bullet \mathbf{M_p}$ and $\mathbf{W} \bullet \mathbf{M_c}$?

d. 1. Was the information displayed in the product matrix $\mathbf{W} \bullet \mathbf{M}$ meaningful? Explain your response.

2. Was the information displayed in the product matrix $\mathbf{W} \bullet \mathbf{M}$ meaningful? Explain your response.

e. Which employee earned more in commissions for the sales shown in matrix **W**? Justify your response.

f. Suppose that Family Snack changes the commissions it pays to 10% of the sales price.

1. Describe how you could determine a matrix **C**, representing commission per case, using the price matrix **P** below.

$$P = \begin{bmatrix} S & G & F \\ \$45.00 & \$70.00 & \$95.00 \end{bmatrix}$$

2. How could you use C^T (the transpose of **C**), along with matrix **W**, to calculate the commissions for Keyes and Zhang?

3. Is it possible to use **C** instead of C^T in your calculations? Explain your response.

Exploration 2

In Exploration **1**, you used matrix multiplication to analyze the sales of two of Family Snack's employees. In this exploration, you use technology to help the company organize and manipulate some additional sales information.

a. Use technology to find the product **W • M**. Compare this product with your results in Part **c** of Exploration **1**.

b. Besides Keyes and Zhang, Family Snack employs another salesperson, Troy, and a new trainee, Lia. In the week represented in matrix **W**, Troy sold 3 cases of Snack Packs, 9 cases of Gift Packs, and 1 case of Family Packs. Lia sold 6 cases of Snack Packs, 0 Gift Packs, and 0 Family Packs.

Combine this information with the information in matrix **W** to create a new matrix W_2.

c. Determine the product matrix $W_2 \cdot M$ and record its dimensions. Describe the information contained in this matrix.

d. Evaluate the product matrix $W \cdot M_2$ and interpret the results.

e. Matrix **V** below shows the cases of nuts, jerky, and jam sold by each salesperson during the week represented in matrix W_2. Combine this information with that in matrix W_2 to create a new matrix W_3.

$$V = \begin{array}{c} \\ K \\ Z \\ T \\ L \end{array} \begin{bmatrix} N & J & M \\ 2 & 3 & 0 \\ 3 & 1 & 6 \\ 3 & 0 & 3 \\ 2 & 4 & 1 \end{bmatrix}$$

Exploration 2

a. Students multiply matrices **M** and **W** using technology. They should observe that the product is the same as that obtained in Exploration **1**.

b. Sample matrix:

$$W_2 = \begin{array}{c} \\ K \\ Z \\ T \\ L \end{array} \begin{bmatrix} S & G & F \\ 4 & 7 & 2 \\ 2 & 6 & 3 \\ 3 & 9 & 1 \\ 6 & 0 & 0 \end{bmatrix}$$

c. Students should use technology to obtain the 4×2 product matrix below. This matrix shows the value of the sales and commissions for each salesperson.

$$W_2 \cdot M = \begin{array}{c} \\ K \\ Z \\ T \\ L \end{array} \begin{bmatrix} \text{Sales} & \text{Com.} \\ 860.00 & 52.80 \\ 795.00 & 51.30 \\ 855.00 & 51.75 \\ 270.00 & 13.50 \end{bmatrix}$$

d. The product does not exist because the number of columns in **M** does not equal the number of rows in W_2. When attempting to multiply $M \cdot W_2$ using technology, students will receive an error message.

e. Sample matrix:

$$W_3 = \begin{array}{c} \\ K \\ Z \\ T \\ L \end{array} \begin{bmatrix} N & J & M & S & G & F \\ 2 & 3 & 0 & 4 & 7 & 2 \\ 3 & 1 & 6 & 2 & 6 & 3 \\ 3 & 0 & 3 & 3 & 9 & 1 \\ 2 & 4 & 1 & 6 & 0 & 0 \end{bmatrix}$$

d. 1. Yes. The entries in the matrix indicate the amount of commission earned by each salesperson.

2. No. The elements in the matrix are not meaningful in this context. (See sample response to Part **d** of Exploration **1**.)

Note: The fact that matrix multiplication is not commutative will be examined in Exploration **2**. You might wish to emphasize that multiplication of matrices does not guarantee a product matrix which contains useful information. Each product must be evaluated in context.

e. Keyes earned $1.50 more in commissions than Zhang as shown in Part **b.2** of Exploration **1**.

f. 1. The commission matrix is found by multiplying $0.10 \cdot P$. The result is:

$$C = \begin{bmatrix} S & G & F \\ \$4.50 & \$7.00 & \$9.50 \end{bmatrix}$$

2. Multiplying $W \cdot C^T$ results in a matrix that shows the total commission earned by each employee.

3. Sample response: In this case, **W • C** cannot be done because the dimensions are not appropriate. Matrix **C** is a 1×3 matrix and **W** is a matrix 2×3. However, C^T is a 3×1 matrix, so the product $W \cdot C^T$ does exist. The product is a 2×1 matrix showing the total commission for each employee.

f. Sample matrix:

$$\mathbf{S}=\begin{array}{c} \\ N \\ J \\ M \\ S \\ G \\ F \end{array}\overset{\text{Price \quad Com.}}{\begin{bmatrix} 6.00 & 0.18 \\ 10.00 & 0.30 \\ 8.00 & 0.32 \\ 45.00 & 2.25 \\ 70.00 & 4.20 \\ 95.00 & 7.20 \end{bmatrix}}$$

g. Students should use technology to obtain the product below. This matrix shows the value of the sales and commissions for each salesperson on Family Snack's entire product line.

$$\mathbf{W_3 \bullet S}=\begin{array}{c} \\ K \\ Z \\ T \\ L \end{array}\overset{\text{Sales \quad Com.}}{\begin{bmatrix} 902.00 & 54.06 \\ 871.00 & 54.06 \\ 902.00 & 53.25 \\ 330.00 & 15.38 \end{bmatrix}}$$

h. The product does not exist because the number of columns in **S** does not equal the number of rows in $\mathbf{W_3}$.

Discussion 2

a. Sample response: To multiply an $m \times n$ matrix by a $p \times q$ matrix, it is first necessary to make sure that n equals p. In other words, the number of columns in the first matrix must equal the number of rows in the second matrix. Once that condition has been met, multiplication of the matrices **A** and **B** below results in the product matrix **C**.

$$\mathbf{A}=\begin{bmatrix} a_{11} & a_{12} & \cdots & a_{1n} \\ a_{21} & a_{22} & \cdots & a_{2n} \\ \vdots & \vdots & \vdots & \vdots \\ a_{m1} & a_{m2} & \cdots & a_{mn} \end{bmatrix} \quad \mathbf{B}=\begin{bmatrix} b_{11} & b_{12} & \cdots & b_{1q} \\ b_{21} & b_{22} & \cdots & b_{2q} \\ \vdots & \vdots & \vdots & \vdots \\ b_{p1} & b_{p2} & \cdots & b_{pq} \end{bmatrix}$$

$$\mathbf{C}=\begin{bmatrix} a_{11}b_{11}+a_{12}b_{21}+a_{13}b_{31}+\cdots+a_{1n}b_{p1} & \cdots & a_{11}b_{1p}+a_{12}b_{2p}+a_{13}b_{3p}+\cdots+a_{1n}b_{pq} \\ \vdots & \vdots & \vdots \\ a_{m1}b_{11}+a_{m2}b_{21}+a_{m3}b_{31}+\cdots+a_{mn}b_{p1} & \cdots & a_{m1}b_{1p}+a_{m2}b_{2p}+a_{m3}b_{3p}+\cdots+a_{mn}b_{pq} \end{bmatrix}$$

b. Sample response: The product $\mathbf{S} \bullet \mathbf{W_3}$ cannot be done because the number of columns in **S** does not equal the number of rows in $\mathbf{W_3}$.

c. Sample response: Matrix multiplication is not commutative because $\mathbf{A} \bullet \mathbf{B}$ does not always equal $\mathbf{B} \bullet \mathbf{A}$. For example, if the dimensions of matrix **A** are 3×4 and the dimensions of **B** are 4×5, then the product of $\mathbf{A} \bullet \mathbf{B}$ exists, but the product of $\mathbf{B} \bullet \mathbf{A}$ is not defined.

If the dimensions of matrix **A** are 3×4 and the dimensions of **B** are 4×3, then both products exist, but their dimensions are different. Therefore, the two product matrices are not equal.

---

f. Family Snack sells nuts for $6.00 per case, jerky for $10.00 per case, and jam for $8.00 per case.

The commission earned for selling a case of nuts is $0.18, for a case of jerky is $0.30, and for a case of jam is $0.32.

Combine this information with that in matrix **M** to create a new matrix **S**.

g. Evaluate the product matrix $\mathbf{W_3} \bullet \mathbf{S}$ and interpret the results.

h. Evaluate the product matrix $\mathbf{S} \bullet \mathbf{W_3}$ and interpret the results.

Discussion 2

a. Describe the process of multiplying an $m \times n$ by a $p \times q$ matrix.

b. Why is the matrix multiplication $\mathbf{S} \bullet \mathbf{W_3}$ not possible?

c. When using real numbers, multiplication is commutative. For example, $6 \bullet 14 = 14 \bullet 6$. Matrix multiplication, however, is not commutative. Explain why this is the case.

Warm-Up

1. Consider the five matrices shown below.

$$\mathbf{A}=\begin{bmatrix} 1 & 2 & 3 & 4 \end{bmatrix} \quad \mathbf{C}=\begin{bmatrix} 3 & -1 & 4 \\ 0 & 1 & -2 \end{bmatrix}$$

$$\mathbf{B}=\begin{bmatrix} -1 \\ -2 \\ -3 \\ -4 \end{bmatrix} \quad \mathbf{D}=\begin{bmatrix} 3 \\ 1 \\ 4 \end{bmatrix} \quad \mathbf{E}=\begin{bmatrix} 2 & 9 & 1 \\ 0 & 6 & 1 \\ 1 & 2 & 6 \\ 0 & 5 & 1 \\ 8 & 3 & 1 \end{bmatrix}$$

If possible, find each of the following product matrices. When matrix multiplication is possible, show how the elements in the product matrix are formed. If multiplication is not possible, explain why not.

   a. $\mathbf{A} \bullet \mathbf{B}$

   b. $\mathbf{C} \bullet \mathbf{D}$

   c. $\mathbf{E} \bullet \mathbf{B}$

2. Matrix **L** has dimensions $p \times q$ and matrix **N** has dimensions $s \times t$.

   a. What must be true for $\mathbf{L} \bullet \mathbf{N}$ to be possible?

   b. If $\mathbf{L} \bullet \mathbf{N}$ is possible, what are the dimensions of the resulting matrix?

Warm-Up

1. a. $\mathbf{A} \bullet \mathbf{B} = [1(-1) + 2(-2) + 3(-3) + 4(-4)] = [-30]$

   b.
$$\mathbf{C} \bullet \mathbf{D} = \begin{bmatrix} 3 \bullet 3 + (-1) \bullet 1 + 4 \bullet 4 \\ 0 \bullet 3 + 1 \bullet 1 + (-2) \bullet 4 \end{bmatrix} = \begin{bmatrix} 24 \\ -7 \end{bmatrix}$$

   c. In this case, matrix multiplication is not possible. Because matrix **E** is 5×3 and matrix **B** is 4×1, the number of columns in **E** is not the same as the number of rows in **B**.

2. a. For multiplication to be possible, q must equal s.

   b. If the matrix multiplication is possible, the product matrix will have dimensions $p \times t$.

Assignment

3.1 Consider the following two matrices.

$$X = \begin{bmatrix} 7 & 2 & 3 \\ -1 & 0 & 4 \end{bmatrix} \qquad Y = \begin{bmatrix} 3 & 1 \\ 2 & 5 \\ 0 & 2 \end{bmatrix}$$

a. 1. Find the product matrix $X \bullet Y$ and describe its dimensions.

2. How are the dimensions of the product matrix related to the dimensions of X and Y?

b. 1. Find the product matrix $Y \bullet X$ and describe its dimensions.

2. How are the dimensions of the product matrix related to the dimensions of X and Y?

c. Describe how your responses to Parts a and b show that matrix multiplication is not commutative.

3.2 A store has placed an order with Family Snack represented by the matrix O shown below. Each element in the matrix indicates the number of a specific item in the order.

$$O = \begin{array}{c} N \\ J \\ M \\ S \\ G \\ F \end{array} \begin{bmatrix} 20 \\ 60 \\ 48 \\ 24 \\ 12 \\ 2 \end{bmatrix}$$

a. The total requirement matrix for Family Snack's product line is matrix R shown below. Use matrix R to determine the number of each simple component needed to fill the order.

$$R = \begin{array}{c} N \\ J \\ M \\ S \\ G \\ F \end{array} \begin{array}{cccccc} N & J & M & S & G & F \\ \begin{bmatrix} 1 & 0 & 0 & 2 & 4 & 12 \\ 0 & 1 & 0 & 6 & 12 & 36 \\ 0 & 0 & 1 & 0 & 3 & 12 \\ 0 & 0 & 0 & 1 & 2 & 6 \\ 0 & 0 & 0 & 0 & 1 & 3 \\ 0 & 0 & 0 & 0 & 0 & 1 \end{bmatrix} \end{array}$$

Assignment

Problems suitable for use as assessment items are identified by an asterisk (*).

3.1 a. 1. The dimensions of the product matrix are 2×2.

$$X \bullet Y = \begin{bmatrix} 25 & 23 \\ -3 & 7 \end{bmatrix}$$

2. The row dimension is the number of rows in X, while the column dimension is the number of columns in Y.

b. 1. The dimensions of the product matrix are 3×3.

$$Y \bullet X = \begin{bmatrix} 20 & 6 & 13 \\ 9 & 4 & 26 \\ -2 & 0 & 8 \end{bmatrix}$$

2. The row dimension is the number of rows in Y, while the column dimension is the number of columns in X.

c. Answers will vary. Students should mention that because the two product matrices have different dimensions and different elements, $X \bullet Y \neq Y \bullet X$. Therefore, matrix multiplication is not commutative.

* 3.2 a. By performing the following matrix multiplication, students should determine that 140 boxes of nuts, 420 pieces of jerky, and 108 jars of jam are needed to fill the order.

$$R \bullet O = \begin{array}{c} N \\ J \\ M \\ S \\ G \\ F \end{array} \begin{bmatrix} 140 \\ 420 \\ 108 \\ 60 \\ 18 \\ 2 \end{bmatrix}$$

b. By performing the matrix multiplication below, students should find that 318 boxes of nuts, 1104 pieces of jerky, and 84 jars of jam are needed to fill the order.

$$R \bullet \begin{array}{c} N \\ J \\ M \\ S \\ G \\ F \end{array}\begin{bmatrix} 150 \\ 600 \\ 48 \\ 60 \\ 12 \\ 0 \end{bmatrix} = \begin{array}{c} N \\ J \\ M \\ S \\ G \\ F \end{array}\begin{bmatrix} 318 \\ 1104 \\ 84 \\ 84 \\ 12 \\ 0 \end{bmatrix}$$

* **3.3 a.** Sample matrix:

$$S = \begin{array}{c} 1 \\ 2 \\ 3 \\ 4 \end{array}\begin{bmatrix} 10 \\ 6 \\ 4 \\ 3 \end{bmatrix}$$

b. The columns of **R** must match the rows of **S** in Part **a.**

$$R = \begin{array}{c} \\ E_1 \\ E_2 \\ E_3 \\ E_4 \end{array}\begin{array}{cccc} 1 & 2 & 3 & 4 \\ \begin{bmatrix} 4 & 0 & 4 & 4 \\ 3 & 4 & 0 & 5 \\ 2 & 5 & 5 & 0 \\ 3 & 3 & 3 & 3 \end{bmatrix}\end{array}$$

c. As shown in the product matrix below, employee 3 was first, employees 2 and 4 tied for second, and employee 1 was fourth.

$$R \bullet S = \begin{array}{c} \\ E_1 \\ E_2 \\ E_3 \\ E_4 \end{array}\begin{array}{c} \text{Pts.} \\ \begin{bmatrix} 68 \\ 69 \\ 70 \\ 69 \end{bmatrix}\end{array}$$

3.4 The matrix below is the product of the requirement matrix **R** and matrix **O**.

$$R \bullet O = \begin{array}{c} N \\ J \\ M \\ S \\ G \\ F \end{array}\begin{array}{ccccc} O_1 & O_2 & O_3 & O_4 & O_5 \\ \begin{bmatrix} 68 & 104 & 272 & 148 & 32 \\ 178 & 270 & 681 & 396 & 74 \\ 52 & 72 & 182 & 130 & 14 \\ 28 & 42 & 106 & 64 & 12 \\ 10 & 16 & 44 & 28 & 2 \\ 2 & 4 & 12 & 8 & 0 \end{bmatrix}\end{array}$$

b. Another customer has ordered 150 boxes of nuts, 600 pieces of jerky, 48 jars of jam, 60 Snack Packs, and 12 Gift Packs. Determine the number of each simple component needed to fill this order.

3.3 Last year, Family Snack offered an incentive program to its sales staff. Employees received 10 incentive points for each month in which they ranked first in sales, 6 points for each month in which they ranked second, 4 points for third, and 3 for fourth.

a. Create a matrix **S** that displays the incentive points awarded for each ranking.

b. Employee 1 ranked first during 4 months, third during 4 months, and fourth during 4 months. Employee 2 ranked first during 3 months, second during 4 months, and fourth during 5 months. Employee 3 ranked first 2 months, second 5 months, and third 5 months. Employee 4 ranked first, second, third, and fourth for 3 months each.

Create a matrix **R** that displays the number of months at each rank for each of the four employees.

c. The employee with the most incentive points receives an all-expenses-paid vacation. Determine the order in which the four employees finished in the contest, along with their scores.

3.4 Matrix **R** is the total requirement matrix for Family Snack's product line. Family Snack has received orders O_1, O_2, O_3, O_4, and O_5 from five different customers, as shown in matrix **O** below.

$$R = \begin{array}{c} N \\ J \\ M \\ S \\ G \\ F \end{array}\begin{array}{cccccc} N & J & M & S & G & F \\ \begin{bmatrix} 1 & 0 & 0 & 2 & 4 & 12 \\ 0 & 1 & 0 & 6 & 12 & 36 \\ 0 & 0 & 1 & 0 & 3 & 12 \\ 0 & 0 & 0 & 1 & 2 & 6 \\ 0 & 0 & 0 & 0 & 1 & 3 \\ 0 & 0 & 0 & 0 & 0 & 1 \end{bmatrix}\end{array} \qquad O = \begin{array}{c} N \\ J \\ M \\ S \\ G \\ F \end{array}\begin{array}{ccccc} O_1 & O_2 & O_3 & O_4 & O_5 \\ \begin{bmatrix} 12 & 20 & 60 & 20 & 8 \\ 10 & 18 & 45 & 12 & 2 \\ 16 & 12 & 14 & 22 & 8 \\ 8 & 10 & 18 & 8 & 8 \\ 4 & 4 & 8 & 4 & 2 \\ 2 & 4 & 12 & 8 & 0 \end{bmatrix}\end{array}$$

a. How many boxes of nuts are needed to fill O_3?

b. How many boxes of nuts are needed to fill all five orders?

c. How many pieces of jerky are needed to fill O_2?

d. How many pieces of jerky are needed to fill all five orders?

e. How many jars of jam are needed to fill all five orders?

* * * * *

a. Family Snack needs 272 boxes of nuts to fill O_3.

b. Family Snack needs 624 boxes of nuts to fill all five orders.

c. Family Snack needs 270 pieces of jerky to fill O_2.

d. Family Snack needs 1599 pieces of jerky to fill all five orders.

e. Family Snack needs 450 jars of jam to fill all five orders.

✳ ✳ ✳ ✳ ✳

3.5 A bicycle shop use matrices to track its monthly sales. The shop sells both mountain bikes (MT) and touring bikes (TR). The number of bikes sold in July are displayed in matrix **J** below.

$$\mathbf{J} = \begin{array}{c} \text{mountain} \\ \text{touring} \end{array} \begin{array}{ccc} 43\text{ cm} & 48\text{ cm} & 54\text{ cm} \end{array} \left[\begin{array}{ccc} 2 & 6 & 5 \\ 5 & 9 & 8 \end{array} \right]$$

Matrix **S** shows the selling price in dollars for each model.

$$\mathbf{P} = \begin{array}{c} 43\text{ cm} \\ 48\text{ cm} \\ 54\text{ cm} \end{array} \begin{array}{cc} \text{MT} & \text{TR} \end{array} \left[\begin{array}{cc} 250 & 280 \\ 270 & 300 \\ 290 & 320 \end{array} \right]$$

a. What matrix operation would allow you to calculate the value of the July sales for each model? Perform this operation. Use the column and row headings for matrices **P** and **J** to determine appropriate headings for the product matrix.

b. Describe what each element in the product matrix represents. If some elements have no clear interpretation, identify them and explain why this occurs.

c. Is it possible to perform the matrix operation in Part **a** if the order of the matrices is reversed? If so, describe the elements that have clear interpretations. If the operation is not possible, explain why not.

d. Are the total July sales for the bicycle shop more or less than $15,000? Explain your response.

3.6 Consider the five matrices shown below.

$$A = \begin{bmatrix} 2 & 3 & 1 \\ -2 & 7 & 8 \end{bmatrix} \quad B = \begin{bmatrix} 3 & 0 & 5 & -2 \\ 1 & 8 & -4 & 9 \\ 11 & 6 & -5 & 0 \end{bmatrix} \quad C = \begin{bmatrix} 2 & 5 & -6 \\ 9 & -4 & 0 \\ 9 & 3 & 1 \end{bmatrix}$$

$$D = \begin{bmatrix} 1 & 0 & 0 \\ 0 & 1 & 0 \\ 0 & 0 & 1 \end{bmatrix} \quad E = \begin{bmatrix} 0 & 7 & -6 & 7 \\ 2 & -1 & 1 & 0 \\ 5 & -8 & 3 & -11 \\ 2 & 9 & 1 & 7 \end{bmatrix}$$

* 3.5 a. As shown below, the value of the sales for each model can be calculated by matrix multiplication.

$$\mathbf{J \cdot P} = \begin{array}{c} \text{MT} \\ \text{TR} \end{array} \begin{array}{cc} \text{MT} & \text{TR} \end{array} \left[\begin{array}{cc} 3570 & 3960 \\ 6000 & 6660 \end{array} \right]$$

b. Because it is the product of the first row in **J** and the first column in **P** (both of which represent values for mountain bikes), $3570 represents the sales of mountain bikes. Similarly, $6660 represents the sales from touring bikes. The other two elements are not relevant because they involve numbers representing mountain bikes multiplied by numbers representing touring bikes.

c. Yes, it is possible to perform the matrix operation in Part **a** if the order of the matrices is reversed. In the product matrix below, $1900 is the income from 43-cm bikes, $4320 is the income from the 48-cm bikes, and $4010 is the income from 54-cm bikes. (As in Part **b**, the only relevant elements are those along the diagonal.)

$$\mathbf{P \cdot J} = \begin{array}{c} 43 \\ 48 \\ 54 \end{array} \begin{array}{ccc} 43 & 48 & 54 \end{array} \left[\begin{array}{ccc} 1900 & 4020 & 3490 \\ 2040 & 4320 & 3750 \\ 2180 & 4620 & 4010 \end{array} \right]$$

d. Total July sales are less than $15,000. To find the total sales, students should add only the relevant elements in the product matrix:

$$\$3570 + \$6660 = \$10{,}230$$

or

$$\$1900 + \$4320 + \$4010 = \$10{,}230.$$

3.6 a. The dimensions of **A • B** are 2×4.

$$\mathbf{A \bullet B} = \begin{bmatrix} 20 & 30 & -7 & 23 \\ 89 & 104 & -78 & 67 \end{bmatrix}$$

The column dimension of **B** does not match the row dimension of **A**, therefore **B • A** is not possible.

b. The dimensions of **A • C** are 2×3.

$$\mathbf{A \bullet C} = \begin{bmatrix} 40 & 1 & -11 \\ 131 & -14 & 20 \end{bmatrix}$$

The column dimension of **C** does not match the row dimension of **A**, therefore **C • A** is not possible.

c. The column dimension of **B** does not match the row dimension of **C**, therefore **B • C** is not possible. The dimensions of **C • B** are 3×4.

$$\mathbf{C \bullet B} = \begin{bmatrix} -55 & 4 & 20 & 41 \\ 23 & -32 & 61 & -54 \\ 41 & 30 & 28 & 9 \end{bmatrix}$$

d. The dimensions of both product matrices are 3×3.

$$\mathbf{C \bullet D} = \begin{bmatrix} 2 & 5 & -6 \\ 9 & -4 & 0 \\ 9 & 3 & 1 \end{bmatrix} \qquad \mathbf{D \bullet C} = \begin{bmatrix} 2 & 5 & -6 \\ 9 & -4 & 0 \\ 9 & 3 & 1 \end{bmatrix}$$

e. The dimensions of **B • E** are 3×4.

$$\mathbf{B \bullet E} = \begin{bmatrix} 21 & -37 & -5 & -48 \\ 14 & 112 & -1 & 114 \\ -13 & 111 & -75 & 132 \end{bmatrix}$$

The column dimension of **E** does not match the row dimension of **B**, therefore **E • B** is not possible.

3.7 Sample response: The value of the stock is $1,995. This is the sum of the elements in the product matrix that results from multiplying the cost matrix and the stock matrix.

Research Project

a. Multiplication of 2×2 matrices is associative, as shown below.

$$(\mathbf{A \bullet B}) = \begin{bmatrix} ae + bg & af + bh \\ ce + dg & cf + dh \end{bmatrix}$$

$$(\mathbf{A \bullet B}) \bullet \mathbf{C} = \begin{bmatrix} (ae + bg)i + (af + bh)k & (ae + bg)j + (af + bh)l \\ (ce + dg)i + (cf + dh)k & (ce + dg)j + (cf + dh)l \end{bmatrix}$$

$$= \begin{bmatrix} a(ei + fl) + b(gi + hk) & a(ej + fl) + b(gj + hl) \\ c(ei + fl) + d(gi + hk) & c(ej + fl) + d(gj + hl) \end{bmatrix}$$

$$(\mathbf{B \bullet C}) = \begin{bmatrix} ei + fk & ej + fl \\ gi + hk & gj + hl \end{bmatrix}$$

$$\mathbf{A \bullet (B \bullet C)} = \begin{bmatrix} a(ei + fk) + b(gi + hk) & a(ej + fl) + b(gj + hl) \\ c(ei + fk) + d(gi + hk) & c(ej + fl) + d(gj + hl) \end{bmatrix}$$

Therefore, $(\mathbf{A \bullet B}) \bullet \mathbf{C} = \mathbf{A \bullet (B \bullet C)}$.

If possible, find each of the following product matrices using a matrix manipulator. When matrix multiplication is possible, identify the dimensions of the product matrix. If multiplication is not possible, explain why not.

a. **A • B** and **B • A**

b. **A • C** and **C • A**

c. **B • C** and **C • B**

d. **C • D** and **D • C**

e. **B • E** and **E • B**

3.7 A shoe store sells three types of boots: low-top, mid-range, and high-top. Each type of boot comes in three styles; slip-on, buckle, and tie. The following matrix lists the store's inventory:

$$\text{I = type } \begin{array}{c} \\ L \\ M \\ H \end{array} \begin{array}{c} \text{style} \\ \begin{array}{ccc} S & B & T \end{array} \\ \begin{bmatrix} 1 & 6 & 35 \\ 10 & 2 & 9 \\ 12 & 7 & 2 \end{bmatrix} \end{array}$$

The wholesale price of a pair of low-top boots is $21, of mid-range is $30, and of high-tops is $23. Use matrix methods to calculate the wholesale value of this inventory

Research Project

In this module, you have explored matrix addition, subtraction, and multiplication. Use the general 2×2 matrices below to further investigate matrix arithmetic.

$$\mathbf{A} = \begin{bmatrix} a & b \\ c & d \end{bmatrix} \qquad \mathbf{B} = \begin{bmatrix} e & f \\ g & h \end{bmatrix} \qquad \mathbf{C} = \begin{bmatrix} i & j \\ k & l \end{bmatrix}$$

a. Is multiplication of 2×2 matrices associative? In other words, does $(\mathbf{A \bullet B}) \bullet \mathbf{C} = \mathbf{A \bullet (B \bullet C)}$?

b. Is the distributive property of multiplication over addition valid for 2×2 matrices? In other words, does $\mathbf{A \bullet (B + C) = A \bullet B + A \bullet C}$?

c. The identity element for real-number multiplication is 1. For example, $25 \bullet 1 = 25$. Is there an identity for multiplication of 2×2 matrices?

d. For all real numbers, multiplication by 0 results in a product of 0 (the Zero Product Property). Is there a matrix which, when multiplied by **A**, **B**, or **C**, results in a matrix whose elements are all zeros? If so, is there more than one such matrix?

b. The distributive property of multiplication over addition is valid for 2×2 matrices, as shown below.

$$\mathbf{A \bullet (B + C)} = \begin{bmatrix} a & b \\ c & d \end{bmatrix} \bullet \begin{bmatrix} e + i & f + j \\ g + k & h + l \end{bmatrix}$$

$$= \begin{bmatrix} a(e + i) + b(g + k) & a(f + j) + b(h + l) \\ c(e + i) + d(g + k) & c(f + j) + d(h + l) \end{bmatrix}$$

$$= \begin{bmatrix} ae + ai + bg + bk & af + aj + bh + bl \\ ce + ci + dg + dk & cf + cj + dh + dl \end{bmatrix}$$

$$(\mathbf{A \bullet B}) + (\mathbf{A \bullet C}) = \begin{bmatrix} ae + bg & af + bh \\ ce + dg & cf + dh \end{bmatrix} + \begin{bmatrix} ai + bk & aj + bl \\ ci + dk & cj + dl \end{bmatrix}$$

$$= \begin{bmatrix} ae + bg + ai + bk & af + bh + aj + bl \\ ce + dg + ci + dk & cf + dh + cj + dl \end{bmatrix}$$

Therefore, $\mathbf{A \bullet (B + C) = A \bullet B + A \bullet C}$.

c. The identity for multiplication of 2×2 matrices is shown below.

$$\mathbf{I} = \begin{bmatrix} 1 & 0 \\ 0 & 1 \end{bmatrix}$$

d. The Zero Product Matrix for 2×2 matrices is shown below. This matrix is unique.

$$\mathbf{Z} = \begin{bmatrix} 0 & 0 \\ 0 & 0 \end{bmatrix}$$

Summary Assessment

1. Family Snack has decided to add crackers to its product line. The new Snack Pack contains 1 box of nuts, 1 box of crackers, 10 pieces of jerky, and 1 jar of jam; the new Gift Pack contains 2 Snack Packs and 2 jars of jam; and the new Family Pack contains 3 Gift Packs and 4 boxes of crackers.

   a. Construct a requirement graph for Family Snack's new product line.

   b. Use your requirement graph to construct a total requirement matrix for the new product line.

2. An apartment complex offers one-, two-, and three-bedroom apartments. The complex contains 10 furnished and 10 unfurnished one-bedroom apartments; 5 furnished and 10 unfurnished two-bedroom apartments; and 5 furnished and 5 unfurnished three-bedroom apartments.

   A furnished one-bedroom apartment rents for $375 a month; an unfurnished one-bedroom rents for $345. A furnished two-bedroom rents for $400 per month; an unfurnished one rents for $370. A furnished three-bedroom rents for $450 per month; an unfurnished one rents for $420.

   a. Create a 2 × 3 matrix that displays the apartment inventory.

   b. Create a 3 × 2 matrix that displays the rent for each type of apartment.

   c. Find the product of the rent matrix from Part b and the inventory matrix from Part a.

   d. Describe the meaning of each element in the matrix from Part c. If some elements in the matrix have no clear interpretation, explain why this occurs.

   e. The managers of the apartment complex wish to raise the rents by 10%. Construct a matrix showing the new rents.

   f. The monthly electric bills average $80 for a one-bedroom apartment, $95 for a two-bedroom apartment, and $105 for a three-bedroom apartment. Show how matrix multiplication can be used to determine the total electric bill for the entire apartment complex.

   g. In addition to the electric bills from Part f, the apartment managers also must pay bills for other utilities, such as water and sewer. Monthly water bills average $18 for one-bedroom apartments, $26 for two-bedroom apartments, and $42 for three-bedroom apartments. Monthly sewer bills average $15 for one-bedroom apartments, $20 for two-bedroom apartments, and $30 for three-bedroom apartments.

   Show how matrix multiplication can be used to find the monthly utility bills for the entire apartment complex. The utility bill should be broken into water, sewer, and electricity.

teacher note

An additional assessment, for use at your discretion, appears in the Teacher Resources for this module.

Summary Assessment

1. **a.** Sample requirement graph:

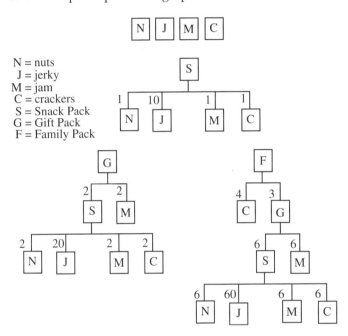

N = nuts
J = jerky
M = jam
C = crackers
S = Snack Pack
G = Gift Pack
F = Family Pack

   b. The corresponding total requirement matrix is shown below.

$$
\mathbf{R} = \begin{array}{c} \\ N \\ J \\ M \\ C \\ S \\ G \\ F \end{array}
\begin{array}{c} \begin{array}{ccccccc} N & J & M & C & S & G & F \end{array} \\
\left[\begin{array}{ccccccc}
1 & 0 & 0 & 0 & 1 & 2 & 6 \\
0 & 1 & 0 & 0 & 10 & 20 & 60 \\
0 & 0 & 1 & 0 & 1 & 4 & 12 \\
0 & 0 & 0 & 1 & 1 & 2 & 10 \\
0 & 0 & 0 & 0 & 1 & 2 & 6 \\
0 & 0 & 0 & 0 & 0 & 1 & 3 \\
0 & 0 & 0 & 0 & 0 & 0 & 1
\end{array} \right] \end{array}
$$

2. Answers may vary, depending on how students organize their matrices.

a. Sample matrix:

$$\mathbf{I} = \begin{array}{c} \\ f \\ u \end{array}\begin{array}{ccc} \text{one} & \text{two} & \text{three} \\ \begin{bmatrix} 10 & 5 & 5 \\ 10 & 10 & 5 \end{bmatrix} \end{array}$$

b. Sample matrix:

$$\mathbf{R} = \begin{array}{c} \\ \text{one} \\ \text{two} \\ \text{three} \end{array}\begin{array}{cc} f & u \\ \begin{bmatrix} 375 & 345 \\ 400 & 370 \\ 450 & 420 \end{bmatrix} \end{array}$$

c. The product of the matrices given in Parts **a** and **b** can be done in two ways.

$$\mathbf{R} \bullet \mathbf{I} = \begin{array}{c} \\ \text{one} \\ \text{two} \\ \text{three} \end{array}\begin{array}{ccc} \text{one} & \text{two} & \text{three} \\ \begin{bmatrix} 7200 & 5325 & 3600 \\ 7700 & 5700 & 3850 \\ 8700 & 6450 & 4350 \end{bmatrix} \end{array}$$

d. The elements along the main diagonal in the product matrix **I** • **R** represent the total rents for the furnished ($8000) and unfurnished ($9250) apartments.

The elements along the main diagonal in the product matrix **R** • **I** represent the total rents for the one-bedroom ($7200), two-bedroom ($5700) and three-bedroom apartments ($4350).

The other elements in both matrices are irrelevant. The irrelevant elements are the result of combining values from different types of apartments. For example, the rent for a one-bedroom apartment multiplied by the number of two-bedroom apartments is meaningless.

e. Students may use scalar multiplication to determine this matrix, as shown below.

$$1.1 \bullet \mathbf{R} = \begin{array}{c} \\ \text{one} \\ \text{two} \\ \text{three} \end{array}\begin{array}{cc} f & u \\ \begin{bmatrix} 412.50 & 379.50 \\ 440.00 & 407.00 \\ 495.00 & 462.00 \end{bmatrix} \end{array}$$

f. Students may have to adjust their matrices so that multiplication is defined (and the product is meaningful). Sample response:

$$\mathbf{I} = \begin{array}{c} \\ \text{one} \\ \text{two} \\ \text{three} \end{array}\begin{bmatrix} 80 \\ 95 \\ 105 \end{bmatrix} = \begin{array}{c} \\ f \\ u \end{array}\begin{bmatrix} 1800 \\ 2275 \end{bmatrix}$$

g. Sample response:

$$\mathbf{I} \bullet \begin{array}{c} \\ \text{one} \\ \text{two} \\ \text{three} \end{array}\begin{array}{ccc} e & s & w \\ \begin{bmatrix} 80 & 15 & 18 \\ 95 & 20 & 26 \\ 105 & 30 & 42 \end{bmatrix} \end{array} = \begin{array}{c} \\ f \\ u \end{array}\begin{array}{ccc} e & s & w \\ \begin{bmatrix} 1800 & 400 & 520 \\ 2275 & 500 & 650 \end{bmatrix} \end{array}$$

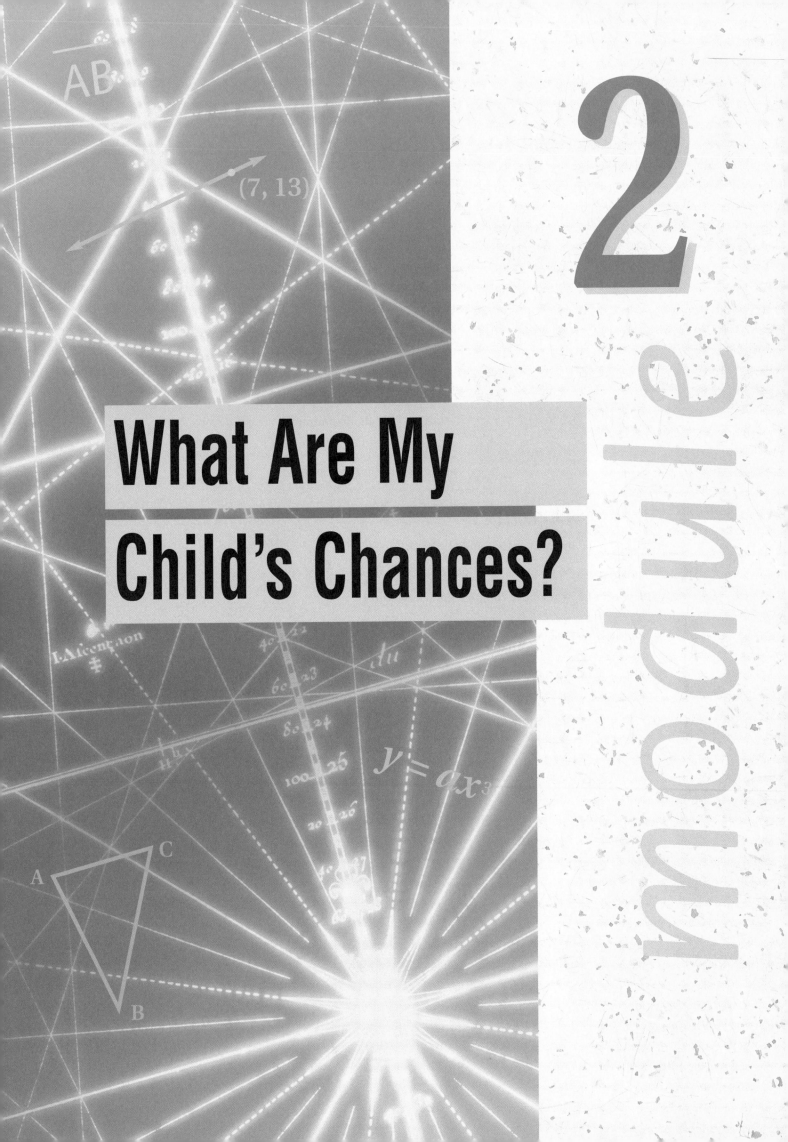

What Are My Child's Chances?

2

module

Overview

Students examine various probability models and their applications to the study of genetics. They use probability to solve problems involving genetic traits and disorders.

Activity 1:   Students review basic terms and concepts associated with probability and calculate experimental probabilities. They identify complementary events and determine their probabilities.

Activity 2:   Students use Venn diagrams, Punnett squares, and tree diagrams to determine theoretical probabilities.

Activity 3:   Students investigate independent and dependent events.

Activity 4:   Students investigate mutually exclusive events.

Activity 5:   Students use simulations to gather data, then compare experimental and theoretical probabilities.

Objectives

In this module, students will:

* receive a brief introduction to the biology of genetics (1, 2)
* identify complementary events (1)
* use Venn diagrams to determine sample spaces and theoretical probabilities (1, 4)
* collect data and calculate experimental probabilities (1, 3, 4, 5)
* compare theoretical and experimental probabilities (2, 4, 5)
* use Punnett squares to determine sample spaces and theoretical probabilitites (2, 3, 4, 5)
* identify independent and dependent events (3, 5)
* investigate formulas for determining the theoretical probability of two or more events, including $P(A \text{ and } B)$ and $P(A \text{ or } B)$, among others (3, 4)
* use tree diagrams to determine sample spaces and theoretical probabilities (3, 4, 5)
* identify mutually exclusive events (4, 5)
* simulate a situation involving independent events (5).

Prerequisites

For this module, students should know:

* how to determine sample spaces
* how to make tree diagrams

* how to use the fundamental counting principle
* how to draw Venn diagrams
* how to calculate expected value.
* how to evaluate exponential expressions.

 Flashbacks, for use at your discretion, appear in the Teacher Resources for this module. These brief problem sets provide a review of some prerequisite skills for each activity.

Planning Guide

Activity	Materials	Technology	Time Line
Activity **1**	■ template for Wheel of Traits (optional)	■ none	2 days
Activity **2**	■ none	■ none	2 days
Activity **3**	■ template for Wheel of Traits (optional)	■ none	2 days
Activity **4**	■ template for Wheel of Traits (optional)	■ none	2 days
Activity **5**	■ coins	■ none	2 days
Assessment Activities	■ none	■ none	3 days **Total: 13 days**

teacher note

This module discusses human characteristics from a biological perspective and uses the vocabulary of genetics. You may wish to present this module in coordination with a biology class or with the cooperation of a science teacher.

The science of genetics is extremely complex. To simplify both the mathematical and scientific focuses of this module, the five traits examined in Activity **1** are assumed to be independent of each other. Throughout the module, each allele in each parent's genotype is assumed to have an equal chance of being passed on to the offspring.

A template for the Wheel of Traits (Figure **2-1** in the student edition) appears in the Teacher Resources for this module.

Introduction

The introduction provides an elementary explanation of genetics and genetic disorders.

Students use five inherited characteristics to explore experimental probability.

Materials List

- template for Wheel of Traits (optional)

teacher note

To ensure that all students obtain the same data set, you might wish to create an overhead transparency of the Wheel of Traits on which to record the classroom totals for each spoke of the wheel. Students should save this data for use in Activities **1, 3,** and **4,** and for the assignments.

A blackline master appears in the Teacher Resources for this module.

Student Outcomes

After completing the following exploration and discussion, students should be able to:

✳ identify a sample space

✳ collect data and calculate experimental probabilities

✳ identify complementary events

✳ use Venn diagrams to show relationships between sets.

Introduction

Genetic diseases are passed on from generation to generation. Many of them can be crippling, even fatal. Even though effective therapies are available for some of these disorders, others are currently untreatable.

Scientists are developing tests to identify genetic diseases in unborn children and to detect adult carriers. Through prenatal screening, and by determining the probability that a particular disease will appear in certain families, many genetic diseases can be prevented. A genetics counselor is an important part of this effort.

The mathematical science of probability, combined with a knowledge of biology and medicine, can help a genetics counselor determine the chances that a child will inherit a genetic disease.

Genetics is the study of **heredity,** the process by which characteristics are passed from one generation to the next. The biological structures that control heredity are **genes.** Your particular combination of genes determines your eye color and hair color, for example, in addition to many of the other characteristics that distinguish you from siblings, parents, and friends.

Most physical traits are determined by several sets of genes. Some, however, such as the presence of free earlobes, are controlled by a single set of genes. Single sets of genes also control blood type and determine the availability of certain hormones and enzymes in the body. How can you calculate a child's chances of having free earlobes or type A blood? In the following activities, you discover how mathematics can help you predict the likelihood of receiving a particular trait.

Exploration

Table **2-1** describes the characteristics associated with five physical traits. Read the descriptions and determine whether or not you have each trait.

30

Exploration

a–d. Students determine and record their personal numbers. For example, a personal number of 10 is reached by moving through the rings as shown in the diagram below:

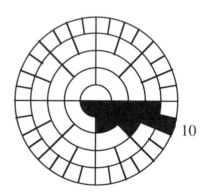

TABLE 2-1 ■ *Five Traits Determined by Single Sets of Genes*	
Trait	**Description**
Mid-digit hair	The middle section of each finger has hair on it.
Widow's peak	When the hair on the head is pulled back, a distinct point in the hairline can be seen in the center of the forehead.
Free earlobes	The bottom parts of the earlobes are not attached to the side of the head.
Rolled tongue	The tongue can be rolled to form a "U" shape.
Folded hands	When the hands are folded so that fingers interlace, the left thumb falls naturally on top.

To explore your own inherited characteristics, you can use a wheel of traits. Figure **2-1** shows a wheel for the five traits described above.

a. Place your finger at the trait in the center of the wheel, "mid-digit hair." If you have this trait, move your finger to the "yes" portion. If you do not have it, move your finger to the "no" portion.

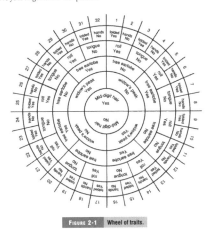

FIGURE 2-1	Wheel of traits.

Module 2 ■ *What Are My Child's Chances?*   31

b. From the portion of the ring where you placed your finger, move outward to the next ring and determine whether or not you have the trait "widow's peak." Again, move your finger to the appropriate portion of the ring.

c. Continue this process for the next three traits, working your way outward through each ring of the wheel.

d. The last portion of the ring where you placed your finger determines your personal number. Record this number.

e. Organize the class results from Parts **a–c** in Table **2-2**. **Note:** Save this table for use in Problem **1.1**.

TABLE 2-2 ■ *Class Results from Wheel of Traits*		
Trait	**No. with Trait**	**No. without Trait**
mid-digit hair		
widow's peak		
free earlobes		
rolled tongue		
folded hands		

f. The set of all possible outcomes for an experiment is the **sample space**. An **event** is a subset of the sample space.

One method of predicting the likelihood of an event is to perform many trials under controlled conditions. The results of these trials provide the **experimental (or empirical) probability** of the event occurring. The experimental probability of an event is the following ratio:

$$\frac{\text{number of times event occurs}}{\text{total number of trials}}$$

Using the class data, calculate the experimental probability of having each of the five traits on the wheel.

Discussion

a. Is each trait on the wheel equally likely to occur in your class? Explain your response.

b. Why does the wheel in Figure **2-1** have 32 different personal numbers?

c. Given the five traits in the wheel in Figure **2-1**, how many different pairs of traits exist?

e. Sample data:

Trait	No. with Trait	No. without Trait
mid-digit hair	18	7
widow's peak	17	8
free earlobes	18	7
rolled tongue	19	6
folded hands	20	5

f. The experimental probabilities in the table below were calculated using the sample data given in Part **e.**

Trait	Experimental Probability
mid-digit hair	18/25
widow's peak	17/25
free earlobes	18/25
rolled tongue	19/25
folded hands	20/25 = 4/5

Discussion

a. Answers will vary, depending on the class data. Sample response: No. Because the probability of having each trait is not the same as the probability of having each of the other traits, the traits are not equally likely.

b. For each of the five traits, there are two possibilities: yes or no. Therefore, the number of possible outcomes is 2^5, or 32.

c. Because order is unimportant in this situation, there are 10 different pairs of traits. Using the letters A, B, C, D, and E to designate each trait, the 10 pairs are: AB, AC, AD, AE, BC, BD, BE, CD, CE, and DE.

d. Sample Venn diagram:

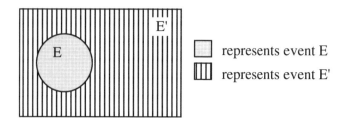

☐ represents event E
▥ represents event E'

e. Given the experimental probability of having a specific trait, the experimental probability of not having that trait can be calculated by subtracting the known probability from 1. For example, if the experimental probability of having a widow's peak is 17/25, the experimental probability of not having this trait is 1 – 17/25 = 8/25.

f. Sample response: If the class is representative of the school population, the product of the school population and the experimental probability of a trait would give a prediction for the number of students with that trait.

Warm-Up

1. **a.** HH, HT, TH, TT
   b. (1,1), (1,2), (1,3), (1,4), (1,5), (1,6), (2,1), (2,2), (2,3), (2,4), (2,5), (2,6), (3,1), (3,2), (3,3), (3,4), (3,5), (3,6), (4,1), (4,2), (4,3), (4,4), (4,5), (4,6), (5,1), (5,2), (5,3), (5,4), (5,5), (5,6), (6,1), (6,2), (6,3), (6,4), (6,5), (6,6)
   c. RR, RS, RP, SR, SS, SP, PR, PS, PP

2. **a.** A flipped coin shows heads.
   b. A yellow or red light is visible at an intersection.
   c. A grade of B, C, D, or F is received in social studies.

3. Sample response: The probability of the complement is equal to the difference between 1 and the probability of the event. In this case, $P' = 5/6$.

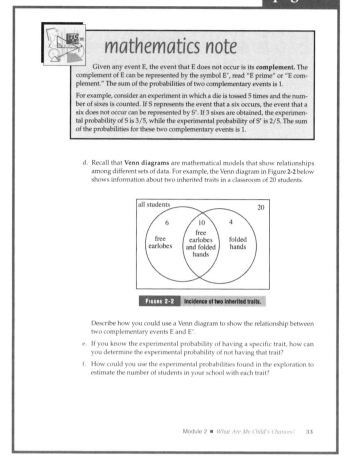

mathematics note

Given any event E, the event that E does not occur is its **complement**. The complement of E can be represented by the symbol E', read "E prime" or "E complement." The sum of the probabilities of two complementary events is 1.

For example, consider an experiment in which a die is tossed 5 times and the number of sixes is counted. If S represents the event that a six occurs, the event that a six does not occur can be represented by S'. If 3 sixes are obtained, the experimental probability of S is 3/5, while the experimental probability of S' is 2/5. The sum of the probabilities for these two complementary events is 1.

d. Recall that **Venn diagrams** are mathematical models that show relationships among different sets of data. For example, the Venn diagram in Figure 2-2 below shows information about two inherited traits in a classroom of 20 students.

FIGURE 2-2   Incidence of two inherited traits.

Describe how you could use a Venn diagram to show the relationship between two complementary events E and E'.

e. If you know the experimental probability of having a specific trait, how can you determine the experimental probability of not having that trait?

f. How could you use the experimental probabilities found in the exploration to estimate the number of students in your school with each trait?

Module 2 ■ *What Are My Child's Chances?*   33

Assignment

Problems suitable for use as assessment items are identified by an asterisk (*).

* 1.1 **a.** Answers will vary, depending on class data. The probabilities in the table at the bottom of the page were calculated using the sample data given in the exploration.
  b. Answers will vary. Students should multiply the experimental probability of having free earlobes by the number of students in the school population.
  c. Because the two events are complementary, the sum of their probabilities is 1.

Trait	Experimental Probability of Having Trait	Experimental Probability of Not Having Trait
mid-digit hair	18/25	7/25
widow's peak	17/25	8/25
free earlobes	18/25	7/25
rolled tongue	19/25	6/25
folded hands	20/25 = 4/5	5/25 = 1/5

Warm-Up

1. For each of the following experiments, list the sample space and describe one event.

    a. A person flips two coins.

    b. A person rolls two ordinary dice.

    c. Two people play "Rock, Paper, Scissors."

2. Describe the complement of each event below.

    a. A flipped coin shows tails.

    b. A green light is visible at an intersection.

    c. A grade of A is received in social studies.

3. If the probability of an event is 1/6, what is the probability of its complement? Justify your response.

Assignment

1.1 a. Use the class data to determine the experimental probability of not having each trait on the wheel. Organize these probabilities in a table like the one below.

Trait	Experimental Probability of Having Trait	Experimental Probability of Not Having Trait
mid-digit hair		
widow's peak		
free earlobes		
rolled tongue		
folded hands		

   b. Using the class data, predict how many students in your school have free earlobes.

   c. What is the sum of the experimental probabilities of having and not having each trait? Why does this occur?

1.2 Suppose that you used the wheel of traits in Figure **2-1** to collect data from across the nation. Do you think the combination of five traits that occurred most often in your class would occur most often in the national data? Why or why not?

1.2 Answers will vary. Students might or might not believe that their class is representative of the national population. Some might argue that the sample size is inadequate to make predictions.

1.3 Because the two events are complementary, the probability of not having a widow's peak in this class is $1 - 0.7 = 0.3$.

* 1.4 The event that is complementary to the trait "folded hands" is "not having folded hands," which means that the right thumb falls naturally on top when hands are folded so that fingers interlace.

✳ ✳ ✳ ✳ ✳

1.5 a. $\dfrac{542{,}000 + 62{,}000 + 36{,}000}{2{,}041{,}000} \approx 0.31 \approx 31\%$

   b. $\dfrac{62{,}000 + 36{,}000}{62{,}000 + 36{,}000 + 542{,}000} \approx 0.15 \approx 15\%$

   c. $1 - \dfrac{428{,}000}{2{,}041{,}000} \approx 0.79 \approx 79\%$

1.3 In one class of students, the experimental probability of having a widow's peak was 0.7. What was the experimental probability of not having a widow's peak in this class? Explain how you determined your response.

1.4 Describe the event that is complementary to having the trait "folded hands."

✳ ✳ ✳ ✳ ✳

1.5 In 2000, approximately 2,041,000 fires were reported in the United States. The table below shows how these fires were distributed by type.

Type of Fire	Number Reported
Structure—accidental	542,000
Structure—incendiary device used	62,000
Structure—suspicious origin	36,000
Outside of structure (includes timber, crops, and outside storage)	54,000
Brush and rubbish	806,000
Vehicle	428,000
Other	113,000

SOURCE: U.S. Bureau of the Census.

   a. What is the probability that a fire reported in 2000 was a structure fire?

   b. What percentage of all structure fires in 2000 involved incendiary devices or suspicious causes?

   c. What is the probability that a fire reported in 2000 was not a vehicle fire?

1.6 In the United States, heart disease is a leading cause of death for adults. The table below shows the number of deaths due to heart disease for men of various age groups in 2000.

Age (years)	No. in Age Group	No. of Deaths
25–34	21,564,000	3278
35–44	18,009,000	18,585
45–54	12,232,000	46,078
55–64	9,955,000	948,276
65–74	7,907,000	1,716,056
75–84	3,745,000	169,828
over 85	841,000	70,864

SOURCE: U.S. Bureau of the Census.

*1.6 **a.** $\dfrac{46,078}{12,232,000} \approx 0.0038 \approx 0.38\%$

b. Because the total number of deaths shown in the table is 2,972,965, the percentage was:

$$\frac{1,716,056}{2,972,965} \approx 0.5772 \approx 58\%$$

c. Because the total number of men represented in the table is 74,253,000, the probability is:

$$\frac{2,972,965}{74,253,000} \approx 0.04 = 4\%$$

d. Sample response:

$$1 - \frac{3,278}{21,564,000} \approx 0.9998 = 99.98\%$$

Students examine the theoretical probabilities of the inherited traits encountered in Activity **1**.

teacher note

A brief assessment of the mathematical content in Activities **1** and **2**, for use at your discretion, appears in the Teacher Resources for this module.

Materials List

■ none

teacher note

Students should have a clear understanding of the biological terms in this activity. You might wish to discuss the differences between *genotype* and *phenotype*, along with *recessive* and *dominant*, before beginning the exploration. Some students might find it helpful to develop a reference sheet of biological terms. All of the terms used in the activity are described briefly in the module summary and in the glossary.

a. For men aged between 45 and 54, what was the probability of dying from heart disease in 2000?

b. What percentage of the men who died from heart disease in 2000 were between 65 and 74 years old?

c. For men aged 25 and over, what was the probability of dying from heart disease in 2000?

d. For men aged between 25 and 34, what was the probability of not dying from heart disease in 2000?

ACTIVITY

The genes you inherited from your parents are carried on 23 pairs of **chromosomes**. Figure **2-3** shows one pair of chromosomes, magnified many thousands of times.

FIGURE 2-3   A pair of human chromosomes.

Like chromosomes, genes also come in pairs. Each member of a pair is called an **allele** (pronounced "uh leel"). During fertilization, two alleles combine—one from each parent. These two alleles may be alike or different. However, only one trait appears for each pair.

The pair of alleles that determines the presence or absence of a particular characteristic is the **genotype.** The trait that actually occurs is referred to as the **phenotype.** When the alleles in a pair are different, the trait that appears is the **dominant** trait. The other is referred to as the **recessive** trait.

Exploration

In the case of earlobes, there are two possible phenotypes: free earlobes or attached earlobes. Having free earlobes is the dominant trait, and having attached earlobes is the recessive trait.

36   Module 2 ■ *What Are My Child's Chances?*

Student Outcomes

After completing the following exploration and discussion, students should be able to:

✷ use Punnett squares to determine sample spaces and theoretical probabilities

✷ compare experimental and theoretical probabilities.

Exploration

a. Answers will vary. The table below shows the possible genotypes for each cross.

Cross	Possible Genotypes
FF × FF	FF
FF × ff	Ff
FF × Ff	FF, Ff
Ff × ff	Ff, ff
Ff × Ff	FF, Ff, ff
ff × ff	ff

In genetics, the dominant trait typically is represented by a capital letter, with the recessive trait represented by the corresponding lowercase letter. If F represents free earlobes and f represents attached earlobes, then the four possible combinations of these two alleles can be written as follows: FF, Ff, fF, and ff.

However, the combinations Ff and fF, which each contain one dominant and one recessive allele, are genetically the same. This means there are only three possible genotypes: FF, Ff, and ff. When the two alleles in a pair are different, the dominant trait masks the recessive one. Since having free earlobes is the dominant trait, the genotypes FF and Ff both result in the phenotype of free earlobes. Only the genotype ff results in the phenotype of attached earlobes.

a. A parent can have any one of the three possible genotypes: FF, Ff, or ff.

  1. Select two genotypes, one to represent each parent.

  2. List all the genotypes that are possible in their children.

b. Describe the method you used in Part **a** to ensure that all possible combinations were identified.

science note

The act of combining genes from two parents is called a **cross**. In a cross, each allele in a parent's genotype is assumed to have an equal chance of being passed on to the offspring.

Given the genotypes of both parents for a particular trait, you can use a **Punnett square** to help identify the possible combinations from a cross. For example, Figure 2-4 shows a Punnett square for the cross of two parents with the same genotype, Ff. The possible genotypes from this cross are FF, Ff, and ff.

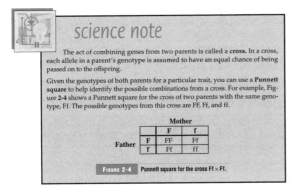

		Mother	
		F	f
Father	F	FF	Ff
	f	Ff	ff

FIGURE 2-4 Punnett square for the cross Ff × Ff.

c. Draw a Punnett square for the cross you chose in Part **a**. Identify all the possible genotypes and all the possible phenotypes.

mathematics note

If each outcome in a sample space has the same chance of occurring, then the **theoretical probability** of an event can be calculated using the following ratio:

$$\frac{\text{number of outcomes in the event}}{\text{total number of outcomes in the sample space}}$$

The theoretical probability of an event E can be written as $P(E)$.

For example, consider the cross of two parents with the same genotype, Ff. As shown in Figure 2-4, the sample space contains 4 equally likely outcomes: FF, Ff, Ff, and ff. Because the FF genotype occurs 1 time in the sample space, its theoretical probability can be expressed as $1/4$. In other words, $P(FF) = 1/4$. Similarly, $P(ff) = 1/4$. Because the genotype Ff occurs 2 times in the sample space, $P(Ff) = 2/4$, or $1/2$. The sum of the probabilities for all the possible outcomes in the sample space is 1.

Because the allele for free earlobes (F) is dominant, the genotypes FF and Ff both result in the phenotype of free earlobes. For the cross shown in Figure 2-4, the probability that a child has free earlobes is $3/4$, while the probability that a child has attached earlobes is $1/4$.

d. For each genotype identified in Part **c**, determine the probability that a child of these parents will possess that genotype.

e. For each possible phenotype identified in Part **c**, determine the probability that a child of these parents will have that phenotype.

Discussion

a. 1. In Part **c** of the exploration, how many different genotypes did you identify?

  2. How many different phenotypes did you identify?

b. Why is it possible for your responses to Part **a** of the discussion to differ from those of your classmates?

c. How do the parents' genotypes affect the probability of the child's phenotype?

Warm-Up

1. Consider the experiment of flipping two fair coins.

  a. Determine the theoretical probability of obtaining one head and one tail.

  b. If you flipped two coins 1200 times, how many times would you expect tails on both coins?

b. Some students might have used tree diagrams to show all the possibilities. Others might have listed the combinations in some pattern in order to consider all possibilities.

c. Answers will vary. The following sample response shows the Punnett square for the cross FF × Ff. The two possible genotypes are FF and Ff. The only possible phenotype is free earlobes.

		Ff	
		F	f
FF	F	FF	Ff
	F	FF	Ff

Note: To ensure that all possible crosses are investigated, you may assign specific crosses to each student or group.

d. Answers will vary. For the sample response given in Part **c**, the probability of each of the two possible genotypes is $1/2$.

e. Answers will vary. For the sample response given in Part **c**, the probability of the phenotype free earlobes is 1.

Discussion

a. 1. Answers will vary. Sample response: For the cross Ff × Ff, there are three possible genotypes: FF, Ff, and FF.

  2. Sample response: For the cross Ff × Ff, there are two possible phenotypes: free earlobes and attached earlobes.

b. Sample response: The genotypes of the parents determine the possible genotypes and phenotypes for the child. For example, in the cross ff × ff, the only possible genotype is ff and the only possible phenotype is attached earlobes.

c. The parents' genotypes determine the sample space of possible genotypes for the child. These genotypes, in turn, determine the possible phenotypes for the child. The frequency of each phenotype in the sample space determines the probability of that phenotype.

Warm-Up

1. a. 0.5
   b. 300 times

2. Sample tree diagram:

	first coin	second coin	third coin	outcome	probability

first coin — second coin — third coin — outcome — probability

1/2 H: 1/2 H: 1/2 H → HHH 1/8
                1/2 T → HHT 1/8
         1/2 T: 1/2 H → HTH 1/8
                1/2 T → HTT 1/8
1/2 T: 1/2 H: 1/2 H → THH 1/8
                1/2 T → THT 1/8
         1/2 T: 1/2 H → TTH 1/8
                1/2 T → TTT 1/8

3. $P(2) = 1/36$ and $P(12) = 1/36$

Assignment

Problems suitable for use as assessment items are identified by an asterisk (*).

* 2.1 a. The Punnett square for this cross is shown below.

	ff	
	f	**f**
FF **F**	Ff	Ff
F	Ff	Ff

b. The only genotype possible from this cross is Ff. Its probability is 1.

c. The only phenotype possible is free earlobes, the dominant trait.

d. The probability of free earlobes is 1.

2.2 a. The Punnett square for this cross is shown below.

	ff	
	f	**f**
Ff **F**	Ff	Ff
f	ff	ff

b. The two possible genotypes are Ff and ff. Each has a probability of 1/2.

c. Because F is the dominant trait, the genotype Ff results in the phenotype free earlobes. The genotype ff results in the phenotype attached earlobes.

d. Each phenotype has a probability of 1/2.

2.3 a. As shown in the following Punnett square, the probability of the genotype RR is 1/2.

	RR	
	R	**R**
Rr **R**	RR	RR
r	Rr	Rr

---

2. Recall that a **tree diagram** shows all the possible outcomes for a series of events. Each line segment in a tree diagram is a **branch.** Each branch may be assigned a probability.

Draw a tree diagram that shows all the outcomes for flipping three fair coins.

3. When rolling two ordinary dice, which sums are the least likely outcomes? Justify your response.

Assignment

2.1 Consider the cross FF × ff, where F represents free earlobes and f represents attached earlobes.

  a. Draw a Punnett square for this cross.

  b. What is the probability of each possible genotype?

  c. Describe the phenotype that results for each possible genotype.

  d. What is the probability of each possible phenotype?

2.2 Repeat Problem **2.1** using the cross Ff × ff.

2.3 Consider the cross Rr × RR, where R represents the ability to roll the tongue, a dominant trait.

  a. Determine the probability of the genotype RR. Justify your response using a Punnett square.

  b. Determine the probability of the genotype rr. Defend your response using a tree diagram.

  c. What is the probability that a child of these parents has the ability to roll the tongue? Explain your response.

2.4 Having a widow's peak is a dominant trait, represented by the capital letter W. Consider the cross Ww × ww, where the father has a widow's peak.

  a. Which pair of alleles belongs to the father? Explain your response.

  b. Using a Punnett square, identify the genotypes that can result from this cross.

  c. Determine the probability that a child of this cross does not have a widow's peak.

---

b. As shown in the tree diagram below, the probability of the genotype rr is 0.

Parent 1 Parent 2 Child

R — R → RR
R — R → RR
r — R → Rr
r — R → Rr

c. Because both of the possible genotypes result in the same phenotype, the probability that a child of these parents has the ability to roll the tongue is 1.

* 2.4 a. Because having a widow's peak is a dominant trait, the father's genotype is Ww.

b. As shown in the following Punnett square, the two possible genotypes are Ww and ww.

	ww	
	w	**w**
Ww **W**	Ww	Ww
w	ww	ww

c. The genotype ww results in a child with no widow's peak, so the probability of this phenotype is $2/4 = 1/2$.

page 40

2.5 Consider the cross Ww × Ww, where W represents the trait widow's peak.

a. What is the probability that a child of this cross receives one dominant allele (W) and one recessive allele (w)?

b. Why do the two outcomes Ww and WW result in the same phenotype?

c. For a child of this cross, what is the ratio of the probability of having a widow's peak to the probability of not having one?

* * * * *

2.6 Both of Deirdre's parents have free earlobes, a dominant gene. Deirdre does not.

a. Use Punnett squares to find all the possible genotypes for a child of Deirdre's parents.

b. Determine the probability that a child of Deirdre's parents does not have free earlobes.

2.7 Cystic fibrosis is a genetic disease. Its victims lack certain chemicals in the body and typically have severe respiratory and digestive problems. For children in the United States, it is the leading cause of death due to disease.

A baby can be born with cystic fibrosis if both its parents are **carriers** of the disease. Carriers are people who show no signs of the disease but can pass it on to their children. Carriers have the genotype Cc, while people with the disease have the genotype cc.

a. Draw a Punnett square that represents a cross between two parents that are carriers of cystic fibrosis.

b. What is the probability that a child with cystic fibrosis is born to parents who are both carriers of the disease?

c. One out of every 25 people in the United States is a carrier of cystic fibrosis. What are the chances that a healthy person chosen at random in the United States is not a carrier of cystic fibrosis?

ACTIVITY 3

In the previous activities, you examined traits one at a time. When genetic counselors advise their clients, however, they must consider the parents' traits as groups. Some characteristics, for example, are associated only with males, and some are associated only with females. A few characteristics are linked to certain other traits regardless of sex. Grouping traits affects the probabilities in each situation. It also affects the way in which those probabilities are calculated.

40 Module 2 ■ *What Are My Child's Chances?*

2.5 **a.** As shown in the Punnett square below, the probability of a child receiving one dominant and one recessive allele (genotype Ww) is 2/4 = 1/2.

		Ww	
		W	**w**
Ww	**W**	WW	Ww
	w	Ww	ww

b. Since having a widow's peak is a dominant trait, both Ww and WW result in the same phenotype.

c. The three outcomes that result in a widow's peak are WW, Ww, and Ww. The genotype ww results in no widow's peak. The ratio of the probabilities is 3/1.

* * * * *

* 2.6 **a.** Attached earlobes is a recessive trait. If F represents the allele for free earlobes, and f represents the allele for attached earlobes, then Deirdre's genotype must be ff. The only possible cross involving parents with free earlobes that results in this genotype is Ff × Ff. As shown in the following Punnett square, the possible genotypes are FF, Ff, and ff.

		Ff	
		F	**f**
Ff	**F**	FF	Ff
	f	Ff	ff

b. The probability that a child of Deirdre's parents has attached earlobes is 1/4.

2.7 **a.** The Punnett square for the cross of two carriers is shown below.

		Cc	
		C	**c**
Cc	**C**	CC	Cc
	c	Cc	cc

b. The probability is 1/4.

c. Because the probability of being a carrier is 1/25, the probability of not being a carrier is 1 – 1/25 = 24/25.

ACTIVITY 3

Students explore probabilities for more than one event. The mathematics note introduces a formula for finding the probability of multiple independent events.

Materials List

- template for Wheel of Traits (optional)

teacher note

To ensure that all students use the same data set, you might wish to display an overhead transparency of the Wheel of Traits data from Activity **1**.

A blackline master appears in the Teacher Resources for this module.

Student Outcomes

After completing the following exploration and discussions, students should be able to:

✳ collect data and calculate experimental probabilities

✳ use Punnett squares to determine sample spaces and theoretical probabilitites

✳ identify independent and dependent events

✳ determine $P(A \text{ and } B)$ for two independent events.

Discussion 1

a. 1. The father has two different alleles, and each has an equal chance of being passed on, therefore the probability is 1/2.

   2. Because the mother has two identical alleles, the probability is 1.

   3. The probability that a child of this couple will have the genotype RR is 1/2.

b. Sample response: No. The probability does not change because the allele passed on by the father is not influenced by the mother's genotype.

c. Because receiving a particular allele from the father is independent of receiving a particular allele from the mother, the probability of a child receiving a given genotype equals the product of the probabilities for receiving each allele from each parent.

   For example, the probability that this child will receive the genotype RR can be calculated as follows:

$$\frac{1}{2} \cdot \frac{1}{2} = \frac{1}{4}$$

Exploration

Students examine the relationship among $P(A)$, $P(B)$, and $P(A \text{ and } B)$ when A and B are independent events.

a–b. The following table shows sample data for the traits folded hands and rolled tongue.

Trait A: folded hands		
Trait B: rolled tongue		
Total Number in Class:		
Trait	**Frequency**	**Experimental Probability**
A	20	20/25
B	19	19/25
A and B	16	16/25

c. Students repeat Part **b** for each of the 10 possible pairs of two traits.

Discussion 1

a. Consider a father with the genotype Rr and a mother with the genotype RR, where R represents a dominant trait.

   1. Assuming that each allele in a parent's genotype has an equal chance of being passed on to any offspring, what is the probability that a child of this couple will receive the dominant allele from the father?

   2. What is the probability that a child of this couple will receive the dominant allele from the mother?

   3. What is the probability that a child of this couple will have the genotype RR?

b. If the mother's genotype were Rr, would this change your response to Part **a1**?

mathematics note

Two events A and B are **independent** if $P(A \text{ and } B) = P(A) \cdot P(B)$. It follows that for independent events A, B, and C, $P(A \text{ and } B \text{ and } C) = P(A) \cdot P(B) \cdot P(C)$. This definition can be extended to any number of independent events.

Given two independent events, the occurrence of one has no effect on the likelihood of the occurrence of the other. Two events that are not independent are said to be **dependent**.

For example, consider tossing a coin heads up and rolling a 4 on a die. These two events are independent if $P(\text{head and } 4) = P(\text{head}) \cdot P(4)$. The sample space for tossing a coin and rolling a die consists of 12 equally likely outcomes: a head with each of the six faces on the die and a tail with each of the six faces. Only one of these outcomes includes a head and a 4. Therefore, $P(\text{head and } 4) = 1/12$.

The theoretical probability of tossing a head is 1/2, and the theoretical probability of rolling a 4 is 1/6. Therefore,

$$P(\text{head}) \cdot P(4) = \frac{1}{2} \cdot \frac{1}{6} = \frac{1}{12}$$

Because $P(\text{head and } 4) = P(\text{head}) \cdot P(4)$, the two events are independent.

c. In the cross Rr × Rr, the probability of the genotypes RR and rr is 1/4, and the probability of Rr is 1/2. How could you find the probability of each genotype using the probabilities of receiving one allele from the father and one from the mother?

Exploration

a. Select two of the following five traits: mid-digit hair, widow's peak, free earlobes, rolled tongue, and folded hands.

b. 1. Determine the number of students in your class who have only the first trait (A), only the second trait (B), and both the first and second traits (A and B). Record this data in a table with headings like those in Table 2-3 below.

TABLE 2-3 ■ *Experimental Probabilities of Two Traits*		
Trait A:		
Trait B:		
Total Number in Class:		
Trait	**Frequency**	**Experimental Probability**
A		
B		
A and B		

   2. Find the experimental probabilities of having trait A, having trait B, and having both A and B. Record these probabilities in Table **2-3**.

c. Choose another pair of traits from the five traits listed in Part **a**. Repeat Part **b** using this pair of traits. Continue this process until you have completed a table for each of the 10 possible pairs of traits.

d. Experimental probabilities often are used to approximate theoretical probabilities. Judging from the experimental probabilities in your tables from Parts **b** and **c**, which pairs of traits appear to represent independent events?

Discussion 2

a. 1. Using the information in your tables, do any of the pairs of traits appear to represent independent events? Explain your response.

   2. Do any of the pairs of traits appear to represent dependent events? Explain your response.

b. 1. Identify two events that appear to be independent. Describe how you could demonstrate that they are independent.

   2. Identify two events that appear to be dependent. Describe how you could demonstrate that they are dependent.

c. Given the theoretical probability of having a particular trait, how would you predict the number of students in your class with that trait?

Warm-Up

1. Identify each pair of events below as independent or dependent.

   a. Event A: Attending Jefferson High School
      Event B: Playing soccer for Jefferson High School

   b. Event A: Going to the movies
      Event B: Eating breakfast each morning

   c. Event A: Driving a car
      Event B: Wearing jeans

2. Calculate $P(A \text{ and } B)$ for each pair of independent events listed below.

   a. $P(A) = 1/3$ and $P(B) = 1/2$

   b. $P(A) = 0.125$ and $P(B) = 0.625$

   c. $P(A) = 5/6$ and $P(B) = 6/7$

3. Determine the theoretical probability of each the following.

   a. Leo flips a fair coin; it shows tails. He draws one card at random from an ordinary deck of playing cards; the card is an ace.

   b. While playing a board game with two ordinary dice, Venus rolls doubles twice in a row.

4. A true/false quiz has four questions. If a student makes a random guess on each question, what is the probability of getting all the answers correct?

Assignment

3.1 Assume that each of the following five traits is independent of the others: mid-digit hair, widow's peak, free earlobes, rolled tongue, and folded hands. Using the class data from the exploration, estimate the probability of having free earlobes and the ability to roll your tongue and no widow's peak.

Warm-Up

1. a. dependent
   b. independent
   c. independent
2. a. $1/6$
   b. 0.078125
   c. $5/7$
3. a. $1/26$
   b. $1/36$
4. $1/16 = 0.0625 = 6.25\%$

Assignment

Problems suitable for use as assessment items are identified by an asterisk (*).

3.1 Answers may vary, depending on class data. Using the sample data given in Activity **1**, the probability of having free earlobes and the ability to roll the tongue and no widow's peak is:

$$\frac{18}{25} \bullet \frac{19}{25} \bullet \frac{8}{25} = \frac{2736}{15{,}625}$$

d. For each pair of traits, students should use experimental probabilities to approximate theoretical probabilities. If $P(A) \bullet P(B) \approx P(A \text{ and } B)$, then they should observe that traits A and B appear to be independent.

Discussion 2

a. 1. Answers may vary, depending on class data.
   2. If $P(A) \bullet P(B)$ is not approximately equal to $P(A \text{ and } B)$, students should observe that traits A and B appear to be dependent.
b. 1. Sample response: Having blond hair and being male appear to be independent events. This could be demonstrated by using the experimental probability of each trait to approximate the theoretical probabilities. If $P(A) \bullet P(B) \approx P(A \text{ and } B)$, then the traits would appear to be independent.
   2. Sample response: Receiving an A in every class and getting on the honor roll are dependent events. This could be demonstrated by using the experimental probability of each event to approximate the theoretical probabilities. If $P(A) \bullet P(B) \neq P(A \text{ and } B)$, then the events would appear to be dependent.
c. Sample response: The product of the probability of that trait and the number of students in the class gives the number of students you could expect to have the trait.

* 3.2 **a.** The probability for each branch is shown on the tree diagram below.

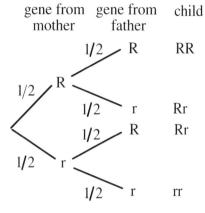

gene from mother gene from father child

b. Receiving an allele from one parent is independent of receiving an allele from the other parent, so the probability for the genotype rr can be found by multiplying the probabilities on the two corresponding branches:

$$P(r) \bullet P(r) = \frac{1}{2} \bullet \frac{1}{2} = \frac{1}{4}$$

The same method can be used to find the probability for genotype RR:

$$P(R) \bullet P(R) = \frac{1}{2} \bullet \frac{1}{2} = \frac{1}{4}$$

Similarly, for each occurrence of the genotype Rr:

$$P(R) \bullet P(r) = \frac{1}{2} \bullet \frac{1}{2} = \frac{1}{4}$$

However, because the genotype Rr occurs twice in the cross, the probabilities of the two occurrences must be added:

$$\frac{1}{4} + \frac{1}{4} = \frac{1}{2}$$

c. The Punnett square for this cross is shown below.

Rr

Rr		R	r
	R	RR	Rr
	r	Rr	rr

Using a Punnett square, the probabilities for rr and RR are 1/4 and the probability for Rr is 1/2.

d. The probabilities found for each genotype are the same using either method.

3.3 The cross Mm × Mm yields the outcomes MM, Mm, Mm, and mm. Because 3 of the 4 result in the phenotype mid-digit hair, the probability that a child of these parents has mid-digit hair is 3/4.

The cross WW × Ww yields the sample space WW, WW, Ww, and Ww. Because all of these outcomes result in a widow's peak, P(widow's peak) = 1.

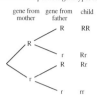

3.2 The tree diagram below shows the possible genotypes for the cross Rr × Rr.

gene from mother gene from father child

R → R RR
R → r Rr
r → R Rr
r → r rr

a. Make a copy of this diagram. On each branch of the tree, write the probability of a child receiving that allele.

b. Use the tree diagram to find the probability of each genotype. Describe the method you used.

c. Create a Punnett square for the cross Rr × Rr. Use it to calculate the probability of each genotype.

d. How do the probabilities you found using the tree diagram compare with the probabilities found using a Punnett square?

3.3 Two potential parents both have the genotype Mm for mid-digit hair. The father has the genotype WW for widow's peak, and the mother has the genotype Ww. Assuming that mid-digit hair and widow's peak are independent traits, determine the probability that a child of these parents has both mid-digit hair and a widow's peak.

3.4 **Antigens** are proteins that can activate the immune system. An individual's blood type is determined by the presence or absence of two antigens, A and B, on red blood cells. Type A and type B blood each have one antigen on red blood cells, type O blood contains neither antigen, while type AB contains both.

Blood type is also affected by another antigen, the Rh factor. Blood that contains this factor is referred to as Rh positive (Rh+), and blood that does not contain this factor is referred to as Rh negative (Rh–). The presence or absence of the Rh factor, along with the four basic blood types, results in eight different kinds of blood: A+, B+, AB+, O+, A–, B–, AB–, and O–.

A biology class has collected data on the blood of 26 students. The following table summarizes this data.

44   Module 2 ■ *What Are My Child's Chances?*

Therefore, the probability that a child of these parents has both traits is:

$$\frac{3}{4} \bullet 1 = \frac{3}{4}$$

* 3.4 **a.** The experimental probability for type A is 10/26 = 5/13, for type B is 4/26 = 2/13, for type AB is 1/26, and for type O is 11/26.

b. The experimental probability for the presence of the Rh factor is 20/26 = 10/13; the experimental probability for the absence of the Rh factor is 6/26 = 3/13.

c. Sample tree diagram:

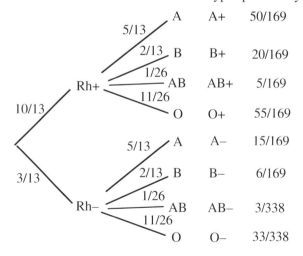

		blood type	probability
Rh+	A	A+	50/169
	B	B+	20/169
	AB	AB+	5/169
	O	O+	55/169
Rh–	A	A–	15/169
	B	B–	6/169
	AB	AB–	3/338
	O	O–	33/338

Blood Type	No. of Students	Rh Factor	No. of Students
A	10	Rh+	20
B	4	Rh–	6
AB	1		
O	11		

a. Determine the experimental probability of each of the following blood types: A, B, AB, and O.

b. Determine the experimental probability each of the following: Rh+ and Rh–.

c. Assuming that blood type and Rh factor are independent traits, draw a tree diagram that shows the estimated probability of each of the eight possible kinds of blood.

✳ ✳ ✳ ✳ ✳

3.5 The presence of curly hair (H) is dominant over straight hair (h). If the parents' genotypes are hh and Hh, determine the probability that both their two children will have curly hair. Assume that the traits of one child are independent of the traits of the other.

3.6 As mentioned in Problem 2.7, 1 out of every 25 people in the United States is a carrier of cystic fibrosis. What is the probability that two people chosen at random are both carriers?

3.7 A marketing firm surveyed 5000 people about their favorite sodas and snack foods. The results of the survey are shown in the table below. Each value in the "percentage" column represents the percentage of the survey group who preferred a particular soda or snack food.

Soda	Percentage	Snack Food	Percentage
cola A	30	corn chips	30
cola B	25	potato chips	40
cherry cola	10	pretzels	10
orange	5	variety mix	15
root beer	15	other	5
other	15		

a. What is the probability that a person chosen at random from this group prefers cola?

b. What is the probability that a person chosen at random from this group prefers cola and pretzels?

c. What is the probability that a person chosen at random from this group does not prefer root beer?

✳ ✳ ✳ ✳ ✳

3.5 Students may use a Punnett square or draw a tree diagram to find the sample space hH, hH, hh, hh. The genotype hH results in curly hair, so the probability of a child having curly hair is 1/2. The probability that two children of these parents have curly hair is $1/2 \cdot 1/2 = 1/4$.

* 3.6 Assuming that two people chosen at random are unrelated, the probability that both are carriers of cystic fibrosis is:

$$\frac{1}{25} \cdot \frac{1}{25} = \frac{1}{625}$$

3.7 a. The probability that a person chosen at random prefers cola is $0.30 + 0.25 + 0.10 = 0.65$.

b. Assuming that preference for soft drink is independent of preference for snack food, the probability that a person chosen at random prefers cola and pretzels is $0.65 \cdot 0.10 = 0.065$.

c. The probability that a person chosen at random prefers root beer is 0.15. Therefore, the probability that a person chosen at random does not prefer root beer is $1 - 0.15 = 0.85$.

* 3.8 **a.** The Punnett square for this cross is shown below.

	Hh	
	H	**h**
h	Hh	hh
h	Hh	hh

(left label: **hh**)

b. $P(hh) = 1/2$

c. Because the births are independent events, the probability that a child is a carrier is the same for each birth: $P(Hh) = 1/2$.

d. Because the births are independent events,

$$P(hh \text{ and } hh) = \frac{1}{2} \cdot \frac{1}{2} = \frac{1}{4}$$

Research Project

Students may contact a local hospital or the March of Dimes Birth Defects Foundation for more information on genetic counseling.

There are more than 2000 diseases with some identifiable genetic component. The following paragraphs briefly describe the diseases listed in the student edition.

- Cystic fibrosis is associated with the failure of the chlorine pump in cell membranes, resulting in a buildup of mucus outside cells. The accumulation of mucus in the pancreas, lungs, and digestive tract makes victims susceptible to pneumonia and other infections.

Untreated victims typically die by age 4 or 5. Treatment with special diets low in chlorine and daily doses of antibiotics can increase life expectancy to an average of 27 years.

In the United States, cystic fibrosis occurs in about 1 of every 2500 births. About 1 in every 25 people is a carrier. The disease occurs in individuals with double recessive genotypes.

- Tay-Sachs disease is caused by the failure of an enzyme that breaks down excess lipids, resulting in a buildup of lipids in the brain. Infants develop seizures and blindness, accompanied by a decline in mental and motor skills. There is currently no treatment. Death occurs a few years after birth.

Tay-Sachs occurs in about 1 of every 360,000 births worldwide. It is more frequent (about 1 in every 3600) in Jewish people whose ancestors came from Central Europe. The disease occurs in individuals with double recessive genotypes.

- Huntington's disease is characterized by a breakdown in the tissues of the nervous system. Victims experience a steady decline in mental and motor skills and typically do not manifest symptoms until middle age (between 35 and 45 years old). There is currently no treatment for the disease.

3.8 Huntington's disease is a rare and deadly genetic disorder. All carriers eventually develop the disease. Since Huntington's disease may lie dormant until a person is between 35 and 45 years old, many carriers have children before they develop symptoms.

a. Draw a Punnett square of a cross between a carrier of Huntington's disease (Hh) and a person who is not a carrier (hh).

b. What is the probability that a child from this cross does not carry the disease?

c. If the parents from Part **a** have one child who is not a carrier, what is the probability that a second child will carry the disease?

d. What is the probability that the parents from Part **a** have two children who are not carriers?

Research Project

Research one of the following genetic diseases: cystic fibrosis, Tay-Sachs disease, Huntington's disease, sickle-cell anemia, or phenylketonuria (PKU). Determine its symptoms, the frequency of its occurrence, and the probability that parents pass the disease to their children.

ACTIVITY 4

Your individual combination of traits makes you different from every other person on the planet. Some of these inherited traits, however, can prevent you from having some others. In this activity, you discover how the probability of having one trait or another can be affected by the relationship between them.

Exploration

a. To complete Steps **1** and **2** below, let trait A represent a preference for writing with the left hand and trait B represent a preference for writing with the right hand.

1. Determine the number of students in your class with trait A only, trait B only, both trait A and trait B, and either trait A or trait B. Record this data in a table with headings like those in Table **2-4**.

Huntington's disease occurs in individuals with one dominant and one recessive allele. Fetuses with double dominant genotypes are spontaneously aborted.

- Sickle-cell anemia is caused by deformed hemoglobin in red blood cells. The malformed red blood cells result in blood clotting, lower blood oxygen levels, and other symptoms of anemia. There is currently no treatment. Although usually not fatal, the disease limits activity and can cause chronic health problems.

In the United States, sickle-cell anemia is most frequent among people of African origins, occurring in about 1 of every 400 births (about 1 in 10 are carriers). Sickle-cell anemia is a co-dominant disease, which means that carriers may have mild symptoms. In tropical regions, carriers have displayed an increased resistance to malaria.

- Phenylketonuria (PKU) is characterized by the inability to metabolize the amino acid, phenylalanine. As a result, phenylpyruvate accumulates in the bloodstream, eventually reaching toxic levels. Maintaining a diet low in phenylalanine has shown to be an effective treatment.

PKU occurs in about 1 of every 15,000 births in the United States. By using a simple blood test, infants can be screened for the disease before they leave the hospital. PKU occurs in individuals with double recessive genotypes.

TABLE 2-4 ■ *Experimental Probabilities of Two Traits*		
Trait A:		
Trait B:		
Total Number in Class:		
Trait	**Frequency**	**Experimental Probability**
A		
B		
A and B		
A or B		

2. Find the experimental probabilities of having trait A only, having trait B only, having both trait A and trait B, and having either trait A or trait B. Record these probabilities in your table.

b. Repeat Part **a** for each of the following pairs of traits.

1. blue eyes and dark hair

2. dark hair and folded hands

mathematics Note

Given two events A and B, the theoretical probability of either A or B occurring can be found as follows:

$$P(A \text{ or } B) = P(A) + P(B) - P(A \text{ and } B)$$

For example, suppose event A is drawing a black card from a standard deck of 52 playing cards, and event B is drawing a king from a standard deck of playing cards. Because there are 26 black cards in a standard deck, $P(\text{black}) = 26/52$. Similarly, because there are 4 kings in the deck, $P(\text{king}) = 4/52$. The probability of either A or B occurring can be calculated as shown below:

$$P(\text{black or king}) = P(\text{black}) + P(\text{king}) - P(\text{black and king})$$

$$= \frac{26}{52} + \frac{4}{52} - \left(\frac{26}{52} \cdot \frac{4}{52}\right)$$

$$= \frac{26}{52} + \frac{4}{52} - \frac{2}{52}$$

$$= \frac{28}{52} = \frac{7}{13}$$

ACTIVITY

4

Students identify mutually exclusive events. Given two events A and B, they use appropriate formulas to find the probability of A or B.

Materials List

■ template for Wheel of Traits (optional)

teacher note

To ensure that all students use the same data set, you might wish to display an overhead transparency of the Wheel of Traits data from Activity **1**.

A blackline master appears in the Teacher Resources for this module.

Student Outcomes

After completing the following exploration and discussion, students should be able to:

✳ collect data and calculate experimental probabilities

✳ determine sample spaces and theoretical probabilities

✳ compare theoretical and experimental probabilities

✳ determine $P(A \text{ or } B)$

✳ identify mutually exclusive events.

Exploration

a. Sample data:

Trait A: left-handedness		
Trait B: right-handedness		
Total Number in Class: 25		
Trait	**Frequency**	**Experimental Probability**
A	10	$10/25 = 2/5$
B	15	$15/25 = 3/5$
A and B	0	$0/25 = 0$
A or B	25	$25/25 = 1$

b. Students repeat Part **a** for two other pairs of traits.

teacher note

You might wish to use the following Venn diagram to help explain the example given in the mathematics note.

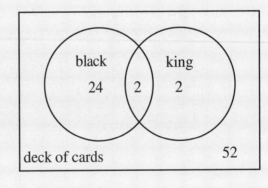

c–d. The calculated values for P(A or B) should be equal to those recorded in the tables. For example, using the sample data given in Part **a**:

$$P(\text{A or B}) = P(\text{A}) + P(\text{B}) - P(\text{A and B})$$
$$= \frac{10}{25} + \frac{15}{25} - 0$$
$$= \frac{25}{25} = 1$$

Discussion

a. Sample response: Yes. The probabilities determined by the formula were equal to those observed in the class.

b. For all classes, P(A and B) should equal 0 for left-handedness and right-handedness. Depending on the class data, this also might be true for other pairs of traits.

c. 1. For all classes, the preferences for writing with the left hand or the right hand should be mutually exclusive. Depending on the class data, other pairs of traits also might be mutually exclusive.

   2. The preferences for writing with the left hand or the right hand are always mutually exclusive because it is not possible to prefer both at the same time. In the general population, the other pairs of traits are not mutually exclusive.

d. Sample response: Since P(A and B) = 0 for mutually exclusive events, that part of the formula can be omitted without affecting the result.

e. Yes. Because the complement of event E is defined as the event that E does not occur, it is impossible for an event and its complement to occur at the same time.

f. No. On a single roll of a die, for example, a roll of six and a roll of three are mutually exclusive. However, they are not complementary. The probability of rolling a six is 1/6. The probability of rolling a three is also 1/6. The sum of their probabilities is 1/3, not 1.

g. When mutually exclusive traits A and B are considered as sets, they do not intersect, as shown in the diagram below. Because there is no intersection, the probability of A and B occurring at the same time is 0.

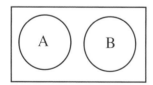

---

c. Use the formula in the mathematics note to determine P(A or B) for each of the following pairs of traits.

   1. left-handedness and right-handedness

   2. blue eyes and dark hair

   3. dark hair and folded hands

d. Compare your results from Part **c** to the experimental probability of A or B for each pair of traits.

Discussion

a. Did your results in Part **c** of the exploration support the formula for determining P(A or B)? Explain your response.

b. For which pair(s) of traits in the exploration was the experimental probability of A and B occurring at the same time 0?

mathematics note

Two events are **mutually exclusive** if they cannot occur at the same time in a single trial. For two mutually exclusive events A and B, P(A and B) = 0.

For example, consider the toss of a single coin. In this case, heads and tails are mutually exclusive, because both cannot occur at the same time on a single toss. However, because one person could be both right-handed and have the ability to roll the tongue, these two events are not mutually exclusive.

c. 1. In your class data, which pairs of traits were mutually exclusive?

   2. Do you think that these traits are always mutually exclusive? Explain your response.

d. For two mutually exclusive events A and B, the theoretical probability of A or B can be calculated using either the formula given in the mathematics note or the one shown below:

$$P(\text{A or B}) = P(\text{A}) + P(\text{B})$$

Why are these two formulas equivalent for mutually exclusive events?

e. Are complementary events always mutually exclusive? Explain your response.

f. Are mutually exclusive events always complementary? Use an example to support your response.

g. Draw a Venn diagram that shows the relationship between two mutually exclusive events. How does this diagram show that P(A and B) = 0?

Warm-Up

1. Identify each pair of events below as mutually exclusive or not mutually exclusive. Justify your responses.

   a. Event A: Being a father
      Event B: Being female

   b. Event A: U.S. citizenship
      Event B: Canadian citizenship

   c. Event A: World War II veteran
      Event B: Born in 1945

   d. Event A: Resident of California
      Event B: Resident of Texas

   e. Event A: Born in the U.S.A.
      Event B: Born to run

2. In each pair of events listed below, A and B are independent and not mutually exclusive. Determine $P(A \text{ or } B)$.

   a. $P(A) = 2/3$, $P(B) = 1/4$

   b. $P(A) = 0.42$, $P(B) = 0.7$

   c. $P(A) = 3/5$, $P(B) = 1/2$

Assignment

4.1 Decide whether or not each of the following pairs of traits represents two mutually exclusive events. Justify your response for each pair.

   a. having the ability to roll the tongue and not having this ability

   b. having a widow's peak and having curly hair

   c. having two blue eyes and having two brown eyes

4.2 Familial hypercholesterolemia causes high levels of cholesterol in the blood and can lead to clogging of the arteries at a young age. This genetic disorder is caused by the dominant allele (D). People with the genotype DD are severely affected, those with the genotype Dd are mildly affected, and those with the genotype dd are not affected at all.

Hank and Erma both have the genotype Dd. Use two different methods to find the probability that a child of this couple is either mildly affected or not affected at all.

Module 2 ▪ *What Are My Child's Chances?* 49

Warm-Up

1. **a.** mutually exclusive
   b. not mutually exclusive
   c. mutually exclusive
   d. mutually exclusive (assuming full-time residency)
   e. not mutually exclusive
2. **a.** 3/4
   b. 0.826
   c. 4/5

Assignment

Problems suitable for use as assessment items are identified by an asterisk (*).

4.1 **a.** Because these two events cannot occur at the same time (and are complementary), they are mutually exclusive.

   b. Because a person can have both traits at the same time, these two events are not mutually exclusive.

   c. Because a person with two blue eyes cannot also have two brown eyes, these two events are mutually exclusive.

* 4.2 One way to determine the probability that a child of this couple is either mildly affected or not affected at all is to use a tree diagram.

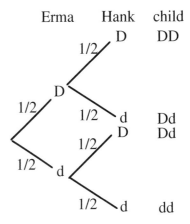

Because the genotype Dd occurs twice, the probability that a child is mildly affected is:

$$\left(\frac{1}{2} \cdot \frac{1}{2}\right) + \left(\frac{1}{2} \cdot \frac{1}{2}\right) = \frac{1}{2}$$

Because the genotype dd occurs only once, the probability that a child is not affected at all is $1/4$. Using the formula for $P(A \text{ or } B)$,

$$P(Dd \text{ or } dd) = \frac{1}{2} + \frac{1}{4} - 0$$

$$= \frac{3}{4}$$

This probability can also be determined using a Punnett square.

		Dd	
		D	**d**
Dd	**D**	DD	Dd
	d	Dd	dd

The genotype Dd occurs twice in a sample space of 4 genotypes, therefore its probability is $1/2$. Because dd occurs once, its probability is $1/4$. As shown above, $P(Dd \text{ or } dd) = 3/4$.

4.3 **a.** For the cross Mm × Mm, the probability of the phenotype mid-digit hair is 3/4. For the cross WW × Ww, the probability of the phenotype widow's peak is 1. The probability that a child of these parents has mid-digit hair or a widow's peak is:

$$\frac{3}{4} + 1 - \left(\frac{3}{4} \bullet 1\right) = 1$$

Note: Students may solve this problem simply by reasoning that because the probability of a widow's peak is 1, the probability of a widow's peak or mid-digit hair is also 1.

b. Because the probability of either a widow's peak or mid-digit hair is 1, all five children would be expected to have one trait or the other.

✳ ✳ ✳ ✳ ✳

4.4 These events are mutually exclusive, therefore the probability can be calculated as follows:

$$\frac{3}{20} + \frac{1}{20} = \frac{4}{20} = \frac{1}{5}$$

* 4.5 **a.** 0.0065

b. $0.0065 \bullet 250 \approx 2$

c. **1.** $0.0065 \bullet 0.0065 \approx 4.2 \bullet 10^{-5}$

2. $0.0065 + 0.0065 - (0.0065 \bullet 0.0065) \approx 0.013$

4.6 **a.** Because there are 10 digits on each tumbler, the number of possible combinations for a three-tumbler lock is $10 \bullet 10 \bullet 10 = 1000$. Therefore, the probability of guessing the right combination on one guess is 1/1000.

b. Sample response: Yes. The number of possible combinations for a five-tumbler lock is $10^5 = 100{,}000$. This lock has 100 times more possible combinations than a three-tumbler lock, which decreases the probability that someone could guess the actual combination.

4.3 The Norgaard family has five children. Both parents have the genotype Mm for mid-digit hair. The father's genotype for widow's peak is WW, while the mother's is Ww.

a. What is the probability that a child of these parents has either mid-digit hair or a widow's peak?

b. How many of the family's five children would you expect to have either mid-digit hair or a widow's peak? Justify your response.

* * * * *

4.4 A survey of 20 students reported the following hair colors: 10 brown, 6 black, 3 blond, and 1 red. If one student is selected randomly from this group, what is the probability that the student has blond hair or red hair? (Assume that each student has only one hair color.)

4.5 In 2003, the Internal Revenue Service audited approximately 0.65% of all tax returns. In that same year, Carla's Accounting Service prepared tax returns for 250 clients. Assume that each taxpayer had the same chance of receiving an audit.

a. What was the probability of receiving an audit in 2003?

b. Estimate the number of Carla's clients who received an audit.

c. Eli and Marc both used Carla's Accounting Service in 2003. Determine the probability of each of the following.

1. both Eli and Marc received audits

2. either Eli or Marc received an audit

4.6 Umberto plans to buy a chain with a tumbler lock to secure his bicycle. The first lock he examines has three tumblers, each of which can be set to any digit from 0 to 9. Only one combination of three numbers will open the lock.

a. What is the probability of guessing the correct combination on the first attempt?

b. The second lock Umberto examines has five tumblers. Is a five-tumbler lock more secure than a three-tumbler lock? Explain your response.

ACTIVITY 5

Like hair color and free earlobes, your gender is an inherited trait. As shown in Figure **2-5**, the sex chromosomes for a female are indicated by XX, and those for a male are indicated by XY. Each parent contributes one chromosome to the child's pair. The father can contribute either an X or a Y chromosome; the mother can contribute only an X chromosome.

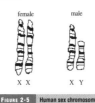

female   male

X X   X Y

FIGURE 2-5 Human sex chromosomes.

Exploration

In this exploration, you use a simulation to investigate the probability that a combination of sex chromosomes results in a female child. You then use another simulation to examine the probability that a family with two children will include one male child and one female child.

a. Assume that the probability of receiving either allele from either parent is the same. Predict the probability that a combination of sex chromosomes results in a female child.

b. 1. To model the mother's chromosomes, label both sides of a coin "X."

    2. To model the father's chromosomes, label a second coin "X" on one side and "Y" on the other.

c. 1. Simulate the combination of male and female chromosomes by tossing the two coins. Determine and record the gender of the resulting combination.

    2. Repeat Step **1** 19 more times.

    3. Determine the experimental probability that a combination of male and female chromosomes results in a female child.

Module 2 ■ *What Are My Child's Chances?* 51

ACTIVITY 5

In this activity, students discover that the gender of each child in a family is an independent event. They apply this fact to finding the probabilities of specific family combinations of boys and girls. (This presents a somewhat simplified view of the determination of gender. Even though it is true that the gender of each child is an independent event, the probabilities of having a boy or girl for any particular family might not be exactly 1/2, due to a range of biological and genetic factors.)

teacher note

A brief assessment of the mathematical content in Activities **3**, **4**, and **5**, for use at your discretion, appears in the Teacher Resources for this module.

Materials List

■ coins (two per group)

Student Outcomes

After completing the following exploration and discussion, students should be able to:

✴ use Punnett squares to determine sample spaces and theoretical probabilitites

✴ use tree diagrams to determine sample spaces and theoretical probabilities

✴ compare theoretical and experimental probabilities

✴ identify independent and dependent events

✴ simulate a situation involving independent events

✴ identify mutually exclusive events.

Exploration

Students use coins to simulate the random selection of the chromosomes that determine gender. (Because the coin that represents the mother's chromosomes always results in an X, students might realize that only the toss of the coin representing the father's chromosomes actually determines the gender of the child.)

a. Answers may vary. Some students may correctly predict 1/2.

b. Students simulate the chromosomes by labeling two coins.

c. Students simulate the combination of male and female chromosomes by tossing the two coins. The experimental probability that the combination results in a female child should be approximately 1/2.

d. As shown below, either method can be used to analyze the cross of genotype XY (male) and genotype XX (female). The sample space from this cross contains four equally likely outcomes: two each of XX and XY. Therefore, the theoretical probability of each outcome is 1/2.

Sample Punnett square:

		XX	
		X	**X**
XY	**X**	XX	XX
	Y	XY	XY

Sample tree diagram:

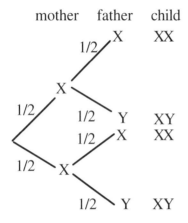

mother   father   child

e. Answers may vary. Some students may correctly predict 1/2.

f. The experimental probability that two independent combinations of male and female chromosomes result in one male and one female child should be approximately 1/2.

g. As shown in the following tree diagram, 2 of the 4 possible outcomes result in one male and one female child. The theoretical probability, therefore, is 1/2.

Child 1   Child 2   Family

G → G → GG
G → B → GB
B → G → BG
B → B → BB

h. The experimental probabilities calculated using the class data should be approximately 1/2.

d. Use a Punnett square or tree diagram to determine the theoretical probability that a combination of male and female chromosomes results in a female child.

e. Predict the probability that two independent combinations of male and female chromosomes result in one male and one female child.

f. 1. To simulate two independent combinations of sex chromosomes, toss the two coins twice. Determine and record the genders of the resulting pair of children.

2. Repeat Step 1 19 more times.

3. Determine the experimental probability that two independent combinations of male and female chromosomes result in one male and one female child.

g. Determine the theoretical probability that two independent combinations of male and female chromosomes result in one male and one female child.

h. Compile the class results from Parts c and f. Using the class results, determine the experimental probability of each of the following.

1. A combination of male and female chromosomes results in a female child.

2. Two independent combinations of male and female chromosomes results in one male and one female child.

Discussion

a. When tossing two coins, why is the outcome for each coin independent of the other?

b. In Part **a** of the exploration, did you predict that a male child and a female child are equally likely? Why or why not?

c. 1. How did the experimental probabilities you calculated using the results of 20 trials compare with the experimental probabilities calculated using the class results?

2. Which probabilities were closer to the theoretical probabilities?

d. In Part **f** of the exploration, you simulated two combinations of sex chromosomes by tossing the coins twice.

1. How many outcomes are there in the sample space for this experiment?

2. How would the size of the sample space change if the experiment simulated three combinations of sex chromosomes?

3. How would the size of the sample space change if the experiment simulated *n* combinations of sex chromosomes?

Discussion

a. Sample response: They are independent events because the outcome of one coin does not affect the outcome of the other coin.

b. Sample response: Yes. They are equally likely because the chance of getting an X on the father coin is the same as the chance of getting a Y on the father coin: 1/2. Because the chance of getting an X on the mother coin is 1, the toss of the mother coin does not affect the outcome.

c. 1. Answers may vary. As the number of trials increases, the experimental probability is more likely to be close to 1/2.

2. The experimental probabilities calculated using the class results are more likely to be close to the theoretical probabilities.

d. 1. The sample space contains 4 items: GG, GB, BG, and BB, where G represents girl and B represents boy.

2. Since there are 2 possibilities for each child, the number of possible outcomes for 3 children is:

$$2 \cdot 2 \cdot 2 = 2^3 = 8.$$

3. 2^n

Warm-Up

1. **a.** Draw a tree diagram to illustrate the sample space for forming three-digit numbers using the digits 3, 5, and 9, *without repetition.*

   b. If the digits are chosen randomly, what is the probability that the number 359 will be formed?

   c. If the digits are chosen randomly, what is the probability that the three-digit number will begin with a 9?

   d. If the digits are chosen randomly, what is the probability that the number formed will be greater than 539?

2. A **prime number** is a number that has exactly two factors, 1 and itself. A **composite number** is a number that has more than two factors. The number 1 is neither prime nor composite.

   a. Create a Venn diagram that shows all of the possible outcomes when rolling an ordinary six-sided die and identifying the roll as prime, composite, or neither.

   b. What is the probability of rolling a prime number?

   c. What is the probability of rolling neither a prime nor a composite number?

   d. What is the probability of rolling two prime numbers followed by a composite number?

Assignment

5.1 **a.** Consider a couple with three children. Draw a tree diagram that shows all the possible outcomes for the genders of the children.

   b. Assume that having a boy and having a girl are equally likely outcomes. Determine the probability that the couple has a girl, a girl, and a boy, in that order.

   c. Determine the probability that exactly two of the children are girls.

   d. Are your responses to Parts **b** and **c** different? Why or why not?

5.2 A family has four boys. Assuming that the birth of each child is an independent event, is their fifth child more likely to be a girl or a boy? Explain your reasoning.

5.3 To find the probability that a family with five children will have five girls, a student used the following formula:

$$P(5 \text{ girls}) = \frac{1}{2} \cdot \frac{1}{2} \cdot \frac{1}{2} \cdot \frac{1}{2} \cdot \frac{1}{2} = \frac{1}{32}$$

Do you agree with this student's method? Why or why not?

Module 2 ■ *What Are My Child's Chances?*   53

Warm-Up

1. **a.** Sample tree diagram:

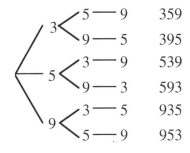

3	5 — 9	359
	9 — 5	395
5	3 — 9	539
	9 — 3	593
9	3 — 5	935
	5 — 9	953

   b. 1/6

   c. 2/6 = 1/3

   d. 3/6 = 1/2

2. **a.** Sample diagram:

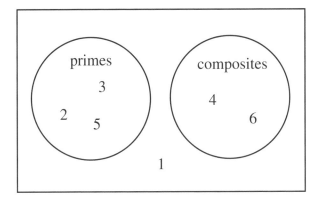

b. 3/6 = 1/2

c. 1/6

d. 1/12

Assignment

Problems suitable for use as assessment items are identified by an asterisk (*).

* **5.1 a.** Sample tree diagram:

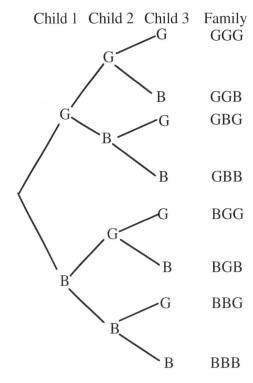

Child 1 Child 2 Child 3 Family

G	G	G	GGG
		B	GGB
	B	G	GBG
		B	GBB
B	G	G	BGG
		B	BGB
	B	G	BBG
		B	BBB

b. Given that a boy and a girl are equally likely, the probability on each branch in the tree diagram is 1/2. Therefore, $P(\text{GGB}) = 1/8$.

c. Two of the three children are girls in 3 of the possible outcomes: GGB, GBG, and BGG. Because the probability of each outcome is 1/8, the total probability is 3/8.

d. The answers to Parts **b** and **c** differ because the event in Part **b** considers the specific order GGB, and the event in Part **c** does not. There are 3 different outcomes that satisfy Part **c,** but only one that satisfies Part **b.** Therefore, their probabilities are different.

5.2 Assuming that the probability of having a boy or girl was equally likely for each of the previous four children, the fifth child is as likely to be a boy as a girl.

5.3 If students assume that each birth is an independent event with the same probability, 1/2, they should agree with this method.

✳ ✳ ✳ ✳ ✳

5.4 **a.** 1/50

b. Assuming that the outcome of one car rental has no effect on the outcome of another, the probability can be calculated as follows:

$$(1/50)^5 = 0.0000000032 \approx 0$$

c. They can expect 250(1/50) = 5 to be involved in accidents.

5.5 **a.** The probability that the fourth digit is a 7 is 1/10.

b–d. The probability that any one sequence of six digits is the winning number is $(1/10)^6 = 1/1,000,000$.

* 5.6 **a.** When rolling two dice, there are 36 equally likely outcomes. Because 6 of them result in a roll of 7 and 2 result in a roll of 11, the probability of winning is:

$$\frac{6}{36} + \frac{2}{36} = \frac{8}{36} = \frac{2}{9}$$

b. Because each roll is an independent event, the probability of winning on three rolls in a row is:

$$\frac{2}{9} \cdot \frac{2}{9} \cdot \frac{2}{9} = \frac{8}{729}$$

* * * * *

5.4 After analyzing its customer data, a rental car agency found that approximately 2% of its customers were involved in accidents.

a. What is the probability that a customer chosen at random is involved in an accident?

b. If 5 different customers are chosen at random, what is the probability that all 5 are involved in accidents? Explain your response.

c. If the agency rents 250 cars in one day, how many should they expect to be involved in accidents?

5.5 In one lottery game, players may choose any sequence of six digits. A computer generates the winning number by randomly selecting one digit at a time, in order from first to sixth.

a. What is the probability that the fourth digit of the winning number is 7?

b. What is the probability that the winning number is 682399?

c. What is the probability that the winning number is 123456?

d. What is the probability that the winning number is 000000?

5.6 In the game of craps, a player rolls two dice. A roll of 7 or 11 results in a win.

a. What is the probability of winning on one roll? Explain your response.

b. What is the probability of winning on three rolls in a row? Explain your response.

Summary Assessment

To ensure a safe and steady supply of blood for medical use, many hospitals maintain banks of donated blood. The human body normally contains about 5 L of blood. Each volunteer donates about 0.5 L. In healthy people, that 0.5 L is readily replenished.

Imagine that you work for a hospital blood bank. The blood bank likes to have at least 5 L of each blood type available—enough for one complete transfusion, if necessary. The hospital is planning to make a public service announcement requesting more donors. Your job is to determine which blood types are most needed.

1. An individual's blood type—O, A, B, or AB—is determined by a combination of the parents' genes, one allele from each parent. The allele for type O blood is always recessive. The alleles for types A and B are always dominant. The combination of alleles A and B produces the blood type AB.

   a. List all the possible genotypes for each blood type.

   b. Assuming that each possible genotype is equally likely to occur in the population, determine the probability of having each blood type.

2. The blood bank currently has a total of 75 L of blood. How many liters of each blood type would you expect it to have?

3. The presence or absence of the Rh factor also affects blood type. In the United States, about 85% of the population is Rh positive (Rh+); the rest is Rh negative (Rh–).

   The presence or absence of the Rh factor, along with the four basic blood types, results in eight different kinds of blood: A+, B+, AB+, O+, A–, B–, AB–, and O–. How many liters of each would you expect the blood bank to have?

4. In its public service announcement, which types of blood should the hospital say are most needed? Explain your response.

teacher note

An additional assessment, for use at your discretion, appears in the Teacher Resources for this module.

Summary Assessment

1. a. The possible genotypes for each blood type are shown below.

Blood Type	A	B	AB	O
Possible Genotype	AA, AO	BB, BO	AB	OO

b. Assuming that each genotype is equally likely, the probability of each phenotype is listed below.

Blood Type	A	B	AB	O
Probability	2/6 = 1/3	2/6 = 1/3	1/6	1/6

Note: The actual distribution of human blood types varies by population.

2. Assuming that the genotypes of blood donors are distributed as in Problem **1,** the expected amounts can be found by multiplying each probability by 75 L and rounding to the nearest 0.5 L. The total should not exceed 75 L.

Blood Type	A	B	AB	O
Expected Amount (L)	25	25	12.5	12.5

3. Assuming that blood type and Rh factor are independent events, the expected amount of each blood type can be multiplied by 85% to determine the expected amount of Rh+ blood, and by 15% to determine the amount of Rh– blood, with the results rounded appropriately. As in Problem **2,** the total should not exceed 75 L.

Blood Type	A+	A–	B+	B–	AB+	AB–	O+	O–
Expected Amount (L)	21	4	21	4	10.5	2	10.5	2

4. As shown in the table in Problem **3,** the expected amount for each Rh– blood type is less than 5 L. The table below shows the amounts needed and the number of donors required for each.

Blood Type	A–	B–	AB–	O–
Amount Needed (L)	1	1	3	3
Donors Needed	2	2	6	6

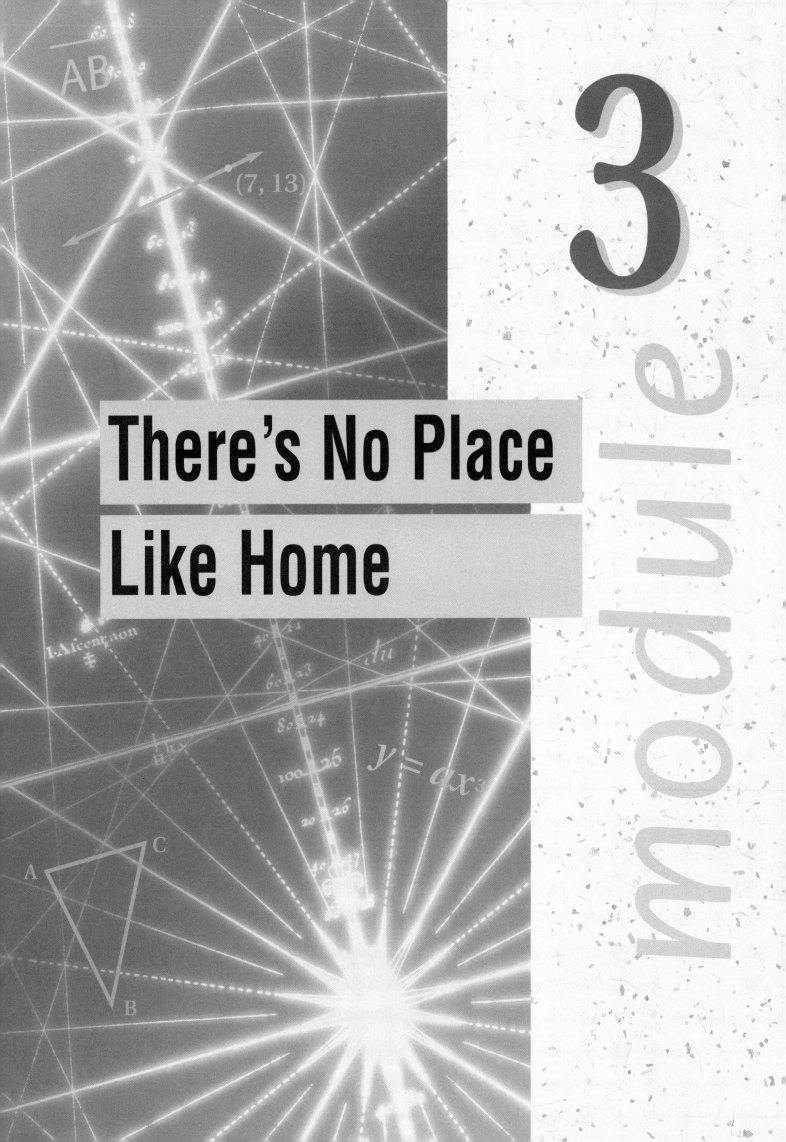

There's No Place Like Home

3 module

Overview

In this module, students use traditional American Indian housing designs to investigate the surface areas and volumes of some common three-dimensional figures.

Activity 1:   An intuitive understanding of limits is developed by exploring a circle as the limit of a progression of regular polygons with an increasing number of sides inscribed in the circle.

Activity 2:   Students use nets to help them calculate the surface area and lateral surface area of cylinders and prisms.

Activity 3:   Students calculate the volumes of cylinders and prisms, and explore the ratio of surface area to volume as a measure of structural efficiency.

Activity 4:   Students develop a method to calculate the surface area of right pyramids. They are introduced to sectors of circles and use them to calculate the lateral surface area of cones.

Activity 5:   Students develop and use formulas for the volumes of cones, spheres, and pyramids.

Objectives

In this module, students will:

✳ construct and inscribe polygons (1)

✳ circumscribe regular polygons (1)

✳ find measures of central angles of regular polygons given the number of sides (1)

✳ determine the areas of regular polygons and circles (1)

✳ identify the limiting shapes for sequences of inscribed regular polygons, prisms, and pyramids (1, 3)

✳ determine the lateral and total surface areas of prisms and cylinders (2, 3)

✳ determine the volumes of prisms and cylinders (3, 5)

✳ given the range of certain dimensions of a prism, find the range of the corresponding volumes (3)

✳ calculate the ratio of surface area to volume for a given figure (3, 5)

✳ find the area of a sector given the measure of its central angle (4)

✳ calculate lateral and total surface area of cones (4)

✳ determine the radius of a cone's base, given the sector that determines its lateral surface area (4)

✳ develop and use a formula for the surface area of a cone (4)

* develop and use a formula for the volume of a cone (5)
* compare the volume of a cone with that of a right cylinder with the same base and height (5)
* develop and use a formula for the volume of a right pyramid (5)
* develop and use a formula for the volume of a sphere (5)
* compare the volumes of right cylinders, hemispheres, and right cones with the same radius and height (5)
* calculate the surface areas and volumes of spheres (5).

Prerequisites

For this module, students should know:

* how to use the sine, cosine, and tangent ratios to determine unknown lengths in right triangles
* how to use $\sin^{-1}$, $\cos^{-1}$, and $\tan^{-1}$ to determine unknown angle measures in right triangles
* the definition of a regular polygon
* how to identify the central angles of a regular polygon
* how to calculate the circumference and area of a circle
* how to determine the volume of a right rectangular prism
* how to make nets of three-dimensional figures
* the Pythagorean theorem.

 Flashbacks, for use at your discretion, appear in the Teacher Resources for this module. These brief problem sets provide a review of some prerequisite skills for each activity.

Planning Guide

Activity	Materials	Technology	Time Line
Activity **1**	■ none	■ geometry utility ■ spreadsheet	2 days
Activity **2**	■ none	■ none	1 day
Activity **3**	■ cubes	■ none	2 days
Activity **4**	■ construction paper ■ scissors ■ tape	■ geometry utility	2 days
Activity **5**	■ construction paper ■ scissors ■ tape ■ compass ■ ruler ■ rice	■ geometry utility ■ graphing utility ■ spreadsheet	2 days
Assessment Activities	■ none	■ none	3 days **Total: 12 days**

Introduction

This module uses traditional American Indian housing designs as a context for studying the surface areas and volumes of prisms, cylinders, pyramids, cones, and spheres.

In this activity, students explore the areas of regular polygons. This provides the basis for determining surface area throughout the module. The idea of a circle as the limit of a progression of its inscribed regular polygons is introduced here.

Materials List

■ none

Technology

■ geometry utility

■ spreadsheet (optional)

Student Outcomes

After completing the following exploration and discussion, students should be able to:

✳ use the measures of central angles to construct regular polygons on a geometry utility

✳ determine the areas of regular polygons

✳ compare the areas and perimeters of circumscribed polygons as the number of sides increases.

✳ compare the areas, perimeters, and apothems of inscribed polygons as the number of sides increases.

teacher note

Because the following exploration can be time consuming, you might wish to divide the polygons in Part **c** among several groups, then ask students to compile their results. (If so, all students should use the same radius when constructing the inscribed polygons.)

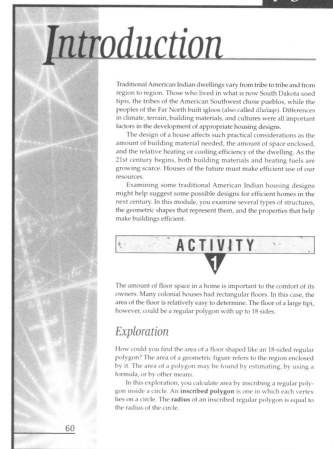

Introduction

Traditional American Indian dwellings vary from tribe to tribe and from region to region. Those who lived in what is now South Dakota used tipis, the tribes of the American Southwest chose pueblos, while the peoples of the Far North built igloos (also called *illuliaqs*). Differences in climate, terrain, building materials, and cultures were all important factors in the development of appropriate housing designs.

The design of a house affects such practical considerations as the amount of building material needed, the amount of space enclosed, and the relative heating or cooling efficiency of the dwelling. As the 21st century begins, both building materials and heating fuels are growing scarce. Houses of the future must make efficient use of our resources.

Examining some traditional American Indian housing designs might help suggest some possible designs for efficient homes in the next century. In this module, you examine several types of structures, the geometric shapes that represent them, and the properties that help make buildings efficient.

ACTIVITY 1

The amount of floor space in a home is important to the comfort of its owners. Many colonial houses had rectangular floors. In this case, the area of the floor is relatively easy to determine. The floor of a large tipi, however, could be a regular polygon with up to 18 sides.

Exploration

How could you find the area of a floor shaped like an 18-sided regular polygon? The area of a geometric figure refers to the region enclosed by it. The area of a polygon may be found by estimating, by using a formula, or by other means.

In this exploration, you calculate area by inscribing a regular polygon inside a circle. An **inscribed polygon** is one in which each vertex lies on a circle. The **radius** of an inscribed regular polygon is equal to the radius of the circle.

60

For example, Figure 3-1 shows a square inscribed in a circle, with the radius of the square drawn from the square's center to one of the vertices.

FIGURE 3-1   Inscribed square with a radius of 2 cm.

a. 1. Construct a circle on a geometry utility. Record its radius, area, and perimeter.

 2. Select three points on the circle to represent the vertices of an inscribed triangle.

 3. Connect the center of the circle to each of the three points to form three central angles. A **central angle** is an angle with its vertex at the center of a circle.

 4. Move the points along the circle, one at a time, until the central angles all have equal measures.

 5. Connect the three points on the circle to form a regular triangle.

b. 1. Use the geometry utility to calculate the triangle's area and perimeter.

 2. Record this information in a table.

c. Using a process similar to that described in Part **a**, inscribe a regular quadrilateral, pentagon, hexagon, octagon, and 18-sided polygon in circles of the same radius.

d. In your table from Part **b**, record the area and perimeter of each regular polygon, along with the area and perimeter of the circle in which they were inscribed. **Note:** Save your data for use in the discussion.

Discussion

a. How did you determine the locations of the vertices for your inscribed polygons?

b. In Parts **a** and **c** of the exploration, why does creating congruent central angles guarantee that a regular polygon will be formed?

c. 1. What methods do you know for determining the area of regular polygons?

 2. What are the advantages and disadvantages of each one?

Module 3 ■ *There's No Place Like Home*   61

Exploration

a–b. Students use a geometry utility to draw an inscribed regular triangle, then determine its perimeter and area.

c–d. The following sample data was collected using a radius of 5 cm.

Regular Polygon	Perimeter (cm)	Area (cm²)
triangle	26.0	32.4
square	28.3	49.9
pentagon	29.4	59.3
hexagon	30.0	64.8
octagon	30.6	70.6
18-gon	31.2	76.8
circle	31.4	78.4

Discussion

a. Sample response: The number of sides in the polygon equals its number of central angles. Because there are 360° in a circle, 360° divided by the number of sides (or vertices) determines how many degrees each central angle must have. To find the vertices, locate the points on the circle where each central angle has the desired measure.

b. The congruent central angles form congruent isosceles triangles in each polygon, with the base of each triangle representing a side of the polygon. The bases of these triangles are all congruent, therefore the sides of the polygon are congruent. Because the base angles of all the isosceles triangles are congruent, the angles of the polygon are congruent.

c. 1. One method divides the regular polygon into congruent isosceles triangles with vertex angles at the center of the polygon and bases as the sides of the polygon. The area of each of these triangles, where a is the height and b is the length of the base, is

$$\frac{1}{2}ab$$

The area of the polygon is equal to the sum of the areas of these triangles. If the polygon has n sides, then the area of the polygon is

$$n\left(\frac{1}{2}ab\right)$$

Because $n \cdot b$ is the perimeter of the polygon, the generalized form of this method is the formula

$$A = \frac{1}{2}ap$$

where a is the apothem and p is the perimeter.

 Note: Some students might recall this formula from the Level 1 module, "A New Look at Boxing." Others might suggest using technology, as described in the exploration.

 2. Sample response: Each method can be useful, depending on the information given. Using a formula is appropriate when you know the required lengths. Using technology can be faster if you already have drawn a model of the polygon.

d. 1. The shape of the polygon approaches a circle.
   2. The area of the polygon approaches the area of the circle.
   3. The perimeter of the polygon approaches the circumference of the circle.

e. 1. The shape of the polygon approaches a circle.
   2. The area of the polygon approaches the area of the circle.
   3. The perimeter of the polygon approaches the circumference of the circle.

f. 1. Sample response: As the number of sides of the polygon increases, the shape of the polygon becomes more and more circular. The apothem approaches a radius (r) of the circle and the perimeter approaches the circumference ($2\pi r$) of the circle.
   2. As the number of sides increases, the formula for the area of a regular polygon approaches the formula for the area of a circle:

$$A = \frac{1}{2}r(2\pi r) = \pi r^2$$

Warm-Up

1. **a.** 30°
   b. 15°
   c. 40°
2. The area is approximately 110 m².

Assignment

Problems suitable for use as assessment items are identified by an asterisk (*).

1.1 **a.** $m\angle ABC = 20°$; $m\angle ABD = 10°$
   b. $AD = 5 \cdot \sin 10° \approx 0.87$ m

---

d. Consider a set of regular polygons inscribed in the same circle. As the number of sides in a polygon increases, describe what happens to each of the following characteristics:

   1. the shape of the polygon
   2. the area of the polygon
   3. the perimeter of the polygon.

e. A **tangent** to a circle is a line, segment, or ray that intersects a circle in one point and is perpendicular to a radius at that point. Consider a pentagon whose sides are each tangent to a circle, as shown in Figure 3-2 below. In this case, the polygon **circumscribes** the circle.

FIGURE 3-2   A circle circumscribed by a regular pentagon.

Consider a set of regular polygons that circumscribe the same circle. As the number of sides in a polygon increases, describe what happens to each of the following characteristics:

   1. the shape of the polygon
   2. the area of the polygon
   3. the perimeter of the polygon.

f. Figure 3-3 below shows a regular pentagon inscribed in a circle. In this case, $\overline{AG}$ is an **apothem**, a segment whose measure is the perpendicular distance from the center of a regular polygon to one of its sides.

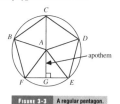

FIGURE 3-3   A regular pentagon.

One formula for the area of a regular polygon is

$$A = \frac{1}{2}ap$$

where a is the length of the apothem and p is the perimeter of the polygon. (See the Level 1 module, "A New Look at Boxing.")

   1. As the number of sides of an inscribed regular polygon increases, what do the values of a and p approach in relation to the circle?
   2. How does this affect the formula for the area of a regular polygon given above?

Warm-Up

1. Find the measure of the central angles of each of the following regular polygons.
   a. dodecagon
   b. 24-gon
   c. nonagon

2. Find the area of a regular pentagon with sides 8 cm long.

Assignment

1.1 The diagram below shows a view of a tipi from above. The floor of the tipi is an 18-sided regular polygon with a radius of 5 m.

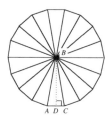

Use this diagram to determine each of the following:

   a. the measures of $\angle ABC$ and $\angle ABD$
   b. the length of $\overline{AD}$ (using trigonometry)

c. the length of $\overline{AC}$

d. the length of $\overline{BD}$

e. the area of $\triangle ABC$

f. the area of the tipi's floor.

1.2 The Powder House in Williamsburg, Virginia, was built in 1714 and used for storing gunpowder. As shown in the diagram below, the structure has a regular octagonal base. Given that the longest diagonals measure 16 m, determine the area of the floor.

1.3 Igloos are built from blocks of snow. The floor of an igloo is a circle. If an igloo has a diameter of 3.5 m, what is the area of its floor?

* * * * *

1.4 The diagram below shows the regular hexagonal floor of a modern domed camping tent. Given that each side is 1 m long, determine the area of the floor.

1 m

Research Project

Choose one American Indian tribe—or several tribes from a single region—and study their traditional buildings. Describe each structure's practical, seasonal, and cultural uses. Then describe each structure from a mathematical point of view, including its shape, geometric properties, and typical dimensions.

64   Module 3 ■ *There's No Place Like Home*

1.3 Using the formula for the area of a circle, the area of the floor is $\pi(3.5/2)^2 \approx 9.6\ \text{m}^2$.

* * * * *

1.4 Student methods may vary. Using the formula for the area of a regular polygon, the area of the floor is:

$$A = \frac{1}{2}a \bullet p$$

$$\approx \frac{1}{2}(0.87 \bullet 6) \approx 2.6\ \text{m}^2$$

Research Project

This research project gives students the opportunity to further explore the geometric and cultural aspects of traditional American Indian housing designs. You might wish to encourage students to build models or make sketches.

---

c. $AC \approx 1.74$ m

d. Using the Pythagorean theorem, $BD \approx 4.9$ m.

e. The area of $\triangle ABC \approx (4.9 \bullet 1.74)/2 \approx 4.3\ \text{m}^2$.

f. The area of the floor is approximately

$$18(4.3) \approx 77\ \text{m}^2.$$

* 1.2 Student methods may vary. Using the points labeled in the diagram below, $AB \approx 8$ m, $\sin 67.5° = BD/8$, and $\cos 67.5° = AD/8$.

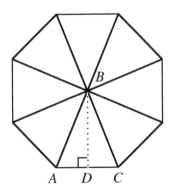

The area of the floor, therefore, can be found as follows:

$$A = \frac{1}{2}a \bullet p$$

$$= \frac{1}{2}(8 \bullet \sin 67.5°) \bullet 2(8 \bullet \cos 67.5°)8 \approx 181\ \text{m}^2$$

ACTIVITY 2

Students examine lateral surface area and total surface area using nets of right prisms and right circular cylinders. (Only right prisms and cylinders are considered in the context of this module.)

Materials List

■ none

Technology

■ geometry utility (optional)

Student Outcomes

After completing the following discussion, students should be able to:

✳ describe the net of a right prism.

✳ describe the net of a right cylinder

✳ find the total surface area of a right prism.

✳ find the total surface area of a right cylinder.

Discussion

a. 1. Sample response: The bases of a prism must be parallel. Because the rectangles are not parallel, the floor cannot be a base.
   2. Sample response: It is called a right prism because the bases are perpendicular to the lateral faces.

b. The length of $\overline{AD}$ (or $\overline{BC}$) equals the perimeter of the base.

c. Sample response: Determine the area of a base by squaring the length of one side of the base. Find the area of the lateral surface by multiplying the perimeter of the base by the height of the prism. Add the area of the two bases to the area of the lateral surface.

d. 1. The length of the rectangle's longer side is the circumference of the cylinder.
   2. The length of the rectangle's shorter side is the height of the cylinder.
   3. The circles represent the two bases of the cylinder.
   4. The length of the rectangle's longer side is $2\pi r$.
   5. Sample response: Multiply the circumference of the cylinder by the height to find the lateral surface area. Find the area of a base by squaring the radius and then multiplying by π. Add the lateral surface area to two times the area of a base.

ACTIVITY 2

When an architect designs a house, the desired amount of floor space is only one consideration. Available building materials also play a role in determining an appropriate design. In some situations, appearance is a primary consideration; in others, durability and cost are the main concerns. In any case, estimating the amount of materials required is an important part of the planning process. When determining the amount of material needed to build a house, it is helpful to calculate the area of the walls, floor, and roof.

American Indian families in the Yukon region of Alaska and Canada often built double lean-tos such as the one shown in Figure 3-4.

FIGURE 3-4
A double lean-to.

A double lean-to can be described as a right triangular prism with bases that are equilateral triangles. The total surface area of a prism is the sum of the lateral surface area and the areas of the two bases. For example, Figure 3-5 shows a net for a right triangular prism. In this case, the three rectangles in the net are the lateral faces of the prism. The sum of their areas is the prism's lateral surface area.

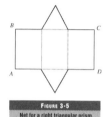

FIGURE 3-5
Net for a right triangular prism.

Module 3 ■ *There's No Place Like Home* 65

Discussion

a. 1. Why is it incorrect to consider a rectangle as a base of the prism in Figure 3-5?
   2. Why is this prism called a "right" prism?

b. How are the dimensions of rectangle *ABCD* in Figure 3-5 related to the perimeter of the prism's base?

c. Describe how to find the surface area of a right prism with a square base.

d. Figure 3-6 shows a net for a right circular cylinder.

FIGURE 3-6 Net for a right circular cylinder.

1. What does the length of the rectangle's longer side represent?
2. What part of the net represents the height of the cylinder?
3. What do the circles represent?
4. Express the length of the rectangle's longer side in terms of the radius of the circle.
5. Describe how to find the total surface area of a cylinder.

Warm-Up

1. The height of a regular hexagonal prism is 24 m and the length of each side is 8 m.
   a. Sketch the prism labeling the information given.
   b. Sketch a net for the prism, labeling the appropriate edges.
   c. Find the lateral area.
   d. Find the area of the bases.
   e. Determine the total surface area of the prism.

Assignment

2.1 The Powder House described in Problem **1.2** can be modeled by a right regular octagonal prism. A similar building, shown in the diagram on the right, is 11 m high. Each side of a base is 6 m long.

  a. Sketch a net for the building.

  b. Label the dimensions of one of the net's lateral faces.

  c. Determine the building's lateral surface area.

  d. Calculate the area of the bases.

  e. Determine the total surface area of the building.

2.2 a. Sketch a net for a prism whose bases are regular heptagons.

  b. As the number of sides in the bases of a prism increase, what geometric shape does the prism approach?

2.3 To help estimate the amount of material needed to build the double lean-to shown in Figure **3-4**, determine its total surface area.

2.4 The Pueblo Indians of the Rio Grande region lived in rectangular flat-roofed homes. As shown in the diagram below, these dwellings resemble an early version of the modern apartment building.

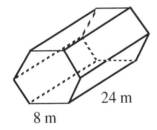

The right rectangular prism below shows some possible dimensions for a single-family unit in a Pueblo village. Use these measurements to determine the total surface area of one family's home.

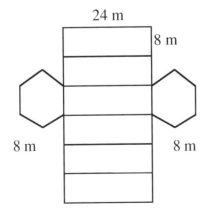

Warm-Up

1. a. Sample sketch:

  b. Sample net:

24 m

8 m

8 m   8 m

  c. The lateral surface area is 1152 m².
  d. The area of the bases is approximately 332.6 m².
  e. The total surface area is approximately 1484.6 m².

Assignment

Problems suitable for use as assessment items are identified by an asterisk (*).

2.1 a–b. Sample response:

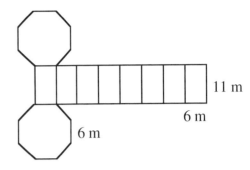

11 m

6 m

6 m

  c. The lateral surface area is 8 • 6 • 11 = 528 m².
  d. Sample response:

$$A = 2 \cdot n\left(\frac{1}{2}ab\right)$$
$$= 2 \cdot 8\left(\frac{1}{2} \cdot 6 \cdot \frac{3}{\tan 22.5°}\right)$$
$$\approx 348 \text{ m}^2$$

  e. The total surface area is 528 + 348 ≈ 876 m².

2.2 a. Sample sketch:

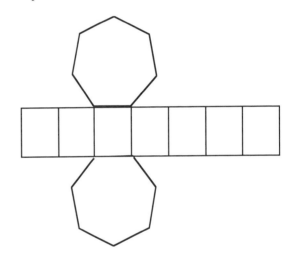

  b. Sample response: As the number of sides increases, the base gets closer and closer to a circle. The shape of the prism approaches a cylinder.

2.3 The lateral surface area, including the floor, is 3 • 3.2 • 4.7 ≈ 45 m². The height of the triangular base is 1.6 • tan 60° ≈ 2.8 m. The area of each base is

$$\frac{1}{2} \cdot 2.8 \cdot 3.2 \approx 4.5 \text{ m}^2$$

The total surface area is 45 + 2(4.5) or approximately 54 m².

2.4 The total surface area is 2 • (3.8 • 3.4) + 2 • (3.8 + 3.4) • 2.2 = 57.5 m².

* 2.5 **a.** The area of the floor is 3.7 • 4.9 ≈ 18.1 m².
    b. The two walls have a total area of π(3.7/2)² ≈ 10.8 m².
    c. The lateral surface area can be found as follows:

$$\frac{1}{2} \cdot 2\pi(3.7/2) \cdot 4.9 \approx 28.5 \text{ m}^2$$

    d. The total surface area is: 18.1 + 28.5 + 10.8 ≈ 57.4 m².

＊ ＊ ＊ ＊ ＊

2.6 Sample response: The amount of bark required to cover the Iroquois house (not including the floor) is the area of the four walls plus the area of the half cylinder that represents the roof:

$$2(5.5 + 18.3) \cdot 2.75 + \pi(2.75)^2 + \frac{1}{2}(2\pi \cdot 2.75) \cdot 18.3$$

$$\approx 313 \text{ m}^2$$

Students compare the volumes of various American Indian structures. They also consider the ratio of surface area to volume as a measure of a building's heating (or cooling) efficiency.

 teacher note

A brief assessment of the mathematical content in Activities **1**, **2**, and **3**, for use at your discretion, appears in the Teacher Resources for this module.

Materials List

■ sets of eight cubes (one or two sets per group)

Student Outcomes

After completing the following exploration and discussion, students should be able to:

＊ describe a formula for the volume of a right prism.

＊ determine the volume of a right prism.

＊ determine the volume of a right cylinder

＊ determine the ratio of surface area to volume for cylinders and prisms.

2.5 A traditional wigwam of the Chippewa tribe and a modern Quonset hut share the same basic shape: a half cylinder. The Chippewas used wigwams as sweat lodges. Quonset huts with translucent walls are commonly used as greenhouses. Complete Parts **a–d** for the Quonset hut shown on the right.

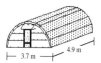

   a. What is the area of the floor?

   b. What is the area of the two walls formed by the semicircles?

   c. What is the lateral surface area?

   d. What is the total surface area, including the floor?

＊ ＊ ＊ ＊ ＊

2.6 The Iroquois Indians of New York lived in rectangular barrel-roofed houses. The roof of each structure was made by bending poles into a semicircular shape (a half barrel). The entire building, except for the floor, was covered with bark. How much tree bark would be needed to cover the house shown in the diagram below?

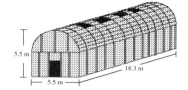

ACTIVITY 3

Like today's families, early American Indian families lived in dwellings of various shapes and sizes. The ease of heating and cooling these structures was an important part of their design. Efficient heating and cooling also are major considerations for nearly all modern homes.

Because you heat the space inside a home (volume) and lose heat through the outside walls, roof, and floor (surface area), you must consider both surface area and volume when estimating efficiency. One way to do this involves calculating the ratio of a building's surface area to its volume. Although this rule of thumb is not always applicable, it does give one indication of a home's potential efficiency.

Exploration

a. 1. Arrange eight cubes so that each cube shares at least one entire face with another cube.

2. Describe the shape you created in Step 1 and make a sketch of it. For example, Figure 3-7 shows a sketch of one possible arrangement.

FIGURE 3-7 An arrangement of eight cubes.

b. Repeat Part **a** for several different arrangements of the cubes.

mathematics note

The **volume** (V) of a right prism can be found by multiplying the area of one of its bases (B) by its height (h). The height of a prism is the distance between the two bases. In general, the formula for the volume of a right prism is:

$$V = B \cdot h$$

For example, consider a right hexagonal prism with a height of 15 m. If the area of each base is 256 m², the volume of the prism can be found as follows:

$$V = B \cdot h = 256 \text{ m}^2 \cdot 15 \text{ m} = 3840 \text{ m}^3$$

c. For each shape you created in Parts **a** and **b**, determine the volume, the total surface area, and the ratio of surface area to volume. Record these values in a table. For example, the volume (V) of the shape in Figure 3-7 is 8 units³, its surface area (S) is 34 units², and the ratio S/V is 4.25.

Discussion

a. 1. Which of the shapes that you created in the exploration has the greatest surface area?

The diagram below shows several arrangements in which the cubes are stacked.

7. **8.** **9.** **10.**

The total surface area and ratio of surface area to volume for each arrangement are shown in the table below.

Arrangement	Surface Area (units²)	Surface Area / Volume
1	34	4.25
2	32	4
3	34	4.25
4	32	4
5	30	3.75
6	28	3.5
7	34	4.25
8	30	3.75
9	34	4.25
10	24	3

Exploration

In this exploration, students investigate the relationship between volume and surface area.

a–b. Students should record each arrangement of the cubes they investigate.

c. In general, the total surface area depends on the number of faces shared by the cubes. The diagram below shows a top view of three sample arrangements with a surface area of 34 units².

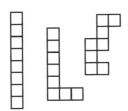

The following diagram shows the top view of six additional arrangements of cubes.

1. **2.** **3.** **4.** **5.** **6.**

Discussion

a. 1. The greatest surface area (34 units²) occurs in several different arrangements.

2. The least surface area (24 units^2) occurs in a $2 \times 2 \times 2$ arrangement.

3. All the arrangements have the same volume, 8 units^3.

b. Sample response: Given that two designs have the same volume, a design with more surface area (and therefore a higher ratio) would be more in contact with the outside air. Even though it might receive more sunlight during the day, it also would lose more heat whenever the outside air was colder than the inside air.

c. 1. The greatest ratio (4.25) occurs in the arrangements with the surface area of 34 units^2.

2. The least ratio (3.0) occurs in the arrangement with the surface area of 24 units^2.

d. Sample response: A cube would be a good choice because it has the smallest surface area for a given volume.

e. Sample response: Because more surface area would provide more area for sunlight to strike, one of the shapes with a high ratio of surface area to volume would be a good choice.

Warm-Up

1. **a.** 1794 cm^3
   b. $\approx$ 1620.7 dm^3
   c. $\approx$ 16,848 cm^3
2. The volume is approximately 11,923 cm^3.

Assignment

Problems suitable for use as assessment items are identified by an asterisk (*).

3.1 **a.** The volume inside a Mohave-type house ranges from $6^2 \bullet 2.2 \approx 79.2$ m^3 to about $7.5^2 \bullet 2.2 \approx 124$ m^3.

b. The ratio of surface area to volume is:

$$\frac{2(6 \bullet 6) + 4(2.2 \bullet 6)}{79.2} \approx 1.58$$

3.2 **a.** The ratio of surface area to volume is:

$$\frac{2(4 \bullet 3.25 + 2.2 \bullet 3.25 + 2.2 \bullet 4)}{2.2(4)3.25} \approx 2.02$$

b. The volume of the Pueblo dwelling is about $13 \bullet 2.2 \approx 29$ m^3. This is about 50 m^3 less space than the smallest Yuma dwelling.

3.3 **a.** The volume of the house is:

$$(4.1 \bullet 3.1 \bullet 1.7) + \left(\frac{3.1 \bullet 1}{2} \bullet 4.1\right) \approx 28 \text{ m}^3$$

b. The surface area of the house is:

$$4.1 \bullet 3.1 + 2(1.7 \bullet 3.1 + 1.7 \bullet 4.1) + 2\left(\frac{3.1 \bullet 1}{2}\right)$$
$$+ 2(1.84 \bullet 4.1) \approx 55 \text{ m}^2$$

The ratio of surface area to volume is $55/28 \approx 1.96$.

---

2. Which has the least surface area?

3. Which has the greatest volume?

b. Why might the ratio of surface area to volume provide a reasonable way to evaluate the heating and cooling efficiency of a house? (Disregard the effects of different building materials or insulation when considering your response.)

c. 1. Which of the shapes you created in the exploration has the greatest ratio of surface area to volume?

2. Which has the smallest ratio of surface area to volume?

d. If you were building a house in a cold climate and needed to conserve heating fuel, which shape would you choose? Explain your response.

e. If you were building a house to collect and store solar energy, which shape would you choose? Explain your response.

Warm-Up

1. Find the volume of each figure described below.

   a. a right octagonal prism with a height of 13 cm and a base area of 38 cm^2

   b. a right cylinder with a base radius of 4.3 dm and a height of 27.9 dm

   c. a right prism with a height of 54 cm whose base is an irregular polygon with an area of 312 cm^2

2. Determine the volume of a hexagonal prism with a height of 24 cm and an apothem of 12 cm.

Assignment

3.1 The Yuma people of the Colorado River region lived in "Mohave-type" houses. Each one-story dwelling was a right rectangular prism with a square floor. These houses were about 2.2 m tall and had flat roofs. The square floors ranged from 6 m to 7.5 m on each side.

   a. What is the range of the volumes for these dwellings?

   b. What is the ratio of surface area to volume for a Yuma dwelling with a square floor 6 m on each side?

3.2 As mentioned in Problem **2.4**, the traditional homes of the Pueblo Indians are rectangular flat-roofed structures that resemble apartment buildings. A typical family room was about 2.2 m high. The dimensions of the floor were approximately 4 m by 3.25 m.

   a. What is the ratio of surface area to volume for this room?

   b. How does the amount of space in a Pueblo dwelling compare with that of the smallest Yuma dwelling?

3.3 The summer houses of one Southeastern tribe were rectangular, gabled dwellings with thatched roofs and mud walls. The gabled roof was open, with smoke holes located along the ridge. One example of this type of house is shown in the diagram below.

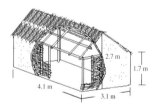

a. What is the volume of this house?

b. What is its ratio of surface area to volume?

3.4 The basic shapes of the two structures shown below were used by many different American Indian tribes.

Consider a structure of each type with identical, rectangular bases measuring 3.0 m by 3.8 m. Each structure has walls of the same height. Each also has the same overall height: 3.4 m.

a. Which structure has the greater surface area? Explain your response.

b. Which has the greater volume? Explain your response.

c. If the two structures were built of the same materials, which one would you expect to retain heat more efficiently? Explain your response.

3.5 The figure below shows the top view of a right prism inscribed in a cylinder. The bases of the prism are many-sided regular polygons.

a. As the number of sides in a base of the prism increases, how does the volume of the prism compare to the volume of the cylinder?

b. The formula for the volume of a right prism is $V = B \cdot h$, where B represents the area of a base and h represents the height.

  1. Can this formula be used to find the volume of a right cylinder? Explain your response.

  2. What formula would you use to determine the area of a base of the cylinder?

* * * * *

3.6 A manufacturer of painting supplies uses a cylindrical container for paint and a container shaped like a rectangular prism for paint thinner. The dimensions of these two containers are shown in the diagram below.

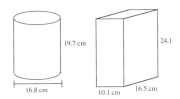

19.7 cm   24.1

16.8 cm   10.1 cm   16.5 cm

a. Determine the lateral surface area, total surface area, and volume of the cylindrical container.

b. Determine the lateral surface area, total surface area, and volume of the container shaped like a rectangular prism.

c. If both containers are made from the same material, which one do you think would be cheaper to make? Explain your response.

---

* **3.4** **a.** Because the floors and side walls are the same sizes, students need only compare those portions of the structures that lie above the side walls. The surface area of this portion of the building with the curved roof is:

$$\frac{2 \cdot \pi \cdot 1.5 \cdot 3.8}{2} + \pi \cdot (1.5)^2 \approx 25 \text{ m}^2$$

The surface area of this portion of the other structure is:

$$2 \cdot \left(\frac{1.5 \cdot 3.0}{2}\right) + 2(1.5\sqrt{2} \cdot 3.8) \approx 21 \text{ m}^2$$

Therefore, the surface area of the building with the curved roof is about 4 m^2 greater than that of the other building.

b. The volume of the portion of the building with the curved roof that lies above the side walls is:

$$\frac{\pi \cdot 1.5^2 \cdot 3.8}{2} \approx 13.4 \text{ m}^3$$

The volume of the corresponding portion of the other building is:

$$\frac{3.0 \cdot 1.5}{2} \cdot 3.8 \approx 8.6 \text{ m}^3$$

Therefore, the volume of the building with the curved roof is about 5 m^3 greater than that of the other building.

c. Sample response: Because heat is lost through surface area, you might expect the building with the curved roof to lose heat more easily. But this structure also has more volume. In fact, the ratio of surface area to volume for the building with the curved roof is $25/13.4 \approx 1.9$, while the ratio for the other building is $21/8.6 \approx 2.4$. Judging from these ratios, the building with the curved roof is likely to be more efficient in retaining heat.

3.5 **a.** Sample response: As the number of sides increases, the volume of the prism approaches the volume of the cylinder.

b. **1.** Sample response: Yes, the formula also can be used to find the volume of a cylinder. You just need to find the area of the circular base and multiply it by the height of the cylinder.

2. Because the base of a cylinder is a circle, the formula for its area is $A = \pi r^2$.

✴ ✴ ✴ ✴ ✴

3.6 **a.** The lateral surface area of the cylindrical container is about 1040 cm^2. The total surface area is approximately 1480 cm^2. The volume is approximately 4360 cm^3.

b. The lateral surface area of the container shaped like a rectangular prism is about 1280 cm^2. The total surface area is approximately 1620 cm^2. The volume is approximately 4020 cm^3.

c. Sample response: Because the cylindrical container has less surface area, it should take less material to manufacture each one. Therefore, it should be cheaper to produce.

Students examine the surface area and volume of both pyramids and cones. Using nets, they also explore the notion of a cone as the limit of a progression of regular polygonal pyramids with the same heights whose bases are inscribed in the same circle.

Materials List

- construction paper (one sheet per student)
- tape
- scissors

Technology

- geometry utility (optional)

Student Outcomes

After completing the following exploration and discussions, students should be able to:

✳ identify the height and slant height of a right pyramid

✳ calculate the lateral and total surface area of a pyramid

✳ construct nets for right pyramids

✳ find the area of a sector of a circle given the measure of its central angle

✳ find the lateral surface area of a cone

✳ find the radius of a cone's base given the radius and measure of the sector that determines the net of the lateral surface.

Discussion 1

a. The lateral faces are congruent isosceles triangles.
b. 1. The shape of the base becomes more and more circular.
   2. The lengths of the bases of the congruent isosceles triangles decrease.
   3. The pyramid looks more like a cone.
c. Sample response: To find the surface area of a pyramid, find the area of the polygonal base and the area of all the lateral triangular faces. Add the area of the base to the area of all the triangles.

ACTIVITY 4

For the American Indian tribes who followed the bison herds, a tipi was the ideal home. It was warm in winter, cool in summer, portable, and easily made from available materials. Figure **3-8** shows one example of a tipi.

FIGURE 3-8 A tipi.

Some tipis approximated the shape of a regular pyramid. The base was a regular polygon, and the number of sides ranged from 6 in smaller tipis to 18 in larger ones. For example, the pyramid in Figure **3-9** represents a tipi with a hexagonal base 6 m on each side. The **height** of a pyramid is the distance from the vertex to the base. The **slant height** of a pyramid is the height of its lateral faces. Each lateral face is a triangle.

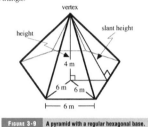

FIGURE 3-9 A pyramid with a regular hexagonal base.

Discussion 1

a. What type of triangle is each of the lateral faces of a regular pyramid?
b. As the number of lateral faces in a pyramid increases, describe what happens to each of the following:
   1. the shape of the base
   2. the shape of the lateral faces
   3. the shape of the pyramid.
c. Describe how to find the surface area of a pyramid.

Exploration

In this exploration, you construct a net for a model of a tipi.

a. 1. Construct a net, including the base, for a regular hexagonal pyramid.
   2. Verify that the net forms a pyramid.
b. 1. Cut out the lateral faces of the net. Arrange them so that the vertex angles of the triangles all meet at a single point and there are no gaps between the sides.
   2. Tape the triangles together to form a net of the **lateral surface** of the pyramid.

Discussion 2

a. 1. Describe the net of the lateral surface of the pyramid.
   2. As the number of lateral faces in a pyramid increases, what happens to the shape of this net?

mathematics note

An **arc** of a circle is a part of the circle whose endpoints are the intersections, with the circle, of the sides of a central angle.

The **measure of an arc** is the measure of its central angle. A **minor arc** has a measure less than 180°; a **major arc** has a measure greater than 180°; a **semicircle** has an arc measure of exactly 180°.

The **length of an arc** is the distance on the circle between the arc's endpoints. This distance can be found by multiplying the circle's circumference by the fractional part of the circle that the arc represents.

A **sector** of a circle is a region bounded by the sides of a central angle and an arc of the circle. The **area of a sector** can be found by multiplying the circle's area by the fractional part of the circle that the sector represents.

For example, Figure **3-10** shows a circle with center at O and a radius of 10 cm. The shaded sector is bounded by a central angle of 40° and the minor arc AB. The unshaded sector has a central angle of 320° and is bounded by the major arc ACB.

FIGURE 3-10   A sector of a circle.

Because the measure of arc AB is 40° and the central angle of the entire circle is 360°, the length of arc AB can be found as follows:

$$\frac{40}{360} \cdot 2\pi(10) \approx 7 \text{ cm}$$

Similarly, the area of the shaded sector is:

$$\frac{40}{360} \cdot \pi(10)^2 \approx 35 \text{ cm}^2$$

b. Consider the expression used to find the length of arc AB in the previous mathematics note. In this expression, what does each of the following quantities represent?

1. $2\pi(10)$

2. 40/360

c. Consider the expression used to find the area of the shaded sector in the previous mathematics note. In this expression, what does the quantity $\pi(10)^2$ represent?

d. As the number of lateral faces in a pyramid increases, how does the net of the lateral surface compare to the sector of a circle?

Module 3 ■ *There's No Place Like Home*   75

Exploration

a. 1. Sample net:

2. Students should fold the net into a pyramid.

b. 1–2. The following diagram shows a sample net of the lateral surface (with tape):

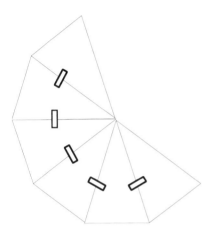

Discussion 2

a. 1. Sample response: The shape of the net looks like a concave polygon.

2. Sample response: As the number of faces increases, the net of the lateral surface would look more like a part of a circle.

b. 1. The quantity $2\pi(10)$ represents the circumference of the circle.

2. The ratio 40/360 represents the fraction of the circle represented by the shaded sector in Figure **3-10.**

c. The quantity $\pi(10)^2$ represents the area of the circle.

d. As the number of faces increases, the net of the lateral surface approaches a sector of a circle.

e. 1. The radius of the sector determines the slant height of the cone.
   2. The arc length of the sector determines the circumference of the cone's base.
   3. Sample response: Find the arc length of the sector. This is the circumference of the base of the cone. Because the circumference is $2\pi r$, you can then solve for the radius of the base of the cone.

Warm-Up

1. **a.** Sample net:

   b. The length of the apothem is approximately 4.3 m.
   c. The area of the base is approximately 65.0 m².
   d. The slant height is approximately 5.9 m.
   e. The lateral surface area is approximately 88.4 m².
   f. The total surface area is approximately 153.3 m².

Assignment

Problems suitable for use as assessment items are identified by an asterisk (*).

4.1 a. $\pi(5)^2 \approx 78.5$ cm²
   b. $2\pi \cdot 5 \approx 31.4$ cm
   c. The fraction of the circle represented by each unshaded sector is shown below:

$$\frac{270°}{360°} = \frac{3}{4}, \quad \frac{240°}{360°} = \frac{2}{3}, \quad \frac{300°}{360°} = \frac{5}{6}$$

   d. The areas of these unshaded sectors are:

$$\frac{3}{4}\pi(5)^2 \approx 58.9 \text{ cm}^2, \quad \frac{2}{3}\pi(5)^2 \approx 52.4 \text{ cm}^2,$$

$$\frac{5}{6}\pi(5)^2 \approx 65.4 \text{ cm}^2$$

   e. The corresponding arc lengths are:

$$\frac{3}{4}(2\pi)5 \approx 23.6 \text{ cm}, \quad \frac{2}{3}(2\pi)5 \approx 20.9 \text{ cm},$$

$$\frac{5}{6}(2\pi)5 \approx 26.2 \text{ cm}$$

e. The lateral surface of a cone can be represented by a sector of a circle. For example, Figure 3-11 shows a sector of a circle of radius r, along with the corresponding cone of slant height s.

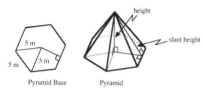

FIGURE 3-11 A sector formed into a cone.

1. What part of the sector determines the slant height of the cone?
2. What part of the sector determines the circumference of the base of the cone?
3. Describe how to find the radius of the cone's base given the radius of the sector and the measure of its central angle.

Warm-Up

1. The diagram below shows a right regular hexagonal pyramid and its base.

Pyramid Base   Pyramid

   a. Sketch a net for the pyramid.
   b. Find the length of the apothem of the base.
   c. What is the area of the base?
   d. Find the length of the slant height.
   e. What is the lateral surface area of the pyramid?
   f. Find the total surface area of the pyramid.

Assignment

4.1 The diagram below shows three circles, each with a radius of 5 cm, along with the measures of the central angles of the unshaded sectors.

270°   240°   300°

   a. What is the area of each circle?
   b. What is the circumference of each circle?
   c. What fraction of the circle is represented by each unshaded sector?
   d. What is the area of each unshaded sector?
   e. What is the length of the arc that bounds each unshaded sector?

4.2 Consider a cone constructed from the sector with a central angle that measures 270° in Problem **4.1**.

   a. What part of the cone is represented by the length of the arc that bounds the sector?
   b. What is the height of the cone?
   c. What is the area of the cone's base?
   d. What is the total surface area of the cone?

4.3 Although tipis are pyramids, their shapes can be modeled by cones. As shown in the diagram on the right, when the covering material for a tipi is cut from a circle and draped over the supporting poles, it resembles a cone without a base. In this case, the covering material represents the lateral surface of the cone.

   a. Sketch a net of a cone, including the base.
      1. Label the radius of the base r.
      2. Label the part of the net that represents the slant height of the cone s.
   b. 1. Determine the length of the "curved" part of the lateral surface in terms of the radius of the cone's base.
      2. Find the circumference of a circle with radius s.
      3. What fraction of a circle with radius s is represented by the lateral surface of the cone? Express your response in terms of r (the radius of the cone's base) and s (the cone's slant height).

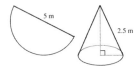

> c. 1. Find the area of a circle with radius *s*.
>   2. Determine the area of the lateral surface of the cone.
> d. Write a formula for the total surface area of a cone.
> e. Describe how to find the height *h* of a cone using *r* and *s*.
>
> 4.4 In some modern tipi designs, the covering material is cut in the shape of a semicircle, then draped over the poles. In the model shown below, the cover was cut from a circle of radius 2.5 m.
>
>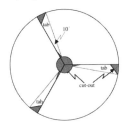
>
> a. What is the diameter of the tipi's floor?
> b. What is the height of the tipi?
> c. Do these seem like reasonable measurements for a tipi? Explain your response.
>
> * * * * *
>
> 4.5 To help customers add engine oil, many service stations provide paper funnels. One manufacturer of such funnels uses the circular template shown in the diagram below. By cutting the template along the solid lines, three funnels (with tabs) can be produced. The dotted lines indicate the folds for the tabs. The circumference of the larger opening of each funnel is 32 cm; the circumference of the smaller opening is 5 cm.
>
> 78   Module 3 ■ *There's No Place Like Home*

* 4.3 a. Sample sketch:

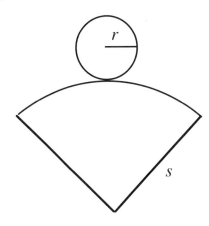

b. 1. $2\pi r$
2. $2\pi s$
3. By comparing the length of the arc of the curved part of the net with the circumference of the large circle, the fraction of the large circle represented by the cone's lateral surface is:

$$\frac{2\pi r}{2\pi s} = \frac{r}{s}$$

c. 1. πs^2
2. The area of the lateral surface of the cone is:

$$\frac{r}{s}(\pi s^2) = \pi r s$$

d. Sample response: The total surface area is the sum of the lateral surface area and the area of the base: $A = \pi r^2 + \pi r s$.

e. Using the Pythagorean theorem, $h = \sqrt{s^2 - r^2}$.

4.4 a. The circumference of the floor is determined by the length of the semicircular arc, $\pi(2.5)$ m. Thus, the diameter of the floor is 2.5 m.

b. Because the radius of the floor is 1.25 m and the slant height of the tipi is 2.5 m, $h = \sqrt{2.5^2 - 1.25^2} \approx 2.2$ m.

c. Sample response: This is a very small tipi. A person could stand up only in the center, and it could sleep no more than two people.

* * * * *

4.2 a. The arc length of the sector is the circumference of the base of the cone.

b. The circumference of the base of this cone is 23.6 cm. The radius of the base, therefore, is $r = 23.6/2\pi \approx 3.8$ cm. The slant height of the cone is the radius of the original circle, 5 cm. Using the Pythagorean theorem, the height of the cone can be found as follows:

$$3.8^2 + h^2 = 5^2$$
$$h = 3.2 \text{ cm}$$

c. The area of the base of the cone is:

$$\pi \cdot 3.8^2 \approx 45.4 \text{ cm}^2.$$

d. The total surface area is:

$$\frac{270}{360} \cdot \pi(5)^2 + \pi(3.8)^2 \approx 104.3 \text{ cm}^2$$

4.5 a. To determine the radius of the template, students first must recognize that the central angle which defines each funnel, including the tab, measures 120°. Because the central angle for the tab measures 10°, the fraction of the circle that forms the funnel is 110°/360°.

Because the length of the arc that forms the larger opening of the funnel is 32 cm, the radius of the circle can be found as follows:

$$\frac{110°}{360°} \cdot 2\pi r = 32$$

$$r = \frac{32}{2\pi} \cdot \frac{360°}{110°}$$

$$r \approx 16.7 \text{ cm}$$

b. Similarly, the radius of the inner circle can be determined as shown:

$$\frac{110°}{360°} \cdot 2\pi r = 5$$

$$r = \frac{5}{2\pi} \cdot \frac{360°}{110°}$$

$$r \approx 2.6 \text{ cm}$$

c. Students should recognize that the height of the funnel is the difference between the height of the cone before the tip is cut off and the height of the small cone which forms the tip.

The slant height of the larger cone is the radius of the larger circle, 16.7 cm. Because the radius of its base is approximately 5.1 cm, its height is $\sqrt{16.7^2 - 5.1^2} \approx 15.9$ cm.

The slant height of the smaller cone (the tip) is the radius of the inner circle, 2.6 cm. Because the radius of its base is approximately 0.8 cm, its height is $\sqrt{2.6^2 - 0.8^2} \approx 2.5$ cm.

The height of the funnel is 15.9 − 2.5 = 13.4 cm.

ACTIVITY 5

In this activity, students explore cones created from sectors of a circle. They also examine volume, surface area, and the ratio of surface area to volume for various cones and spheres.

teacher note

A brief assessment of the mathematical content in Activities **4** and **5,** for use at your discretion, appears in the Teacher Resources for this module.

---

a. Determine the radius of the circular template.

b. Find the radius of the inner circle that is cut from the template.

c. Determine the height of the paper funnel.

ACTIVITY 5

A structure's volume—and its ratio of surface area to volume—are important considerations for heating or cooling the space inside. In the previous activity, you modeled tipi coverings using sectors of a circle. In this activity, you experiment with the size of the sectors and observe the resulting effects on a tipi's volume.

Exploration 1

In this exploration, you investigate the relationship between the volumes of two figures with the same height and radius of the base: a right circular cylinder and a right circular cone.

a. Construct a right circular cone by completing the following steps.

1. On a sheet of paper, draw a circle with a radius of at least 4 cm. As shown in Figure **3-12,** label the center *A* and a point on the circle *B*.

FIGURE 3-12 Circle and radius *AB*.

2. Cut out the circle, then make a cut along $\overline{AB}$.

3. Investigate the right circular cones that you can form by moving point *B* to various points on the circumference of the circle.

4. Select one cone. Tape the overlapping edge to the cone's surface.

b. Measure the height of the cone and the radius of its base in centimeters.

Materials List

■ compass (one per group)
■ scissors (one pair per group)
■ construction paper (four sheets per group)
■ ruler (one per group)
■ tape
■ rice (about 2 cups per group)

Technology

■ geometry utility
■ spreadsheet

Student Outcomes

After completing the following explorations and discussions, students should be able to:

✳ develop a formula for the volume of a right cone

✳ compare the volume of a cone to that of a right cylinder with the same base and height

✳ develop a formula for the volume of a right pyramid

✳ compare the volumes of right cylinders, hemispheres, and right cones with congruent radii and heights.

✳ develop a formula for the volume of a sphere.

c. 1. Create a net for the lateral surface of a right circular cylinder with the same height and radius as your cone. Include a tab on one edge, as illustrated in Figure 3-13.

FIGURE 3-13 Lateral surface of right circular cylinder.

2. Tape the edges of the net together to form the lateral surface of the cylinder.

d. 1. Estimate the ratio of the volume of the cylinder to the volume of the cone.

2. Place the cylinder upright on a flat surface.

3. Fill the cone with rice, then pour the rice into the cylinder. Repeat until the cylinder is full.

4. Record the number of full cones required to fill the cylinder. **Note:** Save the rice for use in Exploration **2**.

Discussion 1

a. Compare the volumes of cones and right circular cylinders with equal heights and radii.

b. Use the formula for the volume of a right circular cylinder and your results in Exploration **1** to determine a formula for the volume of a right circular cone.

Exploration 2

In this exploration, you investigate the relationship between the volumes of two figures with the same height and the same square base: a right prism and a regular pyramid.

a. Use a geometry utility to create a net for a regular pyramid with a square base. Print a copy of the net.

b. Cut the triangular faces from the net and tape them together to form the lateral surface of the pyramid.

c. 1. Measure the height of the pyramid in centimeters.

2. Measure the length of a side of the base in centimeters.

d. 1. Create a net for a right prism with the same height and base as the pyramid from Parts **a–c.**

Exploration 1

Students examine cones made from sectors of a circle with a fixed radius.

a. Students draw a circle, cut it along a radius, and form a cone by overlapping the edges and taping the overlapped edge.

b. Students measure the height and radius of their cones.

c. Students create the lateral surface of a right circular cylinder with the same base and height as their cones. They form a cylinder by taping the edges together at the tab.

d. The ratio of the volume of the cylinder to that of the cone should be 3/1. Student results may vary slightly due to measuring and construction errors.

Discussion 1

a. The volume of the cylinder is three times the volume of a cone with the same base and height.

b. The formula for the volume of a right circular cylinder with radius r and height h is $V = \pi r^2 h$. It follows that the volume of a right circular cone with radius r and height h is

$$V = \frac{1}{3}\pi r^2 h$$

Exploration 2

Students investigate the relationship between the volume of a right prism and the volume of a regular pyramid with the same base and height.

a. Sample net:

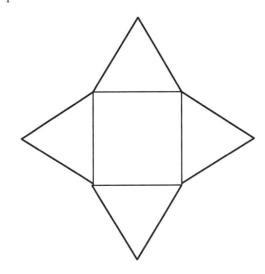

b–c. Students cut the lateral faces from the net and tape them together to form the shape of a pyramid. They then measure the height of the pyramid and a side of the base.

d. Students create a right prism with the same base and height as the pyramid in Parts **a–c.**

e. The ratio of the volume of the prism to that of the pyramid should be 3/1. Student results may vary slightly due to measuring and construction errors.

Discussion 2

a. The volume of the prism is three times the volume of a pyramid with the same base and height.

b. The results of the explorations should agree with the formula given in the mathematics note.

c. Sample response: Find the area of the base by squaring s, multiply the area of the base by the height, and multiply that product by 1/3.

d. 1. Students should rank the figures in the following order: right circular cylinder, hemisphere, right circular cone.

2. The volume of the cylinder is $V = B \bullet h = (\pi r^2)r = \pi r^3$. The volume of the cone is:

$$V = \frac{1}{3} B \bullet h = \frac{1}{3} \pi r^3$$

3. Conjectures will vary. Based on the formulas for the volume of a cone and a cylinder, students probably will guess that the formula involves the product πr^3. Sample response:

$$V = \frac{2}{3} \pi r^3$$

4. Because the volume of a sphere is twice that of a hemisphere with the same radius, students should suggest multiplying their response to Part **d3** of the discussion by 2.

Warm-Up

1. **a.** $V \approx 2411.5 \text{ cm}^3$
   b. $V \approx 268.0 \text{ cm}^3$
   c. $V \approx 401.9 \text{ cm}^3$
2. $V \approx 66.1 \text{ m}^3$

Assignment

Problems suitable for use as assessment items are identified by an asterisk (*).

5.1 **a.** Using the formula for the volume of a cone,

$$V = \frac{1}{3} \pi (10)^2 (15) \approx 1571 \text{ cm}^3$$

b. The height of the cylinder must be 1/3 that of the cone, or 5 cm which can be determined by solving for h in $1571 = \pi(10)^2 \bullet h$.

c. Students may solve for h as follows:

$$1571 = \frac{1}{3} \pi (8)^2 h$$

$$h \approx 23.4 \text{ cm}$$

---

2. Cut out the net, then cut off one of the bases. Tape the edges together to create an open container.

e. 1. Estimate the ratio of the volume of the prism to the volume of the pyramid.

2. Fill the pyramid with rice, then pour the rice into the prism. Repeat until the prism is full.

3. Record the number of full pyramids required to fill the prism.

Discussion 2

a. Compare the volumes of regular pyramids and right prisms with equal heights and congruent bases.

mathematics note

The volume of a pyramid or a cone can be found using the following formula:

$$V = \frac{1}{3} B \bullet h$$

where B is the area of the base and h is the height of the pyramid or cone.

b. 1. Are your results in Exploration **1** consistent with the formula given in the mathematics note? Explain your response.

2. Are your results in Exploration **2** consistent with the formula?

c. Describe how to determine the volume of a regular pyramid with a height of h units and a square base in which each side is s units long.

d. Figure **3-14** below shows a right circular cylinder, a hemisphere, and a right circular cone, with the same radii and "heights." (For the purposes of this comparison, the radius of a hemisphere also can be thought of as its "height.")

FIGURE 3-14 A cylinder, a hemisphere, and a cone.

1. Rank the volumes of each figure from largest to smallest.

2. Express the volumes of the cylinder and the cone in terms of r.

Module 3 ■ *There's No Place Like Home*   81

---

3. Make a conjecture about the formula for the volume of a hemisphere with radius r.

4. Based on your conjecture above, what would be the formula for the volume of a sphere of radius r?

mathematics note

A **sphere** is the set of all points in space that are the same distance from a given point, the **center** of the sphere. The common distance is the **radius** of the sphere. The **diameter** of a sphere is twice the radius.

The volume of a sphere with radius r can be found using the following formula:

$$V = \frac{4}{3} \pi r^3$$

Warm-Up

1. Find the volume of each figure described below.

a. a right circular cylinder with a radius of 8 cm and a height of 12 cm

b. a sphere with a diameter of 8 dm

c. a right circular cone with a diameter of 16 cm and a slant height of 10 cm

2. The base of the figure shown below is a circle. Determine its volume.

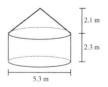

2.1 m

2.3 m

5.3 m

Assignment

5.1 **a.** Find the volume of a right circular cone with a radius of 10 cm and a height of 15 cm.

b. Determine the height of a right circular cylinder with the same radius and volume as the cone in Part **a**.

c. Determine the height of a right circular cone with a radius of 8 cm and the same volume as the cone in Part **a**.

5.2 a. Consider a tipi shaped like a pyramid with a regular dodecagon as its base. (A dodecagon has 12 sides). The tipi's height is 5 m and each side of the base is 2 m long. What is the volume of this tipi?

b. Consider a tipi that can be modeled by a right circular cone. The radius of its base is 3.75 m and its height is 5 m. What is the volume of this tipi?

c. Explain why your responses to Parts **a** and **b** are close in value.

5.3 A cone-shaped structure with a small ratio of surface area to volume might be more efficient to heat than one with a larger ratio. Consider a building shaped like a right circular cone with a slant height of 6 m, a height of *h* meters and a radius of *r* meters.

a. Write an equation that expresses the height *h* in terms of the radius *r*.

b. Use your equation from Part **a** to write a formula for the volume of the cone in terms of *r*.

c. The shaded sector in the diagram on the right represents a net for the lateral surface of a cone with a slant height of 6 m. The arc that bounds the sector has a length equal to the circumference of the base of the cone: $2\pi r$.

Write an expression for the lateral surface area of the cone in terms of *r*.

d. Create a spreadsheet with the following headings. Use the spreadsheet to investigate the ratio of lateral surface area to volume for cones with a slant height of 6 m and radii from 0.1 m to 5.9 m, in increments of 0.1 m.

Radius (m²)	Volume (m³)	Lateral Surface Area (m²)	Surface Area / Volume
0.1			
0.2			
0.3			
⋮			
5.8			
5.9			

e. Identify the height and radius of the cone in Part **d** with the smallest ratio of surface area to volume.

5.2 a. The area of the regular dodecagon can be found as follows:

$$A = \frac{1}{2}ap = \frac{1}{2}\tan 75°(12 \bullet 2) \approx 45\ m^2$$

Using the formula for the volume of a pyramid,

$$V \approx \frac{1}{3} \bullet 45 \bullet 5 \approx 75\ m^3$$

b. $V = \frac{1}{3} \bullet \pi(3.75)^2 5 \approx 74\ m^3$

c. Sample response: The radius of the dodecagon is approximately 7.4 m, which is close to the radius of the base of the cone. Therefore, the areas of the two bases are close in value. Because the pyramid and the cone have the same height, their volumes are also close in value.

* 5.3 a. Using the Pythagorean theorem, $h = \sqrt{36 - r^2}$.

b. Students should substitute for *h* as shown below:

$$V = \frac{1}{3}\pi r^2 h = \frac{1}{3}\pi r^2 \sqrt{36 - r^2}$$

c. The area of the sector is a fraction of the area of the circle with radius 6 m:

$$A = \frac{2\pi r}{12\pi} \bullet \pi(6^2) = 6\pi r$$

d. Sample spreadsheet:

Radius (m)	Volume (m³)	Lateral Surface Area (m²)	Surface Area / Volume
0.1	0.063	1.884	30.004
0.2	0.251	3.768	15.008
⋮	⋮	⋮	⋮
4.1	77.114	77.283	1.002
4.2	79.152	79.168	1.000
4.3	81.023	81.053	1.000
4.4	82.701	82.938	1.003
⋮	⋮	⋮	⋮
5.9	39.765	111.212	2.797

e. Sample response: The smallest ratio of surface area to volume occurs in a cone with a radius somewhere between 4.2 m and 4.3 m. The corresponding range for the heights is also between approximately 4.2 m and 4.3 m.

teacher note

The derivation of the formula for the surface area of a sphere ($s = 4\pi r^2$) requires the use of calculus to find the area of a surface of revolution.

---

* 5.4 **a.** Students should use the diameter of the pit to approximate the radius of the hemisphere. The total volume of the house can be found as follows:

$$V = (\pi \bullet 1.75^2 \bullet 1.5) + \frac{1}{2}\left(\frac{4}{3} \bullet \pi \bullet 1.75^3\right) \approx 25.7 \text{ m}^3$$

b. The total surface area can be found as follows:

$$A = (\pi \bullet 1.75^2) + (2 \bullet \pi \bullet 1.75 \bullet 1.5)$$

$$+ \frac{1}{2}(4 \bullet \pi \bullet 1.75^2) \approx 45.4 \text{ m}^2$$

c. Sample response: Because part of a pit house is buried—and because the earth provides both insulation and heat storage—it would have less heat loss during cold months, and more moderate indoor temperatures during warm months.

✳ ✳ ✳ ✳ ✳

5.5 **a.** The radius of the base of the cone formed by the shaded sector can be determined as shown below:

$$2\pi r = \frac{120°}{360°}(2\pi \bullet 10)$$

$$r \approx 3.3 \text{ cm}$$

The total surface area can be found as follows:

$$A \approx \pi \bullet 3.3^2 + \frac{120°}{360°} \bullet \pi \bullet 10^2 \approx 139 \text{ cm}^2$$

Similarly, the radius of the base of the cone formed by the unshaded sector is:

$$2\pi r = \frac{240°}{360°}(2\pi \bullet 10)$$

$$r \approx 6.7 \text{ cm}$$

The total surface area of this cone is:

$$A \approx \pi \bullet 6.7^2 + \frac{240°}{360°} \bullet \pi \bullet 10^2 \approx 351 \text{ cm}^2$$

b. For the cone formed by the shaded sector, $h \approx \sqrt{10^2 - 3.3^2} \approx 9.4$ cm. Its volume, therefore, is:

$$V \approx \frac{1}{3} \bullet (\pi \bullet 3.3^2) \bullet 9.4 \approx 107 \text{ cm}^3$$

For the cone formed by the unshaded sector, $h \approx \sqrt{10^2 - 6.7^2} \approx 7.4$ cm. Its volume is:

$$V \approx \frac{1}{3} \bullet (\pi \bullet 6.7^2) \bullet 7.4 \approx 348 \text{ cm}^3$$

---

mathematics note

$$S = 4\pi r^2$$

5.4 The traditional house of the Maidu and Miwok tribes of central California was a cylindrical pit covered by a hemispherical dome. These pits ranged from 1.5 m to 3.5 m deep, and 3.5 m to 18 m in diameter. The diagram below shows an example of this type of dwelling.

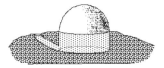

a. The pit in the diagram above is 1.5 m deep and has a diameter of 3.5 m. What is the total volume of this house?

b. What is the total surface area of this house?

c. As shown in the diagram, part of the house lies below ground level. How do you think this will affect the relative efficiency of heating or cooling?

✳ ✳ ✳ ✳ ✳

5.5 The diagram below shows a circle with a radius of 10 cm. The shaded sector has a central angle that measures 120°.

10 cm

Imagine that the two sectors are cut apart, then folded into cones. In each cone, the cut edges touch, but do not overlap.

---

a. Find the total surface area of each cone, including the base.

b. Find the volume of each cone.

c. Find the ratio of surface area to volume for each cone.

5.6 The diagram below shows one example of an igloo. The inside diameter of the igloo is 6.0 m. Its walls are made of packed snow 0.1 m thick.

a. The living space inside this igloo is a hemisphere. What is the volume of the living space?

b. What is the volume of the packed snow in the igloo's walls (ignoring the entryway)?

c. What is the ratio of lateral surface area to volume for the inside of the igloo? What might this ratio tell you about the relative heating efficiency of an igloo?

d. Consider a house built in the shape of a half cylinder (such as a Quonset hut) with the same volume as the igloo in Part **a** and a height of 3 m. Disregarding the floor, what is this home's ratio of surface area to volume?

e. Which shape—a hemisphere or a half cylinder—do you think would be more practical for housing in Arctic regions? Explain your response.

5.7 The bathysphere is a spherical steel vessel designed for undersea research. Designed by American naturalist and explorer William Beebe, it made its first dive in 1930.

a. The outside radius of the bathysphere is approximately 75 cm. Determine the volume of water it displaces.

b. Find the volume of the interior of the bathysphere given that its steel walls are 3.8 cm thick.

c. When the first bathysphere was designed, weight was an important concern. Assuming that weight is proportional to surface area, compare the weight of the bathysphere with that of a cube of equal volume.

Summary Assessment

1. The Miwok people of central California were one of several tribes who built structures with cylindrical walls and conical roofs known as roundhouses. Roundhouses were used to host ceremonial dances and rituals. The diagram below shows one example of a roundhouse.

   The floor of the roundhouse in the diagram has a diameter of 10.6 m. The height of the walls is 2.1 m; the total height of the building is 4.6 m.

   a. What is the total surface area of this roundhouse?

   b. What is its volume?

2. As shown in the following diagram, the living space in an igloo is shaped like a hemisphere and its entryway is shaped like a half-cylinder.

   The inside radius of the igloo in the diagram is 2.5 m. The entryway is 1 m long and has an inside radius of 0.5 m.

   Determine the inside surface area and volume of the igloo, including the entryway. Describe any assumptions you make in solving this problem.

---

e. Answers will vary. Judging only from the calculated ratios of surface area to volume, the hemisphere should be more efficient to heat than the half cylinder of equal volume.

5.7 a. Using the formula for the volume of a sphere,

$$V = \frac{4}{3}\pi(75)^3 \approx 1.8 \cdot 10^6 \text{ cm}^3$$

   b. Subtracting the thickness of the walls,

$$V = \frac{4}{3}\pi(75 - 3.8)^3 \approx 1.5 \cdot 10^6 \text{ cm}^3$$

   c. The surface area of the Bathysphere is $A = 4\pi(75)^2 \approx 71{,}000 \text{ cm}^2$. The surface area of a cube with equal volume would be approximately 88,000 cm². Assuming that weight is proportional to surface area, the ratio of the weight of the Bathysphere to the weight of the cube would be approximately 0.8.

  teacher note

An additional assessment, for use at your discretion, appears in the Teacher Resources for this module.

Summary Assessment

1. a. To find the surface area of this structure, students must find the lateral surface area of a cone and the lateral surface area of a cylinder.

   The slant height s of the cone equals $\sqrt{r^2 + h^2}$, where r is the radius of the base and h is the height of the cone. In this case,

$$s = \sqrt{5.3^2 + 2.5^2} \approx 5.9 \text{ m}$$

   The lateral surface area of the cone, therefore, is:

$$\pi \cdot r \cdot s = \pi \cdot 5.3 \cdot 5.9 \approx 97 \text{ m}^2$$

   The lateral surface area of the cylinder is:

$$2\pi \cdot r \cdot h = 2\pi \cdot 5.3 \cdot 2.1 \approx 69 \text{ m}^2$$

   Adding the surface area of the floor ($\pi(5.3^2) \approx 87 \text{ m}^2$), the total surface area is approximately $97 + 69 + 87 = 253 \text{ m}^2$.

   b. The total volume can be found as follows:

$$V = \frac{1}{3}\pi \cdot 5.3^2 \cdot 2.5 + \pi \cdot 5.3^2 \cdot 2.1 \approx 259 \text{ m}^3$$

---

c. For the cone formed by the shaded sector, the ratio is approximately 1.3. For the cone formed by the unshaded sector, the ratio is approximately 1.0.

5.6 a. Because the inside radius of the hemisphere is 3 m, its volume is:

$$V = \frac{2}{3}\pi(3^3) \approx 57 \text{ m}^3$$

   b. The volume of snow is about 5.9 m³.

   c. The ratio of surface area to volume is approximately 1. Because this ratio is relatively low, one would expect the efficiency to be fairly good—especially when considering the insulating properties of snow. Although some heat will be lost through the floor (which in the Arctic is also frozen), the temperature of the outside air during the cold months is likely to be much lower than that of the tundra.

   d. Given a volume of 57 m³, the length of the half cylinder can be found by solving the following equation for h:

$$57 = \frac{1}{2}(\pi \cdot 3^2 \cdot h)$$

   Because $h \approx 4.1$ m, the surface area of the half cylinder, not including the floor, is:

$$\pi(3^2) + \pi(3)4.1 \approx 67 \text{ m}^2$$

   Therefore, the ratio of surface area to volume is approximately 1.2.

2. The total inside surface area is the surface area of the hemisphere minus the area of the doorway plus the surface area of the entryway. Because the entryway is a half cylinder, its lateral surface area is:

$$\frac{1}{2}(2\pi \bullet r \bullet h) = \pi \bullet 0.5 \bullet 1 \approx 1.6 \text{ m}^2$$

The surface area of the hemisphere minus the area of the doorway can be found as follows, where r_i is the radius of the igloo and r_e is the radius of the entryway:

$$\frac{1}{2}(4\pi r_i^2 - \pi r_e^2) = \frac{1}{2}(4\pi \bullet 2.5^2 - \pi \bullet 0.5^2)$$

$$= 39 \text{ m}^2$$

The total inside surface area, therefore, is about 41 cm². The total volume is the sum of the volume of the half cylinder and the volume of the hemisphere:

$$V = \frac{1}{2}\pi(0.5^2)1 + \frac{1}{2}\left(\frac{4}{3}\pi 2.5^3\right) \approx 33 \text{ m}^3$$

3. **a.** For the Delaware lodge, the total surface area can be found by adding the areas of the floor, four walls, roof, and the two triangular gable ends, respectively.

$$49 + 4(7 \bullet 3) + 2(7 \bullet 3.9) + 2\left(\frac{1}{2} \bullet 7 \bullet 1.7\right) \approx 200 \text{ m}^2$$

Its volume is:

$$3(49) + \left(\frac{1}{2} \bullet 7 \bullet (1.7) \bullet 7\right) \approx 189 \text{ m}^3$$

The ratio of surface area to volume is approximately 1.

For the Miwok roundhouse, the total surface area can be found by adding the areas of the floor, round side wall, and the conical roof, respectively:

$$49 + 2\pi \bullet 3.9 \bullet 3 + \pi(3.9 \bullet 4.3) \approx 175 \text{ m}^2$$

Its volume is:

$$3(49) + \left(\frac{1}{3} \bullet 49 \bullet 1.7\right) \approx 175 \text{ m}^3$$

The ratio of surface area to volume is approximately 1, the same as that for the Delaware lodge.

b. Answers will vary. Sample response: If materials were limited, I would choose the roundhouse. Although it has slightly less volume, it also has less surface area.

c. Answers will vary. Sample response: Judging from ratio of surface area to volume, the two designs appear to be very close in efficiency. The roundhouse might be slightly easier to heat or cool.

3. Oklahoma's Delaware tribe did not build roundhouses. Their ceremonial lodges were shaped like square prisms with gabled roofs. In the diagram below, a Delaware lodge is shown on the left. A Miwok roundhouse appears on the right. For both of these structures, the area of the floor is 49 m², the height of the walls is 3 m, and the total height of the building is 4.7 m.

a. Compare the ratios of total surface area to volume (including the floor) for the two buildings.

b. If you lived in a region where building materials were scarce, which type of structure would you choose: the roundhouse or the gabled lodge? Explain your response.

c. Which design might be easier to heat or cool? Explain your response.

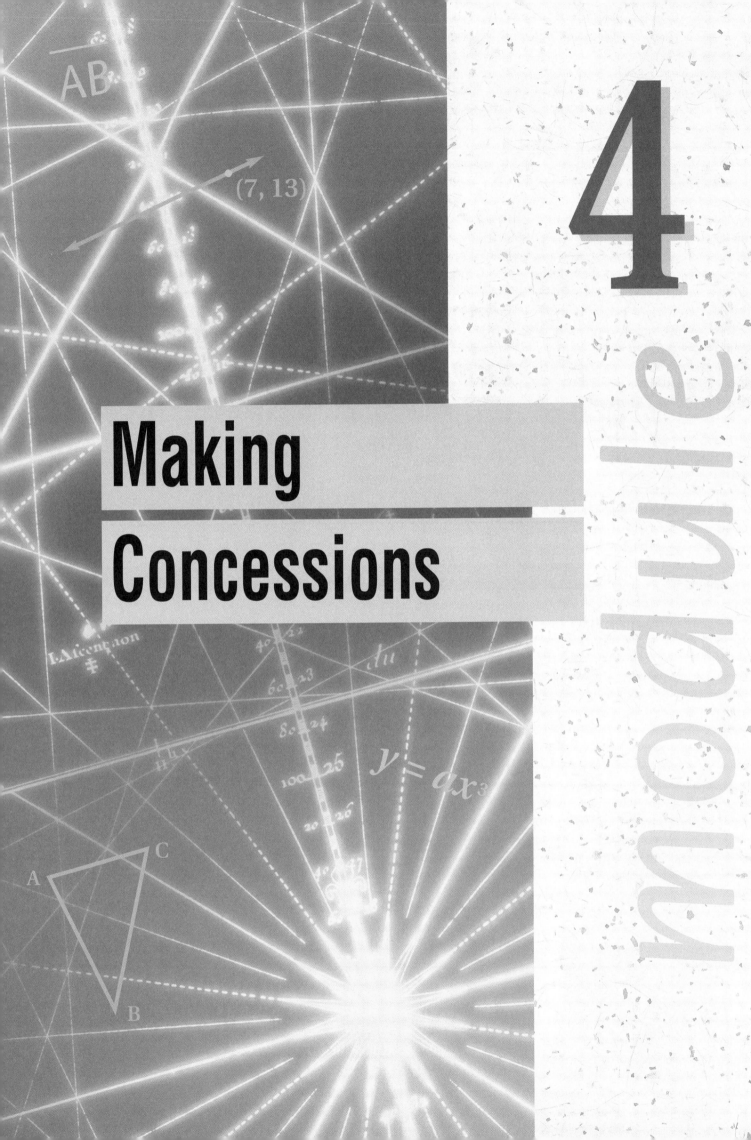

Making Concessions

module 4

Overview

In this module, students investigate step functions in general and three different types of rounding functions in particular: round down, round up, and round to the nearest integer.

Additionally, students examine linear programming in two dimensions and in three dimensions. To find corner points of figures that enclose feasible solutions, they solve systems of linear equations using substitution and matrices.

Activity 1:	Students explore three methods of rounding: rounding up, rounding down, and rounding to the nearest. They represent intervals using graphs, inequalities, and interval notation.
Activity 2:	Students investigate linear programming. They use constraints to construct feasible regions, then determine corner points.
Activity 3:	Students analyze feasible regions and optimize objective functions.
Activity 4:	Students use matrices to solve systems of linear equations in two and three variables.

Objectives

In this module, students will:

* represent real-number intervals using inequalities and interval notation (1)
* graph and interpret step functions (1)
* use the vertical-line test to determine when a graph is not a function (1)
* represent compound inequalities on a number line (1, 2)
* represent compound inequalities algebraically (1, 2, 4)
* determine constraints for linear-programming problems (2)
* find the corner points of a feasible region (2)
* interpret the meaning of points in a feasible region (2)
* identify solution sets for systems of inequalities in two variables (2, 3, 4)
* develop the corner principle for optimization (3, 4)
* write objective functions (3, 4)
* use linear programming to make decisions involving two variables (3, 4)
* use matrices to solve systems of equations in two and three variables (4)
* find inverses of 2×2 and 3×3 matrices (4)
* identify determinants of 2×2 and 3×3 matrices (4)
* use linear programming to make decisions involving three variables (4).

Prerequisites

For this module, students should know:

* how to represent simple inequalities algebraically
* how to round numbers

* how to graph inequalities on a number line
* how to graph inequalities on a coordinate plane
* how to determine the equation of a line
* how to solve a system of linear equations in two variables by substitution
* how to multiply matrices
* how to identify points on a three-dimensional coordinate system.

 Flashbacks, for use at your discretion, appear in the Teacher Resources for this module. These brief problem sets provide a review of some prerequisite skills for each activity.

teacher note

Students were introduced to linear programming in the Level 1 module, "Under the Big Top but Above the Floor." They explored three-dimensional coordinate systems in the Level 1 module, "From Here to There."

Planning Guide

Activity	Materials	Technology	Time Line
Activity **1**	■ graph paper ■ tape ■ scissors ■ freezer paper ■ pay template ■ colored paper	■ graphing utility	3 days
Activity **2**	■ graph paper	■ graphing utility	2 days
Activity **3**	■ graph paper	■ graphing utility	3 days
Activity **4**	■ graph paper ■ tape ■ scissors ■ cardboard box	■ graphing utility ■ three-dimensional graphing utility ■ matrix manipulator	4 days
Assessment Activities	■ none	■ none	4 days **Total: 16 days**

teacher note

Other types of paper available in rolls may be substituted for freezer paper. A blackline master of the pay template appears in the Teacher Resources for this module.

When graphing step functions, some graphing utilities may connect the steps. In such cases, it might be desirable to plot individual points instead. Regardless of the technology used, students should be alerted to the possible pitfalls of relying only on the graphs to interpret step functions. For example, few graphing utilities display the open endpoints on each step.

In Exploration **2** of Activity **4,** students model feasible regions in three dimensions.

Introduction

Step functions and linear programming occur in many everyday settings. For example, step functions can be used to model long-distance telephone rates, postal delivery charges, and pay schedules. Businesses use linear programming to analyze profits and costs. In this module, students use these concepts to help plan a fund-raising project involving concession sales.

teacher note

Some problem contexts used in this module limit students to whole-number solutions. However, while the contexts might restrict acceptable solutions, the methods learned are applicable in any linear-programming setting.

Students should be cautioned to make sure that their solutions are reasonable both mathematically and contextually.

ACTIVITY 1

In this activity, students create and interpret graphs of different rounding methods. Inequalities and interval notation are used to express real-number intervals.

Materials List

- pay template (one per group; a blackline master appears in the Teacher Resources for this module)
- scissors (1 pair per group)
- tape or glue
- freezer paper (about 1.5 m per group)
- graph paper (one sheet per student)
- colored paper (optional)

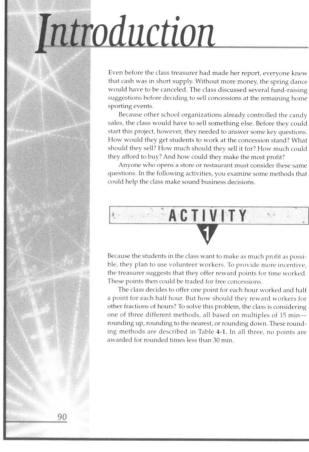

Introduction

Even before the class treasurer had made her report, everyone knew that cash was in short supply. Without more money, the spring dance would have to be canceled. The class discussed several fund-raising suggestions before deciding to sell concessions at the remaining home sporting events.

Because other school organizations already controlled the candy sales, the class would have to sell something else. Before they could start this project, however, they needed to answer some key questions. How would they get students to work at the concession stand? What should they sell? How much should they sell it for? How much could they afford to buy? And how could they make the most profit?

Anyone who opens a store or restaurant must consider these same questions. In the following activities, you examine some methods that could help the class make sound business decisions.

ACTIVITY 1

Because the students in the class want to make as much profit as possible, they plan to use volunteer workers. To provide more incentive, the treasurer suggests that they offer reward points for time worked. These points then could be traded for free concessions.

The class decides to offer one point for each hour worked and half a point for each half hour. But how should they reward workers for other fractions of hours? To solve this problem, the class is considering one of three different methods, all based on multiples of 15 min—rounding up, rounding to the nearest, or rounding down. These rounding methods are described in Table 4-1. In all three, no points are awarded for rounded times less than 30 min.

90

TABLE 4-1 ■ Rounding Methods for Worker Hours

Rounding Method	Rounding Up	Rounding to the Nearest	Rounding Down
Description	rounds to next multiple of 15	rounds to nearest multiple of 15	rounds to previous multiple of 15
For 17 min of Work	reward for 30 min	reward for 15 min	reward for 15 min
For 27 min of Work	reward for 30 min	reward for 30 min	reward for 15 min

Exploration

Each of these rounding methods is an example of a **step function**. In this activity, you examine the step functions that the class encounters as they analyze the cost of doing business.

In this exploration, you create two different graphs of a worker's reward when time is rounded up to the next multiple of 15 min.

a. 1. Obtain a copy of the worker's reward template from your teacher. Each ordered pair on the template represents a number of minutes worked and the corresponding reward earned. Complete the ordered pairs for each minute in the period from 0 min to 79 min.

2. Cut out each square on the template, creating a set of 80 squares each labeled with a different ordered pair. Figure **4-1** shows the ordered pairs for 17 min and 53 min.

FIGURE 4-1   Two paper squares.

3. On a large sheet of paper, create a two-dimensional coordinate system with the origin located near the lower left-hand corner. Represent a worker's reward in tickets on the *y*-axis and time in minutes on the *x*-axis.

teacher note

You might wish to use colored paper for the pay templates in the following exploration. This can make the graphs easier to interpret. Students also might find it easier to create the horizontal scale *after* positioning their paper squares on the graph.

For classroom reference, you might wish to display at least one of the graphs created in this activity during the entire module.

Student Outcomes

After completing the following exploration and discussion, students should be able to:

✳ graph and interpret step functions

✳ represent real-number intervals using number lines, inequalities, and interval notation

✳ use a vertical line test to show when a graph is not a function.

Exploration

Note: To save time, you may complete Part **a** as a class, assigning several ordered pairs to each student. However, creating at least two different graphs allows students to compare results.

a. Students should tape or glue all ordered pairs on a large set of coordinate axes, starting with 0 min and proceeding sequentially. You might wish to display the freezer paper on a wall or bulletin board. The finished graphs should resemble the graph of a step function, with 15 squares of paper forming each step. Sample graph:

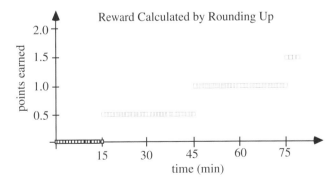

b. Sample graph:

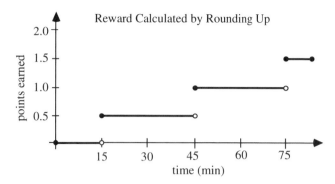

Reward Calculated by Rounding Up

4. As shown in Figure **4-2**, use the paper squares to plot the corresponding ordered pairs on the coordinate system from Step **3**.

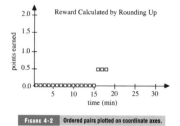

Reward Calculated by Rounding Up

FIGURE 4-2 Ordered pairs plotted on coordinate axes.

b. Another way of representing a worker's reward when rounding up is to graph the 15-min intervals in the period from 0 min to 79 min.

mathematics note

The set of all real numbers between two fixed endpoints is an **interval**. Each of these endpoints may or may not be included in the interval.

When an interval is graphed on a number line, a closed circle indicates that the endpoint is included in the interval. An open circle indicates that the endpoint is not included in the interval.

For example, the graph in Figure **4-3** represents all real numbers between 15 and 30, including 15 but not including 30.

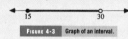

FIGURE 4-3 Graph of an interval.

Another way to describe an interval is with an **inequality**. For example, the interval in Figure **4-3** can be described by the inequality $15 \le x < 30$.

A real-number interval also can be described using **interval notation**. In interval notation, a square bracket,] or [, indicates that the endpoint is included in the interval. A parenthesis,) or (, indicates that the endpoint is not included in the interval. For example, the interval $15 \le x < 30$ shown in Figure **4-3** can be written as [15, 30).

92   Module 4 ■ *Making Concessions*

Discussion

a. Answers will vary. Sample response: The first interval can be represented by the graph below.

It can be written as the inequality $0 \le x < 15$, or using interval notation as [0, 15).

b. Both of the graphs from the exploration should form a series of steps.

c. Sample response: The graph made of paper squares shows time only in whole numbers of minutes. The graph created using intervals represents all the real numbers in each interval.

d. Sample response: The graph in Part **b** of the exploration uses open and closed endpoints to show the exact time when the graph jumps from one step to another. **Note:** Graphs created using technology might not show these endpoints.

e. Yes. This graph is a function because every element in the domain is paired with exactly one element in the range.

f. Yes, This graph passes the vertical line test. No vertical line can be drawn that passes through more than one point on the graph.

   Note: Because the vertical line test does not determine if every element in the domain is paired with an element in the range, it does not guarantee that a graph that passes the test is a function.

1. On a sheet of graph paper, create another two-dimensional coordinate system, representing reward in tickets on the *y*-axis and time in minutes on the *x*-axis.

2. Graphically represent as many 15-min intervals as necessary to show the reward earned for working from 0 min to 79 min. Use open or closed circles to indicate whether or not each endpoint is included in an interval.

Discussion

a. Select one of the intervals that you used in Part **b** of the exploration. Describe three different ways to represent this interval.

b. Describe the general shapes of the graphs created in the exploration.

c. If you consider each paper square as representing a pixel on a screen, the graph you created in Part **a** of the exploration resembles the graphs created by some types of technology. Compare this graph to the graph created in Part **b** of the exploration.

d. Does either graph show the exact time when a worker's reward jumps from one step to another? Explain your response.

e. Recall that a **function** is a relation for which each element of the domain corresponds to exactly one element of the range. In other words, a set of ordered pairs (x, y) is a function if every value of x is paired with a value of y and every value of x occurs in only one ordered pair.

   Is your graph from Part **a** of the exploration a function? Explain your response.

f. Given a graph on a coordinate plane with the domain represented on the horizontal axis and the range on the vertical axis, a **vertical line test** can sometimes be used to determine when the graph is not a function. If a vertical line can be drawn that intersects the graph in more than one point, this indicates that an element of the domain is paired with more than one element of the range. If this occurs, the graph does not represent a function.

   Does your graph from Part **a** of the exploration pass the vertical line test? Explain your response.

Module 4 ■ *Making Concessions*   93

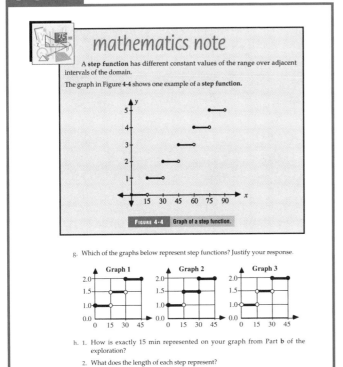

mathematics note

A **step function** has different constant values of the range over adjacent intervals of the domain.

The graph in Figure 4-4 shows one example of a **step function**.

FIGURE 4-4 Graph of a step function.

g. Which of the graphs below represent step functions? Justify your response.

h. 1. How is exactly 15 min represented on your graph from Part **b** of the exploration?

2. What does the length of each step represent?

3. What does the vertical distance between successive steps represent?

i. To determine rewards for parts of hours, the class could round up using multiples of 10 min instead of multiples of 15 min. How would that affect employee earnings?

94 Module 4 ■ *Making Concessions*

---

h. 1. A time of exactly 15 min is represented by a solid endpoint at the coordinates (15,0.5).

2. The length of each step represents the time interval for which an employee receives the same number of reward points.

3. Sample response: The vertical distance between successive steps represents a jump of 0.5 reward points.

i. Using multiples of 10 minutes, the number of points earned is likely to rise. For example, an employee who works 21 min would earn 1 point if time is rounded to the nearest multiple of 10. If time is rounded to the nearest multiple of 15, the employee would earn only 0.5 points.

g. Sample response: Graphs 1 and 3 both represent step functions. Graph 2 is not a function. There are two y-values for $x = 30$. They are 1.5 and 2.0.

teacher note

Students should be cautioned about using the vertical line test to verify that a graph represents a function. Because a graph often does not show every x-value in a relation, the vertical line test should be used only to show that a relation is *not* a function.

j. Since the domain is all non-negative real numbers, it can be written as the interval [0,∞).

teacher note

You might wish to discuss some of the different ways in which functions can be represented (lists of ordered pairs, tables, function mappings, graphs, etc.). You also might wish to describe some everyday situations that can be interpreted as functions (time in toaster versus darkness of bread), and some examples of relationships that are not functions (numbers displayed on the face of an analog clock and hours after midnight).

Warm-Up

1. The responses below show the appropriate inequality and a corresponding graph.

   a. $-7 \le x \le 12$

   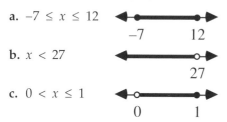

   b. $x < 27$

   c. $0 < x \le 1$

2. **a.** [6,8)
   b. (−4,∞)
   c. [−10,10]

3. Sample response: The domain is the set $D = \{-34,19,27, 45,53\}$. The range is the set $R = \{-14,2,8,63,67\}$. This is a function because each member of the domain is paired with one and only one member of the range.

4. **a.** Sample response: The graph is a function because each member of the domain is paired with one and only one member of the range.
   b. Sample response: The graph does not represent a function. Some members of the domain are paired with more than one member of the range. This can be demonstrated by drawing a vertical line through certain x-values and observing that the vertical line passes through the graph more than once.

j. The symbols ∞ or +∞ can be used to indicate that an interval contains all the numbers greater than a particular value. Similarly, the symbol −∞ can be used to indicate that an interval contains all the numbers less than a particular value. For example, the set of all numbers less than or equal to −2 could be written as (−∞,−2].

The domain of the step function in Figure **4-4** is the set of real numbers greater than or equal to 0. How would you use the symbols described above to represent this domain as an interval?

Warm-Up

1. Use an inequality to represent each of the following intervals, then graph each inequality on a number line.

   a. all real numbers between −7 and 12, inclusive
   b. all real numbers less than 27
   c. all real numbers between 0 and 1, including 1 but not 0

2. Use interval notation to describe each graph below.

3. List the domain and range of the following relation and determine whether or not it is also a function. Justify your response.

   {(19,2), (45,8), (−34,63), (27,−14), (53,67)}

4. Which, if any, of these graphs represents a function? Explain your response.

   a.

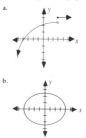

   b.

Assignment

1.1 The class plans to reward workers with one half point per half hour. Assuming that the class treasurer rounds parts of hours down to the previous multiple of 15 min, complete the following table.

Time	Points Earned
29 min	
29 min, 20 sec	
29 min, 57 sec	
30 min	
30 min, 2 sec	
31 min	

1.2 If the class rounds down to the previous multiple of 15 min, there is an interval for which an employee will earn 0 tickets.

 a. Represent this period of time as an inequality.

 b. Describe this period of time in a sentence.

 c. Graph this period of time on a number line.

 d. Express this interval using interval notation.

1.3 The class is selling concessions at an all-day event. Some of the workers begin at 8:00 A.M. The following table includes a column for the tickets earned in each 15-min interval, beginning at 8:00 A.M., when parts of hours are rounded down to the previous multiple of 15.

Interval Start Time	Time Interval (min)	Interval Notation	Number-line Graph	Points Earned
8:00 A.M.	$0 \leq t < 15$			
8:15 A.M.		[15,30)		0
	$30 \leq t < 45$			
	⋮	⋮	⋮	⋮

 a. Use your responses from Problem **1.2** to complete the first row.

 b. Continue to complete each row until the table includes 9:19 A.M.

96 Module 4 ■ *Making Concessions*

Assignment

Problems suitable for use as assessment items are identified by an asterisk (*).

1.1 A completed table is shown below.

Time	Points Earned
29 min	0.0
29 min, 20 sec	0.0
29 min, 57 sec	0.0
30 min	0.5
30 min 2 sec	0.5
31 min	0.5

1.2 a. $0 \leq x < 30$

 b. Sample response: This interval is the time period from 0 min to 30 min, where 0 min is included and 30 min is excluded.

 c. Sample graph:

 d. [0, 30)

1.3 a–b. A completed table is shown below.

Interval Start Time	Time Interval (min)	Interval Notation	Number-line Graph	Tickets Earned
8:00 A.M.	$0 \leq t < 15$	[0, 15)		0.0
8:15 A.M.	$15 \leq t < 30$	[15, 30)		0.0
8:30 A.M.	$30 \leq t < 45$	[30, 45)		0.5
8:45 A.M.	$45 \leq t < 60$	[45, 60)		0.5
9:00 A.M.	$60 \leq t < 75$	[60, 75)		1.0
9:15 A.M.	$75 \leq t < 79$	[75, 79)		1.0

1.4 a–b. Sample graphs:

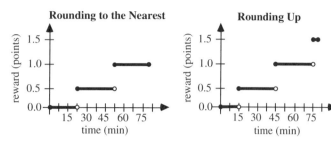

Rounding to the Nearest

Rounding Up

1.5 a. 0 points, 0.5 points, 1 point, or 1.5 points

b. $22.5 \leq x < 52.5$ or $[22.5, 52.5)$

c. $15 < x \leq 45$ or $(15, 45]$

d. A completed table is shown below.

Points Earned	Time Worked in Minutes	
	Rounding Up	**Rounding to the Nearest**
0.0	$x = 0$	$0 \leq x < 7.5$
0.0	$0 < x \leq 15$	$7.5 \leq x < 22.5$
0.5	$15 < x \leq 30$	$22.5 \leq x < 37.5$
0.5	$30 < x \leq 45$	$37.5 \leq x < 52.5$
1.0	$45 < x \leq 60$	$52.5 \leq x < 67.5$
1.0	$60 < x \leq 75$	$67.5 \leq x < 82.5$
1.5	$75 < x \leq 90$	$82.5 \leq x < 90$

e. The intervals for which the two rounding methods reward the same number of points are: $0 \leq x \leq 15$ for 0 points, $22.5 \leq x \leq 45$ for 0.5 points $52.5 \leq x \leq 75$, for 1 point, and $82.5 \leq x \leq 90$ for 1.5 points.

1.6 a. The minimum amount of time that a worker can work to earn 0.5 points when rounding down is 30 min. The minimum time when rounding to the nearest is 22.5 min. When rounding up, any time greater than 15 min will do.

b. Sample response: Rounding up favors workers because the time is never rounded to a lesser value.

c. Sample response: Rounding down favors the class because time is usually rounded to a lesser value.

d. Sample response: Rounding to the nearest might serve as a compromise because time can be rounded both to greater and lesser values.

1.4 As shown in Table **4-1**, rounding to the nearest multiple of 15 min and rounding up to the next multiple of 15 are two different methods for rounding a worker's time. Complete Parts **a** and **b** below using a reward of one-half point per half hour.

   a. On a coordinate plane, create a graph of a worker's earnings from 0 min to 79 min when time is rounded to the nearest multiple of 15 min.

   b. Create a graph as in Part **a** for a worker's earnings from 0 min to 79 min when time is rounded up to the next multiple of 15 min.

1.5 Assume that the class considers time in 15-min intervals. One student has worked x min where x is in the interval $[0, 90]$.

   a. List the different rewards that this student could earn for working x min at the rate of one-half point per half hour.

   b. If time is rounded to the nearest multiple of 15 min, determine the time interval that corresponds with a half-point reward. Write this interval both as an inequality and using interval notation.

   c. If time is rounded up to the next multiple of 15 min, determine the interval both as an inequality and using interval notation.

   d. Complete the table for each 15-min interval in the interval $[0, 90]$.

Points Earned	Time Worked in Minutes	
	Rounding Up	**Rounding to the Nearest**
0	$x = 0$	$0 \leq x < 7.5$
	$0 < x \leq 15$	
⋮	⋮	⋮
	$75 < x \leq 90$	

   e. Identify all the time intervals in the first hour of work for which the two rounding methods result in the same number of points earned.

1.6 Use your graphs for the three different rounding methods to help you answer the following questions.

   a. Using each rounding method, what is the minimum amount of time an employee can work to earn 0.5 points?

   b. Which of the three rounding methods favors workers? Explain your response.

   c. Which of the three rounding methods favors the class? Explain your response.

   d. Which method might serve as a compromise between the workers and the class? Explain your response.

Module 4 ■ *Making Concessions*   97

1.7 Identify all the time intervals in the first hour of work for which all three rounding methods in Table **4-1** result in the same amount of pay.

1.8 The following graph represents a method that an employer uses to pay her employees.

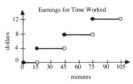

Earnings for Time Worked

a. Using this method, how much would an employee make for working 1 hr?

b. Is the amount you identified in Part **a** the employee's hourly wage? Justify your response.

c. Describe the payment method used by this employer.

* * * * *

1.9 A salesperson in a clothing store receives a commission of $135 for each $1000 in sales. The store "rounds down" when determining commissions. For example, if the amount of merchandise sold is less than $1000, the salesperson gets no commission. If $1200 worth of merchandise is sold, the salesperson gets $135.

a. How much commission would a salesperson receive for $4800 in sales?

b. Identify the intervals of sales for which a salesperson would earn from $0 to $540 in commissions. List the commission earned for each interval.

c. Create a graph of commission earned versus merchandise sold for the intervals identified in Part **b.**

1.10 A cellular phone company uses the schedule shown below to determine charges for outgoing calls less than or equal to 6 min in duration.

Phone Charges for Duration of Call

1.9 **a.** The store rounds $4800 down to $4000. Because the salesperson receives $135 for each $1000 in sales, she would earn 4($135) = $540.

b. The following table shows the appropriate intervals.

Sales (*s*)	Commission
$0 \le x < 1000$	$0
$1000 \le x < 2000$	$135
$2000 \le x < 3000$	$270
$3000 \le x < 4000$	$405
$4000 \le x < 5000$	$540

c. Sample graph:

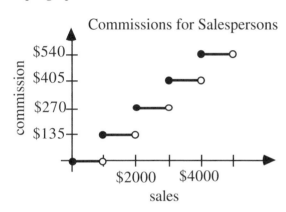

Commissions for Salespersons

1.7 The following table shows the times for which all three rounding methods result in the same reward. **Note:** You may discuss the solutions of systems of simple inequalities with only one variable. Overlaying the graphs of the inequalities might help students visualize the intersection.

Points Earned	Time Worked (min)
0.0	$0 \le x < 15$
0.5	$30 \le x < 45$
1.0	$x = 60$

1.8 **a.** An employee would make $8.00 for working 1 hr.

b. Sample response: The hourly wage is not $8.00. If it were, the time worked would be multiplied by $8.00 to calculate pay. Using this method, the pay for 75 min or 1.25 hr would be $10.00. Based on the graph, the actual pay for 1.25 hr is $12.00.

c. Sample response: Using this method, the employer rounds parts of hours to the nearest multiple of 30 min. Employee pay is then calculated using a rate of $8.00 per hour.

❋ ❋ ❋ ❋ ❋

1.10 **a.** Sample response: Time is "rounded up" to the next minute. For example, a call is considered to have lasted 1 min. even if it lasted only 1 sec. It is considered to have lasted 2 min if it lasted 61 sec.

   b. Sample response: Every minute or part of a minute is assigned one and only one charge. **Note:** Students may attempt to use the vertical line test to show that the graph represents a function. They should be cautioned that the vertical line test is intended to show only that a graph does *not* represent a function.

   c. Sample response: The domain represented on the graph is [0,6] min. It is not possible to use interval notation to identify the range because it is not a continuous set of values. The range is R = {$0.00, $0.40, $0.80, $1.20, $1.60, $2.00, $2.40}.

   d. $2 < x \le 3$ or $(2, 3]$

1.11 Sample response: When rounding up, the interval $(84, 92]$ represents a B. When rounding down, the interval $[85, 93)$ represents a B. When rounding to the nearest, the interval $[84.5, 92.5)$ represents a B.

1.12 **a.** **1.** $f(2.2) = 2$
   2. $f(2.9) = 2$
   3. $f(-2.2) = -3$
   4. $f(-2.9) = -3$

   b. Students should determine the keystrokes necessary to enter $[x]$ in their graphing utility. Using the TI-84 or the Voyage 200, for example, the command is int(x).

   c. On many graphing utilities, graphs of the greatest integer function appear to consist of connected steps. To eliminate this type of graph, students must set the utility to graph individual points rather than continuous lines. (Note that in the sample graph below, it is not possible to determine on which step the integer values lie.)

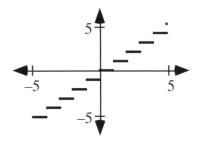

a. Describe the method the company uses for rounding the duration of a phone call.

b. Explain why the graph represents a function.

c. Describe the domain and range of the function using interval notation, if possible.

d. Given a charge of $1.20, determine the interval of minutes for which the call might have lasted. Write this interval both as an inequality and using interval notation.

1.11 Mr. Van DeLay rounds his students' percentage scores to the units place, then uses the grading scale shown in the table on the right. Using inequalities, describe the intervals of percentages that would receive a B if Mr. Van DeLay rounds up, rounds down, or rounds to the nearest integer.

Percentage	Grade
93–100	A
85–92	B
76–84	C
65–75	D
0–64	F

mathematics note

The **greatest integer function** assigns every real number x in the domain to the greatest integer less than or equal to x. This function can be written as $y = [x]$.

Using the greatest integer function, the real number 2.7, for example, would be assigned the value of 2. This can be written as $[2.7] = 2$. Similarly, $[1.9] = 1$, $[0.4] = 0$, and $[-3.4] = -4$.

1.12 The greatest integer function is the parent function for a family of step functions.

a. Evaluate $f(x) = [x]$ for each of the following values of x.

   1. 2.2   **2.** 2.9
   3. –2.2   **4.** –2.9

b. Determine how the technology you use handles the greatest integer function.

c. Use a graphing utility to create a graph of the greatest integer function $f(x) = [x]$.

d. Does your graph look like a step function? Explain your response.

   d. Sample response: My graph looked like a step function because I set the graphing utility to plot individual points. If I had not, each step would have been connected and the graph would have not have looked like a step function.

ACTIVITY 2

This activity focuses on a typical decision-making process in a business setting. Students represent ranges of values on number-line graphs. They then use these ranges to establish feasible regions for linear programming problems.

teacher note

A brief assessment of the mathematical content in Activities **1** and **2**, for use at your discretion, appears in the Teacher Resources for this module.

ACTIVITY 2

To increase their chances for success, businesses gather as much information as possible before making important decisions. Before entering a new market or introducing a new product, businesses often conduct surveys or **feasibility studies**. These studies may identify the type and quantity of products to sell, number of potential customers, and appropriate prices to charge.

Exploration

When the class conducted a feasibility study, they found that students at their school were most interested in buying pizza, canned soda pop, and nachos. The class has asked you to make some recommendations on the remaining questions.

They have about $100 to spend on pizzas, pop, and nachos, and want to earn as much money as possible. Each pizza contains eight slices. Soda pop comes in six-packs. Nachos must be purchased in kits consisting of four bags of tortilla chips and one container of cheese. Each kit makes 16 servings.

a. Estimate the cost to the class of each pizza, six-pack, and nacho kit.

b. Describe how the class should sell each item—by weight, volume, piece, or some other method.

c. Determine how much they should charge for each item sold.

d. Keeping in mind the $100 limit, how many of each item—pizza, pop, and nachos—should the class purchase for resale?

e. Record your decisions from Parts **a–d** in a table with headings like those in Table **4-2** below. Use this information to estimate the potential profit for the class.

TABLE 4-2 ■ Estimated Profit for Concessions

Item	How Sold	Selling Price	Cost per Item	Quantity Purchased	Amount Spent	Potential Profit
pizza						
pop						
nachos						
				Total		

f. Summarize your recommendations in a report. **Note:** Save your report for use in the assignment.

100   Module 4 ■ *Making Concessions*

Student Outcomes

After completing the following exploration and discussion, students should be able to:

✴ identify the constraints in a linear-programming problem

✴ determine equations for linear constraints

✴ write linear inequalities to define boundaries of a feasible region

✴ identify a feasible region given a set of constraints

✴ determine the coordinates of the corner points of a feasible region.

teacher note

The sample data given in the following exploration will be used to generate sample responses throughout the module.

Exploration

Students consider some basic questions concerning the planning and start-up of a concession stand. This works well as a group activity.

a–e. Students make decisions based on their own experiences and wishes. The only restriction is the $100 spending limit. The profits shown in the sample table at the bottom of the page assume that all items are sold.

f. Students write summaries of their recommendations. **Note:** Students use their data on quantity and profit in the assignment.

Materials List

■ graph paper (several sheets per student; optional)

Technology

■ graphing utility (optional)

Item	How Sold	Selling Price	Cost per Item	Quantity Purchased	Amount Spent	Potential Profit
pizza	by piece	$2.00	$5.00	10 pizzas	$50.00	$110.00
pop	by can	$1.00	$2.00	15 six-packs	$30.00	$60.00
nachos	by weight	$1.50	$10.00	2 kits	$20.00	$28.00
				Total	$100.00	$198.00

Discussion

a. Because students have no indication of the potential market or acceptable selling prices, they might have some difficulty deciding how much of each item to buy and how much to charge.

b. Sample response: It would have helped to know the number of people who would buy concessions, the number interested in each item, the cost to the class for each item, the number of home games left, and the availability of storage for unused products.

c. Questions should reflect student concerns in Parts **a** and **b**.

d. Sample response: We assumed that the items could be obtained for a certain price, that we would not have to rent selling space, and that all the food would be sold.

e. 1–2. Answers will vary. Some students might recommend that none of a particular item be bought. The greatest recommended number must keep the total cost below $100.

    3. Sample response: The profit ranges from $40 to $600.

f. Because it is possible to spend $100 and not sell anything, the least possible profit is –$100.

Warm-Up

1. **a.** $n > 5$
   b. $c < -2$
   c. $k \leq 1$
   d. $-4 < x < 2$
   e. $m \geq -12$
   f. $-14 < r \leq -5$

2. **a.** 2 pencils and 5 pens
   b. 5 pencils and 2 pens
   c. 10 pencils and 8 pens
   d. 14 pencils and 13 pens

3. **a.** points C and D
   b. points A and B
   c. points B and C
   d. points A and B

Discussion

a. What difficulties did you encounter in reaching your decisions?

b. What additional information would have been helpful?

c. What other questions might be important to ask in a feasibility study?

d. What assumptions did you make when estimating potential profit?

e. Compare your recommendations with those of others in the class.

   1. For each item, what is the least quantity recommended for purchase?

   2. For each item, what is the greatest quantity recommended for purchase?

   3. What is the range of estimated profit?

f. What would be the least possible profit in this situation? Explain your response.

Warm-Up

1. Write an inequality for each of the following.

   a. n is greater than 5

   b. c is less than –2

   c. k is less than or equal to 1

   d. x is less than 2 but greater than –4

   e. m is greater than or equal to –12

   f. r is less than or equal to –5 but greater than –14

2. Use the following graph to interpret the meaning of the coordinates for each point listed below.

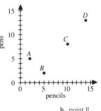

   a. point A **b.** point B

   c. point C **d.** point D

---

3. Identify the points in Problem **2** that are included in each of the following sets.

   a. The number of pencils is greater than 6.

   b. The number of pens is less than or equal to 5.

   c. The number of pencils is greater than or equal to 5 and the number of pens is less than 12.

   d. The number of pens is greater than 0 and less than 6, and the number of pencils is greater than 0 and less than 14.

Assignment

2.1 Use your results from the exploration to complete Parts **a–d** below.

   a. Given that the class might sell none of the items they purchase, what is the least possible profit? What is the greatest possible profit?

   b. Use the two values identified in Part **a** as the endpoints of an interval. Graph this interval on a number line.

   c. Write an inequality to represent your graph in Part **b**.

   d. In your response to Part **c**, did you use the symbols < and > or the symbols ≤ and ≥? Explain how you made your choice.

2.2 Suppose the class recommended that no fewer than 5 but no more than 20 pizzas should be purchased for resale. The illustration below shows a graphical representation of this information on an xy-coordinate system.

The recommended number of pizzas is represented on the x-axis. The recommended number of six-packs of pop—which has not yet been determined—is represented on the y-axis.

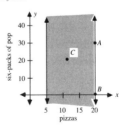

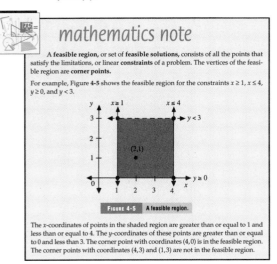

a. Interpret the meaning of the coordinates for each of the following:

   1. point A
   2. point B.

b. If point C represents any point in the shaded region, describe its possible range of coordinates.

c. Is there any portion of the shaded region in which the coordinates of the points are not relevant to this setting? Explain your response.

d. Suppose the class recommended that no fewer than 10 but no more than 40 six-packs of pop be purchased. On a copy of the coordinate system shown above, represent the range of six-packs that might be ordered.

e. Graph the intersection of the region that describes the recommended range of pizzas with the region that describes the recommended range of six-packs of pop.

mathematics note

A **feasible region**, or set of **feasible solutions**, consists of all the points that satisfy the limitations, or linear **constraints** of a problem. The vertices of the feasible region are **corner points**.

For example, Figure **4-5** shows the feasible region for the constraints $x \geq 1$, $x \leq 4$, $y \geq 0$, and $y < 3$.

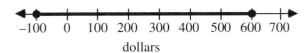

FIGURE 4-5 A feasible region.

The x-coordinates of points in the shaded region are greater than or equal to 1 and less than or equal to 4. The y-coordinates of these points are greater than or equal to 0 and less than 3. The corner point with coordinates (4,0) is in the feasible region. The corner points with coordinates (4,3) and (1,3) are not in the feasible region.

Assignment

Problems suitable for use as assessment items are identified by an asterisk (*).

2.1 **Note:** Part **b** does not ask students to graph an interval for profit on a number line, because the profit in this setting is not a continuous range of values.

a. Sample response: The profit could range from –$100.00 to $600.00.

b. Sample graph:

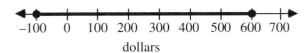

−100   0   100   200   300   400   500   600   700
dollars

c. Answers will vary. The sample response given in Part **a** can be written as –$100.00 $\leq d \leq$ $600.00.

d. Sample response: I used the symbols $\leq$ because $\geq$ the endpoints of the interval were possible values.

2.2 a. 1. Point A represents the purchase of 20 pizzas and 30 six-packs.
      2. Point B represents the purchase of 20 pizzas and 0 six-packs.

b. Sample response: The x-coordinate of point C is always between 5 and 20, inclusive. The y-coordinate can take on any real-number value.

c. Sample response: The shaded region below the x-axis has no meaning because it is impossible to buy a negative number of six-packs. You can't buy fractions of pizzas or six-packs, so any points with non-integer coordinates also have no meaning.

   Because the class has only $100 to spend, the shaded region above the number of six-packs that can be purchased for $100 is not relevant in this setting.

d. Sample graph:

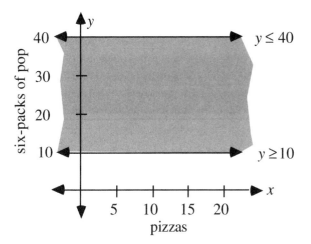

e. Sample graph:

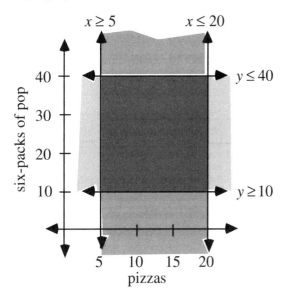

2.3 **a.** For the sample graph given in Problem **2.2e,** the intersection is the set of all ordered pairs such that $5 \le x \le 20$ and $10 \le y \le 40$, where x and y are integers.

    b. Because the boundary lines represent values that satisfy the constraints, the symbols $\le$ and $\ge$ should be used.

    c. Sample response: No. Pizzas, six-packs, and nacho kits can be bought only in whole numbers, so only points whose coordinates are integers [lattice points] should be considered.

* 2.4 **a.** Sample response: Medium pizzas cost $5.00 each and pop costs $2.00 per six-pack. **Note:** The sample responses given below are based on these costs.

    b. 1. $0 \le x \le 20$, where x is an integer

      2. $0 \le y \le 50$, where y is an integer

      3. See sample graph given in Part **d** below.

    c. 1. Sample response: $5x + 2y \le 100$, where x and y are integers

      2. See sample graph given in Part **d** below.

    d. The shaded area in the following sample graph indicates where the combined cost of pizzas and six-packs is less than or equal to $100. The set of feasible solutions includes the ordered pairs with integer values that fall in this region.

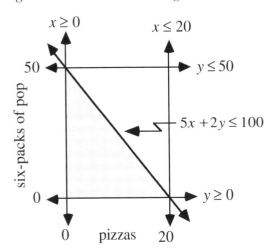

    e. 1. The coordinates of the corner points in the sample graph above are (0,50), (20,0), and (0,0).

      2. Student responses may include descriptions of graphing and tracing, solving a system of linear equations by substitution, or the use of a symbolic manipulator.

＊ ＊ ＊ ＊ ＊

2.5 **a.** In the following sample responses, x represents the number of boys and y represents the number of girls.

    1. $x \ge 30$, where x is a whole number

2.3 Use your graph from Problem **2.2e** to complete Parts **a–c** below.

    a. Write inequalities to describe the set of feasible solutions.

    b. In your inequalities from Part **a**, did you use the symbols < and > or the symbols ≤ and ≥? Explain your choice.

    c. Do all the points in the feasible region indicate reasonable values considering the problem setting? Explain your response.

2.4 The class has decided to start concession sales using only pizza and pop.

    a. Estimate a reasonable cost for each pizza and six-pack of pop. You may consult local merchants on prices.

    b. 1. Write inequalities to represent the number of pizzas that can be purchased for $100 or less, where *x* represents number of pizzas. (Your inequalities should indicate that the class cannot purchase a negative number of pizzas.)

      2. Write inequalities to represent the number of six-packs that can be purchased for $100 or less, where *y* represents number of six-packs. (Your inequalities should indicate that the class cannot purchase a negative number of six-packs.)

      3. Graph these inequalities on a two-dimensional coordinate system where *y* represents number of six-packs and *x* represents number of pizzas.

    c. 1. In Part **b**, you assumed that the entire $100 could be spent on either pizza or pop. Write an inequality in which $100 is the limit for the total cost of both items.

      2. Graph this constraint on the same coordinate system as in Part **b**. You might need to solve the inequality for *y* before graphing.

    d. Label the feasible region on your graph and explain what it represents in this situation.

    e. 1. Determine the coordinates of the corner points of the feasible region and describe the method that you used to identify them.

      2. Describe at least one other method that you could use to determine the coordinates of the corner points.

＊ ＊ ＊ ＊ ＊

2.5 A student newspaper plans to conduct a survey on dating. The editors would like to poll at least 30 boys and 30 girls, but no more than a total of 120 students. To reflect their ratio in the school population, the survey group should consist of at least 5 girls for every 7 boys.

    a. Write an inequality to represent each of the following:

      1. the number of boys to be surveyed

2. the number of girls to be surveyed

3. the total number of students to be surveyed

4. the ratio of the number of girls to be surveyed to the number of boys to be surveyed.

b. Graph the inequalities from Part **a** on a single coordinate system. Identify the feasible region.

c. Determine the coordinates of the corner points and identify those that are included in the feasible region.

2.6 The feasible region shown in the graph below is defined by four constraints.

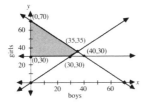

a. Write each constraint as an inequality.

b. Identify the corner points that are included in the feasible region.

c. What might these constraints represent in terms of the number and gender of students in a newspaper survey?

2.7 At G&S Jewelry, two jewelers make rings and necklaces. It takes approximately 1.5 hr to create a ring and about 1 hr to make a necklace. The two jewelers work for a total of 80 hr per week. A ring typically contains about 5 g of metal and a necklace contains about 20 g. The company wants to limit the amount of metal used each week to 500 g.

a. Determine the inequalities that define the feasible region.

b. Find the corner points of the feasible region.

2. $y \geq 30$, where y is a whole number

3. $x + y \leq 120$, where x and y are whole numbers

4. $7y \geq 5x$, where x and y are whole numbers

b–c. As shown in the sample graph below, all of the corner points are in the feasible region.

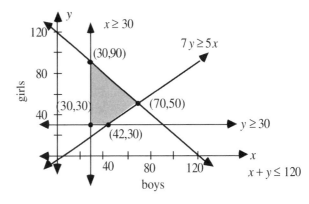

2.6 **a.** $x > 0$, $y \geq 30$, $x + y \leq 70$, and $y \geq x$, where x and y are whole numbers

b. The corner points are (30,30), (35,35), (0,70), and (0,30). Corner points (30,30) and (35,35) lie within the feasible region.

c. Sample response: The constraints indicate that no more than 70 students will be surveyed. Of those surveyed, the number of girls must be greater than or equal to the number of boys. There must be at least 30 girls interviewed.

2.7 **a.** In the following inequalities, r represents the number of rings, while n represents the number of necklaces: $r \geq 0$, $n \geq 0$, $1.5r + n \leq 80$, and $5r + 20n \leq 500$, where r and n are whole numbers.

b. The corner points are (0,0), (0,25), (44,14), and (53.3,0).

ACTIVITY 3

Students continue to graph feasible regions and identify corner points. They explore the use of the corner principle to optimize an objective function.

Materials List

- graph paper (several sheets per student; optional)

Technology

- graphing utility

Student Outcomes

After completing the following explorations and discussions, students should be able to:

✳ write an objective function

✳ use the substitution method to identify the corner points of a feasible region

✳ use the corner principle to optimize an objective function.

Exploration 1

a. Students explore how the graph of an objective function is affected as the value of the objective (in this case, profit) changes.
b. 1. Students should observe that all the lines are parallel.
   2. Sample response: As the value of P increases, so does the y-intercept.

Discussion 1

a. Sample response: The lines are parallel (they all have the same slope).
b. Sample response: All the lines are parallel because the x-coefficient and y-coefficient, which determine the slope, remained the same.
c. Sample response: For a given profit function, the value of P remains constant. As the value of x increases, the value of y decreases.
d. Sample response: The graph representing the greatest profit is located above the others. This happens because the value of P affects the y-intercept. The greater the value of P in the objective function, the greater the y-intercept.

ACTIVITY 3

Business analysts often use feasible regions to examine all the possible solutions to a problem—and eliminate those that do not satisfy one or more constraints. These constraints might include limitations on raw materials, on production costs, or on manufacturing output. The relationships among these constraints affect a company's potential profit.

One method for analyzing potential profit is **linear programming**. To use this method, all the constraints on a situation must be linear. After determining a feasible region, an **objective function**—in this case, an equation representing profit—can be evaluated for points in this region. Using this process, it is possible to identify the conditions that will result in the maximum potential profit.

Linear programming also can be used to identify the conditions that will result in minimum values, such as production costs or manufacturing time. In this activity, you use an objective function to determine the maximum profit that the class can make from its concession stand.

Exploration 1

Suppose that the class makes a profit of $3.00 on each pizza and $2.00 on each six-pack. If x represents number of pizzas, y represents number of six-packs, and P represents profit, the objective function in this situation is $P = 3x + 2y$.

a. Substitute four different values for P in the objective function $P = 3x + 2y$. Use technology to graph these four equations.

b. 1. What similarities or differences do you observe among the graphs?

   2. How is the value of P related to the y-intercept of $P = 3x + 2y$?

Discussion 1

a. What similarities did you observe in the graphs of the four equations?

b. Why do you think these similarities occur?

c. As the values of x increase in any given profit equation, does the profit increase or decrease? Explain your response.

d. In relation to the other graphs, where is the graph that indicates the greatest profit? Why do you think this occurs?

e. In relation to the other graphs, where is the graph that indicates the least profit?

e. Sample response: The graph that represents the least profit is the one with the lowest y-intercept in the feasible region. This line is located below the others.

Exploration 2

a. The set of feasible solutions includes the ordered pairs with integer values that fall in the shaded region of the following sample graph.

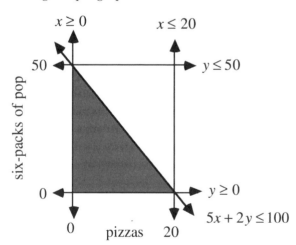

Exploration 2

One method for determining the maximum profit involves substituting the coordinates of a point in the feasible region into the objective function, then calculating the resulting profit. This process is continued for each point until the maximum profit is found. Because it requires checking every point in the feasible region, this method can require an unreasonable amount of time. In this exploration, you develop an alternative method for finding maximum profit.

a. Suppose that the class can buy pizzas for $5.00 each and soda pop for $2.00 per six-pack. Given that they can spend no more than $100.00, the constraints on this situation are $0 \le x \le 20$, $0 \le y \le 50$, and $5x + 2y \le 100$, where x represents number of pizzas and y represents number of six-packs.

Use technology to graph the feasible region described by these constraints.
Note: The technology that you choose might not be able to graph the boundary of a constraint that is not a function. In this case, it might be possible to "draw" a line to represent that boundary.

b. 1. Select a point in the feasible region. Use the objective equation $P = 3x + 2y$ to calculate the profit at that point.

2. Substitute the profit calculated in Step **1** for P in $P = 3x + 2y$. Graph this equation on the coordinate system from Part **a.**

c. 1. As you observed in Exploration **1**, the graphs of $P = 3x + 2y$ for all values of P are parallel.

Use this fact to help you find the location, with respect to the feasible region, of the line that indicates the maximum profit.

2. Determine the maximum profit in this situation.

d. Compare the value that you found for the maximum profit with those of others in the class.

Discussion 2

a. 1. What is the minimum number of boundary lines required to determine a vertex of a feasible region?

2. What is the minimum number of equations required to identify the coordinates of a vertex?

b. Depending on the technology you used, it might not have been possible to graph all of the boundaries of the feasible region. Describe any problems that you encountered when graphing the feasible region, and explain why they occurred.

c. Where did the line that indicates maximum profit intersect the feasible region?

d. In the Level 1 module "Under the Big Top but Above the Floor," you used the substitution method to solve systems of equations. Describe how you could use this method to find the coordinates of the corner points of a feasible region.

mathematics note

The **substitution method** can be used to solve a system of linear equations. The method begins by solving an equation for one variable. The resulting expression is then substituted for that variable in another equation in the system. This process is repeated until a solution can be identified.

For example, Table 4-3 lists the steps necessary to find the solution to a system of two equations with two variables, x and y.

TABLE 4-3 ■ *Substitution Method for Solving a System of Linear Equations*

Consider the given system of equations.	$\begin{cases} 2x + 3y = 6 \\ 9y - 4x = 13 \end{cases}$
Solve one of the equations for y.	$y = 2 - \dfrac{2}{3}x$
Substitute for y in the other equation.	$9\left(2 - \dfrac{2}{3}x\right) - 4x = 13$
Solve for x.	$x = \dfrac{1}{2}$
Substitute for x in one of the original equations.	$2\left(\dfrac{1}{2}\right) + 3y = 6$
Solve the resulting equation for y.	$y = \dfrac{5}{3}$
Write the solution to the system in the form (x, y).	$\left(\dfrac{1}{2}, \dfrac{5}{3}\right)$

To check the solution, you can substitute the coordinates of the point in each of the original equations.

$$2x + 3y = 6 \qquad\qquad 9y - 4x = 13$$
$$2\left(\tfrac{1}{2}\right) + 3\left(\tfrac{5}{3}\right) \overset{?}{=} 6 \quad \text{and} \quad 9\left(\tfrac{5}{3}\right) - 4\left(\tfrac{1}{2}\right) \overset{?}{=} 13$$
$$1 + 5 = 6 \qquad\qquad 15 - 2 = 13$$

Both of these equations are true, therefore the solution is correct.

b. 1. Sample response: The point (10,25) lies in the feasible region. Substituting these values in the equation $P = 3x + 2y$ yields $P = 80$.

2. Substituting 80 for P results in the equation:

$$80 = 3x + 2y.$$

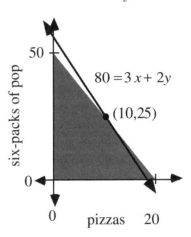

c. 1. The line that indicates the maximum profit intersects the feasible region at the corner point (0,50).

2. Because the equation of this line is $100 = 3x + 2y$, the maximum profit is $100.

d. Students compare values for maximum profit with others in the class.

Discussion 2

a. 1. Two lines must intersect to determine a vertex.

2. Two equations are needed to find the coordinates of the vertex.

b. Many graphing utilities will only graph functions. Constraints in the form $x = c$, where c is a constant, are not functions.

c. The line that indicates the maximum profit passes through the corner point (0,50). All other lines that pass through the feasible region are below that line.

d. Sample response: To find the coordinates of the vertex in the lower right-hand corner of the feasible region, for example, you can use the lines defined by the equations $5x + 2y = 100$ and $x = 20$ (the two intersecting boundary lines). Substituting 20 for the value of x in the equation $5x + 2y = 100$ results in $5(20) + 2y = 100$. Solving this equation for y yields $y = 0$. The point with coordinates (20,0) satisfies both equations; therefore it is a point of intersection and thus a corner point of the feasible region.

e. Sample response: You could find the coordinates for all the corner points of the feasible region and substitute the values of the coordinates into the objective function until you found the greatest value for P.

f. Sample response: The graph of the objective function that maximizes the objective would coincide with the edge of the feasible region. The maximum value would occur at any point along that border, so there might be more than one way to maximize the objective function.

g. The maximum profit can be found by substituting the coordinates into the objective function.

h. Sample response: No. Because 5/8 of a six-pack is equivalent to $3\frac{3}{4}$ cans, this is not a possible amount to buy.

i. Sample response: This means that the maximum value occurs at any point on the segment joining (0,4) and (3,3).

Warm-Up

1. The following pairs of lines are parallel: **a** and **d**, **b** and **f**, **c** and **e**.

2. **a.** (1,2)

   b. (2,–1)

   c. This system has no solution.

   d. (36/11,–6/11)

   e. (1,0)

   f. The solution is the set of all real numbers.

3. Sample graphs:

   a.

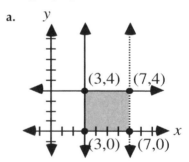

   b.

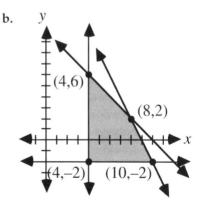

4. **a.** $P = -60$

   b. $P = -68$

   c. $P = 34$

   d. $P = -60$

---

e. How could you determine the maximum profit without substituting the coordinates of every point in the feasible region in the objective equation?

f. Suppose that the graph of the objective function was parallel to the boundary that contained the point where the maximum profit occurred. How would this affect your ability to determine the maximum value?

g. Given the objective function and the coordinates of the point at which the maximum profit occurs, how could you determine the maximum profit?

mathematics note

When the corner points are part of the feasible region, the **corner principle** provides a method of finding the maximum or minimum values of an objective function. According to this principle, the maximum and minimum values of an objective function occur at the corner points of the feasible region.

For example, Figure **4-6** shows a feasible region with five corner points. According to the corner principle, the maximum value of an objective function is located at one of the corner points.

Given the objective function $P = 2x + y$, the maximum value can be found by substituting the coordinates of each of the five corner points in this equation, then comparing the resulting values for P.

As shown in Table **4-4** below, the maximum value of 10 occurs at the corner point with coordinates (4,2).

FIGURE 4-6
Feasible region with five corner points.

TABLE 4-4 ■ Substituting the Coordinates of Corner Points in the Objective Function	
Coordinates (x,y)	Objective Function ($P = 2x + y$)
(0,0)	2(0) + 0 = 0
(0,4)	2(0) + 4 = 4
(3,3)	2(3) + 3 = 9
(4,2)	2(4) + 2 = 10
(4,0)	2(4) + 0 = 8

The minimum value also can be found using the corner principle. For the objective function $P = 2x + y$, the minimum value of 0 occurs at the corner point with coordinates (0,0).

Module 4 ■ *Making Concessions*   109

---

h. What if, by applying the corner principle, you obtained a solution which indicated that the class should buy 5/8 of a six-pack of pop? Is this solution reasonable? Why or why not?

i. Suppose that the objective function for the feasible region in Figure **4-6** is $P = x + 3y$. In this case, the maximum value of P is 12.

The graph of $12 = x + 3y$ contains the segment joining the vertices (0,4) and (3,3). What does this indicate about where the maximum value occurs?

Warm-Up

1. Each of the following equations represents a line. Identify which lines are parallel. Justify your response.

   a. $3x + 4y = 12$ **b.** $2x + 6y = -9$

   c. $y = \frac{3}{4} + 6$ **d.** $y = -\frac{3}{4}x - 10$

   e. $3x = 4y - 2$ **f.** $2x + 6y = 35$

2. Solve each of the following systems of equations.

   a. $\begin{cases} y = 3x - 1 \\ y = -5x + 7 \end{cases}$ **b.** $\begin{cases} 4x - 3y = 11 \\ 6x - y = 13 \end{cases}$ **c.** $\begin{cases} x - y = 3 \\ -\frac{1}{3}x + \frac{1}{3}y = 1 \end{cases}$

   d. $\begin{cases} 2x + y = 6 \\ 3x = 4y + 12 \end{cases}$ **e.** $\begin{cases} 3x + y - 3 = 0 \\ 2x - 3y - 2 = 0 \end{cases}$ **f.** $\begin{cases} 2x + 5y = -20 \\ x = -\frac{5}{2}y - 10 \end{cases}$

3. Graph each system of linear inequalities below. Shade the feasible region and identify the coordinates of the corner points.

   a. $\begin{cases} x \geq 3 \\ x < 7 \\ y \geq 0 \\ y \leq 4 \end{cases}$ **b.** $\begin{cases} x \geq 4 \\ y \geq -2 \\ x + y \leq 10 \\ 2x + y \leq 18 \end{cases}$

4. Find the value of for each of the following ordered pairs.

   a. (0,6)

   b. (–3,5)

   c. (4,–1)

   d. (–10,0)

110   Module 4 ■ *Making Concessions*

5. Which of the lines in the graph below, if any, appear to represent the same profit function for different profit values? Explain your response.

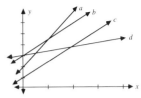

Assignment

3.1 The figure below shows a feasible region with four corner points.

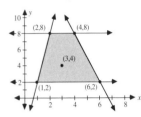

a. Use the information in the graph to represent each of the following with a sketch and with an equation.

1. the maximum value of the objective function $P = 3x + 2y$
2. the maximum value of the objective function $P = 15x + y$
3. the minimum value of the objective function $P = 3x + 2y$
4. the minimum value of the objective function $P = 15x + y$

b. Describe how the slope of the objective function affects your use of the corner principle.

---

5. Sample response: Because lines b and c appear to be parallel, they could represent the same profit function for different values of P.

Assignment

Problems suitable for use as assessment items are identified by an asterisk (*).

3.1 a. Sample graph for Parts **1–4**:

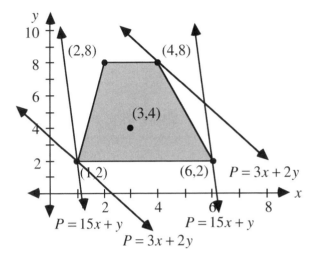

1. $28 = 3(4) + 2(8)$
2. $92 = 15(6) + 2$
3. $7 = 3(1) + 2(2)$
4. $17 = 15(1) + 2$

b. Sample response: The slope of the objective function determines which corner point of the feasible region represents a maximum or minimum value of the function.

3.2 The maximum value of 30 occurs at the corner point (0,6). Sample graph:

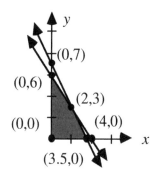

* **3.3 a.** The constraints on the problem can be represented by the inequalities $0 \leq x \leq 16$, $0 \leq y \leq 22$, and $4.96x + 1.84y \leq 100$ where x represents the number of pizzas and y represents the number of six-packs of pop and both x and y are whole numbers.

b. See sample graph given in Part **e** below.

c. The profit is $11.04 on each pizza and $4.16 on each six-pack.

d. Sample response: $P = 11.04x + 4.16y$, where P is profit, x is the number of pizzas, and y is the number of six-packs.

e. The maximum value of $P = 11.04x + 4.16y$ occurs at the corner point (12,22). If all items are sold, the maximum profit is $12(11.04) + 22(4.16)$ or $224.00. Sample graph:

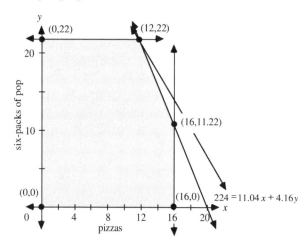

f. Sample response: The class should buy 12 pizzas and 22 six-packs of pop. Because these are whole-number quantities, this seems to be a reasonable answer.

3.2 Graph the feasible region described by the following constraints, label the corner points, and find the maximum value of the objective function $P = 5y - 2x$.

$$\begin{cases} x \geq 0 \\ y \geq 0 \\ 3x + 2y \leq 12 \\ 2x + y \leq 7 \end{cases}$$

3.3 According to the results of their feasibility study, the class should purchase no more than 16 eight-slice pizzas. The study also indicated that the class should buy no more than 22 six-packs of pop. Each pizza costs $4.96 and each six-pack costs $1.84. The class has $100.00 to spend on these items.

   a. Write inequalities to represent the constraints in this situation.

   b. Graph the feasible region defined by these constraints.

   c. The class plans to charge $2.00 for a slice of pizza and $1.00 for a can of pop. How much profit will the class earn by selling one pizza? How much profit will they earn by selling one six-pack?

   d. Use your responses to Part **c** to write an objective function for profit from selling pizzas and pop.

   e. Find the maximum profit the class can earn if they sell all the pizza and pop they purchase. Graph the equation that represents the maximum profit on the coordinate system from Part **b**.

   f. To realize this maximum profit, how many pizzas and six-packs should the class buy? Does this solution seem reasonable? Explain your response.

3.4 **a.** Graph the feasible region described by the following constraints.

$$\begin{cases} 3x + y \leq 15 \\ x + 2y \leq 20 \\ x \geq 0 \\ y \geq 0 \end{cases}$$

   b. Determine the coordinates of the corner points of the feasible region.

   c. Given the constraints in Part **a,** find the minimum value of each of the following objective functions:

     1. $P = 2y - x$ **2.** $P = 3y + 2x$

3.5 **a.** Repeat Problem **3.3** if each pizza costs the class $6.00 and each six-pack costs $2.00.

   b. How would you try to find the maximum profit if the corner principle resulted in a solution that required the purchase of fractional amounts of pizza or six-packs?

   c. What do you think a businessperson might do if faced with the situation in Part **b?**

112   Module 4 ■ *Making Concessions*

3.4 a. Sample graph:

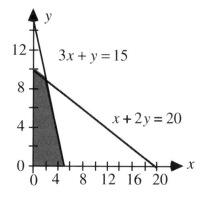

b. The coordinates of the corner points are (0,0), (5,0), (2,9), and (0,10).

c. 1. As shown in the table below, the minimum of −5 occurs at (5,0).

(x,y)	$P = 2y - x$	$P = 3y + 2x$
(0,0)	0	0
(5,0)	−5	10
(2,9)	16	31
(0,10)	20	30

2. As shown in the table above, the minimum of 0 occurs at (0,0).

3.6 Imagine that your class decides to sell nachos and canned soft drinks as a fund-raising project. You have $100.00 available to purchase these items. Determine the maximum potential profit for the class. Describe any assumptions you make in analyzing this situation.

* * * * *

3.7 The feasible region shaded in the following graph is defined by five constraints. Determine the coordinates of the corner points of this region.

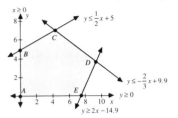

3.8 The graph on the right shows a feasible region with five corner points.

a. 1. Which point in the feasible region results in the maximum value of the objective function $P = 5x + 5y$?

2. Which point in the feasible region results in the minimum value of the objective function $P = 5x + 5y$?

b. 1. Determine the slope of the line that passes through points D and E.

2. Determine the value of the objective function $P = 8x + 5y$ at D and E.

3. Write $P = 8x + 5y$ in slope-intercept form and identify the slope.

4. Describe how your responses to Steps 1 and 2 are related.

5. A graph of the objective function $P = 8x + 5y$ for three values of P would consist of three lines. Describe how these lines would be related to $\overline{DE}$.

c. Find an example of an objective function that has its maximum value at each of the following:

1. both point D and point C 2. point C only   3. point E only.

Module 4 ■ *Making Concessions*   113

3.5 a. The maximum value of the objective function occurs at the corner point $(9\frac{1}{3}, 22)$, where x represents number of pizzas and y represents number of six-packs. Because the value for x is not a whole number, it does represent a reasonable amount of pizza to buy.

b. To find the maximum profit that corresponds to a point with integer coordinates, students may suggest rounding solutions to the nearest integer or substituting the coordinates of points near the corner point into the objective function.

In this case, the point $(9,22)$ results in a profit of $244. Although the points $(10,22)$ and $(10,21)$ produce greater profits, they are not in the feasible region. The point $(10,20)$ is in the feasible region but results in a profit of only $240.

Note: Neither of these methods guarantees that the optimum value will be found.

c. Sample response: A businessperson might buy less if the profit is not greatly affected. They may buy slightly more if they believe they could sell the extra or easily absorb the loss.

3.6 Answers will vary. Students should record the quantities of cheese and chips needed to make an appropriate number of nacho servings, the quantity and cost of each item to be purchased, and the selling price of each item. If the corner principle does not give a solution with integer coordinates, they should use an appropriate strategy to determine the quantities to purchase.

* * * * *

3.7 $A(0,0)$, $B(0,5)$, $C(4.2,7.1)$, $D(9.3,3.7)$, $E(7.45,0)$

3.8 a. 1. $D(10,8)$

2. $A(0,0)$

b. 1. $m = -8/5$

2. At both D and E, the value of the objective function is 120.

3. The equation of this line in slope-intercept form is:

$$y = -\frac{8}{5}x + \frac{P}{5}$$

The slope of the objective function is $-8/5$.

4. Because the slope of the objective function is the same as the slope of the line that passes through D and E, the value of the function is the same at both D and E (and at any other point on $\overline{DE}$).

5. All three lines would be parallel to $\overline{DE}$.

c. 1. Sample response: $P = 2x + 5y$.

2. Sample response: $P = x + 5y$.

3. Sample response: $P = 10x + 2y$.

Research Project

Students plan a fund-raiser that involves selling two different items. To help determine the feasibility of their plan, they conduct a survey. They then prepare a report designed to persuade their classmates to invest in the venture. This works well as a small-group activity.

You might wish to allow students to implement a plan selected by the class. Students then can evaluate the accuracy of their projections.

Students use matrices to solve systems of two equations in two unknowns. Matrix equations are then used to find corner points of feasible regions.

Students also extend linear programming concepts into three dimensions by considering the sale of three items instead of two.

teacher note

A brief assessment of the mathematical content in Activities **3** and **4,** for use at your discretion, appears in the Teacher Resources for this module.

Materials

- graph paper (several sheets per group)
- cardboard boxes (one per group)
- scissors (one pair per group)
- tape

Technology

- graphing utility
- three-dimensional graphing utility (optional)
- matrix manipulator

Research Project

Plan a fund-raiser for your mathematics class that involves selling two items at a dance, game, or other school-related activity. Design a survey to determine what two items to sell, how much to charge for each item, and how much of each item to purchase. Administer the survey. Assume that you can interest enough investors in your plan to raise $50.00. Use this constraint and the results from the survey to determine the constraints for the fund-raiser.

Use linear programming to determine the maximum profit that each investor could expect to earn. Prepare a report for the class to persuade each student to become an investor. You might wish to include the survey questionnaire, survey results, initial costs, expected profit, graphs, and sample advertising posters.

A C T I V I T Y

In Activity **3**, you used the corner principle to determine the maximum or minimum value of an objective function. Identifying the coordinates of corner points often involves solving a system of equations, either by substitution or by some other method. In this activity, you use matrices to solve systems of linear equations.

Exploration 1

Using matrices to solve a system of equations involves two steps: writing a matrix equation to represent the system, then solving the resulting matrix equation.

a. Consider the following system of equations:

$$\begin{cases} -8x + 10y = 40 \\ 10x + 10y = 139 \end{cases}$$

The **matrix equation** for this system is shown below. Simplify this equation by completing the matrix multiplication on the left-hand side of the equals sign.

$$\begin{bmatrix} -8 & 10 \\ 10 & 10 \end{bmatrix} \bullet \begin{bmatrix} x \\ y \end{bmatrix} = \begin{bmatrix} 40 \\ 139 \end{bmatrix}$$

b. Compare the simplified matrix equation with the original system of equations. Describe any similarities you observe.

Student Outcomes

After completing the following explorations and discussions, students should be able to:

✳ write a system of algebraic equations in two variables in matrix form

✳ determine the inverse of a 2×2 matrix

✳ verify that the product of a matrix and its inverse is the identity matrix

✳ use multiplication by an inverse matrix to solve simple matrix equations

✳ use various methods to identify inconsistent systems of equations

✳ calculate the determinant of a 2×2 matrix

✳ model a three-dimensional feasible region

✳ identify the corner points of a three-dimensional feasible region

✳ write a system of equations in three variables in a matrix form

✳ use technology to find the inverse of a 3×3 matrix

✳ use technology to find the determinant of a 3×3 matrix.

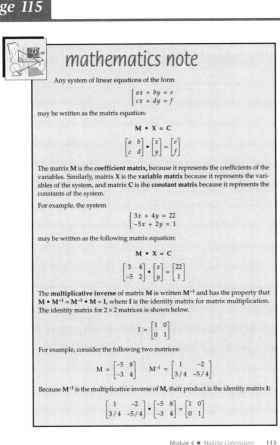

mathematics note

Any system of linear equations of the form

$$\begin{cases} ax + by = e \\ cx + dy = f \end{cases}$$

may be written as the matrix equation:

$$M \cdot X = C$$

$$\begin{bmatrix} a & b \\ c & d \end{bmatrix} \cdot \begin{bmatrix} x \\ y \end{bmatrix} = \begin{bmatrix} e \\ f \end{bmatrix}$$

The matrix **M** is the **coefficient matrix**, because it represents the coefficients of the variables. Similarly, matrix **X** is the **variable matrix** because it represents the variables of the system, and matrix **C** is the **constant matrix** because it represents the constants of the system.

For example, the system

$$\begin{cases} 3x + 4y = 22 \\ -5x + 2y = 1 \end{cases}$$

may be written as the following matrix equation:

$$M \cdot X = C$$

$$\begin{bmatrix} 3 & 4 \\ -5 & 2 \end{bmatrix} \cdot \begin{bmatrix} x \\ y \end{bmatrix} = \begin{bmatrix} 22 \\ 1 \end{bmatrix}$$

The **multiplicative inverse** of matrix **M** is written M^{-1} and has the property that $M \cdot M^{-1} = M^{-1} \cdot M = I$, where **I** is the identity matrix for matrix multiplication. The identity matrix for 2×2 matrices is shown below.

$$I = \begin{bmatrix} 1 & 0 \\ 0 & 1 \end{bmatrix}$$

For example, consider the following two matrices:

$$M = \begin{bmatrix} -5 & 8 \\ -3 & 4 \end{bmatrix} \quad M^{-1} = \begin{bmatrix} 1 & -2 \\ 3/4 & -5/4 \end{bmatrix}$$

Because M^{-1} is the multiplicative inverse of **M**, their product is the identity matrix **I**:

$$\begin{bmatrix} 1 & -2 \\ 3/4 & -5/4 \end{bmatrix} \cdot \begin{bmatrix} -5 & 8 \\ -3 & 4 \end{bmatrix} = \begin{bmatrix} 1 & 0 \\ 0 & 1 \end{bmatrix}$$

Module 4 ■ *Making Concessions*   115

teacher note

In Part **e** of Exploration **1**, students find the inverse of a known matrix. Using the fact that $M \cdot M^{-1} = I$, they then solve for the variable matrix **X** in $M \cdot X = C$.

After students have completed Exploration **1**, you might wish to demonstrate how the inverse of any 2×2 matrix can be found using the equation $M \cdot M^{-1} = I$, where

$$M = \begin{bmatrix} a & b \\ c & d \end{bmatrix} \quad \text{and} \quad M^{-1} = \begin{bmatrix} e & f \\ g & h \end{bmatrix}$$

From this matrix equation, the following systems of equations can be written:

$$\begin{cases} ae + bg = 1 \\ ce + dg = 0 \end{cases} \quad \text{and} \quad \begin{cases} af + bh = 0 \\ cf + dh = 1 \end{cases}$$

Solving for e, f, g, and h, then substituting into M^{-1} yields the solution below:

$$M^{-1} = \begin{bmatrix} \dfrac{-d}{bc-ad} & \dfrac{b}{bc-ad} \\ \dfrac{c}{bc-ad} & \dfrac{-a}{bc-ad} \end{bmatrix} = \begin{bmatrix} \dfrac{d}{ad-bc} & \dfrac{-b}{ad-bc} \\ \dfrac{-c}{ad-bc} & \dfrac{a}{ad-bc} \end{bmatrix}$$

Exploration 1

Students examine the relationship between a system of two equations and two unknowns and the corresponding matrix equation. The concept of inverse matrices is introduced. Students then use technology to solve matrix equations.

a. Students should obtain the following equation:

$$\begin{bmatrix} -8x + 10y \\ 10x + 10y \end{bmatrix} = \begin{bmatrix} 40 \\ 139 \end{bmatrix}$$

b. Sample response: The entries in the matrices are the terms of the equations. The first equation's terms are in the top rows of the matrices; the second equation's terms are in the bottom rows of the matrices.

c. One way for students to verify the value of $\mathbf{M}^{-1}$ is to enter matrix $\mathbf{M}$ in their technology, then use the multiplicative inverse command. A second approach involves entering both $\mathbf{M}$ and $\mathbf{M}^{-1}$, then finding their product—which should be the identity matrix.

d. Matrices will vary. Sample response:

$$\begin{bmatrix} 6 & 4 \\ -2 & 5 \end{bmatrix} \bullet \begin{bmatrix} 1 & 0 \\ 0 & 1 \end{bmatrix} = \begin{bmatrix} 1 & 0 \\ 0 & 1 \end{bmatrix} \bullet \begin{bmatrix} 6 & 4 \\ -2 & 5 \end{bmatrix} = \begin{bmatrix} 6 & 4 \\ -2 & 5 \end{bmatrix}$$

$$\begin{bmatrix} 8 & 3 \\ 10 & -5 \end{bmatrix} \bullet \begin{bmatrix} 1 & 0 \\ 0 & 1 \end{bmatrix} = \begin{bmatrix} 1 & 0 \\ 0 & 1 \end{bmatrix} \bullet \begin{bmatrix} 8 & 3 \\ 10 & -5 \end{bmatrix} = \begin{bmatrix} 8 & 3 \\ 10 & -5 \end{bmatrix}$$

e. 1. The matrix equation is shown below:

$$\begin{bmatrix} 5 & 2 \\ 2 & 1 \end{bmatrix} \bullet \begin{bmatrix} x \\ y \end{bmatrix} = \begin{bmatrix} 22 \\ 9 \end{bmatrix}$$

2. In this case, $\mathbf{M} \bullet \mathbf{M}^{-1} = \mathbf{I}$ is as follows:

$$\begin{bmatrix} 5 & 2 \\ 2 & 1 \end{bmatrix} \bullet \begin{bmatrix} e & f \\ g & h \end{bmatrix} = \begin{bmatrix} 1 & 0 \\ 0 & 1 \end{bmatrix}$$

From this matrix equation, students should write the following systems of equations:

$$\begin{cases} 5e + 2g = 1 \\ 2e + g = 0 \end{cases} \text{ and } \begin{cases} 5f + 2h = 0 \\ 2f + h = 1 \end{cases}$$

Solving these systems results in $e = 1, f = -2, g = -2,$ and $h = 5$. Therefore, the inverse of the coefficient matrix $\mathbf{M}$ is:

$$\mathbf{M}^{-1} = \begin{bmatrix} 1 & -2 \\ -2 & 5 \end{bmatrix}$$

---

c. Use technology to verify that the value of $\mathbf{M}^{-1}$ given in the mathematics note is correct.

d. Use technology to verify that $\mathbf{I} \bullet \mathbf{A} = \mathbf{A} \bullet \mathbf{I} = \mathbf{A}$ for at least two different 2×2 matrices $\mathbf{A}$.

e. A linear equation of the form $a \bullet x = b$ can be solved for x by multiplying both sides of the equation by the multiplicative inverse of a.

Similarly, a matrix equation of the form $\mathbf{M} \bullet \mathbf{X} = \mathbf{C}$ can be solved for $\mathbf{X}$ by multiplying both sides of the equation by the multiplicative inverse of $\mathbf{M}$, as shown below, and by using the associative property for matrix multiplication:

$$\mathbf{M}^{-1} \bullet (\mathbf{M} \bullet \mathbf{X}) = \mathbf{M}^{-1} \bullet \mathbf{C}$$
$$(\mathbf{M}^{-1} \bullet \mathbf{M}) \bullet \mathbf{X} = \mathbf{M}^{-1} \bullet \mathbf{C}$$
$$\mathbf{I} \bullet \mathbf{X} = \mathbf{M}^{-1} \bullet \mathbf{C}$$
$$\mathbf{X} = \mathbf{M}^{-1} \bullet \mathbf{C}$$

Note that each side of the equation must be multiplied on the left by $\mathbf{M}^{-1}$ and recall that $\mathbf{M}^{-1} \bullet \mathbf{M} = \mathbf{M} \bullet \mathbf{M}^{-1} = \mathbf{I}$.

1. Write the following system of linear equations as a matrix equation of the form $\mathbf{M} \bullet \mathbf{X} = \mathbf{C}$:

$$\begin{cases} 5x + 2y = 22 \\ 2x + y = 9 \end{cases}$$

2. To find the inverse $\mathbf{M}^{-1}$ of the coefficient matrix $\mathbf{M}$, again consider that $\mathbf{M}^{-1} \bullet \mathbf{M} = \mathbf{M} \bullet \mathbf{M}^{-1} = \mathbf{I}$.

Let the elements of $\mathbf{M}^{-1}$ be represented by the variables $e, f, g,$ and h, as shown below:

$$\mathbf{M}^{-1} = \begin{bmatrix} e & f \\ g & h \end{bmatrix}$$

The equation $\mathbf{M} \bullet \mathbf{M}^{-1} = \mathbf{I}$ can then be rewritten as follows:

$$\mathbf{M} \bullet \mathbf{M}^{-1} = \mathbf{I}$$
$$\mathbf{M} \bullet \begin{bmatrix} e & f \\ g & h \end{bmatrix} = \mathbf{I}$$
$$\mathbf{M} \bullet \begin{bmatrix} e & f \\ g & h \end{bmatrix} = \begin{bmatrix} 1 & 0 \\ 0 & 1 \end{bmatrix}$$

Use this matrix equation to write two systems of two equations, each with two variables. Solve these systems, then substitute for $e, f, g,$ and h in the inverse matrix $\mathbf{M}^{-1}$.

3. Use technology to verify that the matrix you identified in Step **2** is the inverse of the coefficient matrix **M**.

4. Solve the matrix equation **M • X = C** for the variable matrix **X** by multiplying each side by **M⁻¹**. Write the resulting equation in the form below:

$$\begin{bmatrix} x \\ y \end{bmatrix} = \begin{bmatrix} m \\ n \end{bmatrix}$$

5. Verify by substitution that **M • X = C**.

6. Write the solution as an ordered pair.

7. Verify your solution by substituting these coordinates in the original equations:

$$\begin{cases} 5x + 2y = 22 \\ 2x + y = 9 \end{cases}$$

8. Check the solution by graphing the two equations on the same coordinate system.

f. When a system of equations has no solution, it is said to be **inconsistent**.

1. Verify that the system shown below is inconsistent by graphing the two equations on the same coordinate system.

$$\begin{cases} x + 2y = 4 \\ 2x + 4y = 13 \end{cases}$$

2. When an attempt is made to solve an inconsistent system using matrices, one step of the process cannot be completed. Repeat Part **e** using the system of equations above until you discover where the process fails.

---

mathematics note

The **determinant** of a 2 × 2 matrix **M** (denoted det **M** or |**M**|) is the difference of the two diagonals of the matrix. For a matrix **M** in the form given below, det **M** = ad – bc.

$$M = \begin{bmatrix} a & b \\ c & d \end{bmatrix}$$

For example, consider the following matrix **A**:

$$A = \begin{bmatrix} 2 & 3 \\ -4 & 1 \end{bmatrix}$$

In this case, det **A** = 2(1) – 3(–4) = 2 – (–12) = 14.

---

3. Students verify that **M⁻¹** is the inverse of the coefficient matrix **M**. They can do this by showing that the following equation is true: **M⁻¹ • M = M • M⁻¹ = I**.

4. The resulting equation is:

$$\mathbf{M^{-1} \cdot M \cdot X = M^{-1} \cdot C}$$

$$\begin{bmatrix} 1 & -2 \\ -2 & 5 \end{bmatrix} \cdot \begin{bmatrix} 5 & 2 \\ 2 & 1 \end{bmatrix} \cdot \begin{bmatrix} x \\ y \end{bmatrix} = \begin{bmatrix} 1 & -2 \\ -2 & 5 \end{bmatrix} \cdot \begin{bmatrix} 22 \\ 9 \end{bmatrix}$$

$$\begin{bmatrix} x \\ y \end{bmatrix} = \begin{bmatrix} 4 \\ 1 \end{bmatrix}$$

5. The true matrix equation below verifies the solution:

$$\begin{bmatrix} 5 & 2 \\ 2 & 1 \end{bmatrix} \cdot \begin{bmatrix} 4 \\ 1 \end{bmatrix} = \begin{bmatrix} 22 \\ 9 \end{bmatrix}$$

6. The solution is (4,1).

7. Students should substitute as follows:

$$5(4) + 2(1) = 22 \qquad 2(4) + 1 = 9$$
$$20 + 2 = 22 \qquad 8 + 1 = 9$$
$$22 = 22 \qquad 9 = 9$$

Therefore, (4,1) is a solution to both equations.

8. Because the graphs of the two lines intersect at (4,1), the graph also verifies this solution.

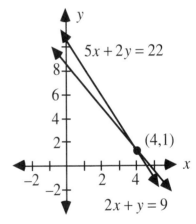

f. 1. The system is inconsistent because the graphs are parallel and do not have a common point.

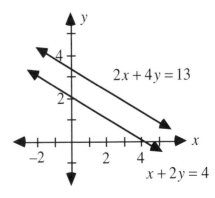

2. The process fails because the coefficient matrix does not have an inverse.

teacher note

To avoid confusion, you may point out that although the notation for a determinant, $|\mathbf{M}|$, resembles the notation for absolute value, determinants and absolute value are not at all related. Determinants can be either positive or negative.

g. 1. The determinant for the coefficient matrix is 1.
   2. The determinant for the coefficient matrix is 0.
   3. Sample response: When the determinant is 0, the lines are parallel and the system has no solution.

h. Students should observe that systems that consist of two parallel lines result in a determinant of 0. If the lines intersect, a solution exists and the determinant is a non-zero number.

Discussion 1

a. Sample response: You can enter the coefficient matrix $\mathbf{M}$ and use the multiplicative inverse button to find $\mathbf{M}^{-1}$. Or you can enter $\mathbf{M}$ and $\mathbf{M}^{-1}$, then find their product to see if you get the identity matrix.

teacher note

Since students were introduced to the determinant for 2×2 matrices in Part **g** of Exploration **1**, you might wish to discuss the following formula for the inverse of a 2×2 matrix $\mathbf{M}$:

$$\mathbf{M}^{-1} = \frac{1}{\det \mathbf{M}} \bullet \begin{bmatrix} d & -b \\ -c & a \end{bmatrix}, \text{ where } \mathbf{M} = \begin{bmatrix} a & b \\ c & d \end{bmatrix}$$

b. Sample response: Matrix multiplication is not commutative. In matrix multiplication, the number of columns in the first matrix must equal the number of rows in the second matrix. Both the coefficient and the constant matrix must be multiplied by the inverse matrix on the left for the dimensions to match.

c. The coefficient matrix does not have an inverse.

d. Sample response: If the determinant of the coefficient matrix for a system of equations is a non-zero number, then the system has a solution. This means that the coefficient matrix has an inverse.

---

g. 1. Find the determinant of the coefficient matrix for the system of equations in Part **e**.
   2. Find the determinant of the coefficient matrix for the system of equations in Part **f**.
   3. Make a conjecture about the relationship between the determinant of the coefficient matrix and the corresponding system of equations.

h. Test your conjecture from Part **g** by completing the following steps.
   1. Write the equations of two intersecting lines. Graph the resulting system of equations and determine its solution. Find the determinant of the coefficient matrix for the system.
   2. Write the equations of two parallel lines. Graph the resulting system of equations and determine its solution. Find the determinant of the coefficient matrix for the system.
   3. Compare your findings with those of other students.

Discussion 1

a. In Part **c** of Exploration **1**, you used technology to verify the value of $\mathbf{M}^{-1}$ given in the mathematics note. Describe two different ways that you can use technology to make this verification.

b. When multiplying both sides of a matrix equation $\mathbf{M} \bullet \mathbf{X} = \mathbf{C}$ by the multiplicative inverse of $\mathbf{M}$, each side of the equation must be multiplied on the left by $\mathbf{M}^{-1}$. Why is this necessary?

c. If a system is inconsistent, what can you conclude about the coefficient matrix $\mathbf{M}$?

d. What does the determinant of the coefficient matrix tell you about the inverse of the coefficient matrix?

e. 1. Describe the coefficient matrix for the following system of equations:
$$\begin{cases} 3x = 7 \\ 5x + 2y = 11 \end{cases}$$
   2. Describe at least two ways to determine if the system has a solution.

f. When considering the sale of two items, the feasible solutions form a region on a coordinate plane. The boundaries of the region are formed by lines whose equations are determined by constraints.

Suppose that the class wanted to decide which two of the three items—pizza, pop, or nachos—to sell. How many coordinate planes would be needed to graph the feasible regions for all the possible pairs?

---

e. 1. The coefficient matrix is a 2×2 matrix in which one of the y-coefficients equals 0:

$$\begin{bmatrix} 3 & 0 \\ 5 & 2 \end{bmatrix}$$

   2. Sample response: You can tell if a system has a solution by graphing the system, by attempting to find the inverse of the coefficient matrix, or by calculating the determinant of the coefficient matrix. If the lines intersect, the system has a solution. If the coefficient matrix has an inverse, the system will have a solution. If the determinant of the coefficient matrix is a non-zero number, the system will have a solution.

f. Sample response: Three planes would be needed: one to graph pizza versus pop, one for pizza versus nachos, and one for pop versus nachos.

g. In Activity **2**, you explored the potential sale of three items at a concession stand: pizza, pop, and nachos. How many variables are necessary to model a situation in which three items are sold?

h. Is it possible to graph the constraints for all three items on a single coordinate plane? Explain your response.

i. Is it possible to represent the constraints on all three items on another type of coordinate system? If not, why not? If so, what geometric figure do you think could be used to represent the boundaries?

Exploration 2

In this exploration, you investigate linear programming in three dimensions.

a. Cut the top, front, and one side from a cardboard box.

b. Use the remaining inside corner to create a three-dimensional coordinate system. As shown in Figure **4-7**, label the two axes that lie in the bottom of the box x and y, respectively. Label the vertical axis z. Divide each axis into intervals of at least 1 cm and label the intervals accordingly.

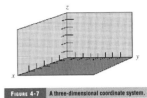

FIGURE 4-7   A three-dimensional coordinate system.

c. The model shown in Figure **4-7** represents the first octant of a three-dimensional coordinate system. On the planes of the first octant, shade and label the regions defined by the following sets of constraints.

   Region A: $0 \leq x \leq 6, \quad 0 \leq y \leq 4, \quad z = 0$

   Region B: $0 \leq y \leq 4, \quad 0 \leq z \leq 5, \quad x = 0$

   Region C: $0 \leq x \leq 6, \quad 0 \leq z \leq 5, \quad y = 0$

d. Cut shapes that approximate these regions from leftover cardboard.

e. 1. Position the cutout of region A on your coordinate system to represent the constraints $0 \leq x \leq 6, \ 0 \leq y \leq 4,$ and $z = 1$. Note its position.

   2. Move the same cutout along the z-axis to the position that represents the constraints $0 \leq x \leq 6, \ 0 \leq y \leq 4,$ and $z = 2$. Compare this position with the position in Step **1**.

teacher note

You might wish to discuss the various ways in which three planes can intersect one another. These are illustrated below.

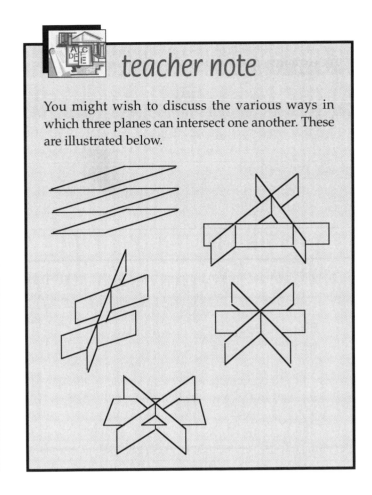

g. Sample response: Three variables are necessary: one each for pizza, pop, and nachos.

h. Sample response: No. One plane can accommodate only two different variables.

i. Sample response: The constraints for three items could be displayed on a three-dimensional coordinate system where planes as described in Part **f** of Discussion **2** would represent the boundaries.

Exploration 2

Students build a model of the first octant of a three-dimensional coordinate system. This activity works well in small groups.

a–b. Students cut cardboard boxes and label the axes of their coordinate systems. **Note:** The leftover cardboard should be saved for use in Part **d.**

c–d. On each plane surface of the first octant, students shade one of three regions defined by inequalities. They then cut a model of each region from the leftover pieces of cardboard.

e.   Students move the model of region A through the various values of the constraint placed on z.

f. Students should tape the model regions to form a rectangular prism in the first octant. This prism defines the set of feasible solutions for the constraints $0 \leq x \leq 6$, $0 \leq y \leq 4$, and $0 \leq z \leq 5$.

g. The coordinates of the eight corner points are: (0,0,0), (0,0,5), (6,0,0), (6,0,5), (0,4,0), (0,4,5), (6,4,0), and (6,4,5).

Discussion 2

a. The set of points includes five rectangular regions that are parallel to Region A, each measuring 4 units by 6 units. The regions are located at $z = 1, 2, 3, 4,$ and 5.

b. **1.** Three planes may intersect in a single point. Two planes may intersect in a line.

2. Each corner point is formed from the intersection of three planes. There are four ways in which three planes can be selected from four planes: *ABC*, *ABD*, *ACD*, and *BCD*.

3. Answers will vary. The maximum number of vertices formed by the intersection of five planes is $_5C_3$ or 10. Given five planes *A, B, C, D,* and *E*, the 10 possible sets of three planes are *ABC, ABD, ABE, ACD, ACE, ADE, BCD, BCE, BDE,* and *CDE*.

Because the feasible space that would contain the maximum number of corner points forms a polyhedron, however, it obeys Euler's equation $V + F - 2 = E$, where *V* represents the number of vertices (corner points), *F* represents the number of faces (planes), and *E* represents the number of edges (intersections of two planes).

Because two planes are required to form an edge, there is a possibility of $_5C_2$ or 10 edges. Substituting into Euler's equation, however, $10 + 5 - 2 = 13$, not 10. Therefore, the feasible space must have less than 10 corner points.

The maximum number of corner points for a feasible space using four planes is 4. These points are the vertices of a tetrahedron. The fifth plane would have to intersect the tetrahedron in such a way as to form another polyhedron defining the feasible space.

c. **1.** The shape is a rectangular prism. A rectangular prism has eight vertices.

2. Sample response: No. Not all sets of constraints that involve six planes would have three pairs of parallel planes. The parallel planes reduce the number of possible corner points.

d. **1.** Sample response: By the corner principle, the maximum will occur at one of the eight corner points. The specific point where the maximum occurs would depend on the objective function.

2. Sample response: The coordinates of each corner point could be substituted into the objective function to determine which represents the maximum value.

3. Repeat the process described in Step **2,** increasing the value of *z* by 1 unit each time, until the cutout is positioned at the edge of the shaded region on the *yz*-plane.

f. Tape the cutouts of regions A, B, and C in the first octant so that they form the boundaries of a shape that includes the set of feasible solutions described by $0 \leq x \leq 6$, $0 \leq y \leq 4$, and $0 \leq z \leq 5$.

g. Identify the corner points of the shape formed in Part **f.**

Discussion 2

a. Describe the set of points obtained as you moved the cutout of region A in Part **e** of the exploration.

b. **1.** What is the least number of planes that can intersect in exactly one point? Explain your response.

2. Imagine that the constraints of a problem indicate that four planes define the set of feasible solutions. Why is 4 the maximum number of corner points in this situation?

3. What is the maximum number of corner points if five planes define the feasible solutions? Explain your response.

c. **1.** What shape is formed in Part **f** of the exploration? How many corner points does this shape have?

2. Would you expect this shape to be the same for every set of feasible solutions involving six planes? Why or why not?

d. **1.** Where would you expect the maximum value of an objective function to occur in terms of the set of feasible solutions from Part **f**?

2. How could you verify the location of the maximum value?

e. Do you think it is possible to graphically represent a situation in which you consider more than three items for sale? Explain your response.

f. Matrices can be used to solve systems of equations involving more than two equations and two unknowns. Consider the following system of three equations and three unknowns:

$$\begin{cases} x + y + z = 6 \\ 2x - y + z = 15 \\ x + 3y - 2z = -7 \end{cases}$$

Describe how you could rewrite this system as a matrix equation including a coefficient matrix, a variable matrix, and a constant matrix.

e. Sample response: No, this would require four dimensions.

f. Using a process similar to that described for systems of two equations and two unknowns, the system can be represented as a matrix equation in the form $\mathbf{M} \bullet \mathbf{X} = \mathbf{C}$ as shown below:

$$\begin{bmatrix} 1 & 1 & 1 \\ 2 & -1 & 1 \\ 1 & 3 & -2 \end{bmatrix} \bullet \begin{bmatrix} x \\ y \\ z \end{bmatrix} = \begin{bmatrix} 6 \\ 15 \\ -7 \end{bmatrix}$$

mathematics note

The determinant of a square matrix larger than 2 × 2 is found by adding a series of partial determinants. Each of these is based on the determinant of a smaller square matrix within the large matrix. The determinants of the smaller matrices are called **minor determinants** or **minors**. Each minor corresponds with an element in the large matrix.

Each minor is multiplied by a **cofactor**. The cofactor is the product of the corresponding element and –1 raised to a power. The exponent for –1 is the sum of the element's row and column position numbers in the large matrix. The sum of the products of minors and cofactors for all the elements equals the determinant of the large matrix.

In the 3 × 3 matrix **M** below, the minor for the element d is the determinant of the 2 × 2 matrix that remains after eliminating the row and column that contain d.

$$\mathbf{M} = \begin{bmatrix} a & b & c \\ d & e & f \\ g & h & i \end{bmatrix}$$

In other words, the minor for the element d is the determinant of the matrix below:

$$\begin{bmatrix} b & c \\ h & i \end{bmatrix}$$

Because element d is in row 2 and column 1 of matrix **B**, its cofactor is the product of d and –1 raised to the power (2 + 1). Therefore, the partial determinant of **B** corresponding with element d is:

$$d(-1)^{(2+1)}\begin{bmatrix} b & c \\ h & i \end{bmatrix} = d(-1)^{3}\begin{bmatrix} b & c \\ h & i \end{bmatrix} = -d\begin{bmatrix} b & c \\ h & i \end{bmatrix}$$

To find the determinant of a 3 × 3 matrix **M**, this process is applied to each of the three elements in a single row or single column of **M**. The determinant of **M** is the sum of the three partial determinants.

g. Consider the matrix below.

$$\mathbf{B} = \begin{bmatrix} 2 & 1 & -3 \\ -1 & 0 & 4 \\ -2 & 3 & -4 \end{bmatrix}$$

g. 1. The minor is the determinant of the 2 × 2 matrix remaining after the row and column containing 0 are removed. The minor is –14.

2. The cofactor is the product of –3 and a power of –1. The exponent equals the sum of the row and column numbers in which –3 is located. In this case, the exponent is 3 + 1 = 4. Therefore, the cofactor is $-3(-1^4) = -3$.

3. Sample response: Enter the matrix **B** into a matrix manipulator. Then enter det**B**.

   Note: The syntax for this varies with the technology used. For Texas Instruments' TI-84 calculator, it is entered as det([B]). For the TI-89 and Voyage 200, the determinant of a matrix **b** is found using det(b).

4. Sample response: The system will have no solutions. When the determinant is 0, the matrix does not have an inverse.

h. Sample response: Yes. The determinant of the coefficient matrix for the system is a non-zero number. Also, there is an inverse matrix for the coefficient matrix.

teacher note

Once students understand how to find the determinant of a matrix larger than 2×2, you may allow them to use technology for this task.

Warm-Up

1. The multiplicative inverse of each matrix is shown below.

a. $\begin{bmatrix} 2 & -1 \\ -7 & 4 \end{bmatrix}$

b. $\begin{bmatrix} 5/11 & 2/11 \\ 2/11 & 3/11 \end{bmatrix}$

c. This matrix has no inverse.

d. $\begin{bmatrix} 1 & 0 & 2 \\ 2 & -1 & 3 \\ 4 & 1 & 8 \end{bmatrix}$

2. Answers will vary. The determinant of both sample responses below is 0. This indicates that the matrix has no inverse.

a. $\begin{bmatrix} 2 & 8 \\ 1 & 4 \end{bmatrix}$

b. $\begin{bmatrix} 1 & -2 \\ -2 & 4 \end{bmatrix}$

3. Students can verify their solutions by substituting the values obtained into the original equations.

a. $\begin{bmatrix} x \\ y \end{bmatrix} = \begin{bmatrix} 3 \\ 5 \end{bmatrix}$

b. $\begin{bmatrix} x \\ y \end{bmatrix} = \begin{bmatrix} -1 \\ 7 \end{bmatrix}$

c. $\begin{bmatrix} x \\ y \end{bmatrix} = \begin{bmatrix} 4 \\ 2 \end{bmatrix}$

d. $\begin{bmatrix} x \\ y \\ z \end{bmatrix} = \begin{bmatrix} -1 \\ 3 \\ 7 \end{bmatrix}$

In this case, the partial determinant for the element 4 can be found as follows:

$$4(-1)^5\left(\det \begin{bmatrix} 2 & 1 \\ -2 & 3 \end{bmatrix}\right) = 4(-1)^5(8) = -32$$

1. Describe how you would find the minor for the element 0 in **B**.
2. Describe how you would find the cofactor for the element −3 in **B**.
3. Describe how you could use technology to find det **B**.
4. If **B** is the coefficient matrix for a system of equations and det **B** = 0, what does that tell you about the solution to the system? Explain your response.

h. Does the system of three equations in Part **f** of Discussion **2** have a solution? Justify your response.

Warm-Up

1. Find the multiplicative inverse of each of the following matrices.

a. $\begin{bmatrix} 4 & 1 \\ 7 & 2 \end{bmatrix}$ b. $\begin{bmatrix} 3 & -2 \\ -2 & 5 \end{bmatrix}$ c. $\begin{bmatrix} 3 & 7 & -1 \\ 3 & 2 & -5 \end{bmatrix}$ d. $\begin{bmatrix} -11 & 2 & 2 \\ -4 & 0 & 1 \\ 6 & -1 & -1 \end{bmatrix}$

2. Change the matrices in Problems **1a** and **b** so that they do not have inverses. Defend your responses.

3. Solve each of the following matrix equations and verify your solutions.

a. $\begin{bmatrix} 2 & 1 \\ -3 & 2 \end{bmatrix} \cdot \begin{bmatrix} x \\ y \end{bmatrix} = \begin{bmatrix} 11 \\ 1 \end{bmatrix}$ b. $\begin{bmatrix} 5 & 2 \\ 4 & -2 \end{bmatrix} \cdot \begin{bmatrix} x \\ y \end{bmatrix} = \begin{bmatrix} 9 \\ -18 \end{bmatrix}$

c. $\begin{bmatrix} 1 & 1 \\ 5 & -8 \end{bmatrix} \cdot \begin{bmatrix} x \\ y \end{bmatrix} = \begin{bmatrix} 6 \\ 4 \end{bmatrix}$ d. $\begin{bmatrix} 2 & -5 & 1 \\ 1 & 2 & 3 \\ -3 & -4 & 2 \end{bmatrix} \cdot \begin{bmatrix} x \\ y \\ z \end{bmatrix} = \begin{bmatrix} -10 \\ 26 \\ 5 \end{bmatrix}$

4. Use matrices to solve each of the following systems of equations.

a. $\begin{cases} 0.1x + 0.2y = 0.7 \\ 0.01x - 0.01y = 0.04 \end{cases}$ b. $\begin{cases} 4x = 7y - 6 \\ 12x = -9y + 12 \end{cases}$

c. $\begin{cases} 80x + 33y = 466 \\ -20x + 73y = 46 \end{cases}$ d. $\begin{cases} x + y + z = 4 \\ 3x - 2y + z = 6 \\ 2x + 5y + 3z = 11 \end{cases}$

e. $\begin{cases} 2x + y + z = 2 \\ 4x - 2y + z = 6 \\ -2x - y - 3z = -6 \end{cases}$

4. a. $\begin{bmatrix} x \\ y \end{bmatrix} = \begin{bmatrix} 5 \\ 1 \end{bmatrix}$

b. $\begin{bmatrix} x \\ y \end{bmatrix} = \begin{bmatrix} 0.25 \\ 1 \end{bmatrix}$

c. $\begin{bmatrix} x \\ y \end{bmatrix} = \begin{bmatrix} 5 \\ 2 \end{bmatrix}$

d. $\begin{bmatrix} x \\ y \\ z \end{bmatrix} = \begin{bmatrix} 1 \\ 0 \\ 3 \end{bmatrix}$

e. $\begin{bmatrix} x \\ y \\ z \end{bmatrix} = \begin{bmatrix} 0.5 \\ -1 \\ 2 \end{bmatrix}$

page 123

5. Plot the following points on a three-dimensional coordinate system.

   a. (3,5,1)

   b. (−2,3,4)

   c. (5,−3,−2)

6. Write the inequalities that describe the shaded regions below.

   a.

   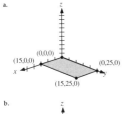

   b.

   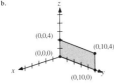

Assignment

4.1 a. Graph the feasible region described by the following constraints.

$$\begin{cases} 3x + 8y \le 48 \\ 3x + 2y \le 24 \\ -x + y \le 0 \\ x \ge 0 \\ y \ge 0 \end{cases}$$

   b. Determine the coordinates of the corner points of the feasible region.

   c. Given these constraints, find the maximum value of the objective function $P = 2y + 3x$.

Module 4 ■ *Making Concessions*   123

Assignment

Problems suitable for use as assessment items are identified by an asterisk (*).

4.1 a. Sample graph:

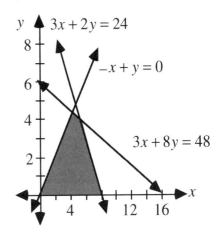

b. $(0,0)$, $(8,0)$, $(5\frac{1}{3},4)$, $(4\frac{4}{11},4\frac{4}{11})$

c. As shown in the table below, the maximum of 24 occurs at two corner points. Therefore, the maximum occurs at any point on the segment connecting these two points.

(x,y)	$P = 2y + 3x$
$(0,0)$	0
$(8,0)$	24
$(5\frac{1}{3},4)$	24
$(4\frac{4}{11},4\frac{4}{11})$	$21\frac{9}{11}$

5. a–c. Sample graph:

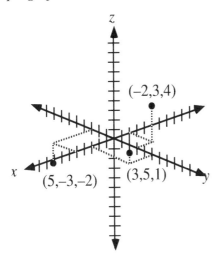

6. a. $\begin{cases} 0 \le x \le 15 \\ 0 \le y \le 25 \\ z = 0 \end{cases}$

   b. $\begin{cases} x = 0 \\ 0 \le y \le 10 \\ 0 \le z \le 4 \end{cases}$

4.2 **a.** This graph shows the constraints on pizza and pop. The shaded region is defined by $0 \le x \le 10$, $0 \le y \le 12$, and $z = 0$.

   b. This graph shows the constraints on pop and nachos. The shaded region is defined by $0 \le y \le 12$, $0 \le z \le 14$, and $x = 0$.

   c. This graph shows the constraints on pizza and nachos. The shaded region is defined by $0 \le x \le 10$, $0 \le z \le 14$, and $y = 0$.

4.3 Sample response: The class should purchase from 0 to 10 pizzas, from 0 to 12 six-packs of pop, and from 0 to 14 nacho kits.

4.4 **a.** $y = 12, y = 0, z = 14, z = 0$

   b. $x = 10, x = 0, z = 14, z = 0$

   c. Sample response: The points of intersection consist of all the possible combinations of ordered triples formed by the x-values, y-values, and z-values of the equations.

4.5 **a.** Sample sketch:

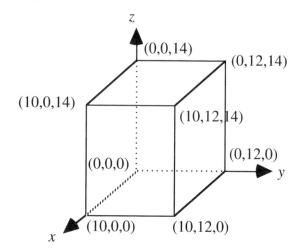

   b. As shown in the table below, the maximum value of $P = x + y + z$ occurs at the point (10,12,14).

(x,y,z)	P = x + y + z
(0,0,0)	0
(10,0,0)	10
(0,12,0)	12
(0,0,14)	14
(10,12,0)	22
(10,0,14)	24
(0,12,14)	26
(10,12,14)	36

4.2 In the three graphs below, x represents the number of pizzas, y the number of six-packs, and z the number of nacho kits. For each graph, identify the items whose constraints are represented, and write inequalities to describe the shaded region.

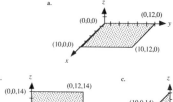

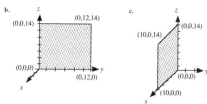

4.3 Describe what the inequalities in Problem **4.2** mean in terms of the number of pizzas, six-packs, and nacho kits that the class should purchase.

4.4 In Problem **4.2a**, the boundaries of the feasible region are line segments. The equations of the lines that form these boundaries are $x = 10$, $x = 0$, $y = 12$, and $y = 0$. You can use these equations to determine the intersection of this plane with other planes.

   a. Write the equations that represent the boundary lines for the region in Problem **4.2b**.

   b. Write the equations that represent the boundary lines for the region in Problem **4.2c**.

   c. Describe how you could find the points of intersection of the boundary lines, given only their equations.

4.5 **a.** Sketch the shape that defines the feasible solutions when the constraints on all three items in Problem **4.2** are considered at once. List the coordinates of the corner points of this shape.

   b. Use the corner points to find the maximum value for the objective function $P = x + y + z$. Describe the method you used to find the maximum value.

124   Module 4 ■ *Making Concessions*

4.6 Your class has $100.00 to buy pizza and canned soda pop for a concession booth. Each pizza costs $5.00 and each six-pack costs $2.00. The constraints on your purchases are listed below:

- no more than $100.00 can be spent on pizza and pop
- at least $10.00 must be spent on pop
- no more than $80.00 can be spent on pizza
- the amount spent on pizza cannot exceed 4 times that spent on pop.

  a. Express these constraints as inequalities.

  b. Graph the feasible region described by these constraints.

  c. The class expects a profit of $11.00 on each pizza and $2.00 on each six-pack. Determine the maximum potential profit in this situation.

4.7 Suppose that the class decides to sell pizza, pop, and nachos. Each pizza costs the class $5.00 and each six-pack costs $2.00. Nacho kits contain four bags of tortilla chips and one container of cheese. Each bag of tortilla chips costs $2.00; each container of cheese also costs $2.00.

There are eight slices in each pizza and the class plans to sell them for $2.00 a slice. A can of pop sells for $1.00. Each nacho kit contains enough chips and cheese to make 16 orders of nachos. One order of nachos sells for $1.50.

  a. Determine the profit on each pizza, six-pack, and nacho kit sold.

  b. Let x represent the number of pizzas, y the number of six-packs, and z the number of nacho kits purchased by the class. Write an objective function to calculate the maximum profit the class can expect to earn.

4.8 a. The class in Problem 4.7 plans to spend no more than $50.00 on any one of the three items to be sold: pizza, pop, and nachos. Write inequalities to describe these constraints.

  b. How many planes enclose the feasible solutions for these constraints?

  c. How many points of intersection must be examined to determine the maximum profit? Explain your response.

4.9 Using the information determined in Problems 4.7 and 4.8, find the maximum profit the class can expect to earn.

* * * * *

* 4.6 a. In the following inequalities, x represents number of pizzas and y represents number of six-packs:

$$5x + 2y \leq 100$$
$$2y \geq 10$$
$$5x \leq 80$$
$$5x \leq 8y$$
$$x \geq 0$$

  b. Sample graph:

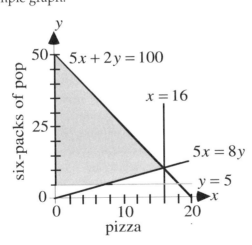

c. As shown below, the profit function $P = 11x + 2y$ has its maximum value at the corner point (16,10).

(x,y)	$P = 11x + 2y$
(0,5)	10
(8,5)	98
(16,10)	196
(0,50)	100

The maximum potential profit of $196 occurs if the class buys (and sells) 16 pizzas and 10 six-packs.

4.7 a. The profit is $11.00 on each pizza, $4.00 on each six-pack of pop, and $14.00 on each nacho kit.

  b. $P = 11x + 4y + 14z$

* 4.8 a. The constraints are $0 \leq x \leq 10$, $0 \leq y \leq 25$, and $0 \leq z \leq 5$.

  b. Six planes enclose the feasible solutions.

  c. Sample response: Eight points must be examined to find the maximum profit. There are eight corner points because the figure formed by the planes is a rectangular prism. **Note:** Students who do not visualize the prism may respond that 20 points must be examined (the maximum number of ways in which six planes can be chosen three at a time).

4.9 The maximum value of $P = 11x + 4y + 14z$ occurs at the corner point (10,25,5). The profit at this point is $11(10) + 4(25) + 14(5) = $280.

✻ ✻ ✻ ✻ ✻

4.10 a. The following inequalities represent the constraints.

$$x + y \geq 20 \bullet 10^6$$
$$x \leq 12 \bullet 10^6$$
$$y \geq 14 \bullet 10^6$$
$$y \leq 20 \bullet 10^6$$
$$x \geq 0$$

b. In the following sample graph, units on the axes represent millions of liters. The feasible region is shaded.

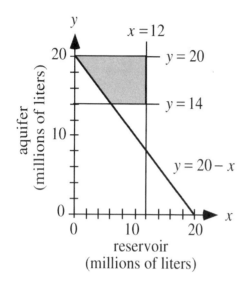

c. As shown below, the minimum value of the objective function $C = 80x + 100y$ occurs at the corner point (6,14). The maximum occurs at the point (12,20).

(x,y)	C = 80x + 100y
(0,20)	2000
(6,14)	1880
(12,14)	2360
(12,20)	2960

1. $1880
2. $2960

4.11 The objective function $P = 5.50b + 6.00m$ is maximized at (20,30) for a profit of $290.

4.12 The team scored 8 three-point shots, 23 two-point shots, and 11 free throws.

4.10 The manager of a municipal water system must decide how to provide the town with at least 20 • 10⁶ L per day. Some of this water can be drawn from a nearby reservoir. The rest must be purchased from a company that pumps water from a large underground aquifer.

To maintain the level of the reservoir, no more than 12 • 10⁶ L per day can be drawn from this source. The town's contract with the water company states that the city must purchase at least 14 • 10⁶ L per day, but no more than 20 • 10⁶ L per day.

a. Express these constraints as inequalities.

b. Graph the feasible region described by these constraints.

c. Water from the reservoir costs the town $80.00 for 1 • 10⁶ L. Water from the water company costs $100.00 for 1 • 10⁶ L.

1. Determine the town's smallest possible daily water bill.

2. Determine the town's largest possible daily water bill.

4.11 After interviewing for a summer job, Jayse decided to work as a box boy at a local grocery store and to mow lawns for his neighbors. The grocery manager said he may work a minimum of 20 hr per week but no more than 30 hr per week.

Jayse decides that he should work no more that 50 hr per week at his two jobs, with no more than 35 hr of lawn mowing.

If the grocery store pays $5.50 per hr and mowing lawns pays $6.00 per hr, what schedule will give Jayse the maximum weekly earnings?

4.12 During a recent basketball game, the Crestview Tigers scored 81 points. The number of two-point shots was 1 more than twice the number of free throws (worth one point each). The number of three-point shots was 3 less than the number of free throws. How many three-point shots, two-point shots and free throws did the Tigers make in the game?

126   Module 4 ▪ *Making Concessions*

Summary Assessment

1. The shipping costs in many mail-order catalogs can be modeled by step functions. One retailer lists the following table of shipping charges:

Purchase ($)	Shipping ($)
0.00–49.99	5.00
50.00–99.99	10.00
100.00–149.99	15.00
150.00–199.99	20.00
200.00–249.99	25.00
250.00–299.99	30.00
300.00–349.99	35.00
350.00–399.99	40.00
400.00–449.99	45.00
450.00+	50.00

a. Create a graph of the data in the table.

b. Which rounding function would best model your graph? Explain your response.

2. As shift manager of a fast-food restaurant, you must make sure that enough meals are prepared to serve customers quickly—but not so many that food is wasted.

During a typical lunchtime rush, you sell no more than 100 single burgers and no more than 90 double burgers. A single burger requires 100 g of hamburger and a double burger requires 200 g. To help avoid spoilage, you plan to use no more than 20 kg of hamburger during the rush.

Before being served to a customer, each single burger requires 6 sec in a microwave oven and each double burger requires 8 sec. During the lunchtime rush, there is no more than 16 min of time available in the microwave.

The restaurant earns a profit of $0.70 on each single burger and $0.90 on each double burger. Assuming that customers purchase every burger prepared, determine how many of each type should be made so as to maximize profits.

teacher note

An additional assessment, for use at your discretion, appears in the Teacher Resources for this module.

Summary Assessment

1. a. Sample graph:

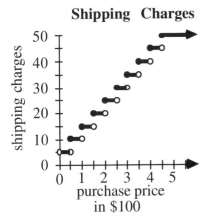

b. Sample response: The greatest integer function best describes the shipping charges until the purchase price reaches $500. The decimal portion is removed from the positive values in the same fashion.

2. Sample response: Let x represent the number of double hamburgers and y represent the number of single hamburgers. The following inequalities are the constraints that define the feasible region: $0.2x + 0.1y \le 20$, $x \ge 0$, $y \ge 0$, $x \le 90$, $y \le 100$, and $8x + 6y \le 960$.

The profit function is the equation $p = 0.90x + 0.70y$. The graph below shows the feasible region.

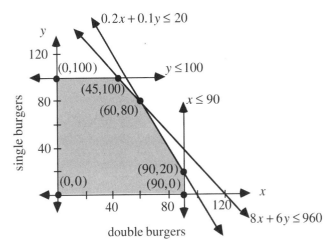

Because the maximum profit of $110.50 occurs at the corner point (45,100), the restaurant should prepare 45 double burgers and 100 singles for the lunchtime rush.

3. Sample response: Using h for the number of hot dogs, c for the number of bags of chips, and p for the number of cans of pop, the three constraints can be expressed as:

$$\begin{cases} 0.15h + 0.2c + 0.35p \leq 108 \\ h \geq 2c \\ p \geq 3(c + h) \end{cases}$$

The corresponding matrix equation for the boundaries of these constraints is:

$$\begin{bmatrix} 0.15 & 0.2 & 0.35 \\ -1 & 2 & 0 \\ 3 & 3 & -1 \end{bmatrix} \bullet \begin{bmatrix} h \\ c \\ p \end{bmatrix} = \begin{bmatrix} 108 \\ 0 \\ 0 \end{bmatrix}$$

An approximate solution to this system is (59,30,266). This solution may not maximize the objective function because it does not occur exactly at a corner point.

The profit equation is $P = 0.85h + 0.8c + 0.65p$. At the approximate solution above, the profit is $247.05.

3. As class president, you are analyzing the best way for your class to earn money with its concession stand. The class officers have decided to sell hot dogs, potato chips, and soda pop. The table below shows the cost and selling price for each of these items.

Item	hot dog	bag of chips	can of pop
Cost	$0.15	$0.20	$0.35
Selling Price	$1.00	$1.00	$1.00

The class has $108.00 in its fundraising account. The total cost for hot dogs, chips, and pop cannot exceed this amount. Judging from last year's sales, the class will sell at least twice as many hot dogs as bags of chips, and at least 3 times as many cans of pop as the combined numbers of chips and hot dogs. Determine the profit at the corner point defined by these three constraints.

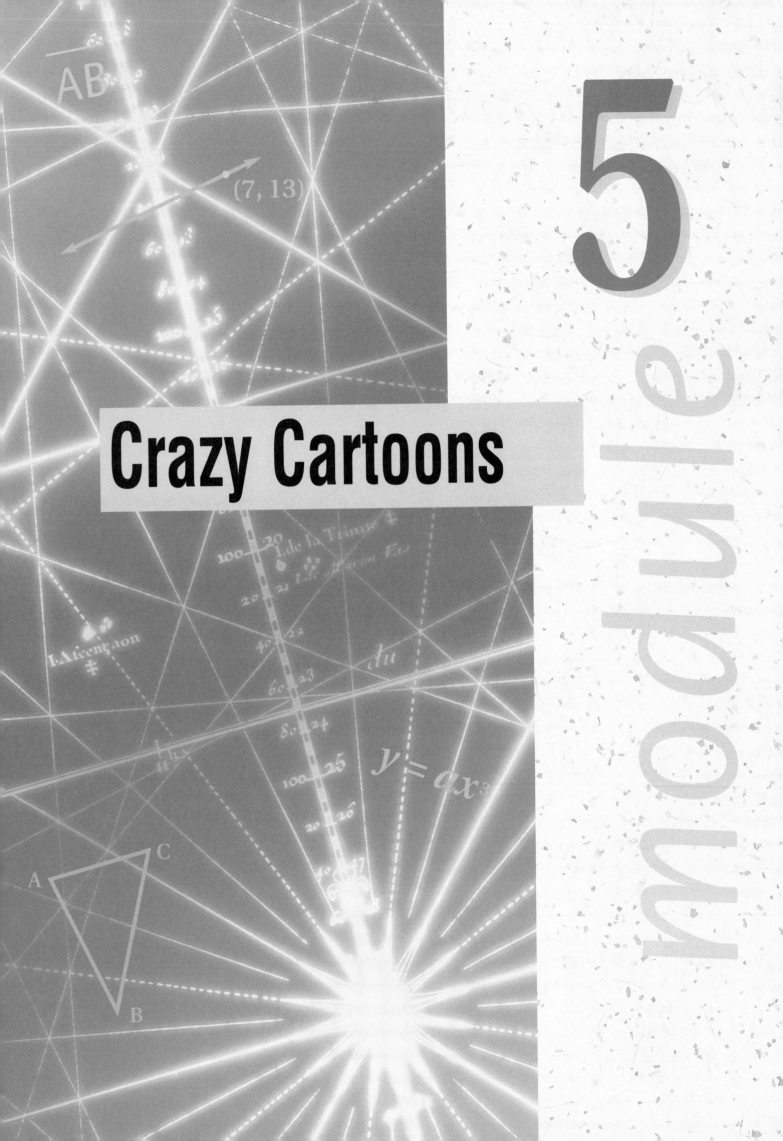

Crazy Cartoons

5 module

Overview

Students explore transformations in a plane, including dilations, translations, reflections, and compositions of transformations. They use matrices to represent two-dimensional figures, and use matrix operations to perform transformations.

Activity 1:   Students investigate translations using vectors. They also explore dilations and scale factors.

Activity 2:   Students translate figures using matrices.

Activity 3:   Students use scalar and matrix multiplication to create dilations.

Activity 4:   Students use matrix multiplication to perform reflections in various lines.

Objectives

In this module, students will:

* use the properties of similar figures (1)
* define a transformation as a one-to-one correspondence between the plane and itself (1)
* identify the preimage and image for a given transformation (1)
* calculate distances between points in the Cartesian plane (1)
* examine the relationship between the distance formula and the Pythagorean theorem (1)
* explore geometric relationships in perspective drawings, dilations centered at the origin, and translations (1)
* describe a dilation in terms of its center and scale factor (1)
* translate objects given a translation vector (1)
* determine the vertical and horizontal components of a vector (1)
* calculate the magnitude and angular direction of a vector (1)
* use and interpret mathematical notation for geometric transformations (1, 2, 3, 4)
* use matrix addition and matrix multiplication to describe translations (2)
* determine the 3×3 identity matrix for matrix multiplication (2)
* solve systems of equations using matrices (2, 3)
* use matrix multiplication to describe dilations with center at the origin (3)
* perform compositions of transformations using matrix multiplication (3, 4)
* explore the geometric relationships found in reflections in a line (4)
* use matrix multiplication to perform reflections (4)
* determine single transformation matrices to perform compositions of transformations (4).

Prerequisites

For this module, students should know:

* how to graph points in the Cartesian plane
* how to determine the domain and range of a function
* the relationships between similar figures

114

* how to use $\tan^{-1}$ to determine angle measures in right triangles
* the Pythagorean theorem
* how to solve systems of linear equations
* how to perform operations on matrices, including scalar multiplication, matrix addition, and matrix multiplication
* how to perform a reflection in a line.

 Flashbacks, for use at your discretion, appear in the Teacher Resources for this module. These brief problem sets provide a review of some prerequisite skills for each activity.

Planning Guide

Activity	Materials	Technology	Time Line
Introduction and Activity **1**	■ rulers ■ graph paper ■ protractors ■ acetate or tracing paper ■ overhead markers	■ geometry utility ■ graphing utility	4 days
Activity **2**	■ rulers ■ graph paper	■ geometry utility ■ graphing utility ■ spreadsheet ■ matrix manipulator	3 days
Activity **3**	■ rulers ■ graph paper ■ template for Problem **3.8**	■ graphing utility ■ spreadsheet ■ matrix manipulator	2 days
Activity **4**	■ rulers ■ graph paper ■ acetate or tracing paper ■ overhead markers	■ graphing utility ■ spreadsheet ■ matrix manipulator	2 days
Assessment Activities	■ rulers ■ graph paper ■ protractors	■ geometry utility ■ graphing utility ■ spreadsheet ■ matrix manipulator	3 days **Total: 14 days**

 teacher note

Students may use graph paper, tracing paper, MIRAs™, transparent grids, graphing calculators, spreadsheets, or other appropriate graphing utilities to perform transformations. In addition, you might wish to allow the use of technology to solve matrix equations or simultaneous equations.

In Activities **2–4**, students use matrices to represent the coordinates of preimages and images. The program that appears at the beginning of Activity **2** allows students to plot these preimages and images using Texas Instruments' TI-84, TI-89, or Voyage 200 calculators.

If you wish to transfer images between calculators and computers, you should download the appropriate version of the TI Connect software. Although this software is free, you must purchase a connecting cable. Information about both TI Connect and the required cable is available on the Texas Instruments website.

A blackline master of the template for Problem **3.8** appears in the Teacher Resources for this module.

Introduction

Students describe transformations in general terms, without the use of coordinates.

Student Outcomes

After completing the following discussion, students should be able to:

✳ identify reflections in a line

✳ identify other transformations using their own words

✳ suggest the use of a two-dimensional coordinate system for describing locations in a plane.

Discussion

a. Sample response: The bug in frame B is a reflection of the bug in frame A with respect to a vertical line. The bug in frame C is a shift of the bug in frame A. The bug in frame D is a 90° counterclockwise rotation of the bug in frame A. The bug in frame E is a scaled-down version of the bug in frame A. The bug in frame F is a scaled-up version of the bug in frame A.

b. Sample response: Using a two-dimensional coordinate system with its origin in the lower left-hand corner of the frame, you could identify the coordinates of the bug's eyes and antennae, the center of each circle in the bug's body, and the endpoints of each segment representing the bug's legs.

ACTIVITY 1

In this activity, students explore translations and dilations by graphing shapes in the coordinate plane. They create and measure transformed shapes and examine the relationships that exist between the preimage and image under both transformations.

Materials List

■ graph paper (several sheets per student)

■ acetate (one per group) or tracing paper (four per group)

■ overhead marker for acetate (one per group)

■ rulers (one per student)

■ protractors (one per student)

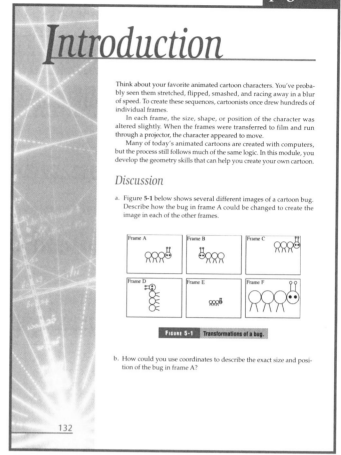

Introduction

Think about your favorite animated cartoon characters. You've probably seen them stretched, flipped, smashed, and racing away in a blur of speed. To create these sequences, cartoonists once drew hundreds of individual frames.

In each frame, the size, shape, or position of the character was altered slightly. When the frames were transferred to film and run through a projector, the character appeared to move.

Many of today's animated cartoons are created with computers, but the process still follows much of the same logic. In this module, you develop the geometry skills that can help you create your own cartoon.

Discussion

a. Figure **5-1** below shows several different images of a cartoon bug. Describe how the bug in frame A could be changed to create the image in each of the other frames.

FIGURE 5-1 Transformations of a bug.

b. How could you use coordinates to describe the exact size and position of the bug in frame A?

132

Technology

■ geometry utility

■ graphing utility (optional)

teacher note

Students receive a formal introduction to vectors, including vector addition, in the Level 3 module, "Fly the Big Sky with Vectors."

Each change of the bug in Figure 5-1 is an example of a **transformation**. In this activity, you investigate the mathematics of two different types of transformations: translations and dilations.

mathematics note

A **one-to-one correspondence** is a function between two sets: the domain and the range. It pairs each element in the domain with exactly one element in the range, and each element in the range with exactly one element in the domain.

For example, Figure 5-2 shows a one-to-one correspondence between the fingers of the left hand and the fingers of the right hand.

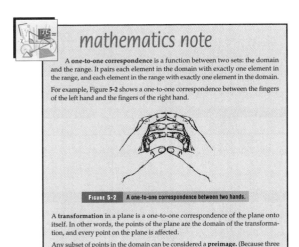

FIGURE 5-2   A one-to-one correspondence between two hands.

A **transformation** in a plane is a one-to-one correspondence of the plane onto itself. In other words, the points of the plane are the domain of the transformation, and every point on the plane is affected.

Any subset of points in the domain can be considered a **preimage**. (Because three non-collinear points determine a plane, a triangle is often used to track the change that occurs under a given transformation.) The corresponding subset of points that results from the transformation is an **image**.

For example, Figure 5-3 shows a reflection in the *y*-axis. In this transformation, preimage point *A*(2,5) is paired with its image point *A*′(−2,5). This type of pairing occurs for every point in the plane.

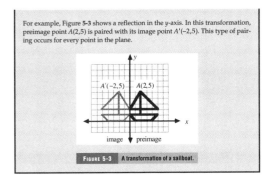

FIGURE 5-3   A transformation of a sailboat.

Exploration 1

Before drawing a cartoon of your own, some experience with transformations of simple figures might be helpful. In this exploration, you examine **translations**.

A translation results in a change of position. For example, Figure 5-4 shows a picture of a skier and its image under a translation.

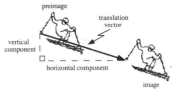

FIGURE 5-4   Translation of a skier.

The skier's change in position can be represented by a **translation vector**. The length of the translation vector represents the distance moved by the preimage; the arrow indicates the direction of travel. A translation vector has a **horizontal component** and a **vertical component**.

Student Outcomes

After completing the following explorations and discussions, students should be able to:

✳ represent translations using vectors

✳ resolve a vector into its horizontal and vertical components

✳ identify preimage and image points under a transformation

✳ calculate the distance between two points in the plane using the distance formula

✳ use tan⁻¹ to find measures of acute angles in right triangles

✳ create a point-perspective drawing and relate its properties to those of similar figures

✳ determine scale factors for dilations

✳ create an image under a dilation given its center and scale factor

✳ use mathematical notation to describe transformations, vectors, and images.

Exploration 1

Students use vectors to examine translations in the coordinate plane.

a–b. Sample graph:

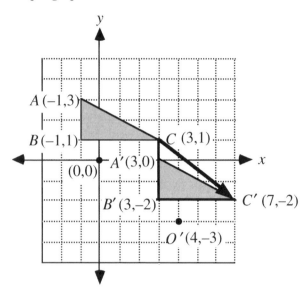

c–e. Students should observe that the order in which they slide the triangle along the components has no effect on the final position of the image.

f. Students repeat Parts **a–e** for other vectors.

Discussion 1

a. Sample response: They are the same. The order in which the preimage is moved along the components of the translation vector has no effect on the final position of the image.

b. Sample response: The preimage and image are congruent under a translation.

   Note: When all preimages and corresponding images are congruent under a transformation, the transformation is said to be an *isometry*.

c. 1. The vertical component is the difference between the y-coordinates of the preimage and the corresponding image, or $y_2 - y_1$. The horizontal component is the difference between the x-coordinates of the preimage and the corresponding image, or $x_2 - x_1$.

   2. The coordinates of the image of T are $(x_1 + h, y_1 + k)$.

   3. The x-coordinate of the image of the origin under a translation corresponds with the horizontal component of the translation vector. The y-coordinate corresponds with the vertical component.

a. Create a two-dimensional coordinate system on a sheet of graph paper. Draw △*ABC* and record the coordinates of its vertices.

mathematics note

A **translation** is a transformation that pairs every preimage point $P(x,y)$ with an image point $P'(x + h, y + k)$. A translation of this type moves every point h units horizontally and k units vertically. A translation from P to P' is denoted as $T_{P,P'}$.

Because translations have both magnitude and direction, they can be represented as vectors. A **translation vector** from $P(x,y)$ to $P'(x + h, y + k)$ can be denoted by the ordered pair $\langle h,k \rangle$. The first value in the ordered pair is the horizontal component. The second is the vertical component. To avoid confusion with coordinate points, angle brackets are used instead of parentheses.

Vectors also can be represented by a bold, lowercase letter or with an arrow. For example, Figure 5-5 shows the translation of a triangle. In this case, the preimage point $R(-5,2)$ corresponds with the image point $R'(3,8)$. The translation vector is vector **v**, or $\vec{v}$, and can be denoted as $\langle (3 - (-5)), (8 - 2) \rangle$ or $\langle 8,6 \rangle$.

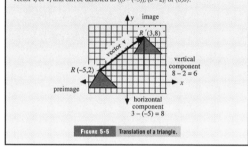

FIGURE 5-5 Translation of a triangle.

b. 1. Select one vertex of your △*ABC*. Draw the translation vector $\langle 4,-3 \rangle$ from this vertex.

   2. Draw the vertical and horizontal components of the translation vector.

c. Place a sheet of tracing paper or clear acetate on top of your graph paper. Trace a copy of △*ABC* and the coordinate axes.

d. 1. Slide the copy along the translation vector. Make sure that the axes of the preimage (original) and image (copy) remain parallel.

   2. Note the location of the image points for the origin and for the triangle's vertices. Label these points on your graph paper.

   3. Record the coordinates of the image points for the origin and the triangle's vertices.

e. Repeat Part **d** by sliding the triangle along one component of the translation vector, then the other. Compare your results with those in Part **d**.

f. 1. On another sheet of graph paper, repeat Parts **a–e** using a translation that has a positive vertical component and a positive horizontal component.

   2. On another sheet of graph paper, repeat Parts **a–e** using a translation that has a negative vertical component and a negative horizontal component.

   3. On another sheet of graph paper, repeat Parts **a–e** using a translation that has a negative vertical component and a positive horizontal component.

Discussion 1

a. How did your results in Part **d** of the exploration compare with your results in Part **e**?

b. Under a translation, how do the size and shape of the preimage compare with those of the image?

c. 1. If the preimage point $P(x_1, y_1)$ has an image point $P'(x_2, y_2)$, what are the horizontal and vertical components of the translation vector? Explain your response.

   2. If the image of the origin under a translation is at the point (h, k), where is the image of the point $T(x_1, y_1)$ located? Justify your response.

   3. How does the location of the origin's image under a translation relate to the horizontal and vertical components of the translation vector?

d. Figure 5-6 shows segments connecting two preimage points to their corresponding image points under a translation. What is true about these two segments? Justify your response.

FIGURE 5-6
Segments connecting preimage and image points.

e. Consider the translation vector ⟨–3,–5⟩. How far is each image point from its preimage under this translation?

f. Describe how you could use the coordinates of the two ends of a translation vector to find its horizontal and vertical components.

mathematics note

Figure 5-7 below shows two points, (x_1,y_1) and (x_2,y_2), on a coordinate plane.

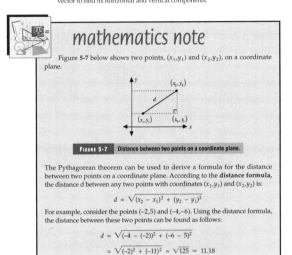

FIGURE 5-7 Distance between two points on a coordinate plane.

The Pythagorean theorem can be used to derive a formula for the distance between two points on a coordinate plane. According to the **distance formula**, the distance d between any two points with coordinates (x_1,y_1) and (x_2,y_2) is:

$$d = \sqrt{(x_2 - x_1)^2 + (y_2 - y_1)^2}$$

For example, consider the points (–2,5) and (–4,–6). Using the distance formula, the distance between these two points can be found as follows:

$$d = \sqrt{(-4 - (-2))^2 + (-6 - 5)^2}$$
$$= \sqrt{(-2)^2 + (-11)^2} = \sqrt{125} \approx 11.18$$

g. Describe how the distance formula can be derived from the Pythagorean theorem.

h. Describe how to find the distance between any point in a preimage to the corresponding point in the image.

i. In the Level 1 module "A New Look at an Old Pyramid," you used the inverse tangent to find the measures of acute angles in right triangles. How could you use $\tan^{-1}$ to find the measure of the angle formed by a translation vector and its horizontal component?

Module 5 ■ *Crazy Cartoons*   137

---

d. Sample response: The two segments are congruent and parallel. Each segment can be thought of as a vector. The triangles formed by the horizontal and vertical components of the vectors and the vectors themselves are congruent by SAS, making the segments congruent. Drawing a line through a pair of corresponding endpoints forms two lines cut by a transversal. Because the corresponding angles are congruent, the segments are parallel.

e. Student should realize that a vector, its horizontal component, and its vertical component form a right triangle. Using the Pythagorean theorem:

$$\sqrt{(-5)^2 + (-3)^2} = \sqrt{34} \approx 5.8 \text{ units}$$

f. Sample response: The vertical component equals the difference between the y-coordinates of the vector's endpoints. The horizontal component equals the difference between the x-coordinates.

g. Sample response: The segment connecting two points can be thought of as the hypotenuse of a right triangle. The length of the horizontal side is $|x_2 - x_1|$ and the length of the vertical side is $|y_2 - y_1|$. Using the Pythagorean theorem, the distance d between the two points is:

$$d^2 = (x_2 - x_1)^2 + (y_2 - y_1)^2$$
$$d = \sqrt{(x_2 - x_1)^2 + (y_2 - y_1)^2}$$

h. Sample response: The distance between a point in the preimage and the corresponding point in the image is the length of the translation vector. Given a vector in the form ⟨h,k⟩, you can use the Pythagorean theorem to find its length.

i. Sample response: The tangent of the angle between the horizontal component and the translation vector is the ratio of the vertical component to the horizontal component. To find the angle measure, you determine the inverse tangent of that ratio.

   Note: You might wish to remind students that, in this setting, the magnitude of a component vector is a distance (and, therefore, always a positive value). The sign indicates direction only.

Exploration 2

Students use point-perspective drawings to examine dilations in the coordinate plane.

a–b. Sample graph:

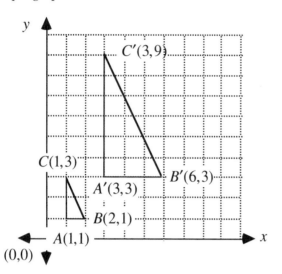

c. In the following sample table, lengths are measured in centimeters and angles are measured in degrees.

Preimage		Image	
AB	1	$A'B'$	3
BC	$\sqrt{5} \approx 2.2$	$B'C'$	$3\sqrt{5} \approx 6.6$
CA	2	$C'A'$	6
$m\angle ABC$	63°	$m\angle A'B'C'$	63°
$m\angle BCA$	27°	$m\angle B'C'A'$	27°
$m\angle CAB$	90°	$m\angle C'A'B'$	90°

Exploration 2

In this exploration, you use graph paper to construct a **point-perspective drawing.** Artists use point-perspective drawings to represent three-dimensional objects in two dimensions. For example, Figure **5-8** shows two rectangular prisms drawn using this method, with point P as the **point of perspective.**

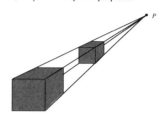

FIGURE 5-8 Point-perspective drawing of two rectangular prisms.

a. On a sheet of graph paper, plot the ordered pairs $A(1,1)$, $B(2,1)$, and $C(1,3)$. Draw triangle ABC.

b. On the same sheet of graph paper, plot the following ordered pairs: $A'(3,3)$, $B'(6,3)$, and $C'(3,9)$. Draw triangle $A'B'C'$.

c. Use your drawing, the Pythagorean theorem, and the inverse trigonometric functions to complete Table **5-1** below.

TABLE 5-1 ■ *Measures of Corresponding Parts of △ABC and △A'B'C'*

Preimage		Image	
AB		$A'B'$	
BC		$B'C'$	
CA		$C'A'$	
$m\angle ABC$		$m\angle A'B'C'$	
$m\angle BCA$		$m\angle B'C'A'$	
$m\angle CAB$		$m\angle C'A'B'$	

d. Determine each of the following ratios:

 1. $A'B'/AB$

 2. $B'C'/BC$

 3. $C'A'/CA$

e. Draw $\overline{AA'}$, $\overline{BB'}$, and $\overline{CC'}$. Extend these segments until they intersect at a common point, the point of perspective. Label this point P and identify its coordinates.

f. Use the distance formula to find the lengths of each of the following segments: $\overline{PA}$, $\overline{PB}$, $\overline{PC}$, $\overline{PA'}$, $\overline{PB'}$, and $\overline{PC'}$.

g. Determine each of the following ratios:

 1. PA'/PA

 2. PB'/PB

 3. PC'/PC

h. Compare the ratios you determined in Part **g** with those found in Part **d.**

Discussion 2

a. What did you observe about the ratios of corresponding lengths in Parts **d** and **g** of Exploration **2**?

mathematics note

A **dilation** is a transformation that pairs a point P, the **center**, with itself and any other point X with a point X' on ray PX so that $PX'/PX = r$, where r is the **scale factor.** A dilation with center C and scale factor r is denoted as $\mathbf{D}_{C,r}$. When the center is the origin, the dilation is written as $\mathbf{D}_{O,r}$.

A dilation with its center at the origin is a transformation such that every point Q with coordinates (x,y) has an image Q' with coordinates (rx, ry), where r is the scale factor, and $r \neq 0$. The scale factor also may be written as a ratio of the corresponding dimensions of the image to the preimage.

---

d. The ratio of corresponding lengths is 3/1.

e. Sample graph:

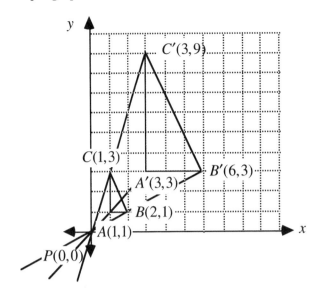

f. $PA = \sqrt{2} \approx 1.4$, $PB = \sqrt{5} \approx 2.2$, $PC = \sqrt{10} \approx 3.2$, $PA' = 3\sqrt{2} \approx 4.2$, $PB' = 3\sqrt{5} \approx 6.6$, $PC' = 3\sqrt{10} \approx 9.5$

g–h. As in Part **d,** the ratios of corresponding lengths are 3/1.

teacher note

This module does not address dilations with scale factors less than 0. You might wish to encourage students to explore such transformations. (The scale factor is negative for dilations in which the center is located between the preimage and the image.)

Discussion 2

a. The ratios of corresponding lengths are equal.

b. Sample response: They seem to be the same. In a point-perspective drawing, the point of perspective is the center of dilation.

c. The corresponding angles are congruent.

d. 1. $\triangle ABC \sim \triangle A'B'C'$

2. $\triangle PAC \sim \triangle P'A'C'$, $\triangle PAB \sim \triangle P'A'B'$, and $\triangle PBC \sim \triangle P'B'C'$

e. 1. The scale factor equals the ratio of corresponding lengths.

2. The scale factor equals the ratio of perimeters.

3. The ratio of the areas is the square of the scale factor.

f. Sample response: Yes, because the two triangles still would be similar.

g. A scale factor x, where $-1 < x < 1$, reduces the size of the original shape.

h. The ratio is the scale factor.

i. 1. The corresponding angles remain congruent.

2. The preimage and image are congruent.

j. Sample response: Under a dilation with a positive scale factor other than 1, the preimage and image would be similar, but in a translation they would be congruent.

k. Sample response: A dilation by a scale factor of 1 would result in an image that is congruent to the preimage. This would be the same as a translation by the vector $\langle 0,0 \rangle$.

Warm-Up

1. a. translation

b. reflection

c. dilation

2. a. $x = \sqrt{7^2 + 3^2} = \sqrt{58} \approx 7.62$; $\tan^{-1}\left(\dfrac{3}{7}\right) \approx 23.2°$

b. $x = \sqrt{12^2 - 10^2} = \sqrt{44} \approx 6.63$; $\tan^{-1}\left(\dfrac{6.63}{10}\right) \approx 33.5°$

c. $x = \sqrt{s^2 - r^2}$; $\tan^{-1}\left(\dfrac{r}{\sqrt{s^2 - r^2}}\right)$

3. a. $\sqrt{(3-9)^2 + (6-18)^2} = \sqrt{100} = 10$

b. $\sqrt{[0-(-2)]^2 + (5-0)^2} = \sqrt{29} \approx 5.39$

c. $\sqrt{(r-t)^2 + (s-v)^2}$

4. a. $J'(10, 7)$; $U'(10, -1)$; $M'(4, -1)$; $P'(4, 7)$

b. $J'(1, 9)$; $U'(1, 1)$; $M'(-5, 1)$; $P'(-5, 9)$

c. $J'(-8, -10)$; $U'(-8, 6)$; $M'(4, 6)$; $P'(4, -10)$

d. $J'(6, 7.5)$; $U'(6, -4.5)$; $M'(-3, -4.5)$; $P'(-3, 7.5)$

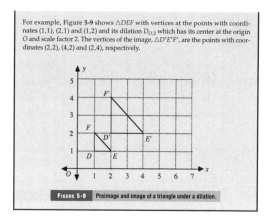

For example, Figure 5-9 shows $\triangle DEF$ with vertices at the points with coordinates (1,1), (2,1) and (1,2) and its dilation $D_{O,2}$ which has its center at the origin O and scale factor 2. The vertices of the image, $\triangle D'E'F'$, are the points with coordinates (2,2), (4,2) and (2,4), respectively.

FIGURE 5-9   Preimage and image of a triangle under a dilation.

b. The transformation of $\triangle ABC$ to $\triangle A'B'C'$ is a dilation. Describe the similarities between a dilation and a point-perspective drawing.

c. In Part **c** of Exploration **2**, what did you observe about the measures of corresponding angles of $\triangle ABC$ and $\triangle A'B'C'$?

d. 1. Describe the geometric relationship between $\triangle ABC$ and $\triangle A'B'C'$.

2. Identify any other triangles on your graph that share this same relationship.

e. 1. How does the scale factor for the dilation compare to the ratios of corresponding lengths for $\triangle ABC$ and $\triangle A'B'C'$?

2. How does the scale factor compare to the ratio of the perimeters of the two triangles?

3. How does the scale factor compare to the ratio of the areas of the two triangles?

f. If you moved the center of the dilation, do you think that the relationships identified in Parts **d** and **e** of this discussion still would be true?

g. How could you change the scale factor to produce an image that is smaller than the preimage?

h. In general, what is the ratio of the distance from the center of dilation to a point on the preimage to the distance from the center of dilation to the corresponding point on the image?

i. 1. In a dilation, what geometric properties appear to remain the same in both the image and the preimage?

2. In a translation, what geometric properties appear to remain the same in both the image and the preimage?

j. How could you tell the difference between a translation and a dilation by a positive scale factor other than 1?

k. What is the result of a dilation by a scale factor of 1?

Warm-Up

1. The skier on the left is the preimage in each of the transformations shown below. Identify each transformation as a dilation, translation, or reflection.

a.

b.

c.

2. Each right triangle below has a horizontal leg and a vertical leg. Find the unknown length in each triangle, then determine the angle formed by the hypotenuse and the horizontal leg.

a.

b.

c.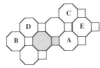

3. Determine the distance between each of the following pairs of points.

a. (9,14) and (3,6)

b. (–2,0) and (0,5)

c. (r,s) and (t,v)

4. The vertices of square JUMP are the points J(4,5), U(4,–3), M(–2,–3), and P(–2,5). For each transformation listed below, determine the coordinates of J'U'M'P'.

a. ⟨6,2⟩

b. ⟨–3,4⟩

c. $D_{O,2}$

d. $D_{O,3/2}$

Assignment

1.1 The pattern shown on the right was created by repeated translations of the shaded figure. The preimage consists of an octagon and a square. The octagon is 20 units across, both horizontally and vertically, and the square measures 10 units on each side.

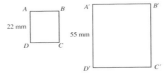

To complete Parts a–e below, assume that the center of the shaded octagon is the origin of a two-dimensional coordinate system with a horizontal x-axis and a vertical y-axis.

a. Determine the translation vector that results in image **A**. Find the angle in degrees formed with the positive portion of the x-axis.

---

b. Determine the translation vector that results in image **B**. Find the angle in degrees formed with the positive portion of the x-axis.

c. Determine the translation vector that results in image **C**. Find the angle in degrees formed with the positive portion of the x-axis.

d. Determine the translation vector that results in image **D**. Find the angle in degrees formed with the positive portion of the x-axis.

e. Determine the translation vector that results in image **E**. Find the angle in degrees formed with the positive portion of the x-axis.

1.2 The two figures in the diagram below are similar.

a. Describe how to find the center of the dilation that transforms ABCD to A'B'C'D'.

b. Identify the scale factor of the dilation.

c. Use mathematical notation to describe a dilation with the scale factor in Part b and center at the origin.

1.3 Is it possible to find a point of perspective in the drawing below, where either figure can be the preimage and the other its image? Explain your response.

1.4 a. Draw the triangle formed by the points A(5,10), B(–5,5), and C(10,–15).

b. Graph the image of △ABC under the translation that transforms P(–5,7) to P'(2,3). Label the vertices of the image and identify their coordinates.

c. Where is the image of the origin located under this translation? Justify your response.

Assignment

Problems suitable for use as assessment items are identified by an asterisk (*).

1.1 a. The translation vector is ⟨30,0⟩. The angle formed with the x-axis is 0°.

b. The translation vector is ⟨–30,0⟩. The angle formed with the x-axis is 180°.

c. The translation vector is ⟨30,30⟩. The angle formed with the x-axis is 45°.

d. The translation vector is ⟨–15,15⟩. The angle formed with the x-axis is 135°.

e. The translation vector is ⟨45,15⟩. The angle formed with the x-axis is 18.4°.

1.2 a. Sample response: The center of the dilation can be found by drawing a line through A and A' and another line through C and C' (or through any two pairs of corresponding points in the image and the preimage). The point of intersection of the two lines is the center of dilation.

b. The scale factor is the ratio of corresponding lengths:

$$\frac{55}{22} = \frac{5}{2} = \frac{2.5}{1}$$

c. $D_{0,2.5}$

1.3 Sample response: No. The figures are not similar; therefore, they could not have been produced by a dilation. There is no point of perspective.

* 1.4 a–b. Sample graph:

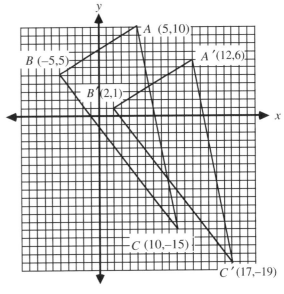

c. The image of the origin is located at (7,–4). The horizontal component of the translation vector is the x-coordinate of the image of the origin. The vertical component of the translation vector is the y-coordinate of the image of the origin. The horizontal component is 2 – (–5) = 7. The vertical component is 3 – 7 = –4.

d. Sample response: The triangle would appear to move 5 units in the direction of the vector.

1.5 a. Sample graph:

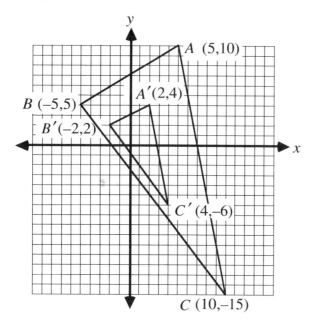

b. 1. 2

   2. –1/5

   3. 2.5

c. Sample response: The sides of the triangle would appear to shrink to about 60% of their original lengths. The triangle itself would appear to shrink to about 36% of its original area.

1.6 a. Sample response: Looking from the side, the plane's apparent size would not change as it landed, but its position would change. This would make translations the right choice for the animation. Looking from in front, the plane would appear to grow larger as it came closer. That makes dilations the right choice.

b. Sample response: Neither animation would be completely realistic. From any given point of perspective, both the plane's position and its apparent size would change as the plane was landing.

* * * * *

1.7 a. Sample response: Because each step is 18 cm high and the vertical distance between floors is 360 cm, there are 20 steps on the escalator. This means that the horizontal distance traveled is 20 steps × 24 cm = 480 cm. The translation vector is ⟨480,–360⟩.

b. The angle is $\tan^{-1}\left(\dfrac{360}{480}\right) \approx 36.9°$.

d. Suppose that you drew five successive images of △*ABC*, each a translation of the previous image by a vector 1 unit long with the same direction. If you taped each image to a separate card and flipped the cards like the pages of a book, what would you see?

1.5 a. Graph the image of △*ABC* in Problem **1.4a** under a dilation with center at the origin *O* and a scale factor of 2/5. Label the vertices of the image and identify their coordinates.

b. Determine the scale factor of the dilation of △*ABC* for each of the following images:

   1. *A*′(10,20), *B*′(–10,10), and *C*′(20,–30)

   2. *A*′(–1,–2), *B*′(1,–1), and *C*′(–2,3)

   3. *A*′(12.5,25), *B*′(–12.5,12.5), and *C*′(25,–37.5)

c. Suppose that you drew five successive images of △*ABC*, each dilated by a scale factor of 9/10, with the same center of dilation. If you taped each image to a separate card and flipped the cards like the pages of a book, what would you see?

1.6 a. An animator wants to show an airplane descending to land. Explain why the animator might use translations to depict a side view of the plane, while using dilations to depict a front view.

b. Would either of the animations described in Part **a** provide a realistic depiction of a plane's descent? Explain your response.

* * * * *

1.7 At the local mall, an escalator carries people from the ground floor to the basement. The basement is 3.6 m below the ground floor. Each step on the escalator measures 24 cm wide and 18 cm high.

a. The change in position of a person on the escalator can be modeled using a translation. Describe the translation vector for a person starting at the top and riding to the bottom. Justify your response.

b. What is the measure of the angle formed by the escalator and the basement floor? Justify your response.

1.8 The similar triangles below represent different images of a cartoon character's eye.

a. Determine the scale factor of a dilation that transforms triangle 1 to triangle 2.

b. Determine the scale factor of a dilation that transforms triangle 2 to triangle 3.

c. Determine the scale factor of a dilation that transforms triangle 1 to triangle 3.

d. Considering the arrangement of the triangles in the diagram above, could the dilations in Parts **a** and **b** have the same center? Explain your response.

1.9 The coordinates of the vertices of quadrilateral *ABCD* are *A*(0,0), *B*(0,3), *C*(5,3), and *D*(5,0). The coordinates of the vertices of its image are *A*′(0,0), *B*′(0,6), *C*′(10,6), and *D*′(10,0). Find the center of dilation and the scale factor for this transformation.

In Activity **1,** you explored the transformation of some simple figures such as triangles and quadrilaterals. Shapes like these require only a few points to define. The figures of most cartoon characters, however, are much more complicated to draw—either by hand or with the aid of a computer. For example, Figure **5-10** below shows the face of Skip.

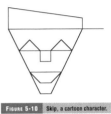

FIGURE 5-10 Skip, a cartoon character.

Although Skip is relatively easy to draw, his face still requires 19 ordered pairs to define. In this activity, you use matrices to store the ordered pairs that define Skip and his images.

Materials List

- graph paper
- ruler (one per student)

teacher note

When using some types of technology (such as spreadsheets or graphing calculators, for example) to draw closed figures, it might be necessary to repeat the coordinates of some points in a matrix to complete the figure. For example, a triangle can be defined on a coordinate grid by listing the coordinates of the three vertices in homogeneous form in a 3×3 matrix. However, to use technology to draw the same triangle from a matrix, it may be necessary to list the coordinates of both a starting point and a stopping point (or four points in all).

Alternately, students simply may use technology to create an unconnected scatterplot, then print the scatterplot and connect the points by hand.

Technology

- geometry utility
- matrix manipulator
- graphing utility
- spreadsheet

* 1.8 **a.** 3/1

  b. 1/2

  c. 3/2

  d. Sample response: They could not have the same center. When you draw lines through corresponding points in the images and preimages, they do not intersect at the same point.

1.9 Sample response: The center of dilation is the origin because it is the only fixed point. The scale factor is 2/1.

In this activity, students explore translations in the coordinate plane using 2×2 and 3×3 matrices.

teacher note

A brief assessment of the mathematical content in Activities **1** and **2,** for use at your discretion, appears in the Teacher Resources for this module.

teacher note

The programs listed below allow students to plot preimages and images defined by matrices on Texas Instruments' TI-84, TI-89, or Voyage 200 calculators. These programs require students to enter both beginning and ending points to create a closed figure. This requires a matrix with at least one more set of coordinates than the actual number of vertices.

Before running a program, students should set the viewing window to an appropriate size, then enter the desired matrix.

Using the TI-84, students enter a matrix with the MATRIX button. The program then asks students where the matrix is stored. They should then use the MATRIX button to indicate the matrix they wish to plot.

Using the TI-89 and Voyage 200, students enter a matrix with the DATA/MATRIX application. To run the program, students should enter plotpts(*matrix name*) and press RETURN, then enter the name of the matrix.

PLOTPTS—A program for the TI-84

```
PROGRAM:PLOTPTS
: PlotsOff
: FnOff
: Disp "WHERE IS THE"
: Disp "MATRIX STORED?"
: Input [A]
: dim([A])→L1
: L1(2)–1→N
: For((I,1,N)
: Line([A](1,I),[A](2,I),[A](1,I+1),[A](2,I+1))
: End
```

plotpts—A program for the TI-89 and Voyage 200

```
: plotpts(list)
: Prgm
: Local siz,pts,i
: dim(list)→siz
: siz[2]–1→pts
: For i,1,pts
: Line list[1,i], list[2,i], list[1,i+1], list[2,i+1]
: EndFor
: EndPrgm
```

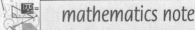

Exploration 1

In this exploration, you examine how matrices can be used to represent cartoon figures and their translations.

a. Create a graph of Skip on a coordinate grid with his chin on the *x*-axis and the highest point of his cap on the *y*-axis.

Label your axes so that the coordinates for Skip's cap can be represented by the following points: (9,6), (0,6), (0,8), (7,7), and (7,6).

Note: Keep this graph for use in Activity **3**.

mathematics note

A point *P* with coordinates (x,y) can be represented in a matrix as shown below.

$$P = \begin{bmatrix} x \\ y \end{bmatrix}$$

Using matrices to represent several points in this way can be helpful in many applications. For example, considering the coordinates given in Part **a** of Exploration **1**, Skip's left eye is a triangle with vertices at (1,4), (2,5), and (3,4). These points can be mathematically described by the following matrix:

$$\begin{bmatrix} 1 & 2 & 3 \\ 4 & 5 & 4 \end{bmatrix}$$

b. Matrix **C** below represents Skip's cap. Matrix **C'** represents his cap after a translation.

$$C = \begin{bmatrix} 9 & 0 & 0 & 7 & 7 \\ 6 & 6 & 8 & 7 & 6 \end{bmatrix} \qquad C' = \begin{bmatrix} 13 & 4 & 4 & 11 & 11 \\ 3 & 3 & 5 & 4 & 3 \end{bmatrix}$$

Graph the positions of Skip's cap as defined by these matrices.

c. Determine the changes that have occurred in the coordinates of each point of Skip's cap.

Student Outcomes

After completing the following exploration and discussion, students should be able to:

✳ determine the dimensions of a matrix

✳ use $2 \times n$ matrices to represent images and preimages as sets of coordinates

✳ represent translations using matrix addition and $2 \times n$ matrices

✳ use $3 \times n$ matrices to represent images and preimages as sets of coordinates in homogeneous form

✳ represent translations using matrix multiplication and $3 \times n$ matrices

✳ use matrix multiplication to translate figures

✳ recognize the 3×3 identity matrix for matrix multiplication.

Exploration 1

Students examine the use of matrix addition to translate figures on a coordinate plane. ■

a. Students graph Skip on a coordinate plane. Sample graph:

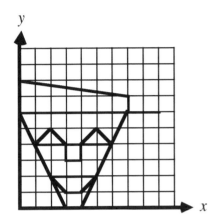

b. Sample graph:

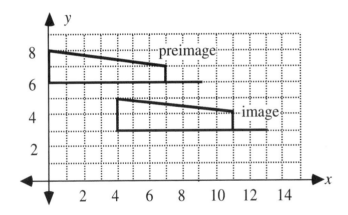

c. Students should observe that every *x*-value in matrix **C** is increased by 4 and every *y*-value is decreased by 3.

d–e. Students should write and verify the following equation:

$$\mathbf{C} + \mathbf{T} = \mathbf{C}'$$

$$\begin{bmatrix} 9 & 0 & 0 & 7 & 7 \\ 6 & 6 & 8 & 7 & 6 \end{bmatrix} + \begin{bmatrix} 4 & 4 & 4 & 4 & 4 \\ -3 & -3 & -3 & -3 & -3 \end{bmatrix} = \begin{bmatrix} 13 & 4 & 4 & 11 & 11 \\ 3 & 3 & 5 & 4 & 3 \end{bmatrix}$$

Discussion 1

a. Sample response: The image has been moved 4 units to the right and 3 units down from the preimage.

b. Sample response: The vector indicates a translation of 5 units down and 4 units to the left. The following matrix translates the five points in matrix **C** the amount indicated by the vector.

$$\mathbb{T}_{C,C'} = \begin{bmatrix} -4 & -4 & -4 & -4 & -4 \\ -5 & -5 & -5 & -5- & -5 \end{bmatrix}$$

c. Sample response: Because Skip's face is defined by 19 ordered pairs, the dimensions of the translation matrix would have to be 2×19.

---

d. A matrix equation in the following form, where **T** is a translation matrix, can be used to represent the change in position of Skip's cap:

$$\mathbf{C} + \mathbf{T} = \mathbf{C}'$$

Determine the matrix **T** that makes this equation true.

e. Use technology to verify your equation from Part **d.**

Discussion 1

a. Describe the change in position of Skip's cap in Part **b** of the exploration.

mathematics note

A translation can be described using matrix addition. In this case, the number of columns in the translation matrix must match the number of points used to define the figure to be translated.

A matrix **T** for the translation from $P(x,y)$ to $P'(x + h, y + k)$ is represented in the following form:

$$\mathbf{T}_{P,P'} = \begin{bmatrix} h & h & h \\ k & k & k \end{bmatrix} \cdots$$

For example, consider the triangle whose vertices are represented in matrix **A**.

$$\mathbf{A} = \begin{bmatrix} 2 & 7 & 5 \\ 3 & 8 & -1 \end{bmatrix}$$

To find the vertices of the image of this triangle under a translation described by the vector $\langle -7,3 \rangle$, you can perform the following matrix addition:

$$\mathbf{A} + \mathbf{T} = \mathbf{A}'$$

$$\begin{bmatrix} 2 & 7 & 5 \\ 3 & 8 & -1 \end{bmatrix} + \begin{bmatrix} -7 & -7 & -7 \\ 3 & 3 & 3 \end{bmatrix} = \begin{bmatrix} -5 & 0 & -2 \\ 6 & 11 & 2 \end{bmatrix}$$

b. What translation matrix would you use to move Skip's cap by the translation vector $\langle -4,-5 \rangle$? Justify your response.

c. What are the dimensions of the matrix necessary to translate Skip's entire face by matrix addition? Explain your response.

d. Describe how you would determine the dimensions of a matrix necessary to translate any given figure by matrix addition.

e. What disadvantages might there be to using matrix addition to translate a complicated figure?

Exploration 2

In Exploration 1, you found that translations can be performed using matrix addition. This methods works reasonably well for simple figures, but would not be efficient for more complicated ones.

In this exploration, you investigate another way to create translations using matrix operations. This method requires that the points of the preimage be represented in **homogeneous form**.

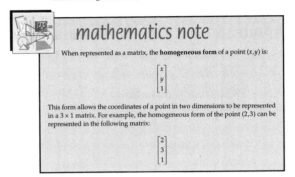

mathematics note

When represented as a matrix, the **homogeneous form** of a point (x,y) is:

$$\begin{bmatrix} x \\ y \\ 1 \end{bmatrix}$$

This form allows the coordinates of a point in two dimensions to be represented in a 3×1 matrix. For example, the homogeneous form of the point $(2,3)$ can be represented in the following matrix:

$$\begin{bmatrix} 2 \\ 3 \\ 1 \end{bmatrix}$$

a. Represent the points that define Skip's left eye, in homogeneous form, as matrix **E**.

b. Translate Skip's left eye 7 units down and 5 units to the right. Record the coordinates of the resulting points, in homogeneous form, in matrix **E′**.

c. Using matrix multiplication, the equation that results in this translation of Skip's eye can be written as follows, where **T** is the translation matrix:

$$\mathbf{T} \cdot \mathbf{E} = \mathbf{E'}$$

What dimensions are required of matrix **T**? Explain your response.

---

d. Sample response: The translation matrix would have 2 rows. The number of columns would be the same as the number of points in the preimage.

e. Sample response: If the preimage had many points, the translation matrix would be tedious to create, because it would require a column for each point in the preimage.

Exploration 2

Students use matrix multiplication to translate figures on a coordinate plane.

a. A matrix for these points, in homogeneous form, is:

$$\mathbf{E} = \begin{bmatrix} 1 & 2 & 3 \\ 4 & 5 & 4 \\ 1 & 1 & 1 \end{bmatrix}$$

b. The resulting image matrix is:

$$\mathbf{E'} = \begin{bmatrix} 6 & 7 & 8 \\ -3 & -2 & -3 \\ 1 & 1 & 1 \end{bmatrix}$$

c. Sample response: For multiplication to be possible, the column dimension of the left matrix must equal the row dimension of the right matrix. This dimension is 3. The product matrix has dimensions equal to the row dimension of the right matrix and the column dimension of the left matrix. So the dimensions of the translation matrix must be 3×3.

d. 1. The left-hand side of the equation is:

$$\mathbf{T} \bullet \mathbf{E} = \begin{bmatrix} a & b & c \\ d & e & f \\ g & h & i \end{bmatrix} \bullet \begin{bmatrix} 1 & 2 & 3 \\ 4 & 5 & 4 \\ 1 & 1 & 1 \end{bmatrix}$$

The resulting product matrix is:

$$\mathbf{T} \bullet \mathbf{E} = \begin{bmatrix} a + 4b + c & 2a + 5b + c & 3a + 4b + c \\ d + 4e + f & 2d + 5e + f & 3d + 4e + f \\ g + 4h + i & 2g + 5h + i & 3g + 4h + i \end{bmatrix}$$

2. The resulting matrix equation is:

$$\mathbf{T} \bullet \mathbf{E} = \mathbf{E}'$$

$$\begin{bmatrix} 1a+4b+c & 2a+5b+c & 3a+4b+c \\ 1d+4e+f & 2d+5e+f & 3d+4e+f \\ 1g+4h+i & 2g+5h+i & 3g+4h+i \end{bmatrix} = \begin{bmatrix} 6 & 7 & 8 \\ -3 & -2 & -3 \\ 1 & 1 & 1 \end{bmatrix}$$

3. Students should write the following system of equations:

$$\begin{cases} a + 4b + c = 6 \\ 2a + 5b + c = 7 \\ 3a + 4b + c = 8 \end{cases}$$

4. The system can be solved using matrices as follows:

$$\begin{bmatrix} 1 & 4 & 1 \\ 2 & 5 & 1 \\ 3 & 4 & 1 \end{bmatrix} \bullet \begin{bmatrix} a \\ b \\ c \end{bmatrix} = \begin{bmatrix} 6 \\ 7 \\ 8 \end{bmatrix}$$

$$\begin{bmatrix} 1 & 4 & 1 \\ 2 & 5 & 1 \\ 3 & 4 & 1 \end{bmatrix}^{-1} \bullet \begin{bmatrix} 1 & 4 & 1 \\ 2 & 5 & 1 \\ 3 & 4 & 1 \end{bmatrix} \bullet \begin{bmatrix} a \\ b \\ c \end{bmatrix} = \begin{bmatrix} 1 & 4 & 1 \\ 2 & 5 & 1 \\ 3 & 4 & 1 \end{bmatrix}^{-1} \bullet \begin{bmatrix} 6 \\ 7 \\ 8 \end{bmatrix}$$

$$\begin{bmatrix} a \\ b \\ c \end{bmatrix} = \begin{bmatrix} 1 \\ 0 \\ 5 \end{bmatrix}$$

5. The three equations containing the variables d, e, and f are:

$$\begin{cases} d + 4e + f = -3 \\ 2d + 5e + f = -2 \\ 3d + 4e + f = -3 \end{cases}$$

This system can be solved using matrices as follows:

$$\begin{bmatrix} 1 & 4 & 1 \\ 2 & 5 & 1 \\ 3 & 4 & 1 \end{bmatrix} \bullet \begin{bmatrix} d \\ e \\ f \end{bmatrix} = \begin{bmatrix} -3 \\ -2 \\ -3 \end{bmatrix}$$

$$\begin{bmatrix} 1 & 4 & 1 \\ 2 & 5 & 1 \\ 3 & 4 & 1 \end{bmatrix}^{-1} \bullet \begin{bmatrix} 1 & 4 & 1 \\ 2 & 5 & 1 \\ 3 & 4 & 1 \end{bmatrix} \bullet \begin{bmatrix} d \\ e \\ f \end{bmatrix} = \begin{bmatrix} 1 & 4 & 1 \\ 2 & 5 & 1 \\ 3 & 4 & 1 \end{bmatrix}^{-1} \bullet \begin{bmatrix} -3 \\ -2 \\ -3 \end{bmatrix}$$

$$\begin{bmatrix} d \\ e \\ f \end{bmatrix} = \begin{bmatrix} 0 \\ 1 \\ -7 \end{bmatrix}$$

d. In the matrix equation $\mathbf{T} \bullet \mathbf{E} = \mathbf{E}'$, the translation matrix $\mathbf{T}$ is of the following form:

$$\mathbf{T} = \begin{bmatrix} a & b & c \\ d & e & f \\ g & h & i \end{bmatrix}$$

To find the elements of $\mathbf{T}$, you must solve several systems of equations. Use the following steps to help complete this process.

1. Write out the matrices for the left-hand side of the equation $\mathbf{T} \bullet \mathbf{E} = \mathbf{E}'$. Multiply $\mathbf{T} \bullet \mathbf{E}$ and determine the resulting product matrix.

   Each element in the product matrix should contain three variables. For example, the element in row 1, column 1 should be $a + 4b + c$.

2. The product matrix from Step **1** equals matrix $\mathbf{E}'$. Because they are equal, each element in the product matrix is equal to the corresponding element in $\mathbf{E}'$.

   Write a matrix equation that relates the values of each pair of corresponding elements. For example, $a + 4b + c = 6$.

3. Write a system of the three equations that contain the three variables a, b, and c.

4. In the Level 2 module, "Making Concessions," you used matrices to solve systems of equations.

   Use that method to solve the system in Step **3**.

5. Repeat Steps **3** and **4** for the variables d, e, and f.

6. Repeat Steps **3** and **4** for the variables g, h, and i.

7. Substitute the value you determined for each variable in matrix $\mathbf{T}$.

e. In Part **d** above, you identified the matrix that, using matrix multiplication, produces a translation of 7 units down and 5 units to the right.

Identify the matrix that, using matrix multiplication, produces the translation defined by the vector $\langle -2, 6 \rangle$.

f. Write the matrix that, using matrix multiplication, produces the translation defined by the vector $\langle h, k \rangle$.

g. In Exploration **1**, you used matrix addition to translate Skip's cap 3 units down and 4 units to the right.

1. Write the matrix $\mathbf{T}$ that, using matrix multiplication, produces the same translation as in Exploration **1**.

2. Write the coordinates of the points that define Skip's cap, in homogeneous form, in a matrix $\mathbf{C}$.

6. The three equations containing the variables g, h, and i are:

$$\begin{cases} g + 4h + i = 1 \\ 2g + 5h + i = 1 \\ 3g + 4h + i = 1 \end{cases}$$

This system can be solved using matrices as follows:

$$\begin{bmatrix} 1 & 4 & 1 \\ 2 & 5 & 1 \\ 3 & 4 & 1 \end{bmatrix} \bullet \begin{bmatrix} g \\ h \\ i \end{bmatrix} = \begin{bmatrix} 1 \\ 1 \\ 1 \end{bmatrix}$$

$$\begin{bmatrix} 1 & 4 & 1 \\ 2 & 5 & 1 \\ 3 & 4 & 1 \end{bmatrix}^{-1} \bullet \begin{bmatrix} 1 & 4 & 1 \\ 2 & 5 & 1 \\ 3 & 4 & 1 \end{bmatrix} \bullet \begin{bmatrix} g \\ h \\ i \end{bmatrix} = \begin{bmatrix} 1 & 4 & 1 \\ 2 & 5 & 1 \\ 3 & 4 & 1 \end{bmatrix}^{-1} \bullet \begin{bmatrix} 1 \\ 1 \\ 1 \end{bmatrix}$$

$$\begin{bmatrix} g \\ h \\ i \end{bmatrix} = \begin{bmatrix} 0 \\ 0 \\ 1 \end{bmatrix}$$

7. When using matrix multiplication, the matrix $\mathbf{T}$ for a translation of 5 units horizontally and -7 units vertically is:

$$\mathbf{T} = \begin{bmatrix} 1 & 0 & 5 \\ 0 & 1 & -7 \\ 0 & 0 & 1 \end{bmatrix}$$

3. Determine the product of following multiplication: T • C.
4. Compare the coordinates of the image found in Step **3** to those described in Part **b** of Exploration **1**, shown below:

$$C' = \begin{bmatrix} 13 & 4 & 4 & 11 & 11 \\ 3 & 3 & 5 & 4 & 3 \end{bmatrix}$$

h. Matrix **I** below is the 3 × 3 **identity matrix** for matrix multiplication:

$$I = \begin{bmatrix} 1 & 0 & 0 \\ 0 & 1 & 0 \\ 0 & 0 & 1 \end{bmatrix}$$

Describe the product of the following multiplication: **I** • **C**.

Discussion 2

a. Describe the elements of the matrix **T** you identified in Part **d** of Exploration **2**.
b. What 3 × 3 matrix, when multiplied on the left, would produce a translation of vector ⟨x,y⟩?
c. In the matrices described in Parts **a** and **b** of this discussion, what is the significance of the portion shown below?

$$\begin{bmatrix} 1 & 0 \\ 0 & 1 \end{bmatrix}$$

d. The **identity transformation** preserves the size, shape, and position of a figure. What 3 × 3 matrix, when multiplied on the left, produces the identity transformation? Justify your response.
e. What differences did you observe between the use of matrix addition and matrix multiplication to represent translations?
f. Would multiplying the preimage matrix on the right by a 3 × 3 translation matrix result in the same image as when multiplying on the left? Explain your response.

Warm-Up

1. **a.** What must be true about the dimensions of two matrices to add them?
   b. What must be true about the dimensions of two matrices to multiply them?

e. When using matrix multiplication, the translation matrix for the vector ⟨–2,6⟩ is:

$$T = \begin{bmatrix} 1 & 0 & -2 \\ 0 & 1 & 6 \\ 0 & 0 & 1 \end{bmatrix}$$

f. When using matrix multiplication, the general translation matrix is:

$$T = \begin{bmatrix} 1 & 0 & h \\ 0 & 1 & k \\ 0 & 0 & 1 \end{bmatrix}$$

g. 1. When using matrix multiplication, the matrix that results in a translation of 3 units down and 4 units to the right is:

$$T = \begin{bmatrix} 1 & 0 & 4 \\ 0 & 1 & -3 \\ 0 & 0 & 1 \end{bmatrix}$$

2. The matrix is:

$$\begin{bmatrix} 9 & 0 & 0 & 7 & 7 \\ 6 & 6 & 8 & 7 & 6 \\ 1 & 1 & 1 & 1 & 1 \end{bmatrix}$$

3. The resulting matrix equation is:

$$T \bullet C = \begin{bmatrix} 1 & 0 & 4 \\ 0 & 1 & -3 \\ 0 & 0 & 1 \end{bmatrix} \bullet \begin{bmatrix} 9 & 0 & 0 & 7 & 7 \\ 6 & 6 & 8 & 7 & 6 \\ 1 & 1 & 1 & 1 & 1 \end{bmatrix} = \begin{bmatrix} 13 & 4 & 4 & 11 & 11 \\ 3 & 3 & 5 & 4 & 3 \\ 1 & 1 & 1 & 1 & 1 \end{bmatrix}$$

4. The coordinates of the image are (13,3), (4,3), (4,5), (11,4), and (11,3). These are the same coordinates for **C'** as in Exploration **1**.

h. Sample response: No translation results. The preimage and image are the same.

Discussion 2

a. The translation matrix is:

$$T = \begin{bmatrix} 1 & 0 & 4 \\ 0 & 1 & -3 \\ 0 & 0 & 1 \end{bmatrix}$$

b. When using matrix multiplication, the matrix for a translation of x units horizontally and y units vertically is:

$$T = \begin{bmatrix} 1 & 0 & x \\ 0 & 1 & y \\ 0 & 0 & 1 \end{bmatrix}$$

c. Sample response: It represents the 2 × 2 identity matrix for matrix multiplication.
d. Sample response: The identity transformation preserves size, shape, and position, therefore the matrix of points must remain the same after multiplication. This occurs when multiplied on the left by the 3 × 3 identity matrix.

$$I = \begin{bmatrix} 1 & 0 & 0 \\ 0 & 1 & 0 \\ 0 & 0 & 1 \end{bmatrix}$$

e. Sample response: Using matrix addition, the row dimension of the translation matrix is always 2, while the column dimension varies with the number of preimage points involved. Using matrix multiplication, the translation matrix is always a 3 × 3 matrix.
f. Sample response: No. To multiply on the right by a 3 × 3 matrix, the preimage matrix also must be a 3 × 3 matrix. For any other dimensions, multiplication on the right by a 3 × 3 matrix is undefined.

Warm-Up

1. **a.** The dimensions must be the same.
   b. The column dimension of the matrix on the left must be the same as the row dimension of the matrix on the right.

2. Using matrix addition, matrix **E** corresponds with the translation vector $\langle -2,4 \rangle$. Using matrix multiplication, matrix **H** corresponds with the translation vector $\langle 3,-1 \rangle$.

3. **a.** Sample response: The product is a 3×4 matrix with the coordinates of four points represented in homogeneous form. All of the x-coordinates have been changed by 3, while all of the y-coordinates have been changed by -1. This is a translation of 3 units to the right and 1 unit down.

   b. The product is undefined. A 3×2 matrix cannot be multiplied on the right by a 3×3 matrix.

   c. Sample response: The product does not represent a translation because the x-coordinates have been changed by differing amounts, as have the y-coordinates.

   Note: The transformation represented in this problem is a dilation. Students explore dilations using matrices in Activity **3**.

   d. Sample response: In the sum, all of the x-coordinates have been changed by -2, while all of the y-coordinates have been changed by 4. This represents a translation of 2 units to the left and 4 units up.

4. **a.** The translation matrix for matrix addition is:

$$\mathbf{T} = \begin{bmatrix} 7 & 7 & 7 & 7 & 7 \\ -10 & -10 & -10 & -10 & -10 \end{bmatrix}$$

The translation matrix for matrix multiplication is:

$$\mathbf{T} = \begin{bmatrix} 1 & 0 & 7 \\ 0 & 1 & -10 \\ 0 & 0 & 1 \end{bmatrix}$$

   b. The translation matrix for matrix addition is:

$$\mathbf{T} = \begin{bmatrix} -3 & -3 & -3 & -3 & -3 & -3 & -3 \\ 4 & 4 & 4 & 4 & 4 & 4 & 4 \end{bmatrix}$$

The translation matrix for matrix multiplication is:

$$\mathbf{T} = \begin{bmatrix} 1 & 0 & -3 \\ 0 & 1 & 4 \\ 0 & 0 & 1 \end{bmatrix}$$

2. Which of the following matrices could be used to translate a pentagon? For those matrices that can produce a translation, describe the appropriate matrix operation and the corresponding translation vector.

$$D = \begin{bmatrix} 4 & 0 & 0 \\ 0 & 4 & 0 \\ 0 & 0 & 1 \end{bmatrix} \quad E = \begin{bmatrix} -2 & -2 & -2 & -2 & -2 \\ 4 & 4 & 4 & 4 & 4 \end{bmatrix} \quad F = \begin{bmatrix} 1/2 & 0 \\ 0 & 1/2 \\ 1 & 1 \end{bmatrix}$$

$$G = \begin{bmatrix} -7 & -5 & 9 & 5 \\ 5 & -2 & -5 & 7 \\ 1 & 1 & 1 & 1 \end{bmatrix} \quad H = \begin{bmatrix} 1 & 0 & 3 \\ 0 & 1 & -1 \\ 0 & 0 & 1 \end{bmatrix} \quad J = \begin{bmatrix} -1 & 0 & 1 & 2 & 3 \\ 5 & 0 & 2 & 0 & 5 \end{bmatrix}$$

3. Use the matrices in Problem **2** to evaluate each of the following matrix expressions. If an expression cannot be evaluated, explain why not. If it can, explain why the result does or does not represent a translation.

   a. H • G   **b.** F • D

   c. D • G   **d.** E + J

4. In each of Parts **a** and **b** below, write a matrix that produces the transformation by matrix addition and one that produces it by matrix multiplication.

   a. the translation of a pentagon 7 units to the right and 10 units down

   b. the change in position of a heptagon by the translation vector $\langle -3,4 \rangle$.

Assignment

2.1 A quadrilateral has vertices at $(1,1)$, $(5,1)$, $(4,4)$, and $(0,4)$. Determine its image under the translation vector $\langle 4,-2 \rangle$ by completing Parts **a–c**.

   a. Write a matrix equation for the translation using matrix addition.

   b. Write a matrix equation for the translation using matrix multiplication.

   c. Create a graph of this translation on a coordinate plane.

2.2 The following diagram shows the translation of a letter M.

translation vector

Assignment

Problems suitable for use as assessment items are identified by an asterisk (*).

2.1 **a.** Sample matrix equation:

$$\begin{bmatrix} 1 & 5 & 4 & 0 \\ 1 & 1 & 4 & 4 \end{bmatrix} + \begin{bmatrix} 4 & 4 & 4 & 4 \\ -2 & -2 & -2 & -2 \end{bmatrix} = \begin{bmatrix} 5 & 9 & 8 & 4 \\ -1 & -1 & 2 & 2 \end{bmatrix}$$

   b. Sample matrix equation:

$$\begin{bmatrix} 1 & 0 & 4 \\ 0 & 1 & -2 \\ 0 & 0 & 1 \end{bmatrix} \bullet \begin{bmatrix} 1 & 5 & 4 & 0 \\ 1 & 1 & 4 & 4 \\ 1 & 1 & 1 & 1 \end{bmatrix} = \begin{bmatrix} 5 & 9 & 8 & 4 \\ -1 & -1 & 2 & 2 \\ 1 & 1 & 1 & 1 \end{bmatrix}$$

   c. Sample graph:

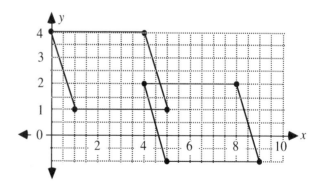

a. Describe the translation using vector notation.

b. Write a matrix equation for the translation using matrix addition.

c. Write a matrix equation for the translation using matrix multiplication.

d. What is the measure of the angle formed by the translation vector and its horizontal component?

e. What is the length of the translation vector?

2.3 a. Use technology to draw the preimage and image of the letter M in Problem **2.2**.

b. Suppose that you drew five more images of the letter M, all evenly spaced between the preimage and image in Part **a**. If you taped each image to a separate card and flipped the cards like the pages of a book, what would you see?

c. Describe how to find a translation matrix that transforms each image in Part **b** to the next, given only the coordinates of the original preimage and final image.

2.4 a. Describe a translation matrix that could be used to slide Skip's face to a region below and to the left of its original position on a grid.

b. Describe the matrix that contains the coordinates of the image points.

c. Determine the measure of the angle formed by the translation vector and its horizontal component.

* * * * *

2.5 a. Describe the translation shown in the diagram below using vector notation.

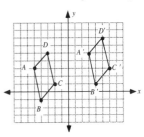

* 2.2 a. $\langle 7, -6 \rangle$

b. Sample response: The translation matrix could be a 2×5 matrix. Each entry in the first row is 7, to represent the horizontal movement. Each entry in the second row is −6, to represent the vertical movement.

$$\begin{bmatrix} 1 & 2 & 3 & 4 & 5 \\ 1 & 6 & 4 & 6 & 1 \end{bmatrix} + \begin{bmatrix} 7 & 7 & 7 & 7 & 7 \\ -6 & -6 & -6 & -6 & -6 \end{bmatrix} = \begin{bmatrix} 8 & 9 & 10 & 11 & 12 \\ -5 & 0 & -2 & 0 & -5 \end{bmatrix}$$

c. Sample matrix equation:

$$\begin{bmatrix} 1 & 0 & 7 \\ 0 & 1 & -6 \\ 0 & 0 & 1 \end{bmatrix} \bullet \begin{bmatrix} 1 & 2 & 3 & 4 & 5 \\ 1 & 6 & 4 & 6 & 1 \\ 1 & 1 & 1 & 1 & 1 \end{bmatrix} = \begin{bmatrix} 8 & 9 & 10 & 11 & 12 \\ -5 & 0 & -2 & 0 & -5 \\ 1 & 1 & 1 & 1 & 1 \end{bmatrix}$$

d. The measure of the angle is approximately 41.6°.

e. The length of the translation vector can be found as follows:

$$\sqrt{(8-1)^2 + (-5-1)^2} = \sqrt{49 + 36} = \sqrt{85} \approx 9.22.$$

2.3 a. See Teacher Note at the beginning of this activity for calculator programs that may be used to draw the figure.

b. Sample response: As you flipped through the cards, the M would appear to move down the page.

Note: Students might wish to create such flip cards. If so, the origin must be in the same position on each card, and each drawing must be taped in the appropriate location relative to the origin.

For those students with Texas Instruments' TI-89 or Voyage 200 calculators, the built-in program **CyclePic** (see TI *Guidebook*), in conjunction with the "**plotpts**" program, will simulate the flip-card effect.

c. Sample response: Determine the translation vector $\langle h, k \rangle$. Then multiply h and k by $1/n$, where n is the total number of images desired. Then use these values to create the appropriate translation matrix for either matrix addition or matrix multiplication.

* 2.4 a. Students choose their own translations, so answers will vary. In each translation matrix, both h and k should be less than 0.

b. To obtain the image matrix **S'**, h is added to each element in row 1 and k is added to each element in row 2.

c. The angle formed by the translation vector and its horizontal component is $\theta = \tan^{-1}(h/k)$.

2.5 a. The translation vector is $\langle 8, 2 \rangle$, representing a shift of 8 units to the right and 2 units up.

b. $\begin{bmatrix} 8 & 8 & 8 & 8 \\ 2 & 2 & 2 & 2 \end{bmatrix}$ or $\begin{bmatrix} 1 & 0 & 8 \\ 0 & 1 & 2 \\ 0 & 0 & 1 \end{bmatrix}$

c. The distance between each point X and its image X' is

$$\sqrt{8^2 + 2^2} = \sqrt{64 + 4} = \sqrt{68} \approx 8.25.$$

2.6 a. The coordinates are $A''(0,2)$, $B''(-6,4)$, and $C''(-1,-4)$.

b. The translation vector is $\langle 5,-4 \rangle$.

c. The translation vector is $\langle -7,2 \rangle$.

d. The translation vector is $\langle -2,-2 \rangle$.

e. Sample response: The sum of the first numbers in the vectors from Parts **b** and **c** gives you the first number in the vector from Part **d**. The sum of the second numbers in the vectors from Parts **b** and **c** gives you the second number in the vector from Part **d**.

f. The distance between each point X and its image X' is .

$$\sqrt{(-2)^2 + (-2)^2} = \sqrt{4 + 4} = \sqrt{8} \approx 2.83.$$

g. $\tan^{-1}(2/2) = 45°$

h. $\begin{bmatrix} 2 & -4 & 1 \\ 4 & 6 & -2 \end{bmatrix} + \begin{bmatrix} -2 & -2 & -2 \\ -2 & -2 & -2 \end{bmatrix} = \begin{bmatrix} 0 & -6 & -1 \\ 2 & 4 & -4 \end{bmatrix}$

i. $\begin{bmatrix} 1 & 0 & -2 \\ 0 & 1 & -2 \\ 0 & 0 & 1 \end{bmatrix} \bullet \begin{bmatrix} 2 & -4 & 1 \\ 4 & 6 & -2 \\ 1 & 1 & 1 \end{bmatrix} = \begin{bmatrix} 0 & -6 & -1 \\ 2 & 4 & -4 \\ 1 & 1 & 1 \end{bmatrix}$

In this activity, students again use matrices to store the coordinates of points that define a figure. They discover that a dilation with center at the origin can be represented by multiplication on the left by a 3×3 matrix.

Materials List

- graph paper (one sheet per student)
- ruler (one per student)
- template for Problem **3.8** (one per student; a blackline master appears in the Teacher Resources for this module)

Technology

- matrix manipulator
- spreadsheet
- graphing utility

---

b. Write two different matrices that can be used to represent the translation $T_{A,A'}$.

c. Determine the distance between each point in the preimage and its corresponding point in the image.

2.6 Consider $\triangle ABC$ with vertices $A(2,4)$, $B(-4,6)$ and $C(1,-2)$. A translation using the following matrix results in the image $\triangle A'B'C'$.

$$\begin{bmatrix} 5 & 5 & 5 \\ -4 & -4 & -4 \end{bmatrix}$$

A translation of $\triangle A'B'C'$ by the matrix below produces the image $\triangle A''B''C''$.

$$\begin{bmatrix} -7 & -7 & -7 \\ 2 & 2 & 2 \end{bmatrix}$$

a. Find the coordinates of $\triangle A''B''C''$.

b. Describe the translation $T_{A,A'}$ using vector notation.

c. Describe the translation $T_{A',A''}$ using vector notation.

d. Describe the translation $T_{A,A''}$ of using vector notation.

e. How could you use the translation vectors in Parts **b** and **c** to find the translation vector in Part **d**?

f. Determine the distance between each point in $\triangle ABC$ and its corresponding point in $\triangle A''B''C''$.

g. Determine the measure of the angle formed by the translation vector for $T_{A,A'}$ and its horizontal component.

h. Write a matrix equation for the translation $T_{A,A''}$ using matrix addition.

i. Write a matrix equation for the translation $T_{A,A''}$ using matrix multiplication.

ACTIVITY

When an object moves away from you, it appears to get smaller. When it moves toward you, it appears to become larger. Animators can use this phenomenon—along with the appropriate dilations—to create the illusion of motion.

 *teacher note*

Students may use technology to create graphs of the transformations found in this activity. Three sample calculator programs appear at the beginning of Activity **2**.

Student Outcomes

After completing the following exploration and discussion, students should be able to:

✷ use scalar multiplication to perform dilations

✷ use 3×3 matrix multiplication to perform dilations.

Exploration

In this exploration, you use matrix multiplication to produce dilations.

a. Refer to the graph of Skip you created in Activity **2.** List the coordinates for Skip's mouth, in homogeneous form, in matrix **M.**

b. 1. Using matrix **M,** draw Skip's mouth on another sheet of graph paper.

  2. On the same graph as in Step **1,** draw a dilation of Skip's mouth with center at the origin and a scale factor of 2.

  3. Write the matrix **M′** for the points that define the image of Skip's mouth, in homogeneous form.

c. Like translations, dilations also can be accomplished using matrix multiplication. For example, Skip's mouth can be dilated by a factor of 2 with center at the origin $(D_{O,2})$, by multiplying **M** on the left by a 3×3 dilation matrix **D.**

  The equation **D • M = M′** defines the dilation, where matrix **D** is of the following form:

$$D = \begin{bmatrix} a & b & c \\ d & e & f \\ g & h & i \end{bmatrix}$$

  Write out the matrices for the left-hand side of the equation **D • M = M′.** Multiply **D • M** and determine the resulting product matrix. Then, using the same method you employed in Exploration 2 of Activity **2,** determine the value of each variable in matrix **D.**

d. List the coordinates for Skip's entire face, in homogeneous form, in a matrix **S.**

  Note: When using some forms of technology to draw closed figures, you should enter the coordinates of each vertex in the order in which you would like them to be connected.

  To determine this order, trace your graph of Skip without lifting your pencil from the paper or retracing any segments. Mark both your starting and stopping points. You might have to list both of these points in the matrix—even if they have the same coordinates.

  Enter the coordinates of your starting point in the first column, the coordinates of the second point in the second column, those of the third point in the third column, and so on. List the coordinates of the stopping point in the last column of the matrix.

e. Use the matrix **D** you identified in Part c to dilate Skip's face by a factor of 2, with center at the origin.

Exploration

In this exploration, students draw and transform Skip on a coordinate plane.

a. Sample matrix:

$$\mathbf{M} = \begin{bmatrix} 2 & 5 & 4 & 3 \\ 2 & 2 & 1 & 1 \\ 1 & 1 & 1 & 1 \end{bmatrix}$$

b. 1–2. Sample graph:

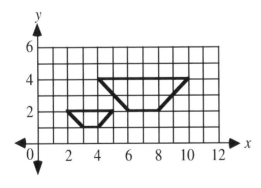

3. Sample matrix:

$$\mathbf{M'} = \begin{bmatrix} 4 & 10 & 8 & 6 \\ 4 & 4 & 2 & 2 \\ 1 & 1 & 1 & 1 \end{bmatrix}$$

c. As in Exploration **2** of Activity **2,** students use systems of equations to determine the elements of the dilation matrix. To identify the appropriate equations, students should create this product matrix:

$$\mathbf{D \bullet M} = \begin{bmatrix} 2a + 2b + c & 5a + 2b + c & 4a + b + c & 3a + b + c \\ 2d + 2e + f & 5d + 2e + f & 4d + e + f & 3d + e + f \\ 2g + 2h + i & 5g + 2h + i & 4g + h + i & 3g + h + i \end{bmatrix}$$

Setting the product matrix equal to the image matrix yields the resulting matrix equation:

$$\begin{bmatrix} 2a + 2b + c & 5a + 2b + c & 4a + b + c & 3a + b + c \\ 2d + 2e + f & 5d + 2e + f & 4d + e + f & 3d + e + f \\ 2g + 2h + i & 5g + 2h + i & 4g + h + i & 3g + h + i \end{bmatrix} = \begin{bmatrix} 4 & 10 & 8 & 6 \\ 4 & 4 & 2 & 2 \\ 1 & 1 & 1 & 1 \end{bmatrix}$$

The three equations containing *a*, *b*, and *c* correspond with the following system:

$$\begin{cases} 2a + 2b + c = 4 \\ 5a + 2b + c = 10 \\ 4a + b + c = 8 \end{cases}$$

This system can be solved using matrices as follows:

$$\begin{bmatrix} 2 & 2 & 1 \\ 5 & 2 & 1 \\ 4 & 1 & 1 \end{bmatrix} \bullet \begin{bmatrix} a \\ b \\ c \end{bmatrix} = \begin{bmatrix} 4 \\ 10 \\ 8 \end{bmatrix}$$

$$\begin{bmatrix} 2 & 2 & 1 \\ 5 & 2 & 1 \\ 4 & 1 & 1 \end{bmatrix}^{-1} \bullet \begin{bmatrix} 2 & 2 & 1 \\ 5 & 2 & 1 \\ 4 & 1 & 1 \end{bmatrix} \bullet \begin{bmatrix} a \\ b \\ c \end{bmatrix} = \begin{bmatrix} 2 & 2 & 1 \\ 5 & 2 & 1 \\ 4 & 1 & 1 \end{bmatrix}^{-1} \bullet \begin{bmatrix} 4 \\ 10 \\ 8 \end{bmatrix}$$

$$\begin{bmatrix} a \\ b \\ c \end{bmatrix} = \begin{bmatrix} 2 \\ 0 \\ 0 \end{bmatrix}$$

The three equations containing *d*, *e*, and *f* correspond with the following system:

$$\begin{cases} 2d + 2e + f = 4 \\ 5d + 2e + f = 4 \\ 4d + e + f = 2 \end{cases}$$

This system can be solved using matrices as follows:

$$\begin{bmatrix} 2 & 2 & 1 \\ 5 & 2 & 1 \\ 4 & 1 & 1 \end{bmatrix} \bullet \begin{bmatrix} d \\ e \\ f \end{bmatrix} = \begin{bmatrix} 4 \\ 4 \\ 2 \end{bmatrix}$$

$$\begin{bmatrix} 2 & 2 & 1 \\ 5 & 2 & 1 \\ 4 & 1 & 1 \end{bmatrix}^{-1} \bullet \begin{bmatrix} 2 & 2 & 1 \\ 5 & 2 & 1 \\ 4 & 1 & 1 \end{bmatrix} \bullet \begin{bmatrix} d \\ e \\ f \end{bmatrix} = \begin{bmatrix} 2 & 2 & 1 \\ 5 & 2 & 1 \\ 4 & 1 & 1 \end{bmatrix}^{-1} \bullet \begin{bmatrix} 4 \\ 4 \\ 2 \end{bmatrix}$$

$$\begin{bmatrix} d \\ e \\ f \end{bmatrix} = \begin{bmatrix} 0 \\ 2 \\ 0 \end{bmatrix}$$

The three equations containing *g*, *h*, and *i* correspond with the following system:

$$\begin{cases} 2g + 2h + i = 1 \\ 5g + 2h + i = 1 \\ 4g + h + i = 1 \end{cases}$$

This system can be solved using matrices as follows:

$$\begin{bmatrix} 2 & 2 & 1 \\ 5 & 2 & 1 \\ 4 & 1 & 1 \end{bmatrix} \bullet \begin{bmatrix} g \\ h \\ i \end{bmatrix} = \begin{bmatrix} 1 \\ 1 \\ 1 \end{bmatrix}$$

$$\begin{bmatrix} 2 & 2 & 1 \\ 5 & 2 & 1 \\ 4 & 1 & 1 \end{bmatrix}^{-1} \bullet \begin{bmatrix} 2 & 2 & 1 \\ 5 & 2 & 1 \\ 4 & 1 & 1 \end{bmatrix} \bullet \begin{bmatrix} g \\ h \\ u \end{bmatrix} = \begin{bmatrix} 2 & 2 & 1 \\ 5 & 2 & 1 \\ 4 & 1 & 1 \end{bmatrix}^{-1} \bullet \begin{bmatrix} 1 \\ 1 \\ 1 \end{bmatrix}$$

$$\begin{bmatrix} g \\ h \\ i \end{bmatrix} = \begin{bmatrix} 0 \\ 0 \\ 1 \end{bmatrix}$$

The matrix that, when multiplied on the left, produces a dilation with a scale factor of 2 and center at the origin is:

$$\mathbf{D} = \begin{bmatrix} 2 & 0 & 0 \\ 0 & 2 & 0 \\ 0 & 0 & 1 \end{bmatrix}$$

d. Skip can be drawn without lifting a pencil or retracing a segment using the circuit shown below. Because Skip can be drawn with a circuit, students can use technology to graph the cartoon without adding additional, unwanted segments. **Note:** There are several other ways to trace through the figure. Only one possibility is shown here.

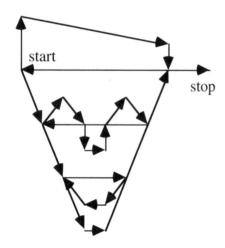

In the following sample matrix, the coordinates of some points have been repeated, to obtain the graph of a closed figure.

$$\mathbf{S} = \begin{bmatrix} 0 & 0 & 7 & 7 & 0 & 1 & 2 & 3 & 3 & 4 & 4 & 5 & 6 & 1 & 2 & 5 & 4 & 3 & 2 & 3 & 4 & 7 & 9 \\ 6 & 8 & 7 & 6 & 6 & 4 & 5 & 4 & 3 & 3 & 4 & 5 & 4 & 4 & 2 & 2 & 1 & 1 & 2 & 0 & 0 & 6 & 6 \end{bmatrix}$$

e. The elements in matrix **S′** are two times greater than the corresponding elements in matrix **S**.

Discussion

a. In Part **e** of the exploration, why must matrix **S** be multiplied on the left by matrix **D**?

b. What 3×3 matrix, when multiplied on the left, would result in each of the following dilations?

   1. $D_{O,3}$
   2. $D_{O,1/4}$
   3. $D_{O,1}$

c. In **scalar multiplication**, each element of a matrix is multiplied by a constant.

   Describe how the product of a scalar and the 3×3 identity matrix could be used to find the matrix that, when multiplied on the left, produces a dilation with center at the origin.

d. How could you represent a dilation by a factor of 2, with center at the origin ($D_{O,2}$), using scalar multiplication by 2?

e. If Skip is transformed by $D_{O,n}$, how could you determine the matrix of points, in homogeneous form, that represents Skip's image?

f. In a dilation, what is the geometric relationship between an image and its preimage?

Warm-Up

1. Write a 3×3 matrix for a dilation by each of the following scale factors, with center at the origin.

   a. 3.3

   b. 1/4

   c. n

2. Without using a calculator, determine the product of each matrix multiplication below.

   a. $\begin{bmatrix} 2 & 0 & 0 \\ 0 & 2 & 0 \\ 0 & 0 & 1 \end{bmatrix} \bullet \begin{bmatrix} 1 & 3 & -5 & 7 & 9 \\ 0 & -3 & 4 & 8 & 6 \\ 1 & 1 & 1 & 1 & 1 \end{bmatrix}$

   b. $\begin{bmatrix} 1/2 & 0 & 0 \\ 0 & 1/2 & 0 \\ 0 & 0 & 1 \end{bmatrix} \bullet \begin{bmatrix} 10 & -4 & 5 \\ -3 & 8 & 2 \\ 1 & 1 & 1 \end{bmatrix}$

Discussion

a. To multiply matrices, the number of columns in the matrix on the left must equal the number of rows in the matrix on the right.

b. 1. $\begin{bmatrix} 3 & 0 & 0 \\ 0 & 3 & 0 \\ 0 & 0 & 1 \end{bmatrix}$

   2. $\begin{bmatrix} 1/4 & 0 & 0 \\ 0 & 1/4 & 0 \\ 0 & 0 & 1 \end{bmatrix}$

   3. $\begin{bmatrix} 1 & 0 & 0 \\ 0 & 1 & 0 \\ 0 & 0 & 1 \end{bmatrix}$

c. Sample response: The following equation shows the product of the identity matrix and a scalar k. In a dilation matrix, the element in row 3, column 3, is 1, not k.

$$k \bullet \begin{bmatrix} 1 & 0 & 0 \\ 0 & 1 & 0 \\ 0 & 0 & 1 \end{bmatrix} = \begin{bmatrix} k & 0 & 0 \\ 0 & k & 0 \\ 0 & 0 & k \end{bmatrix}$$

d. Sample response: If the preimage points are not represented in homogeneous form, a dilation of scale factor 2, with center at the origin, could be produced by multiplying the preimage matrix by the scalar 2.

e. Sample response: To determine the matrix that represents the image of Skip, you could multiply each entry in the first two rows by n. Or you could multiply on the left by the 3×3 matrix:

$$\begin{bmatrix} n & 0 & 0 \\ 0 & n & 0 \\ 0 & 0 & 1 \end{bmatrix}$$

f. Sample response: In a dilation, the image and preimage are similar. They have the same shape and their corresponding angles are congruent. The lengths of corresponding sides are proportional.

 teacher note

In Problem **3.5**, students are introduced to compositions of transformations. They must complete this problem before proceeding to Activity **4**.

To complete Problem **3.8**, each student will require a copy of the template. A blackline master appears in the Teacher Resources for this module.

Warm-Up

1. a. $\begin{bmatrix} 3.3 & 0 & 0 \\ 0 & 3.3 & 0 \\ 0 & 0 & 1 \end{bmatrix}$

   b. $\begin{bmatrix} 1/4 & 0 & 0 \\ 0 & 1/4 & 0 \\ 0 & 0 & 1 \end{bmatrix}$

   c. $\begin{bmatrix} n & 0 & 0 \\ 0 & n & 0 \\ 0 & 0 & 1 \end{bmatrix}$

2. a. $\begin{bmatrix} 2 & 6 & -10 & 14 & 18 \\ 0 & -6 & 8 & 16 & 12 \\ 1 & 1 & 1 & 1 & 1 \end{bmatrix}$

   b. $\begin{bmatrix} 5 & -2 & 5/2 \\ -3/2 & 4 & 1 \\ 1 & 1 & 1 \end{bmatrix}$

c. $\begin{bmatrix} 2 & 4 & -10 & -14 & 6 \\ 0 & -2 & 8 & -4 & 4 \\ 1 & 1 & 1 & 1 & 1 \end{bmatrix}$

3. a. $\begin{bmatrix} -7 & -14 & -21 & 28 \\ 21 & 7 & 0 & -28 \\ 1 & 1 & 1 & 1 \end{bmatrix}$

   b. $\begin{bmatrix} -7 & -14 & -21 & 28 \\ 21 & 7 & 0 & -28 \end{bmatrix}$

4. Sample response: Both products represent a dilation with a scale factor of 7 and center at the origin. Only the form in which they are written is different. The matrix in Part **a** is written in homogeneous form.

Assignment

Problems suitable for use as assessment items are identified by an asterisk (*).

3.1 The dilation of Skip by a scale factor of 3 with center at the origin can be accomplished using the matrix operation $3 \bullet \mathbf{S}$, where **S** is a $2 \times n$ matrix representation for Skip. Sample graph:

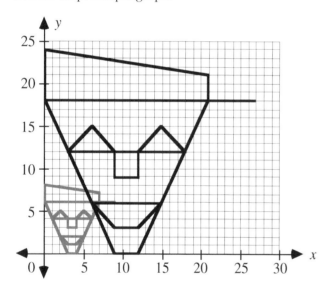

3.2 a. Answers may vary. Sample matrix:
$$\mathbf{P} = \begin{bmatrix} 0 & 2 & 5 & 6 & 3 & 0 \\ 3 & 7 & 5 & 2 & 0 & 3 \\ 1 & 1 & 1 & 1 & 1 & 1 \end{bmatrix}$$

   b. Sample response using multiplication by a 3×3 matrix:
$$\mathbf{P'} = \begin{bmatrix} 3.5 & 0 & 0 \\ 0 & 3.5 & 0 \\ 0 & 0 & 1 \end{bmatrix} \bullet \begin{bmatrix} 0 & 2 & 5 & 6 & 3 & 0 \\ 3 & 7 & 5 & 2 & 0 & 3 \\ 1 & 1 & 1 & 1 & 1 & 1 \end{bmatrix}$$

c. $\begin{bmatrix} 2/3 & 0 & 0 \\ 0 & 2/3 & 0 \\ 0 & 0 & 1 \end{bmatrix} \bullet \begin{bmatrix} 3 & 6 & -15 & 0 & 9 \\ 0 & -3 & 12 & -6 & 6 \\ 1 & 1 & 1 & 1 & 1 \end{bmatrix}$

3. Determine the product of each of the following matrix expressions.

   a. $\begin{bmatrix} 7 & 0 & 0 \\ 0 & 7 & 0 \\ 0 & 0 & 1 \end{bmatrix} \bullet \begin{bmatrix} -1 & -2 & -3 & 4 \\ 3 & 1 & 0 & -4 \\ 1 & 1 & 1 & 1 \end{bmatrix}$

   b. $7 \bullet \begin{bmatrix} -1 & -2 & -3 & 4 \\ 3 & 1 & 0 & -4 \end{bmatrix}$

4. Explain why the two products in Warm-Up **3**, when plotted on a rectangular coordinate system, result in the same graph.

Assignment

3.1 Use scalar multiplication to represent a dilation of Skip by a scale factor of 3, with center at the origin. Graph both the preimage and the image.

3.2 a. Write a matrix of points, in homogeneous form, to represent the vertices of the polygon below. List the points in an order that results in a closed figure when graphed using technology.

   b. Write a matrix expression that produces a dilation of the polygon in Part **a** by a scale factor of 3.5, with center at the origin.

   c. Determine the coordinates of the image polygon. Write the results in a matrix.

3.3 In Parts **a–c** below, represent all points in homogeneous form.

   a. Write a matrix expression that shows the transformation of Skip under the dilation $D_{O,5}$.

156 Module 5 ■ *Crazy Cartoons*

c. Sample matrix:
$$\mathbf{P'} = \begin{bmatrix} 0 & 7 & 17.5 & 21 & 10.5 & 0 \\ 10.5 & 24.5 & 17.5 & 7 & 0 & 10.5 \\ 1 & 1 & 1 & 1 & 1 & 1 \end{bmatrix}$$

3.3 a. Sample response:
$$\mathbf{S'} = \begin{bmatrix} 5 & 0 & 0 \\ 0 & 5 & 0 \\ 0 & 0 & 1 \end{bmatrix} \bullet \mathbf{S}$$

   b. Sample response:
$$\mathbf{C'} = \begin{bmatrix} 3/4 & 0 & 0 \\ 0 & 3/4 & 0 \\ 0 & 0 & 1 \end{bmatrix} \bullet \begin{bmatrix} 9 & 0 & 0 & 7 & 7 \\ 6 & 6 & 8 & 7 & 6 \\ 1 & 1 & 1 & 1 & 1 \end{bmatrix}$$

   c. Using matrix **M** from Part **b** of the exploration:

$$\mathbf{D} \bullet \mathbf{M} = \mathbf{M'}$$

$$\begin{bmatrix} 2/3 & 0 & 0 \\ 0 & 2/3 & 0 \\ 0 & 0 & 1 \end{bmatrix} \bullet \begin{bmatrix} 2 & 5 & 4 & 3 \\ 2 & 2 & 1 & 1 \\ 1 & 1 & 1 & 1 \end{bmatrix} = \mathbf{M'}$$

$$\begin{bmatrix} 8/3 & 10/3 & 8/3 & 2 \\ 4/3 & 4/3 & 4/3 & 4/3 \\ 1 & 1 & 1 & 1 \end{bmatrix} = \mathbf{M'}$$

b. Write a matrix expression that shows the transformation of Skip's cap under the dilation $D_{O,0.75}$.

c. Use technology to find the coordinates of the image of Skip's mouth under the dilation $D_{O,2/3}$.

3.4 The following diagram shows three similar polygons. In Parts **a–d** below, represent all points in homogeneous form.

a. Write a matrix to represent polygon *B*.

b. If polygon *B* is the preimage, what scale factors are needed to create polygons *A* and *C*, respectively?

c. Consider a dilation, with center at the origin, in which polygon *B* is the preimage and polygon *A* is the image. Write a matrix equation to describe this transformation.

d. Consider a dilation, with center at the origin, in which polygon *A* is the preimage and polygon *C* is the image. Write a matrix equation to describe this transformation.

3.5 When more than one transformation is performed on a figure, the result is a **composition of transformations.**

a. Consider the hexagon described by matrix **P** below.

$$\mathbf{P} = \begin{bmatrix} 3 & 2 & -1 & -2 & -1 & 2 \\ 1 & 7 & 7 & 1 & -4 & -4 \\ 1 & 1 & 1 & 1 & 1 & 1 \end{bmatrix}$$

1. Write a matrix equation to translate matrix **P** by the vector $\langle 3, -8 \rangle$.

2. Write a matrix equation to dilate the image from Step **1** by a scale factor of 2, with center at the origin.

3. Create a graph of the preimage **P** and the image of the composite transformation (after Step **2**).

---

* 3.4 **a.** Sample matrix:

$$\mathbf{B} = \begin{bmatrix} a & i & g & e & c \\ b & j & h & f & d \\ 1 & 1 & 1 & 1 & 1 \end{bmatrix}$$

b. The scale factor from *B* to *A* is 1/2 or 0.5. The scale factor from *B* to *C* is 3/1.

c. Sample response:

$$\mathbf{A} = \mathbf{D} \bullet \mathbf{B}$$

$$\mathbf{A} = \begin{bmatrix} 1/2 & 0 & 0 \\ 0 & 1/2 & 0 \\ 0 & 0 & 1 \end{bmatrix} \bullet \begin{bmatrix} a & i & g & e & c \\ b & j & h & f & d \\ 1 & 1 & 1 & 1 & 1 \end{bmatrix}$$

$$\mathbf{A} = \begin{bmatrix} a/2 & i/2 & g/2 & e/2 & c/2 \\ b/2 & j/2 & h/2 & f/2 & d/2 \\ 1 & 1 & 1 & 1 & 1 \end{bmatrix}$$

d. The scale factor from polygon *A* to polygon *C* is 6. The matrix equation below results in the dilation of polygon *A* to polygon *C*, where matrix **D** is the dilation matrix.

$$\mathbf{C} = \mathbf{D} \bullet \mathbf{A}$$

$$\mathbf{C} = \begin{bmatrix} 6 & 0 & 0 \\ 0 & 6 & 0 \\ 0 & 0 & 1 \end{bmatrix} \bullet \begin{bmatrix} a/2 & i/2 & g/2 & e/2 & c/2 \\ b/2 & j/2 & h/2 & f/2 & d/2 \\ 1 & 1 & 1 & 1 & 1 \end{bmatrix}$$

$$\mathbf{C} = \begin{bmatrix} 3a & 3i & 3g & 3e & 3c \\ 3b & 3j & 3h & 3f & 3d \\ 1 & 1 & 1 & 1 & 1 \end{bmatrix}$$

✳ ✳ ✳ ✳ ✳

* 3.5 **a. 1.** Sample response:

$$\mathbf{P}' = \mathbf{T} \bullet \mathbf{P}$$

$$\mathbf{P}' = \begin{bmatrix} 1 & 0 & 3 \\ 0 & 1 & -8 \\ 0 & 0 & 1 \end{bmatrix} \bullet \begin{bmatrix} 3 & 2 & -1 & -2 & -1 & 2 \\ 1 & 7 & 7 & 1 & -4 & -4 \\ 1 & 1 & 1 & 1 & 1 & 1 \end{bmatrix}$$

$$\mathbf{P}' = \begin{bmatrix} 6 & 5 & 2 & 1 & 2 & 5 \\ -7 & -1 & -1 & -7 & -12 & -12 \\ 1 & 1 & 1 & 1 & 1 & 1 \end{bmatrix}$$

2. Sample response:

$$\mathbf{P}'' = \mathbf{D} \bullet \mathbf{P}'$$

$$\mathbf{P}'' = \begin{bmatrix} 2 & 0 & 0 \\ 0 & 2 & 0 \\ 0 & 0 & 1 \end{bmatrix} \bullet \begin{bmatrix} 6 & 5 & 2 & 1 & 2 & 5 \\ -7 & -1 & -1 & -7 & -12 & -12 \\ 1 & 1 & 1 & 1 & 1 & 1 \end{bmatrix}$$

$$\mathbf{P}'' = \begin{bmatrix} 12 & 10 & 4 & 2 & 4 & 10 \\ -14 & -2 & -2 & -14 & -24 & -24 \\ 1 & 1 & 1 & 1 & 1 & 1 \end{bmatrix}$$

3. The final image has vertices at $(12, -14)$, $(10, -2)$, $(4, -2)$, $(2, -14)$, $(4, -24)$, and $(10, -24)$. Sample graph:

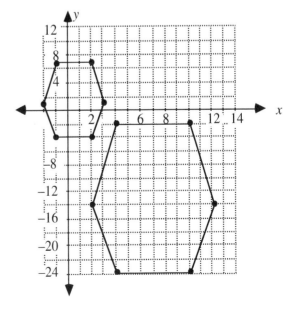

4. In the sample equation below, **P″** is the matrix representation of the final image, **D** is the dilation matrix, **T** is the translation matrix, and **P** is the matrix representation of the original preimage: **P″ = D • T • P.**

The single transformation matrix that results in the final image **P″** is the product of **D** and **T:**

$$\mathbf{D \bullet T} = \begin{bmatrix} 2 & 0 & 0 \\ 0 & 2 & 0 \\ 0 & 0 & 1 \end{bmatrix} \bullet \begin{bmatrix} 1 & 0 & 3 \\ 0 & 1 & -8 \\ 0 & 0 & 0 \end{bmatrix} = \begin{bmatrix} 2 & 0 & 6 \\ 0 & 2 & -16 \\ 0 & 0 & 1 \end{bmatrix}$$

b. 1. Performing the dilation first:

P′ = D • P

$$\mathbf{P'} = \begin{bmatrix} 2 & 0 & 0 \\ 0 & 2 & 0 \\ 0 & 0 & 1 \end{bmatrix} \bullet \begin{bmatrix} 3 & 2 & -1 & -2 & -1 & 2 \\ 1 & 7 & 7 & 1 & -4 & -4 \\ 1 & 1 & 1 & 1 & 1 & 1 \end{bmatrix}$$

$$\mathbf{P'} = \begin{bmatrix} 6 & 4 & -2 & -4 & -2 & 4 \\ 2 & 14 & 14 & 2 & -8 & -8 \\ 1 & 1 & 1 & 1 & 1 & 1 \end{bmatrix}$$

2. Followed by the translation:

P″ = T • P′

$$\mathbf{P''} = \begin{bmatrix} 1 & 0 & 3 \\ 0 & 1 & -8 \\ 0 & 0 & 1 \end{bmatrix} \bullet \begin{bmatrix} 6 & 4 & -2 & -4 & -2 & 4 \\ 2 & 14 & 14 & 2 & -8 & -8 \\ 1 & 1 & 1 & 1 & 1 & 1 \end{bmatrix}$$

$$\mathbf{P''} = \begin{bmatrix} 9 & 7 & 1 & -1 & 1 & 7 \\ -6 & 6 & 6 & -6 & -16 & -16 \\ 1 & 1 & 1 & 1 & 1 & 1 \end{bmatrix}$$

3. The final image has vertices at (9,–6), (7,6), (1,6), (–1,–6), (1,–16), and (7,–16). Sample graph:

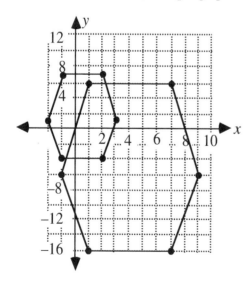

4. If possible, write a single matrix equation that describes the composition of transformations. If a single matrix equation is not possible, explain why not. If it is, determine a single transformation matrix that produces the final image.

b. Reverse the order of the transformations, then repeat Part **a.**

c. Compare your results from Parts **a** and **b.** Did you think they would be the same? Were they? Why or why not?

3.6 a. Draw the triangle formed by the points A(5,10), B(–5,5), and C(10,–15). On the same sheet of graph paper, draw the images of this triangle under four dilations with center at the origin O and scale factors of 5/4, 3/2, 7/4, and 2.

b. Suppose that each image was taped to a separate file card and the cards arranged in the order given in Part **a.** If you flipped the cards like the pages of a book, what would appear to happen to the original triangle?

c. For any pair of images in Part **a,** describe how to find a dilation that transforms one image to the other.

* * * * *

3.7 The following figure shows two views from the window of a spacecraft traveling at a constant velocity. As the spacecraft approaches earth, the planet's image appears to dilate.

6:00 P.M. Tuesday   1:00 A.M. Wednesday

a. Use a ruler to determine the difference in scale between the two images of earth.

b. If the spacecraft continues to approach earth at the same velocity, what will the diameter of the earth's image be after another 7 hr?

4. In the sample equation below, **P″** is the matrix representation of the final image, **T** is the translation matrix, **D** is the dilation matrix, and **P** is the matrix representation of the original preimage: **P″ = T • D • P.**

The single transformation matrix that results in the final image **P″** is the product of **T** and **D:**

$$\mathbf{T \bullet D} = \begin{bmatrix} 1 & 0 & 3 \\ 0 & 1 & -8 \\ 0 & 0 & 0 \end{bmatrix} \bullet \begin{bmatrix} 2 & 0 & 0 \\ 0 & 2 & 0 \\ 0 & 0 & 1 \end{bmatrix} = \begin{bmatrix} 2 & 0 & 3 \\ 0 & 2 & -8 \\ 0 & 0 & 1 \end{bmatrix}$$

c. Sample response: The transformations are not equivalent. The two figures are congruent, but positioned differently. The image in Part **a** is 3 units to the right and 8 units down from the image in Part **b.** I did not think they would be the same, because matrix multiplication is not commutative.

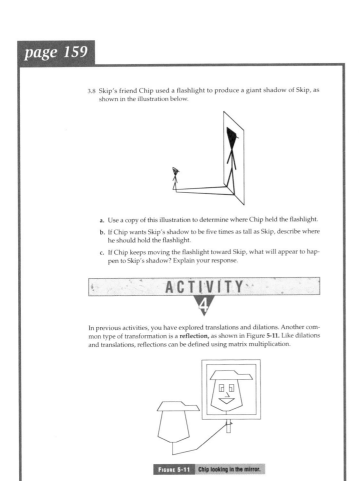

3.8 Skip's friend Chip used a flashlight to produce a giant shadow of Skip, as shown in the illustration below.

a. Use a copy of this illustration to determine where Chip held the flashlight.

b. If Chip wants Skip's shadow to be five times as tall as Skip, describe where he should hold the flashlight.

c. If Chip keeps moving the flashlight toward Skip, what will appear to happen to Skip's shadow? Explain your response.

ACTIVITY 4

In previous activities, you have explored translations and dilations. Another common type of transformation is a **reflection**, as shown in Figure 5-11. Like dilations and translations, reflections can be defined using matrix multiplication.

FIGURE 5-11 Chip looking in the mirror.

Module 5 ■ *Crazy Cartoons* 159

3.6 **a.** Sample graph:

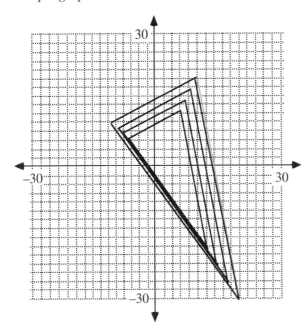

b. Sample response: The triangle's sides would appear to double in length, making the triangle appear to grow or move closer like an animated cartoon.

---

c. Sample response: Assign one figure to represent the preimage and the other to represent the image. Using the origin as the center of dilation, dilate the preimage by a scale factor equivalent to the ratio of the corresponding lengths of the image to the preimage.

✳ ✳ ✳ ✳ ✳

3.7 **a.** Sample response: At 6:00 P.M. on Tuesday, the diameter of the earth's image appears to be about 0.8 cm. At 1:00 A.M. on Wednesday, the diameter of the earth's image appears to be about 2.3 cm. The scale factor is about $2.3/0.8 \approx 2.9$.

b. Sample response: If the effect on the size of the apparent image is the same as in the previous 7 hr, the diameter of the earth's image should appear to be about 6.7 cm, which is 2.9 times larger than 2.3 cm.

3.8 **a.** As shown in the diagram below, the position of the flashlight can be determined by drawing the lines that connect corresponding vertices.

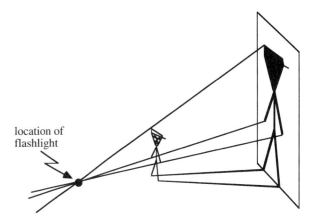

location of flashlight

b. Sample response: Chip should hold the flashlight so that its distance from the wall is five times its distance from Skip. Then the ratio PX'/PX, or the scale factor, will equal 5.

c. Sample response: As Chip moves the flashlight toward Skip, his shadow will grow larger. This is because the ratio of the distance from the flashlight to the wall to the distance from the flashlight to Skip becomes larger.

ACTIVITY 4

In this activity, students examine reflections in the coordinate plane. The exploration builds on students' previous experiences with reflections in the Level 1 module, "Reflect on This."

teacher note

A brief assessment of the mathematical content in Activities **3** and **4,** for use at your discretion, appears in the Teacher Resources for this module.

Materials List

- graph paper (one sheet per student)
- ruler (one per student)
- acetate (one sheet per group) or tracing paper (four sheets per group)
- overhead markers for use with acetate (one per group)
- MIRAs™ (optional replacement for tracing paper and acetate)

Technology

- matrix manipulator
- spreadsheet
- geometry utility (optional)

Student Outcomes

After completing the following exploration and discussion, students should be able to:

✴ use matrix multiplication to perform reflections in the lines $x = 0$, $y = 0$, $y = x$, and $y = -x$

✴ describe the geometric relationships between the preimage and the image in reflections, translations, and dilations.

teacher note

To save time, you may wish to conduct the following exploration as a class demonstration.

Exploration

In this exploration, students examine the use of matrix multiplication to produce reflections in the x- and y-axes and the lines $y = x$ and $y = -x$.

Exploration

In this exploration, you determine 3×3 transformation matrices to produce reflections in various lines.

a. Matrix **P** below describes the vertices of a triangle in homogeneous form.

$$\mathbf{P} = \begin{bmatrix} 2 & 4 & 5 \\ 1 & 3 & 1 \\ 1 & 1 & 1 \end{bmatrix}$$

1. Graph this triangle on a coordinate plane.
2. Consider the x-axis as a mirror. Graph the reflection of the triangle in the x-axis.
3. Write a matrix **P′** for the coordinates of the image in homogeneous form.
4. Draw line segments connecting the corresponding vertices of the preimage and the image.
5. Describe the relationship between the line of reflection and each segment that you drew in Step **4.**

b. Matrix **H** below describes the vertices of a quadrilateral.

$$\mathbf{H} = \begin{bmatrix} -1 & 2 & 6 & 8 \\ 0 & 3 & 4 & -2 \\ 1 & 1 & 1 & 1 \end{bmatrix}$$

1. Graph this quadrilateral on a coordinate plane.
2. Graph the reflection of the quadrilateral in the x-axis.
3. Write a matrix **H′** for the coordinates of the image.

c. Repeat Parts **a** and **b** using the y-axis as a mirror.

d. 1. On a new coordinate system, graph the line $y = x$.
   2. Reflect the triangle described by matrix **P** in this line and write a matrix for the coordinates of the image.
   3. Repeat Steps **1** and **2** using the quadrilateral defined by matrix **H**.

e. Reflect the polygons described by matrices **P** and **H** in the line $y = -x$.

160   Module 5 ■ *Crazy Cartoons*

a. 1–2. Sample graph:

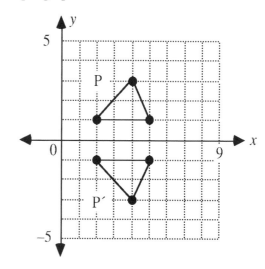

3. Sample matrix:

$$\mathbf{P′} = \begin{bmatrix} 2 & 4 & 5 \\ -1 & -3 & -1 \\ 1 & 1 & 1 \end{bmatrix}$$

4–5. The x-axis is the perpendicular bisector of the segments that connect the corresponding points of the preimage and image.

b. 1–2. In the following sample graph, the solid lines represent the preimage:

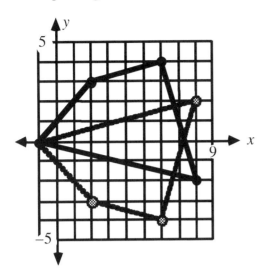

3. Sample matrix:

$$\mathbf{H}' = \begin{bmatrix} -1 & 2 & 6 & 8 \\ 0 & -3 & -4 & 2 \\ 1 & 1 & 1 & 1 \end{bmatrix}$$

c. The following sample graph shows the triangle represented by matrix **P** reflected in the *y*-axis:

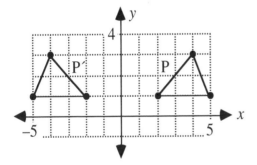

The coordinates of the image can be represented in the matrix below:

$$\mathbf{P}' = \begin{bmatrix} -2 & -4 & -5 \\ 1 & 3 & 1 \\ 1 & 1 & 1 \end{bmatrix}$$

The following sample graph shows the quadrilateral represented by matrix **H** reflected in the *y*-axis:

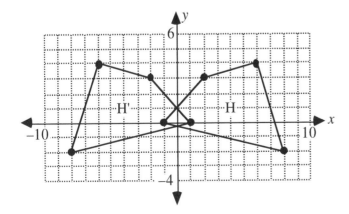

The coordinates of the image can be represented in the matrix below:

$$\mathbf{H}' = \begin{bmatrix} 1 & -2 & -6 & -8 \\ 0 & 3 & 4 & -2 \\ 1 & 1 & 1 & 1 \end{bmatrix}$$

d. 1. Sample graph:

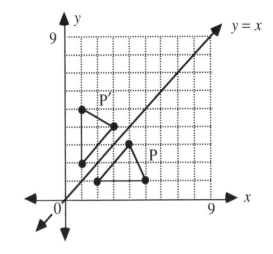

2. Sample image matrix:

$$\mathbf{P}' = \begin{bmatrix} 1 & 3 & 1 \\ 2 & 4 & 5 \\ 1 & 1 & 1 \end{bmatrix}$$

3. Sample graph:

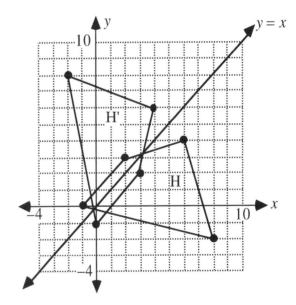

The coordinates of the image can be represented in the matrix below:

$$\mathbf{H}' = \begin{bmatrix} 0 & 3 & 4 & -2 \\ -1 & 2 & 6 & 8 \\ 1 & 1 & 1 & 1 \end{bmatrix}$$

e. Sample graph for the triangle represented by matrix **P**:

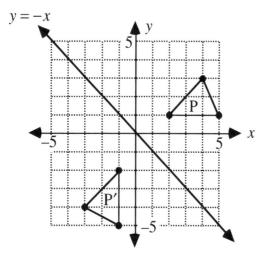

The coordinates of the image can be represented in the matrix below:

$$\mathbf{P'} = \begin{bmatrix} -1 & -3 & -1 \\ -2 & -4 & -5 \\ 1 & 1 & 1 \end{bmatrix}$$

Sample graph for the quadrilateral represented by matrix **H**:

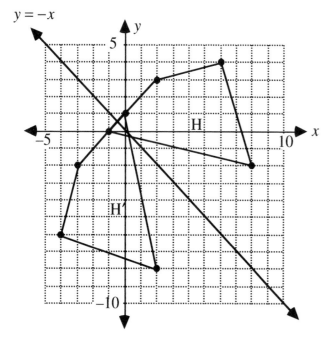

The coordinates of the image can be represented in the matrix below:

$$\mathbf{H'} = \begin{bmatrix} 0 & -3 & -4 & 2 \\ 1 & -2 & -6 & -8 \\ 1 & 1 & 1 & 1 \end{bmatrix}$$

f. Matrix **A** reflects a set of points with respect to the line $y = x$. Matrix **B** reflects a set of points with respect to the y-axis. Matrix **C** reflects a set of points with respect to the line $y = -x$. Matrix **D** reflects a set of points with respect to the x-axis.

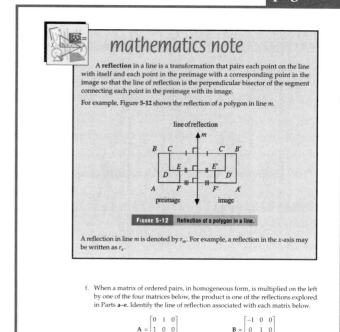

mathematics note

A **reflection** in a line is a transformation that pairs each point on the line with itself and each point in the preimage with a corresponding point in the image so that the line of reflection is the perpendicular bisector of the segment connecting each point in the preimage with its image.

For example, Figure **5-12** shows the reflection of a polygon in line *m*.

FIGURE 5-12   Reflection of a polygon in a line.

A reflection in line *m* is denoted by r_m. For example, a reflection in the *x*-axis may be written as r_x.

f. When a matrix of ordered pairs, in homogeneous form, is multiplied on the left by one of the four matrices below, the product is one of the reflections explored in Parts **a–e**. Identify the line of reflection associated with each matrix below.

$$\mathbf{A} = \begin{bmatrix} 0 & 1 & 0 \\ 1 & 0 & 0 \\ 0 & 0 & 1 \end{bmatrix} \qquad \mathbf{B} = \begin{bmatrix} -1 & 0 & 0 \\ 0 & 1 & 0 \\ 0 & 0 & 1 \end{bmatrix}$$

$$\mathbf{C} = \begin{bmatrix} 0 & -1 & 0 \\ -1 & 0 & 0 \\ 0 & 0 & 1 \end{bmatrix} \qquad \mathbf{D} = \begin{bmatrix} 1 & 0 & 0 \\ 0 & -1 & 0 \\ 0 & 0 & 1 \end{bmatrix}$$

Discussion

a. 1. What patterns did you observe in the preimage and image matrices when reflecting an object in the x-axis?

   2. What patterns did you observe when reflecting in the y-axis?

b. Using your results from Parts **d** and **e** of the exploration, suggest a general statement that describes a reflection in each of the following lines:

   1. $y = x$
   2. $y = -x.$

c. Describe the effect that each matrix in Part **f** of the exploration has on the x- and y-coordinates of the preimage.

d. 1. Compare the 3×3 reflection matrices with the 3×3 matrices for dilations and translations.

   2. What reflection would you expect from the matrix below?

$$\begin{bmatrix} 1 & 0 & 0 \\ 0 & 1 & 0 \\ 0 & 0 & 1 \end{bmatrix}$$

e. How would you summarize the geometric relationships between the preimage and the image in reflections, translations, and dilations?

Warm-Up

1. Identify the letters that could be formed by reflecting half of the letter in a mirror.

A B C D E F G H I J K L M N O
P Q R S T U V W X Y Z

2. Find the image of point (–2,7) under each of the following:

   a. a reflection in the x-axis
   b. a reflection in the y-axis
   c. a reflection in the line $y = x$
   d. a reflection in the line $y = -x.$

3. Matrix **M** defines the vertices of a triangle.

$$\mathbf{M} = \begin{bmatrix} -5 & -5 & -10 \\ 6 & 3 & 3 \\ 1 & 1 & 1 \end{bmatrix}$$

Discussion

a. 1. Sample response: When reflecting in the x-axis, the x-values remain unchanged but each y-value is the additive inverse of the corresponding y-value in the preimage.

   2. Sample response: When reflecting in the y-axis, the y-values remain unchanged but each x-value is the additive inverse of the corresponding x-value in the preimage.

b. 1. Sample response: When reflecting in the line $y = x$, the x and y-values are switched.

   2. Sample response: When reflecting in the line $y = -x$, the x and y-values are switched and the signs are changed.

c. Sample response: When multiplied on the left, matrix A switches the x- and y-coordinates of the preimage. Matrix **B** negates the x-coordinates of the preimage. Matrix **C** switches and negates the x- and y-coordinates of the preimage. Matrix **D** negates the y-coordinates of the preimage.

d. 1. Sample response: All three transformations can be done using multiplication on the left by a 3×3 matrix. In reflections and dilations, the elements in rows 1 and 2, columns 1 and 2 determine the transformation. In a translation, the elements in rows 1 and 2, column 3 determine the transformation.

   2. Sample response: No reflection would occur because the matrix is the 3×3 identity matrix.

e. Sample response: Dilations with positive scale factors other than 1 produce images that are similar to the preimage. Translations and reflections produce images that are congruent to the preimage.

Warm-Up

1. A, B, C, D, E, H, I, M, O, T, U, V, W, X, and Y
2. a. (–2,–7)
   b. (2,7)
   c. (7,–2)
   d. (–7,2)

3. **a.** $\begin{bmatrix} 5 & 5 & 10 \\ 6 & 3 & 3 \\ 1 & 1 & 1 \end{bmatrix}$; r_y where y is the y-axis

b. $\begin{bmatrix} -6 & -3 & -3 \\ 5 & 5 & 10 \\ 1 & 1 & 1 \end{bmatrix}$; r_l where l is the line $y = -x$

c. $\begin{bmatrix} -15 & -15 & -30 \\ 18 & 9 & 9 \\ 1 & 1 & 1 \end{bmatrix}$; $D_{O,3}$

d. $\begin{bmatrix} -1 & -1 & -6 \\ 13 & 10 & 10 \\ 1 & 1 & 1 \end{bmatrix}$; $T_{P,P'}$ where P to P' is represented by $\langle 4,7 \rangle$

e. $\begin{bmatrix} 6 & 3 & 3 \\ -5 & -5 & -10 \\ 1 & 1 & 1 \end{bmatrix}$; r_m where m is the line $y = x$

f. $\begin{bmatrix} -5 & -5 & -10 \\ -6 & -3 & -3 \\ 1 & 1 & 1 \end{bmatrix}$; r_x where x is the x-axis

4. **a.** $\begin{bmatrix} -a & -b & -c & -d \\ e & f & g & h \\ 1 & 1 & 1 & 1 \end{bmatrix}$; r_y where y is the y-axis

b. $\begin{bmatrix} -e & -f & -g & -h \\ -a & -b & -c & -d \\ 1 & 1 & 1 & 1 \end{bmatrix}$; r_l where l is the line $y = -x$

c. $\begin{bmatrix} 3a & 3b & 3c & 3d \\ 3e & 3f & 3g & 3h \\ 1 & 1 & 1 & 1 \end{bmatrix}$; $D_{O,3}$

d. $\begin{bmatrix} a+4 & b+4 & c+4 & d+3 \\ e+7 & f+4 & g+4 & h+4 \\ 1 & 1 & 1 & 1 \end{bmatrix}$; $T_{P,P'}$ where P to P' is $\langle 4,7 \rangle$

e. $\begin{bmatrix} e & f & g & h \\ a & b & c & d \\ 1 & 1 & 1 & 1 \end{bmatrix}$; r_m where m is the line $y = x$

f. $\begin{bmatrix} a & b & c & d \\ -e & -f & -g & -h \\ 1 & 1 & 1 & 1 \end{bmatrix}$; r_x where x is the x-axis

Assignment

Problems suitable for use as assessment items are identified by an asterisk (*).

In Parts **a–f** below, perform the indicated operations and use mathematical notation to describe the resulting transformation.

a. $\begin{bmatrix} -1 & 0 & 0 \\ 0 & 1 & 0 \\ 0 & 0 & 1 \end{bmatrix} \bullet \mathbf{M}$

b. $\begin{bmatrix} 0 & -1 & 0 \\ -1 & 0 & 0 \\ 0 & 0 & 1 \end{bmatrix} \bullet \mathbf{M}$

c. $\begin{bmatrix} 3 & 0 & 0 \\ 0 & 3 & 0 \\ 0 & 0 & 1 \end{bmatrix} \bullet \mathbf{M}$

d. $\begin{bmatrix} 1 & 0 & 4 \\ 0 & 1 & 7 \\ 0 & 0 & 1 \end{bmatrix} \bullet \mathbf{M}$

e. $\begin{bmatrix} 0 & 1 & 0 \\ 1 & 0 & 0 \\ 0 & 0 & 1 \end{bmatrix} \bullet \mathbf{M}$

f. $\begin{bmatrix} 1 & 0 & 0 \\ 0 & -1 & 0 \\ 0 & 0 & 1 \end{bmatrix} \bullet \mathbf{M}$

4. Repeat Problem **3** for the matrix **M** below.

$$\mathbf{M} = \begin{bmatrix} a & b & c & d \\ e & f & g & h \\ 1 & 1 & 1 & 1 \end{bmatrix}$$

Assignment

4.1 **a.** The following graph shows the coordinates of the vertices of a hexagon. Write a matrix equation that describes the reflection of this hexagon in the y-axis, including a matrix for the coordinates of the image.

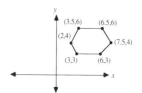

b. Graph the preimage and the image of the hexagon in Part **a**. Reflect each of these figures in the x-axis.

c. Select any one of the four figures from Part **b**. Using this figure as the preimage, can each of the other figures be generated by a single reflection in a line? Explain your response.

4.1 **a.** Sample response:

$$\mathbf{F}' = \mathbf{B} \bullet \mathbf{F}$$

$$\mathbf{F}' = \begin{bmatrix} -1 & 0 & 0 \\ 0 & 1 & 0 \\ 0 & 0 & 1 \end{bmatrix} \bullet \begin{bmatrix} 2 & 3.5 & 6.5 & 7.5 & 6 & 3 \\ 4 & 6 & 6 & 4 & 3 & 3 \\ 1 & 1 & 1 & 1 & 1 & 1 \end{bmatrix}$$

$$\mathbf{F}' = \begin{bmatrix} -2 & -3.5 & -6.5 & -7.5 & -6 & -3 \\ 4 & 6 & 6 & 4 & 3 & 3 \\ 1 & 1 & 1 & 1 & 1 & 1 \end{bmatrix}$$

b. In the following sample graph, polygon 1 is the original preimage. Polygon 2 is a reflection of polygon 1 in the y-axis. Polygons 3 and 4 are the reflections in the x-axis of polygons 1 and 2, respectively.

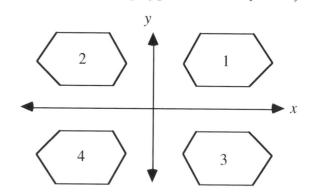

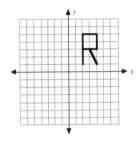

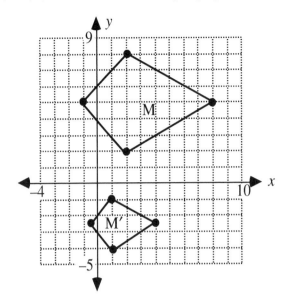

page 164

4.2 Use matrices to produce a reflection of Skip in the line $y = x$ or the line $y = -x$, followed by a reflection in the x-axis or the y-axis. Show the resulting image on a sheet of graph paper.

4.3 The matrix **M** below lists the vertices of a quadrilateral.

$$\mathbf{M} = \begin{bmatrix} -1 & 2 & 8 & 2 \\ 5 & 8 & 5 & 2 \\ 1 & 1 & 1 & 1 \end{bmatrix}$$

  a. 1. Create a graph of the quadrilateral described by matrix **M**.

    2. Reflect the quadrilateral in the x-axis.

    3. Dilate the image from Step **2** by a scale factor of 1/2, with center at the origin.

    3. Graph the result of this composition of transformations and identify the coordinates of the vertices.

  b. Verify your results in Part **a** by writing a matrix representation of the composition of transformations.

4.4 The figure below shows a letter R graphed on a coordinate plane.

  a. Reflect the letter R in the x-axis, then reflect the resulting image in the y-axis.

  b. Reflect the letter R in the y-axis, then reflect the resulting image in the x-axis.

  c. Compare the images you obtained in Parts **a** and **b**. Use matrix multiplication to confirm your observations.

164   Module 5 ■ *Crazy Cartoons*

---

c. Sample response: No, you can't. For any preimage, one of the three possible images is the result of two reflections: one in the x-axis and one in the y-axis. Therefore, there is always one image that cannot be created by a single reflection.

* **4.2** Answers will vary. The following sample graph shows Skip reflected in the line $y = -x$, then in the y-axis.

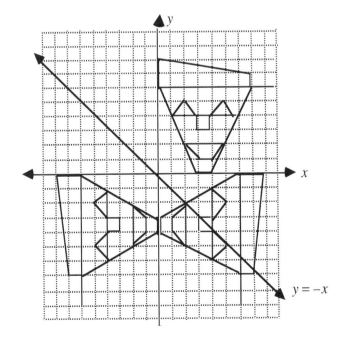

4.3 a. The coordinates of the vertices are $(-0.5, -2.5)$, $(1, -4)$, $(4, -2.5)$, and $(1, -1)$. Sample graph:

b. The composition of transformations can be described by the matrix equation below where **D** is the dilation matrix for $D_{O, 0.5}$ and **R** is the reflection matrix for r_x:

$$\mathbf{M}'' = \mathbf{D} \bullet \mathbf{R} \bullet \mathbf{M}$$

$$\mathbf{M}'' = \begin{bmatrix} 0.5 & 0 & 0 \\ 0 & 0.5 & 0 \\ 0 & 0 & 1 \end{bmatrix} \bullet \begin{bmatrix} 1 & 0 & 0 \\ 0 & -1 & 0 \\ 0 & 0 & 1 \end{bmatrix} \bullet \begin{bmatrix} -1 & 2 & 8 & 2 \\ 5 & 8 & 5 & 2 \\ 1 & 1 & 1 & 1 \end{bmatrix}$$

$$\mathbf{M}'' = \begin{bmatrix} -0.5 & 1 & 4 & 1 \\ -2.5 & -4 & -2.5 & -1 \\ 1 & 1 & 1 & 1 \end{bmatrix}$$

4.4 Students should observe that a reflection in the x-axis, followed by a reflection in the y-axis, is equivalent to a reflection in the y-axis, followed by a reflection in the x-axis. Multiplication of the corresponding matrices confirms this result.

* 4.5 **a.** A regular hexagon has six lines of symmetry, as shown below.

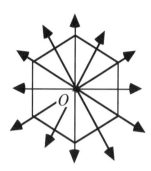

b. A line has an infinite number of lines of symmetry, including line *l* itself and all lines perpendicular to line *l*.

c. An ellipse has two lines of symmetry, as shown below.

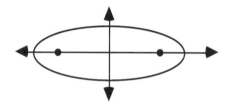

d. A circle has an infinite number of lines of symmetry; all intersect at the center *C*.

4.6 Sample response: Skip does not have a line of symmetry, unless we exclude his hat.

✳ ✳ ✳ ✳ ✳

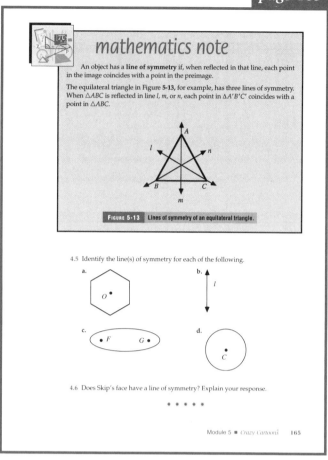

mathematics note

An object has a **line of symmetry** if, when reflected in that line, each point in the image coincides with a point in the preimage.

The equilateral triangle in Figure **5-13**, for example, has three lines of symmetry. When △*ABC* is reflected in line *l*, *m*, or *n*, each point in △*A'B'C'* coincides with a point in △*ABC*.

FIGURE 5-13 Lines of symmetry of an equilateral triangle.

4.5 Identify the line(s) of symmetry for each of the following.

4.6 Does Skip's face have a line of symmetry? Explain your response.

✳ ✳ ✳ ✳ ✳

Module 5 ■ *Crazy Cartoons* 165

4.7 The vertices of a quadrilateral are (–3,1), (–6,2), (–4,4), and (–2,3). When this quadrilateral is reflected in a line, the vertices of the image are (–1,3), (–2,6), (–4,4), and (–3,2).

   a. What is the equation of the line of reflection? Justify your response.

   b. Identify a matrix that, when multiplied on the left, will produce this transformation.

   c. Use a matrix equation to verify your response to Part **b**.

4.8 Parts **a** and **b** below each describe compositions of two transformations. For each part, use matrix operations to determine if the final images are the same.

   a. 1. A dilation with center at the origin and a scale factor of 4 is followed by a translation 2 units to the left and 5 units up.

   2. A translation 2 units to the left and 5 units up is followed by a dilation with center at the origin and a scale factor of 4.

   b. 1. A reflection in the line $y = x$ is followed by a dilation with center at the origin and a scale factor of 7.

   2. A dilation with center at the origin and a scale factor of 7 is followed by a reflection in the line $y = x$.

4.9 Make a sketch of an object that has at least three different lines of symmetry.

Research Project

Create your own animated cartoon using the transformations examined in this module. (Your collection of Skip's transformations should help you consider the possibilities.) Your cartoon should be at least 20 frames long. So that others may view your cartoon, tape each image onto a 3 × 5 card. Include a written summary with a mathematical description of the transformations from each frame to the next. You also may create a cartoon on a programmable calculator. See your teacher for details.

4.7 a. Sample response: Because the x- and y-coordinates are both switched and negated, this is a reflection in the line $y = -x$.

b. The matrix that describes this transformation is:

$$\mathbf{R} = \begin{bmatrix} 0 & -1 & 0 \\ -1 & 0 & 0 \\ 0 & 0 & 1 \end{bmatrix}$$

c. The following matrix equation verifies the responses given above:

$$\mathbf{D'} = \mathbf{R} \bullet \mathbf{D}$$

$$\mathbf{D'} = \begin{bmatrix} 0 & -1 & 0 \\ -1 & 0 & 0 \\ 0 & 0 & 1 \end{bmatrix} \bullet \begin{bmatrix} -3 & -6 & -4 & -2 \\ 1 & 2 & 4 & 3 \\ 1 & 1 & 1 & 1 \end{bmatrix}$$

$$\mathbf{D'} = \begin{bmatrix} -1 & -2 & -4 & -3 \\ 3 & 6 & 4 & 2 \\ 1 & 1 & 1 & 1 \end{bmatrix}$$

4.8 Note: Students may use graphs to illustrate the answers below. It is important to point out in that, in the case of Part **a,** one false instance is enough to show that the compositions are *not* equivalent. However, a single demonstration of equivalent compositions, such as the one in Part **b,** is *not* enough to show that the two compositions are *always* equivalent. A general point must be used, as in the sample solution to Part **b.**

a. Sample response: These do not create equivalent transformations. An example for $P(3,4)$ is shown below.

$$\begin{bmatrix} 4 & 0 & 0 \\ 0 & 4 & 0 \\ 0 & 0 & 1 \end{bmatrix} \bullet \begin{bmatrix} 1 & 0 & -2 \\ 0 & 1 & 5 \\ 0 & 0 & 1 \end{bmatrix} \bullet \begin{bmatrix} 3 \\ 4 \\ 1 \end{bmatrix} \neq \begin{bmatrix} 1 & 0 & -2 \\ 0 & 1 & 5 \\ 0 & 0 & 1 \end{bmatrix} \bullet \left(\begin{bmatrix} 4 & 0 & 0 \\ 0 & 4 & 0 \\ 0 & 0 & 1 \end{bmatrix} \bullet \begin{bmatrix} 3 \\ 4 \\ 1 \end{bmatrix} \right)$$

$$\begin{bmatrix} 4 \\ 36 \\ 1 \end{bmatrix} \neq \begin{bmatrix} 10 \\ 21 \\ 1 \end{bmatrix}$$

b. These create equivalent transformations, as shown below for $P(a,b)$.

$$\begin{bmatrix} 7 & 0 & 0 \\ 0 & 7 & 0 \\ 0 & 0 & 1 \end{bmatrix} \bullet \begin{bmatrix} 0 & 1 & 0 \\ 1 & 0 & 0 \\ 0 & 0 & 1 \end{bmatrix} \bullet \begin{bmatrix} a \\ b \\ 1 \end{bmatrix} = \begin{bmatrix} 0 & 1 & 0 \\ 1 & 0 & 0 \\ 0 & 0 & 1 \end{bmatrix} \bullet \left(\begin{bmatrix} 7 & 0 & 0 \\ 0 & 7 & 0 \\ 0 & 0 & 1 \end{bmatrix} \bullet \begin{bmatrix} a \\ b \\ 1 \end{bmatrix} \right)$$

$$\begin{bmatrix} 7b \\ 7a \\ 1 \end{bmatrix} = \begin{bmatrix} 7b \\ 7a \\ 1 \end{bmatrix}$$

4.9 Answers will vary. Sample response: The following regular heptagon has seven lines of symmetry.

Research Project

Whether done by hand or using technology, these flip-card cartoons should demonstrate students' knowledge of the various transformations and their matrix representations.

When taping or pasting images to index cards, students should take care to ensure that images appear in the proper positions. In a sequence of dilations, for example, the center of dilation must be placed in the same point on each card.

Students who choose to use technology, such as Texas Instruments' TI-84, TI-89, and Voyage 200 calculators, can create individual images with a program such as the one described in Activity **2** (**plotpts**). Such images can be exported to a computer using TI Connect software, then printed.

For those students with Texas Instruments' TI-89 or Voyage 200 calculators, the built-in program **CyclePic** (see TI *Guidebook*), in conjunction with the "**plotpts**" program, will simulate the flip-card effect.

teacher note

An additional assessment, for use at your discretion, appears in the Teacher Resources for this module.

Summary Assessment

1. a. Sample response: A reflection in the line $y = x$ followed by a reflection in the line $y = -x$ followed by a reflection in the line $y = x$ followed by a reflection in the line $y = -x$ will begin and end with the same figure.

   Note: Student responses must specify an even number of reflections.

   b. The matrix equation below corresponds with the sample response given in Part **a**:

$$\begin{bmatrix} 0 & 1 & 0 \\ 1 & 0 & 0 \\ 0 & 0 & 1 \end{bmatrix} \bullet \begin{bmatrix} 0 & -1 & 0 \\ -1 & 0 & 0 \\ 0 & 0 & 1 \end{bmatrix} \bullet \begin{bmatrix} 0 & 1 & 0 \\ 1 & 0 & 0 \\ 0 & 0 & 1 \end{bmatrix} \bullet \begin{bmatrix} 0 & -1 & 0 \\ -1 & 0 & 0 \\ 0 & 0 & 1 \end{bmatrix} \bullet \begin{bmatrix} x \\ y \\ 1 \end{bmatrix} = \begin{bmatrix} x \\ y \\ 1 \end{bmatrix}$$

   c. The single matrix that, when multiplied on the left, results in the same preimage and image is the identity matrix.

$$\mathbf{I} = \begin{bmatrix} 1 & 0 & 0 \\ 0 & 1 & 0 \\ 0 & 0 & 1 \end{bmatrix}$$

2. a. Sample graph:

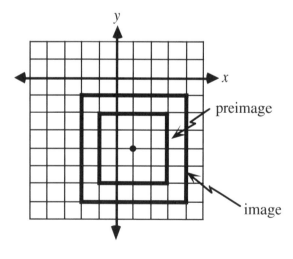

The vertices of the image are $(-2,-1)$, $(-2,-7)$, $(4,-7)$, and $(4,-1)$. They can be found using the matrix equation below.

$$\mathbf{S}' = \begin{bmatrix} 1 & 0 & 1 \\ 0 & 1 & -4 \\ 0 & 0 & 1 \end{bmatrix} \bullet \begin{bmatrix} 1.5 & 0 & 0 \\ 0 & 1.5 & 0 \\ 0 & 0 & 1 \end{bmatrix} \bullet \begin{bmatrix} 1 & 0 & -1 \\ 0 & 1 & 4 \\ 0 & 0 & 1 \end{bmatrix} \bullet \begin{bmatrix} -1 & -1 & 3 & 3 \\ -2 & -6 & -6 & -2 \\ 1 & 1 & 1 & 1 \end{bmatrix}$$

$$\mathbf{S}' = \begin{bmatrix} -2 & -2 & 4 & 4 \\ -1 & -7 & -7 & -1 \\ 1 & 1 & 1 & 1 \end{bmatrix}$$

   b. Sample response: The single dilation matrix can be found by multiplying the three transformation matrices together. The resulting transformation matrix is:

$$\begin{bmatrix} 1.5 & 0 & -0.5 \\ 0 & 1.5 & 2 \\ 0 & 0 & 1 \end{bmatrix}$$

   c. Sample response: The general transformation matrix can be found by substituting variables into the transformation matrices used in Part **a**. If n represents the scale factor and the ordered pair (a,b) represents the center of dilation, the general transformation matrix is:

$$\begin{bmatrix} 1 & 0 & a \\ 0 & 1 & b \\ 0 & 0 & 1 \end{bmatrix} \bullet \begin{bmatrix} n & 0 & 0 \\ 0 & n & 0 \\ 0 & 0 & 1 \end{bmatrix} \bullet \begin{bmatrix} 1 & 0 & -a \\ 0 & 1 & -b \\ 0 & 0 & 1 \end{bmatrix} = \begin{bmatrix} n & 0 & a(1-n) \\ 0 & n & b(1-n) \\ 0 & 0 & 1 \end{bmatrix}$$

Summary Assessment

1. a. Identify a sequence of at least three reflections that results in an image which coincides with the preimage.

   b. Use a matrix equation to verify your response to Part **a**.

   c. Write a single matrix that, when multiplied on the left, produces the composition of transformations described in Part **a**.

2. In this module, you used matrices to perform dilations only with their centers at the origin. However, any point on a coordinate plane can serve as the center of dilation. The following steps describe one way to dilate a figure using a different point as the center.

   Step 1. Select the point that you wish to use as the center of dilation.

   Step 2. Determine a 3×3 matrix that, when multiplied on the left, translates the point selected in Step **1** to the origin.

   Step 3. Translate the preimage using the translation matrix found in Step **2**.

   Step 4. Dilate the image from Step **3** by the desired scale factor with center at the origin.

   Step 5. Determine a 3×3 matrix that, when multiplied on the left, translates the origin to the point selected in Step **1**.

   Step 6. Translate the image from Step **4** using the translation matrix in Step **5**.

   The image under this composition of transformations coincides with the image under the dilation with center at the point selected in Step **1**.

   a. On a coordinate plane, create a square with its center at the point $(1,-4)$ and a side length of 4 units.

   Use the steps outlined above to find the image of this square under the dilation $D_{(1,-4),1.5}$.

   b. Identify a single transformation matrix that could be used to create the dilation in Part **a**. Describe how you determined this matrix.

   c. Write a general 3×3 dilation matrix in which n represents the scale factor and (a,b) represents the center of dilation.

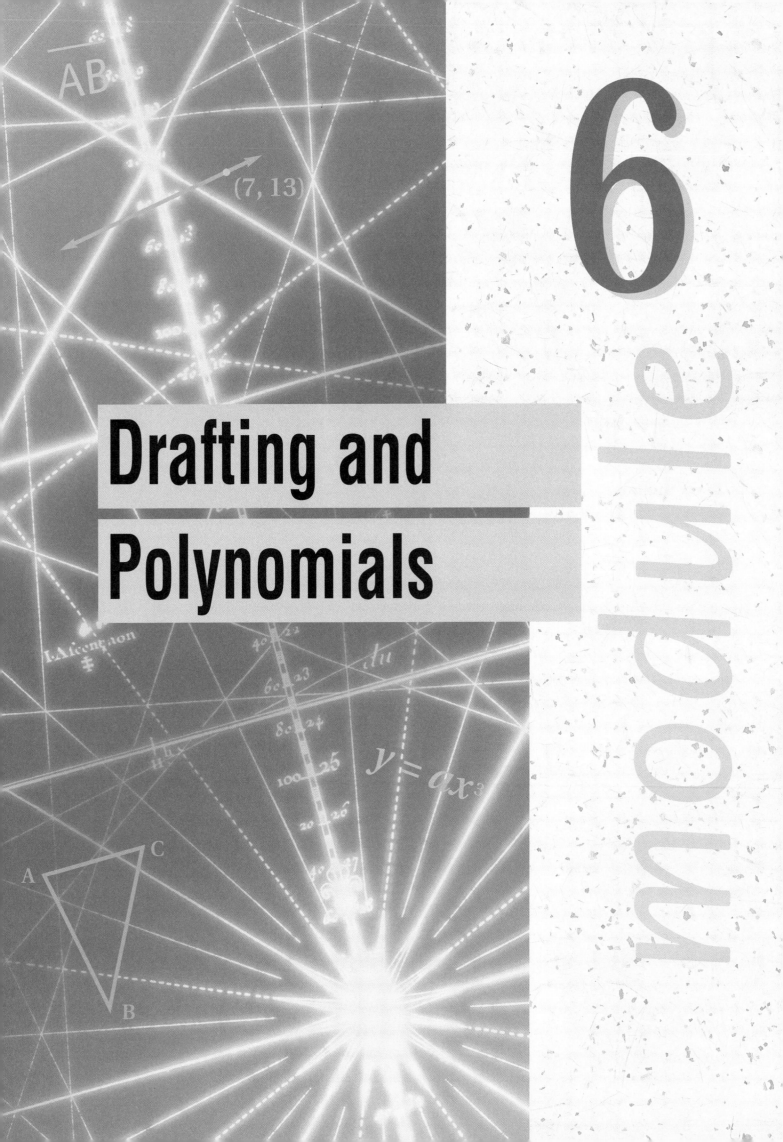

Drafting and Polynomials

6

module

Overview

Students investigate polynomial functions and their corresponding graphs through the context of computer-assisted graphic design. **Note:** Special thanks to the Microsoft and Adobe companies for their assistance with this module.

Activity 1:   Students are introduced to polynomials in one variable and their zeros. They express equations in factored form and investigate linear equations as first-degree polynomials.

Activity 2:   Students explore second-degree polynomials (quadratics) and their zeros.

Activity 3:   Students investigate polynomials with degrees greater than 2.

Activity 4:   Students examine the roots and end behavior of even- and odd-degree polynomials.

Objectives

In this module, students will:

* write polynomial equations in one variable and identify their degrees (1)

* investigate the graphs of polynomial functions (1, 2, 3, 4)

* use the distributive property to expand polynomials (1, 2, 3, 4)

* recognize the relationships among the zeros, factors, and degree of a polynomial function (1, 2 ,3, 4)

* describe the effects of changing the lead coefficient on the graph of a polynomial function (1, 2, 3, 4)

* identify the domain and range of a given polynomial function (1, 2, 3, 4)

* determine roots and factors of a polynomial from its graph (1, 2, 3, 4)

* factor binomials and trinomials (1, 2, 3, 4)

* identify multiple roots of polynomial functions (2)

* use polynomial functions and their graphs as mathematical models (3, 4)

* identify horizontal and vertical translations of polynomial functions (4)

* examine end behavior of polynomial functions (4).

Prerequisites

For this module, students should know:

✳ the distributive property of multiplication over addition

✳ how to multiply binomials

✳ the definition and properties of a function, including its domain and range

✳ function notation

✳ interval notation

✳ the definition of collinearity

✳ how to determine the equation of a line given two points

✳ how to calculate the sum of the square of the residuals.

 Flashbacks, for use at your discretion, appear in the Teacher Resources for this module. These brief problem sets provide a review of some prerequisite skills for each activity.

Planning Guide

Activity	Materials	Technology	Time Line
Introduction and Activity **1**	▪ straightedge ▪ graph paper	▪ graphing utility ▪ symbolic manipulator	2 days
Activity **2**	▪ graph paper ▪ cooked spaghetti or string licorice	▪ graphing utility	3 days
Activity **3**	▪ graph paper ▪ cooked spaghetti or string licorice	▪ graphing utility	2 days
Activity **4**	▪ none	▪ graphing utility	2 days
Assessment Activities	▪ none	▪ graphing utility	3 days **Total: 12 days**

Introduction

The introduction describes situations in which polynomial curves are used in graphic design. In the remainder of the module, students explore a simplified form of the process a computer graphics program might use to characterize a section of a curve. Such programs may employ a variety of strategies for coordinatizing the screen. For example, one program coordinatizes the screen pixel by pixel with the origin in the lower left-hand corner.

teacher note

You might wish to discuss the general form of a polynomial and how to determine the degree before proceeding to Activity **1**.

Students should recall the general and vertex forms of quadratic functions (second-degree polynomials) from the Level 1 module, "Graphing the Distance."

ACTIVITY 1

In this activity, students experiment with one method of fitting a line to a set of points and expressing it in factored form. (This method can be generalized for any polynomial function with all real roots.)

Materials List

- straightedge
- graph paper

Technology

- graphing utility
- symbolic manipulator

Introduction

Builders learned long ago that drawing preliminary sketches makes the construction process easier and more exact. Turning that first sketch into a set of detailed plans can simplify the process even more.

Drafting accurate plans once required special drawing equipment. In recent years, however, drafting tools have changed dramatically. Computer-aided design has made precise drawing much easier and faster. For example, Figure 6-1 shows the front view of a Viking ship originally built around 900 A.D. The curves in the hull were simulated using a computer graphics program.

FIGURE 6-1 Computer representation of a Viking ship.

Computer software typically represents complicated curves by piecing together parts of several simpler curves. These simpler curves are normally defined by functions made up of **polynomials**.

mathematics note

A **polynomial** in one variable, x, is an algebraic expression of the general form

$$a_n x^n + a_{n-1} x^{n-1} + a_{n-2} x^{n-2} + \cdots + a_1 x^1 + a_0$$

where n is a whole number and the **coefficients** a_i are real numbers for $i = 0, 1, 2, \ldots, n$.

The **degree** of a polynomial is equal to the greatest exponent of the variable in the expression. A polynomial in the general form shown above has a degree of n, provided that $a_n \neq 0$.

172

For example, the expression $2x^5 + 4x^4 - 2x^3 - 3x^2 + 5x^1 + 6$ is a polynomial in one variable with a degree of 5. In this expression, the coefficients are 2, 4, −2, −3, 5, and 6. The expression $2x^5 + 6$ is also a fifth-degree polynomial. In this case, the coefficients are 2, 0, 0, 0, 0, and 6.

Some additional examples of polynomials are shown in Table 6-1 below.

TABLE 6-1 ■ Some Polynomials and Their Degrees

Polynomial	Degree
5	0
$2x + 4$	1
$3.6x^2 - 5x + 2$	2
$-5x^3 + x$	3
$\frac{3}{7}x^6 + 3x^5 - \frac{2}{9}x^2 - 11$	6

There are many practical applications for curves described by polynomials. For example, the outlines of many letter designs, or fonts, are created using polynomial functions. In fact, the letters of the words you are reading right now were defined using the graphs of polynomials.

ACTIVITY 1

Imagine that you are a graphics designer who has been asked to connect several points in a drawing with a smooth curve. One way to accomplish this task involves using a two-dimensional coordinate system to identify the coordinates of each point. You could then sketch a curve that passes through the points, determine a mathematical equation that models the curve, and enter that equation in a graphing utility.

Determining the equation that describes a curve, however, can be a complicated task. In the following exploration, you examine the simple case of connecting two points with a curve and determining the corresponding equation.

Exploration

a. Create an xy-coordinate system on a sheet of graph paper.

b. Plot two points with different x-coordinates on the graph paper: one above the x-axis, and one below it. Label each point with its coordinates.

---

c. A line is the simplest and smoothest continuous curve that contains two points. Draw the line that contains the two points in Part **b**.

d. Determine the equation of the line in Part **c**.

e. Estimate the coordinates of the point where the line intersects the *x*-axis. The *x*-coordinate of this point is the **x-intercept**.

This *x*-coordinate is also a **root** or **zero** of the function that describes the curve. It is called a *zero* because, when substituted for *x* in the function, the value of the function is 0.

mathematics note

Factoring is the process of using the distributive property to represent a mathematical expression as a product.

For example, the expression $2x + 6$ can be factored into the equivalent expression $2(x + 3)$. Similarly, the expression $2x^2 + 3x - 5$ can be expressed as $(2x + 5)(x - 1)$.

f. Using the distributive property, a linear equation in the form $y = mx + b$ can be rewritten as:

$$y = m\left(x + \frac{b}{m}\right)$$

1. Express the equation from Part **d** in the form above.

2. Describe how the zero identified in Part **e** relates to this form of the equation.

Discussion

a. Is the graph you drew in the exploration a function? Explain your response.

b. What is the degree of a linear function?

c. If for a given function g, $g(7) = 0$, what does this imply about the graph of g?

d. Consider the graph of a line that intersects the *x*-axis at 12. What are some possible equations for this line?

e. The form of a linear equation described in Part **f** of the exploration,

$$y = m\left(x + \frac{b}{m}\right)$$

can be rewritten by replacing m with a and b/m with $-c$. This results in an equation of the form $y = a(x - c)$.

174   Module 6 ■ *Drafting and Polynomials*

teacher note

When using a graphing utility to create graphs of functions, students should plot points so that both a scatterplot and a function can be illustrated simultaneously.

Throughout this module, students are asked to create "smooth" curves containing several points. In the case of two points, the "smoothest, simplest" curve is a line. Many graphics programs consider a curve "smooth" when it is continuous or could be drawn without lifting a pencil from the paper.

Student Outcomes

After completing the following exploration and discussion, students should be able to:

✳ identify the zero (if any) of a first-degree polynomial

✳ write a first-degree polynomial in factored form

✳ recognize the relationships among the zeros, factors, and degree of a polynomial function

✳ recognize a relationship between the lead coefficient of a polynomial and the behavior of its graph.

Exploration

a–b. Students should plot two points not on the same vertical line. (If both points are on the same vertical line, the line does not represent a function from *x* to *y*.) Sample response: (7,3) and (2,–6).

c. In the case of two points, the "smoothest, simplest" curve is a line.

d. Answers will vary. The equation of the line that contains (7,3) and (2,–6) is:

$$y = \frac{9}{5}x - \frac{48}{5}$$

e. Student graphs should intersect the *x*-axis in only one point. The *x*-intercept of the line that contains the points (7,3) and (2,–6) is 16/3.

f. Students express the equation from Part **d** in the form $y = m(x + b/m)$.
   1. Sample response:

$$y = \frac{9}{5}\left(x - \frac{16}{3}\right)$$

   2. The zero of the function is equal to $-b/m$. For the sample equation given above, the zero is 16/3 or approximately 5.3.

Discussion

a. Sample response: Yes, there is exactly one value of *y* that corresponds to every value of *x*.

b. The degree of a linear function is 1.

c. The graph of function g intersects the *x*-axis at $x = 7$.

d. Students should suggest equations of the form below, where $b/m = 12$.

$$y = a\left(x - \frac{b}{m}\right)$$

e. 1. Sample response: Changing the value of a changes the slope of the line.

   2. Sample response: Using the distributive property, $y = a(x - c)$ is equivalent to $y = ax - ac$. Interpreting this form as the slope-intercept form of a line means that the value of a represents the slope of the line and the quantity $-ac$ is the y-intercept.

f. Sample response: An equation of the form $y = a(x - c)$ contains the zero c and the slope a.

g. 1. The factors of the polynomial function are $(x + 5)$ and $(x - 6)$.

   2. The zeros of the polynomial function are: 3, -4, 2, and 0. Its degree is 4.

Warm-Up

1. a. $3x + 6$

   b. $4y - 12$

   c. $-2x + 8$

2. a. $x^2 + 3x - 28$

   b. $x^2 + 7x + 12$

   c. $x^2 - 16$

   d. $x^2 - 6x + 9$

   e. $(x^2 + 5x + 6)(x - 1) = x^3 + 4x^2 + x - 6$

3. a. degree 7

   b. $a_7 = 3, a_6 = 0, a_5 = 0, a_4 = 0, a_3 = 0, a_2 = 0, a_1 = 0, a_0 = 1$

   c. degree 2

   d. Yes, 17 is a polynomial of degree 0.

4. Sample response: The expression $\sqrt{x}$ can be rewritten as $x^{1/2}$. It is not a polynomial because the exponent of x is not a whole number. For the same reason, the expression $x^{-3} + 6$ is not a polynomial. The expression $x(x + 1)(x + 2)$ is a polynomial because it can be written as $x^3 + 3x^2 + 2x$.

1. What role does the value of a play in the graph of $y = a(x - c)$?

2. How is the equation of a line in the form $y = a(x - c)$ related to its equation in slope-intercept form? Explain your response.

f. In this module, you will model curves by examining their zeros. What advantages are there to writing the equation of a line in the form $y = a(x - c)$?

mathematics note

A function f is a **polynomial function** if $f(x)$ is defined as a polynomial in x.

When the roots or zeros of a non-zero polynomial function are known, and all of these roots are real numbers, the function can be written as a product of factors, as shown below:

$$f(x) = a(x - c_1)(x - c_2)(x - c_3) \cdots (x - c_n)$$

In general, if $f(c) = 0$, c is a zero of $f(x)$ and $(x - c)$ is a factor of $f(x)$.

For example, Figure 6-2 shows a graph of $f(x) = x^2 + 5x - 6$. From the graph, $f(-6) = 0$ and $f(1) = 0$. Therefore, $(x - (-6)) = (x + 6)$ and $(x - 1)$ are factors of $f(x)$. The function can be written in **factored form** as $f(x) = (x + 6)(x - 1)$.

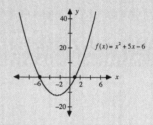

FIGURE 6-2 Graph of a polynomial function $f(x) = x^2 + 5x - 6$.

When a function is expressed in factored form, its zeros can be determined from the factors. For example, if $g(x) = 4(x - 3)(x - 5)(x + 2)$ then 3, 5, and -2 are zeros of $g(x)$. Likewise, if $h(x) = (x - 3)(x - 5)(x + 2)$, then 3, 5, and -2 are its zeros.

Module 6 ■ *Drafting and Polynomials* 175

Figure 6-3 shows the graphs of these two functions. Notice that although the graphs of the two functions are different, their zeros are the same.

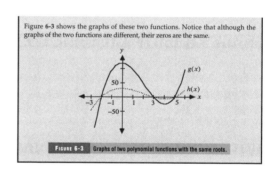

FIGURE 6-3 Graphs of two polynomial functions with the same roots.

g. 1. The zeros (or roots) of a polynomial function are -5 and 6. What are the factors of this function?

   2. The polynomial function $h(x)$ can be written in factored form as $h(x) = (x - 3)(x + 4)(x - 2)x$. What are the zeros of this function? What is the degree of the function?

Warm-Up

1. The distributive property can be used to find the product of 8 and 16 by expressing 16 as $(10 + 6)$ and distributing the 8 as follows:

$$8(10 + 6) = 80 + 48$$
$$= 128$$

Use the distributive property to find each product below.

a. $3(x + 2)$

b. $4(y - 3)$

c. $-2(x - 4)$

2. The product of 20 and 16 can be found by expressing 21 as $(20 + 1)$ and 16 as $(10 + 6)$, then using the distributive property as follows:

$$(20 + 1)(10 + 6) = 20(10 + 6) + 1(10 + 6)$$
$$= (200 + 120) + (10 + 6)$$
$$= 336$$

176 Module 6 ■ *Drafting and Polynomials*

Use the distributive property to find each product below.

a. $(x + 7)(x - 4)$

b. $(x + 3)(x + 4)$

c. $(x - 4)(x + 4)$

d. $(x - 3)^2$

e. $(x + 2)(x + 3)(x - 1)$

3. a. What is the degree of the following polynomial: $3x^7 + 1$?

b. In the polynomial in Part a, what are the coefficients of each of the following terms: x^7, x^6, x^5, x^4, x^3, x^2, x^1, and x^0?

c. What is the degree of the polynomial below?

$$\frac{x^2}{1000} + 10^6$$

d. Is the number 17 a polynomial? If so, identify its degree. If not, explain why not.

4. Which of the following expressions are polynomials? Justify your responses.

a. $\sqrt{x}$

b. $x^{-3} + 6$

c. $x(x + 1)(x + 2)$

Assignment

1.1 a. Using the method described in the exploration, find the equation of a first-degree polynomial function whose graph contains the points $(1, 2)$ and $(3, 6)$. Express the equation in factored form.

b. Identify the root(s) of this polynomial function.

1.2 a. Predict the zero(s) for each of the following polynomial functions.

1. $f(x) = 2(x + 3)$

2. $h(x) = x$

3. $g(x) = -0.2(x - 3)(x + 2)(x - 7)$

4. **Note:** The function below is said to have a **double root** because the factor $(x - 2)$ appears twice.

$$m(x) = (x - 2)(x - 2)$$

b. Create a graph of each function in Part a and estimate the zeros.

c. To verify your estimates in Part c, substitute the value of each predicted zero for x in the corresponding function.

Assignment

Problems suitable for use as assessment items are identified by an asterisk (*).

1.1 a. Using a method similar to that described in the exploration, the equation of the line in factored form is $y = 2(x - 0)$. Sample response:

$$(y - y_1) = \left(\frac{y_2 - y_1}{x_2 - x_1}\right)(x - x_1)$$

$$(y - 2) = \left(\frac{6 - 2}{3 - 1}\right)(x - 1)$$

$$y = 2x - 0$$

$$y = 2(x - 0)$$

b. The root of the equation $y = 2(x - 0)$ is 0.

1.2 a. Since each function except $h(x)$ is written as a product of factors in the form $(x - c_n)$, students should predict that the zeros equal the values of c.

b–c. 1. The function $f(x) = 2(x + 3)$ has a zero of -3 because $f(-3) = 0$. Sample graph:

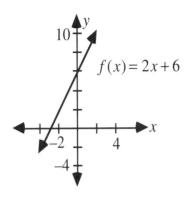

2. The function $h(x) = x$ has a zero of 0 since $h(0) = 0$. Sample graph:

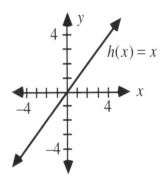

3. The function $g(x) = -0.2(x - 3)(x + 2)(x - 7)$ has zeros of 3, -2, and 7 since $g(3)$, $g(-2)$, and $g(7)$ all equal 0. Sample graph:

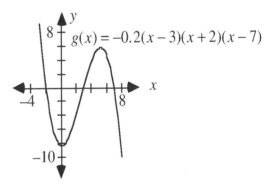

4. The function $m(x) = (x - 2)(x - 2)$ has a zero of 2 because $m(2) = 0$. Sample graph:

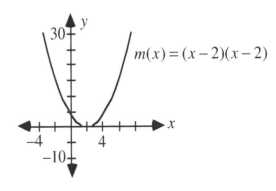

* 1.3 Answers will vary. The following sample responses use the roots 3, 2, –1, and –4.

    a. One polynomial function with roots of 3, 2, –1, and –4 is $f(x) = (x - 3)(x - 2)(x + 1)(x + 4)$.

    b. Another polynomial function with the same roots is $g(x) = 3(x - 3)(x - 2)(x + 1)(x + 4)$.

    c. The two graphs have the same x-intercepts and the same basic shape, but the coefficient of 3 makes the graph of $g(x)$ vary more from the x-axis in the interval $-4 < x < 3$.

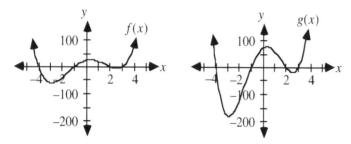

1.4 Sample response: The roof can be formed by $f(x) = -x + 22$ for x in [8, 14] and $f(x) = x + 6$ for x in [2, 8]. The sides of the birdhouse can be formed by $f(x) = -3(x - 6)$ for x in [3, 5] and $f(x) = 3(x - 10)$ for x in [11, 13]. The floor can be formed by $f(x) = 3$ for x in [5, 11]. A graph of the design is shown below:

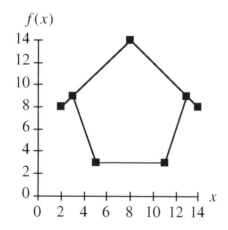

* 1.5 Sample response: The functions that correspond to each letter are shown in the following table.

Letter	Function	Domain
W	$f(x) = -5(x - 1)$	[0, 2]
W	$f(x) = 10(x - 2.5)$	[2, 3]
W	$f(x) = -10(x - 3.5)$	[3, 4]
W	$f(x) = 5(x - 3.5)$	[4, 6]
A	$f(x) = -5(x - 9)$	[8, 10]
A	$f(x) = 5(x - 7)$	[6, 8]
A	$f(x) = 0$	[7, 9]
X	$f(x) = -5(x - 12)$	[11, 13]
X	$f(x) = 5(x - 12)$	[11, 13]

1.3 **a.** Select four different real numbers. Write a polynomial function whose roots are these numbers.

    b. Determine a different polynomial function with the same roots.

    c. Compare the graphs of the two functions in Parts **a** and **b.**

1.4 The birdhouse design shown in the following diagram was created using polynomial functions. The functions were graphed on the same coordinate system, then segments of each graph were used to form the birdhouse. Determine a set of polynomial functions that could be used in this process, including the necessary restrictions on the domain of each one.

1.5 Determine a set of polynomial functions, along with their respective domains, that could be used to create the word WAX in capital letters on a computer screen.

               * * * * *

1.6 **a.** Use the distributive property to multiply the factors of each function below. Identify the degree of each resulting polynomial.

      1. $f(x) = 2(x + 3)$ **2.** $g(x) = -0.8(x - 4)$

      3. $h(x) = (x - 2)(x - 2)$ **4.** $m(x) = 0.2(x - 3)(x + 2)(x - 7)$

    b. Use a symbolic manipulator to verify the products you found in Part **a.**

    c. Use the products in Part **a** to graph each polynomial function. Compare the zeros of each function with its factors.

1.7 A local swimming pool is 20 m wide and 30 m long. As shown in the diagram below, the sidewalk surrounding the pool has a constant width.

    a. Let w represent the width of the concrete sidewalk. Represent the area of the sidewalk using a polynomial function in w.

    b. Use the distributive property to express this polynomial function in a simplified form.

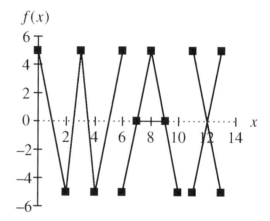

         ❋ ❋ ❋ ❋ ❋

ACTIVITY 2

Drafting by hand can be a challenging, painstaking task. Although a straightedge works fine for connecting points with straight lines, drawing shapes that are not straight can be more difficult. One instrument used for tracing smooth, precise curves by hand is a spline. Modern splines are made of flexible plastic or metal which allows them to retain their shape when bent. Curves drawn using this method are known as spline curves.

To draw smooth, precise shapes, computer-aided design programs frequently make use of both spline curves and Bézier curves. Bézier curves are named after the French mathematician Pierre Bézier, who pioneered computer modeling of curved surfaces for Renault, the automobile manufacturer. Both types of curves actually contain many polynomial curves pieced together mathematically. Figure **6-4** shows the profile of a boat hull created on a computer graphics program. This drawing consists of a Bézier curve and its reflection.

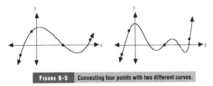

FIGURE 6-4 A boat hull.

To create a similar drawing by hand, a boat builder might plot four points on a grid, then use a spline to draw the curve. In this activity, you experiment with polynomial curves that connect noncollinear points.

Exploration

A drafter or graphic designer usually attempts to draw curves as smoothly and simply as possible. Figure **6-5** shows two smooth polynomial curves that connect the same four points. Because the polynomial on the left connects the points with a simpler curve, typically it would be the preferred model.

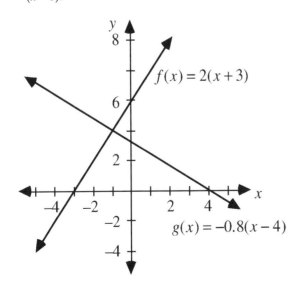

FIGURE 6-5 Connecting four points with two different curves.

Module 6 ■ *Drafting and Polynomials*   179

1.6 a. 1. $y = 2x + 6$; degree 1
  2. $y = -0.8x + 3.2$; degree 1
  3. $y = x^2 - 4x + 4$; degree 2
  4. $y = 0.2x^3 - 1.6x^2 + 0.2x + 8.4$; degree 3

b. Students verify the products in Part **a** using a symbolic manipulator.

c. 1–2. Sample graphs of $f(x) = 2x + 6$ and $g(x) = 0.8x + 3.2$ are shown below. In each case, the zero is the value of the constant c in the factor $(x - c)$.

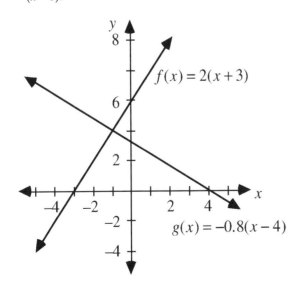

$f(x) = 2(x + 3)$

$g(x) = -0.8(x - 4)$

3–4. Sample graphs of $m(x) = 0.2x^3 - 1.6x^2 + 0.2x + 8.4$ and $h(x) = x^2 - 4x + 4$ are shown below. In each case, the zeros are the values of the constants c in the factors $(x - c)$.

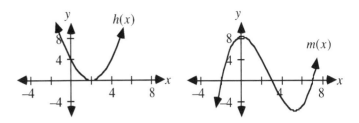

1.7 a. The polynomial function in w that represents the area of the sidewalk is $f(w) = (20 + 2w)(30 + 2w) - (20)(30)$.

b. Using the distributive property, the function can be simplified as follows:

$$f(w) = (20 + 2w)(30 + 2w) - (20)(30)$$
$$= 600 + 100w + 4w^2 - 600$$
$$= 4w^2 + 100w$$

ACTIVITY 2

Students experiment with connecting three noncollinear points using smooth curves.

 teacher note

A brief assessment of the mathematical content in Activities **1** and **2**, for use at your discretion, appears in the Teacher Resources for this module.

Materials List

■ graph paper
■ cooked spaghetti or string licorice

Technology

■ graphing utility

teacher note

In the exploration, students use spaghetti as a model spline. String, pipe cleaners, or wire may be substituted for the pasta. However, pasta models curves extremely well and also sticks to the paper.

In Part **c**, each curve should represent a function and intersect the *x*-axis at two points. This ensures that all roots are real roots. In Parts **g** and **h,** you might wish to point out to students that it might not be possible to model a curve formed with a spline precisely using a single, simple function— even though the spline curve and the function have the same *x*-intercepts.

In this exploration, you use a spline to create a polynomial curve containing three noncollinear points.

a. Create an *xy*-coordinate system on a sheet of graph paper.

b. Draw three noncollinear points on the graph so that as the *x*-coordinates increase in value, the *y*-coordinates alternate between positive and negative values. This will result in two points on one side of the *x*-axis, and one on the other side. The three points selected should satisfy the conditions of a function. Label each point with its coordinates.

c. Fit a model spline to the points so that the spline crosses the *x*-axis the fewest possible number of times. The curve formed by the spline also should represent a function.

d. Trace the curve formed by the spline.

e. Estimate the zeros of the function that describes the curve.

f. Use the zeros from Part **e** to determine the factors of a polynomial with the same *x*-intercepts as the spline curve.

g. Use the factors to write a polynomial function in the form below that appears to approximate the curve.

$$f(x) = a(x - c_1)(x - c_2)(x - c_3) \cdots (x - c_n)$$

h. Plot the three points from Part **b** and the function from Part **g** on a graphing utility. If necessary, modify the function to obtain a better approximation of the three points.

Check your approximation by calculating the sum of the square of the residuals. (Recall that a smaller sum indicates a better approximation.)

Discussion

a. When is it appropriate to use a line as the smoothest, simplest curve connecting a set of points?

b. What is the degree of your polynomial from the exploration?

c. Is it possible to connect three points with a polynomial curve that has a lesser degree than the one you found? Explain your response.

d. How could you use the coordinates of a point from Part **b** of the exploration to find the value of *a* for the function you wrote in Part **g**?

e. 1. How can you change the equation of a polynomial function without changing its zeros?

   2. How do these changes affect the function's graph?

Student Outcomes

After completing the following exploration and discussion, students should be able to:

✻ connect three noncollinear points using a smooth curve

✻ identify the graphs of second-degree polynomial functions

✻ identify roots and factors of a polynomial from its graph

✻ use the distributive property to expand polynomials

✻ recognize the relationships among the zeros, factors, and degree of a polynomial function

✻ describe the effects of changing the lead coefficient on the graph of a second-degree polynomial.

Exploration

a–b. Since three noncollinear points can always be connected with a parabola, students will be modeling the graphs of second-degree polynomials.

c. The curve formed by the spline should intersect the *x*-axis in two points.

d. The following sample graph uses the points $(-4,-2)$, $(1,5)$, and $(7,-2)$:

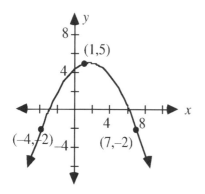

e. Students approximate the two zeros of the polynomial. For the sample response given in Part **d,** the zeros are approximately −3.2 and 6.2.

f. The factors which correspond to the sample response given in Part **d** are $(x + 3.2)$ and $(x - 6.2)$.

g. One function that approximates the three points given in the sample response to Part **d** is $f(x) = -0.23(x + 3.2)(x - 6.2)$. Because the graph opens downward in this case, the value of *a* is negative.

h. Sample response: The sum of the squares of the residuals for $f(x) = -0.23(x + 3.2)(x - 6.2)$ is approximately 0.03.

Discussion

a. Sample response: A line is appropriate as a smooth curve when joining any two points, or any three or more collinear points.

b. Students should obtain second-degree polynomials. Although it is possible to fit higher-order polynomials to three points, the curves will contain unnecessary "bends."

c. Sample response: Yes. If the points are collinear, then a first-degree polynomial (a line) would model them.

d. Answers will vary. Students could substitute one of the points to solve for the coefficient *a* in a polynomial of the form $y = a(x - c_1)(x - c_2)$.

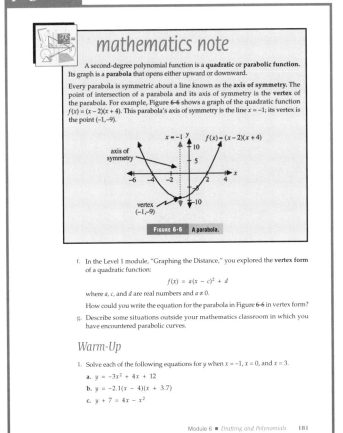

mathematics note

A second-degree polynomial function is a **quadratic** or **parabolic function.** Its graph is a **parabola** that opens either upward or downward.

Every parabola is symmetric about a line known as the **axis of symmetry.** The point of intersection of a parabola and its axis of symmetry is the **vertex** of the parabola. For example, Figure 6-6 shows a graph of the quadratic function $f(x) = (x-2)(x+4)$. This parabola's axis of symmetry is the line $x = -1$; its vertex is the point $(-1,-9)$.

FIGURE 6-6 A parabola.

f. In the Level 1 module, "Graphing the Distance," you explored the **vertex form** of a quadratic function:

$$f(x) = a(x-c)^2 + d$$

where a, c, and d are real numbers and $a \neq 0$.

How could you write the equation for the parabola in Figure 6-6 in vertex form?

g. Describe some situations outside your mathematics classroom in which you have encountered parabolic curves.

Warm-Up

1. Solve each of the following equations for y when $x = -1$, $x = 0$, and $x = 3$.

a. $y = -3x^2 + 4x + 12$

b. $y = -2.1(x-4)(x+3.7)$

c. $y + 7 = 4x - x^2$

e. 1. If $a \neq 0$ in a function of the form $f(x) = a(x - c_1)(x - c_2)$, changing the value of a changes the function without changing its zeros.

2. Changing $|a|$ stretches the graph vertically. If the sign of a is changed, the graph of the function is reflected in the x-axis.

f. Sample response: Since the vertex of the parabola is $(-1,-9)$, $c = -1$ and $d = -9$. The equation then can be written as $f(x) = a(x + 1)^2 - 9$. Because $f(x) = (x-2)(x+4)$,

$$(x - 2)(x + 4) = a(x + 1)^2 - 9$$
$$x^2 + 2x - 8 = a(x + 1)^2 - 9$$
$$x^2 + 2x + 1 = a(x + 1)^2$$
$$x^2 + 2x + 1 = a(x^2 + 2x + 1)$$
$$1 = a$$

g. Because projectiles follow parabolic trajectories, students may describe the paths of a thrown ball or a model rocket (after its engines burn out). Some brands of downhill skis are designed using parabolic curves, as are certain types of fishing rods. Cross-sections of many satellite dish antennas and headlight reflectors also are parabolas.

teacher note

In Part **g** of the discussion above, some students might suggest the curves of telephone or power lines as possible examples of a parabola. Although this shape resembles a parabola, it is in fact a catenary—which is not defined by a polynomial function.

A general equation for a catenary curve is shown below, where a determines how fast the curve opens.

$$f(x) = 0.5a\left(e^{\frac{x}{a}} + e^{-\frac{x}{a}}\right) = a\cosh\left(\frac{x}{a}\right)$$

One example of a catenary curve is the Gateway Arch in St. Louis, Missouri. The following figure shows an outline of the arch and the graph of a parabola containing points on the arch.

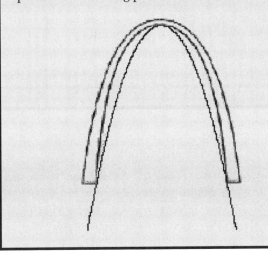

Warm-Up

1. a. When $x = -1$, $y = 5$. When $x = 0$, $y = 12$. When $x = 3$, $y = -3$.

b. When $x = -1$, $y = 29.61$. When $x = 0$, $y = 31.08$. When $x = 3$, $y = 14.07$.

c. When $x = -1$, $y = -12$. When $x = 0$, $y = -7$. When $x = 3$, $y = -4$.

2. **a.** The domain is the set of all real numbers; the range is the set of real numbers less than or equal to 15.

    b. The roots are –4 and 4.

    c. In the interval [–5,0), y-values are increasing.

    d. Sample response: $y = -0.9375(x - 4)(x + 4)$.

    e. Sample response: $y = -0.9375(x - 0)^2 + 15$.

teacher note

Students must complete Problem **2.2** if you wish to assign Problem **4.4** in Activity **4**.

Assignment

Problems suitable for use as assessment items are identified by an asterisk (*).

2.1 **a.** Students may use the trace feature on a graphing utility to find the coordinates of the vertex: (5,25).

    b. Sample response: Because the vertex lies on the parabola's axis of symmetry, the x-coordinate of the vertex is the mean of the values of the two zeros. This value can be substituted into the equation to find the y-coordinate of the vertex.

    c. The method described in Part **b** should work for any parabolic function with two real zeros.

2.2 Answers will vary. The sample response below uses the following functions: $y = x^2$ for x in $[-\sqrt{6}, \sqrt{6}]$, $y = 0.5(x + 2)(x - 2)$ for x in $[-4,4]$, and $y = 6$ for x in $[-4, -\sqrt{6}]$ and $[\sqrt{6}, 4]$.

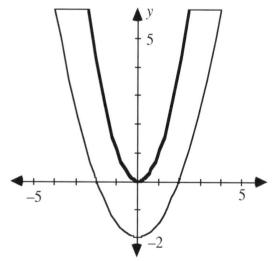

Note: The shapes that students create with parabolas might look more like the letter V than the letter U. They will have an opportunity to create another version in Activity **4**. The outline of the sample letter above contains only four distinct curves. The outline of the letter U shown in the student edition requires at least 12 equations to describe.

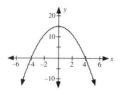

2. Use the following graph to complete Parts **a–e** below.

    a. Describe the domain and range of this function.

    b. Identify the roots, if any.

    c. Consider the interval of x-values [–5,0). Are y-values increasing or decreasing over this interval? Explain your response.

    d. Write an equation for this function in factored form.

    e. Write an equation for this function in vertex form.

Assignment

2.1 **a.** Find the coordinates of the vertex of the parabola described by the equation $y = -x(x - 10)$.

    b. Consider a parabola that intersects the x-axis at two points. Explain how the zeros of the corresponding function can be used to find the vertex of the parabola.

    c. Test your theory from Part **b** using another parabolic function. Describe your test and report on its outcome.

2.2 As mentioned in the introduction, the outlines of the letters in a type font can be described by polynomial functions. Although defining the different parts of a letter's outline might require up to 20 polynomial equations, graphic artists can change the size or shape of letters easily with the help of design software. For example, the three different G's in the diagram on the right show how a letter created using Bézier curves can be altered on a drawing program.

Use two parabolic functions and two line segments to design a simplified version of the letter U. Describe how your design differs from the letter printed on the right.

2.3 The diagram below shows a portion of a stained glass window 12 cm wide and 9 cm high. Determine a set of polynomial functions, along with their respective domains, that could be used to describe the curves in the window.

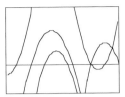

2.4 A graphic artist is producing a poster 40 cm wide and 55 cm long. The poster will feature a rectangular design surrounded by a border of uniform width.

a. Write a polynomial function *f* that represents the possible area of the rectangular design in terms of the width of the border.

b. Explain what each variable in the function represents.

c. If the border must represent no more than half of the total area of the poster, determine an appropriate domain and range for the function.

* * * * *

2.5 One application of polynomial functions is the study of projectile motion. A projectile is any object thrown or projected into the air. The path of a projectile is its trajectory.

The drawing below was made from a flash photograph of the trajectory of a golf ball over a portion of its flight. The flashes were made 1/30 of a second apart. The vertical axis represents the height of the ball above the ground in meters; the horizontal axis represents distance in meters.

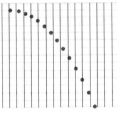

Module 6 ■ *Drafting and Polynomials* 183

2.3 Sample response: The functions that correspond to each curve are shown in the following table.

Function	Domain
a. $f(x) = (x - 1)(x + 1)$	$[0, 2.6]$
b. $f(x) = -0.7(x - 2.5)(x - 7)$	$[1.6, 7.8]$
c. $f(x) = (x - 9)(x - 10.5)$	$[7.2, 12]$
d. $f(x) = -(x - 9)(x - 12)$	$[8.2, 12]$
e. $f(x) = -0.9(x - 4)(x - 6.5)$	$[3, 7.5]$

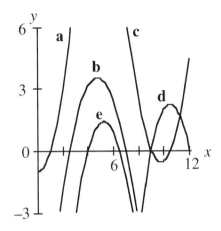

* 2.4 **a.** One polynomial function *f* in *x* that represents the possible area of the rectangular design is $f(x) = (55 - 2x)(40 - 2x)$.

b. Sample response: The value of $f(x)$ represents the area of the rectangular design in square centimeters; the value of *x* represents the width of the border in centimeters.

c. The domain of the function is approximated by the interval $[0, 6.7]$; its range is approximated by the interval $[0, 1100]$.

* * * * *

2.5 a. Answers may vary. If students place the origin at the bottom of the grid, directly under the first image at the left, some points might be: (0,13), (3,12), (5.8,10), (10,3.8), (11.6,0).

b. Answers may vary. Using the sample points given in Part **a,** one possible model is $y = -0.1(x + 11.5)(x - 11.5)$; in vertex form $y = -0.1(x - 0)^2 + 13$.

2.6 a. Sample graph:

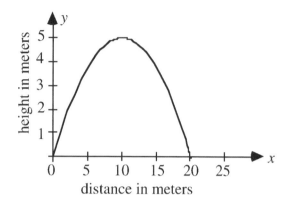

b. The zeros are 0 and 20; the coordinates of the vertex are (10,5).

c. In factored form, $y = -0.05x(x - 20)$. In vertex form, $y = -0.05(x - 10)^2 + 5$.

d. Sample response: The point from which the ball was kicked is assumed to be the origin. The variable y is the height of the ball above the ground (the vertical distance); x is the horizontal distance the ball has traveled.

Students explore connecting several points with smooth curves and examine the graphs of higher-degree polynomials.

Materials List

■ graph paper
■ cooked spaghetti or string licorice

Technology

■ graphing utility

a. Identify a location for the origin in the figure above and determine the approximate coordinates for five of the images of the golf ball.

b. Plot these points on a graphing utility and find a polynomial function that models them. Write the function in both factored form and vertex form.

2.6 While playing at a city park, Coretta kicks a soccer ball high into the air. The ball hits the ground 20 m away. Someone watching from a nearby window claims that the ball went as high as the window ledge, about 5 m above the ground.

a. Sketch a graph of the flight of the ball. Let the x-axis represent distance from the spot where it was kicked, and the y-axis represent distance above the ground.

b. Identify the zeros of the function that describes your sketch and estimate the coordinates of the vertex.

c. Find an equation that describes the path of the ball. Write the equation in both factored form and vertex form.

d. Explain what each variable in your equation represents.

Given any set of points, it is possible to model them with a variety of polynomial functions. This fact has some important consequences in both computer-aided design and mathematical modeling. Figure **6-7** shows two polynomial functions of different degrees which model the same set of three points. Although both curves contain all of the points, they vary in simplicity and degree.

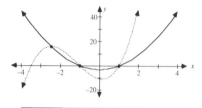

FIGURE 6-7 Two polynomial functions fitting the same points.

184 Module 6 ■ *Drafting and Polynomials*

teacher note

The following exploration focuses on the relationship between a function's factors and its roots—not on fitting curves to data points. As in the previous activity, you may point out that it might not be possible to model a curve formed with a spline precisely using a single, simple function—even though the spline curve and the function have the same x-intercepts.

Exploration

In this exploration, you use smooth curves to connect five points. You then model each curve with polynomials of degrees greater than 2.

a. Create an xy-coordinate system on a sheet of graph paper.

b. Plot five noncollinear points on the graph paper. Select these five points so that a spline curve containing all the points crosses the x-axis a maximum number of times. The five points also should satisfy the conditions of a function. Label each point with its coordinates.

c. Place your model spline so that it connects all five points. The resulting curve should be as smooth and simple as possible.

d. Trace the curve formed by the spline.

e. Estimate the zeros of the function that describes the curve.

f. Use the zeros from Part **e** to determine the factors of a polynomial.

g. Use the factors to write a polynomial function (in factored form) that approximates the graph.

h. Plot the points from Part **b** and the function from Part **g** on a graphing utility. If necessary, modify the lead coefficient in the function to obtain a curve that approximates the points as closely as possible.

Discussion

a. Describe the curve you used to connect the points in the exploration.

b. What is the degree of the polynomial that models the curve?

c. Is it possible for a polynomial function of the same degree as the one found in the exploration to have fewer x-intercepts than the curve in the exploration?

d. Describe some physical structures outside the mathematics classroom in which you have seen curves like the ones described in Part **a**.

Warm-Up

1. The volume V of a sphere with radius r can be found using the following polynomial equation:

$$V = \frac{4}{3}\pi r^3$$

a. Does this equation represent a function? If so, describe its domain and range. If not, explain why not.

b. What is the degree of this polynomial?

c. Identify the zeroes of the polynomial, if any.

Module 6 ■ *Drafting and Polynomials*   **185**

Student Outcomes

After completing the following exploration and discussion, students should be able to:

✳ identify roots and factors of a polynomial from its graph

✳ write and graph polynomials with degrees greater than 2

✳ recognize the relationships among the zeros, factors, and degree of a polynomial function

✳ use polynomials and their graphs as mathematical models.

Exploration

Students use smooth curves to connect five noncollinear points and model polynomials of degrees higher than 2.

a–d. Sample response based on the points $(-5,1)$, $(-2,-2)$, $(2,2)$, $(5,-2)$, and $(7,3)$:

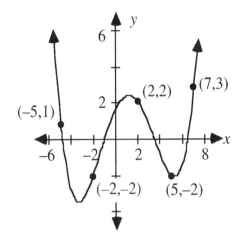

e. Students approximate the zeros of the polynomial. For the sample response above, the zeros are approximately $x = -4.8$, $x = -1$, $x = 3.5$ and $x = 6.5$.

f. Using the sample response above, the factors of the polynomial are $(x + 4.8)$, $(x + 1)$, $(x - 3.5)$, and $(x - 6.5)$.

g. Using the factors from Part **f,** one function that approximates the graph is $f(x) = 0.1(x + 4.8)(x + 1)(x - 3.5)(x - 6.5)$.

h. Students should modify their graphs by adjusting the value of the coefficient a.

Discussion

a. Students may describe their curves in terms of the number of "bends" and the number of x-intercepts. For the sample response given in the exploration, there are three bends and four x-intercepts.

b. The polynomial should be of degree 4 or higher.

c. Sample response: Yes, a polynomial with multiple roots of the same value can have fewer x-intercepts but the same degree. It is also possible to change the number of zeros in a polynomial by translating it vertically, without affecting its degree.

d. Sample responses may include an S-shaped curve on a highway, the cross section of a ship's hull, the "scalloped" contours of some furniture, or the tracks of a roller coaster.

Warm-Up

1. **a.** This equation represents a function. Both the domain and the range are the set of real numbers greater than 0.

   b. This is a third-degree polynomial.

   c. This polynomial has a "triple root": $x = 0$.

2. **a.** Both the domain and the range are the set of real numbers.
   b. The roots are $x = -4$, $x = -1$, and $x = 2$.
   c. In this interval, y-values are decreasing.
   d. $y = 2(x + 4)(x + 1)(x - 2)$

Assignment

Problems suitable for use as assessment items are identified by an asterisk (*).

3.1 **a.** Answers will vary. The following three functions could be used to create the outline of the letter M:
$f(x) = -1.5(x - 2)(x - 4)(x - 7)(x - 9)$ for x in [1.6,9.4];
$f(x) = -0.9(x - 1)(x - 5)(x - 6)(x - 10)$ for x in [0.7,10.3]; and $f(x) = -57.5$ for x in [0.7,1.6] and [9.4,10.3].

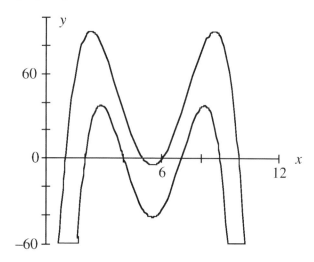

   b. Student responses should include a list of functions along with their appropriate domains.

2. Use the following graph to complete Parts **a–d** below.

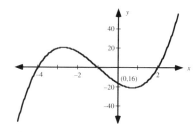

   a. Describe the domain and range of this function.
   b. Identify the roots, if any.
   c. Consider the interval of x-values [−2,0). Are y-values increasing or decreasing over this interval? Explain your response.
   d. Write an equation for this function in factored form.

Assignment

3.1 **a.** Determine a set of polynomial functions that could be used to create the outline of the letter M below. Include the appropriate restrictions on the domain of each function.

   b. Create the outline of another letter using polynomial functions. Record the functions you used along with the appropriate restrictions on the domain of each one.

3.2 **a.** Sample response: $f(x) = 0.05(x - 0.5)(x - 4)^2$ for x in [0,7]
   b. Sample response: $f(x) = -0.05(x + 0.5)(x + 4)^2$ for x in [−7,0]
   c. Sample response: The right side and left side of the design are reflections of each other in the y-axis. The roots and leading coefficients (a) of the corresponding functions are additive inverses.

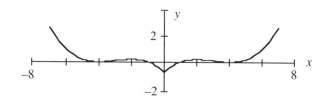

3.2 The diagram below shows a cross section of a ship's hull.

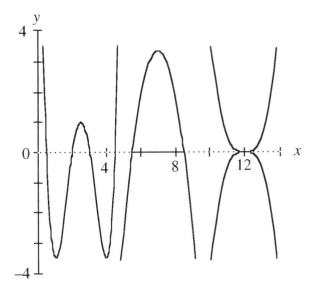

  a. Determine a polynomial function that could be used to create the curve which defines the right-hand side of the hull. Assume that the axis of symmetry for the entire diagram is the *y*-axis.

  b. Determine a polynomial function that could be used to create the curve which defines the left-hand side of the hull.

  c. How are the two functions in Parts **a** and **b** related? Explain your response.

3.3 Use polynomials with degrees other than 1 to produce the letters WAX. Include the domain and the range for each function used.

3.4 Use polynomial functions to design a picture of your choice. Your response should include a sketch of the picture, a list of the functions and their zeros, and a description of the domain and range used to view the picture on a graphing utility.

* * * * *

3.5 The formula for calculating the total amount in an interest-bearing savings account is:

$$A = P\left(1 + \frac{r}{n}\right)^{nt}$$

where *P* is the initial amount invested, *r* is the annual interest rate in decimal form, *n* is the number of times interest is calculated per year, and *t* is the time in years.

  a. Christine's grandparents started a savings account for her on her 13th birthday. They invested $250 at an annual interest rate of 5.5%. What was the amount in the account after 1 year if interest is calculated yearly and no money was withdrawn during the year?

  b. On each of Christine's next five birthdays, her grandparents deposited $200, $325, $450, $400, and $675, respectively, into the account. If no money was withdrawn from the account during these five years, what was the balance on Christine's 18th birthday?

  c. Letting *x* = 1 + *r/n*, write a polynomial equation in *x* that models the amount of money in the saving account on Christine's 18th birthday.

  d. If interest is calculated yearly and no money added or withdrawn after Christine's 18th birthday, write a polynomial equation in *x* that models the amount in the saving account on her 30th birthday.

3.3 Sample response: The functions that correspond to each letter are shown in the table at the bottom of the page, along with the intervals that approximate their domains and ranges.

* 3.4 Answers will vary. Student responses should include a sketch of the design, a list of the functions used, their zeros, and a description of the domain and range used to view the picture.

✹ ✹ ✹ ✹ ✹

3.5 **a.** After one year, the account balance was $250(1 + 0.055)^1 = \$263.75$.

  b. The account balance after these five years can be found as follows:

$$f(x) = 250(1.055)^5 + 200(1.055)^4 + 325(1.055)^3 + 450(1.055)^2 + 400(1.055)^1 + 675(1.055)^0$$
$$= \$2553.99$$

  c. If $x = 1 + r/n$, a polynomial function in *x* that models the account balance on Christine's 18th birthday is:

$$f(x) = 250x^5 + 200x^4 + 325x^3 + 450x^2 + 400x^1 + 675$$

  d. If $x = 1 + r/n$, a polynomial function in *x* that models the account balance on Christine's 30th birthday is:

$$f(x) = 250x^{17} + 200x^{16} + 325x^{15} + 450x^{14} + 400x^{13} + 675x^{12}$$

Letter	Function	Domain	Range
W	$f(x) = (x - 0.5)(x - 2)(x - 3)(x - 4.5)$	[0.32, 4.69]	[−3.52, 3.50]
A	$f(x) = -1.5(x - 5.5)(x - 8.5)$	[4.86, 9.14]	[−3.49, 3.38]
A	$f(x) = 0$	[5.5, 8.5]	[0, 0]
X	$f(x) = 0.3(x - 12)^3$	[9.73, 14.27]	[−3.51, 3.51]
X	$f(x) = -0.3(x - 12)^3$	[9.73, 14.27]	[−3.51, 3.51]

3.6 The length of the box is $(96 - 2x)$. The width of the box is $(54 - 2x)$. The height is x.

a. 1. The polynomial function that models the surface area of the box is:

$$A(x) = (96)(54) - 4(x^2)$$
$$= -4(x^2 - 1296)$$
$$= -4(x - 36)(x + 36)$$

2. The domain of the function is all real numbers, $(-\infty, \infty)$. In the context of this problem, however, only the interval $(0, 27)$ should be considered, because a box cannot be formed for any x-value outside this interval.

3. The zeros of this function are $x = 36$ and $x = -36$. Both are outside the interval of values that should be considered in this context. Therefore, the zeros of this function have no meaning in this setting.

b. 1. The polynomial function in x that models the volume of the box is:

$$V(x) = x(96 - 2x)(54 - 2x)$$
$$= 4x^3 - 300x^2 + 5184x$$
$$= 4x(x - 48)(x - 27)$$

2. The domain of the function is all real numbers, $(-\infty, \infty)$. In the context of this problem, however, only the interval $(0, 27)$ should be considered, because a box cannot be formed for any x-value outside this interval.

3. The zeros of the function are 0, 27, and 48. All of these values are outside the interval to be considered in this problem, so they have no meaning in this setting.

c. Students may trace a graph of the function to determine the approximate maximum volume of about 26,000 cm^3. This occurs when x is approximately 11 cm.

d. The surface area of the open-topped box with the maximum volume is approximately 4700 cm^2, since $A(11) = 5184 - 4(11)^2 = 4700$.

ACTIVITY 4

In this activity, students explore the graphs of polynomials of higher degrees. They determine the domain and range of the corresponding polynomial functions and investigate the end behavior of such functions.

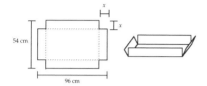

3.6 A container company plans to create an open-topped box from a sheet of cardboard 54 cm wide and 96 cm long. As shown in the following diagram, a square with length x is cut from each corner of the cardboard. The box is formed by folding the cardboard along the resulting seams and fastening the sides together.

a. 1. Determine a polynomial function in x that represents the surface area of the open-topped box.

2. What is the domain of this function? Explain your response.

3. Find the zeros of the function and explain what they represent in terms of the box.

b. Repeat Part a for a polynomial function in x that represents the volume of the box.

c. Determine the value of x that results in a box with the maximum possible volume.

d. Find the surface area of the box with the maximum volume.

ACTIVITY 4

While polynomials of lower degrees can provide simple curves for graphic design, polynomials of higher degrees can be used to model more complex curves. In this activity, you explore the degrees of polynomials whose graphs have similar characteristics.

Exploration 1

The degree of a polynomial function has an effect on the shape of its graph. For example, consider polynomial functions of the form $y = x^n$ and $y = -x^n$, where n is a positive integer.

teacher note

A brief assessment of the mathematical content in Activities **3** and **4**, for use at your discretion, appears in the Teacher Resources for this module.

Materials List

■ none

Technology

■ graphing utility

Student Outcomes

After completing the following exploration and discussion, students should be able to:

✳ write and graph polynomial functions with higher degrees

✳ describe the general shapes of the graphs of some polynomials

a. Let *n* be a positive, even integer. Using a graphing utility, graph at least three different functions of the form $y = x^n$ on the same set of axes. Compare the graphs and determine the domain and range of each function.

b. Let *n* be positive, even integer. Graph some polynomial functions of the form $y = -x^n$. Compare the graphs and determine the domain and range of each function.

c. Compare the domains and ranges of the functions in Part **a** with the domains and ranges of the functions in Part **b**.

d. Let *n* be odd and greater than 1. Using a graphing utility, graph at least three different equations of the form $y = x^n$ on the same set of axes. Compare the graphs and determine the domain and range of each function.

e. Let *n* be odd and greater than 1. Graph some polynomial functions of the form $y = -x^n$. Compare the graphs and determine the domain and range of each function.

f. Compare the domains and ranges of the functions in Part **d** with the domains and ranges of the functions in Part **e**.

g. Investigate graphs of functions of the form $y = ax^n$ for various values of *a* and *n*. Note the shapes of the graphs and the corresponding domains and ranges.

Discussion 1

a. 1. What effect does *a* have on the general shape of the graph of $y = ax^n$?

   2. What general statement can you make about the domain and range of the function $y = ax^n$?

b. 1. Describe the *y*-values of a graph of $y = x^n$ when *n* is even, as *x* increases from −5 to 5.

   2. Describe the *y*-values of a graph of $y = x^n$ when *n* is odd, as *x* increases from −5 to 5.

c. As the *x*-values of a polynomial function increase (or decrease) without bound, the change in the corresponding *y*-values is referred to as the **end behavior** of the function. What generalizations, if any, can you make about the end behaviors of the graphs in Exploration **1**?

d. Is it possible for the range of a polynomial function with an even degree to contain all the real numbers? Explain your response.

e. Is it possible to predict the range of a polynomial function with an odd degree? Explain your response.

✳ identify the domain and range of polynomial functions with higher degrees

✳ use the distributive property to expand polynomials

✳ recognize the relationships among the zeros, factors, and degree of a polynomial function

✳ recognize relationships between the lead coefficient of a polynomial and the behavior of its graph

✳ use graphs to identify factors of polynomials

✳ use technology to factor polynomials

✳ use polynomials and their graphs as mathematical models

✳ identify horizontal and vertical translations of polynomial functions

✳ describe the end behavior of polynomial functions.

Exploration 1

Students compare graphs of polynomials of the form $y = ax^n$.

a. Students should observe that these graphs have the same general shape. The domain of all functions of the form $y = x^n$, when *n* is an even, positive integer, is the set of real numbers. The corresponding range is the set of non-negative real numbers.

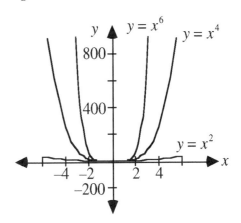

b. Students should again observe that the graphs have the same general shape. The domain of all functions of the form $y = -x^n$, when *n* is an even, positive integer, is the set of real numbers. The corresponding range is the set of nonpositive real numbers.

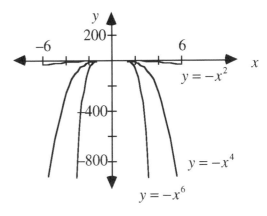

c. Sample response: For a given value of *n*, the domains of $f(x) = x^n$ and $f(x) = -x^n$ are the same; the respective values in the ranges are additive inverses.

d. The graphs have the same general shape. The domain of all functions of the form $y = x^n$, when *n* is an odd integer greater than 1, is the set of real numbers. The corresponding range is also the set of real numbers.

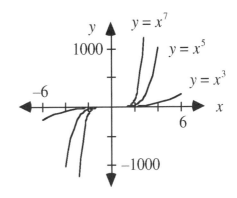

e. The graphs have the same general shape. The domain of all functions of the form $y = -x^n$, when n is an odd integer greater than 1, is the set of real numbers. The corresponding range is also the set of real numbers.

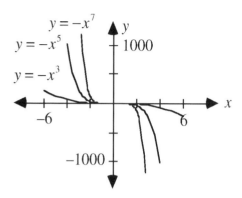

f. Sample response: The domains are equal and the ranges are equal.

g. Sample response: When n is even, the graph is U-shaped like a parabola and the domain is the set of real numbers, or the interval $(-\infty,\infty)$. If a is positive, the range is the set of non-negative real numbers, or the interval $[0,\infty)$. If a is negative, the range is the set of non-positive real numbers, or the interval $(-\infty,0]$.

When n is odd and a is positive, the graphs rise from left to right and are nearly horizontal in the vicinity of the origin. The domain and range of each function is the set of real numbers, or the interval $(-\infty,\infty)$.

When n is odd and a is negative, the graphs fall from left to right and are nearly horizontal in the vicinity of the origin. The domain and range of each function is the set of real numbers, or the interval $(-\infty,\infty)$.

c. For functions of the form $y = x^n$, where n is even, the y-values increase without bound as $|x|$ increases. For functions of the form $y = -x^n$, where n is even, the y-values decrease without bound as $|x|$ increases.

For functions of the form $y = x^n$, where n is odd, the y-values approach $-\infty$ as x decreases without bound. As x increases without bound, the y-values approach $+\infty$. For functions of the form $y = -x^n$, where n is odd, the y-values approach $+\infty$ as x decreases without bound. As x increases without bound, the y-values approach $-\infty$.

d. Sample response: It is not possible. Either the subset of positive real numbers or negative real numbers will be missing because of the effects of raising a value to an even power.

e. Sample response: The range for a polynomial function of odd degree will always be the set of real numbers because of its end behavior. As the absolute values of x increase, one end of the graph increases without bound, while the other end decreases without bound.

Discussion 1

a. 1. Sample response: If n is even, $|a|$ affects the shape of the graph—the greater the $|a|$, the narrower the curve. If n is odd, $|a|$ affects how steep the curve is—the greater the $|a|$ is, the steeper the curve becomes and the less flat it is in the vicinity of the origin. In either case, if a is negative, the curve is reflected in the x-axis.

2. For each value of n, the domain is always the set of real numbers, or the interval $(-\infty,\infty)$. If n is even, the range is either the set of non-negative real numbers or the set of nonpositive real numbers. If n is odd, the range is always the set of real numbers.

b. 1. The y-values decrease from a positive value at $x = -5$ to a value of 0 at $x = 0$. The y-values then increase as x increases in value from 0 to 5.

2. The y-values increase across the domain from a negative value at $x = -5$, to 0 at $x = 0$, to positive values when $x > 0$.

Exploration 2

Earlier in this module, you discovered a relationship between the zeros of a polynomial function and its real-number factors. In this exploration, you investigate this relationship for another group of polynomial functions of the form $f(x) = a_n x^n + a_{n-1} x^{n-1} + \cdots + a_1 x^1 + a_0$.

a. Using a graphing utility, graph each of the following equations on a separate coordinate system. Approximate the roots of each function.

   1. $f(x) = x^2 - 3x + 2$

   2. $f(x) = x^3 - 6x^2 + 11x - 6$

   3. $f(x) = x^4 - 10x^3 + 35x^2 - 50x + 24$

   4. $f(x) = x^5 - 15x^4 + 85x^3 - 225x^2 + 274x - 120$

b. Using technology, factor each polynomial function in Part **a**. Do the results support the approximate roots determined from the graphs?

c. One way to translate the graph of a function involves adding a real number to its equation. Experiment with this technique by adding various real numbers to each function in Part **a** and graphing the results.

d. 1. Consider the function $f(x) = x^2 - 3x + 2$. Write a new function $g(x)$ that represents a vertical translation of $f(x)$.

   2. Graph $g(x)$ and adjust the translation until $g(x)$ has a different number of roots than $f(x)$.

   3. Use the graph of $g(x)$ to approximate its roots.

   4. Use technology to factor $g(x)$. Do the results support the approximate roots determined from the graph?

e. Repeat Part **d** for each of the remaining functions listed in Part **a**.

Discussion 2

a. When a linear function is translated vertically, how does this transformation affect the roots of the function? Explain your response.

b. Does translating a polynomial function change its degree?

c. In Parts **d** and **e** of Exploration **2**, was it possible to express each vertically translated function as a product of first-degree polynomials? How do the graphs of the vertically translated functions support your response?

d. 1. How is the number of real roots of a polynomial function of the form $f(x) = a(x - c_1)(x - c_2)(x - c_3) \cdots (x - c_n)$ related to its degree?

   2. Is this same relationship true for all polynomial functions of the form $f(x) = a_n x^n + a_{n-1} x^{n-1} + \cdots + a_1 x^1 + a_0$? Explain your response.

Exploration 2

In this exploration, students discover that some polynomial functions cannot be expressed as the product of first-degree factors.

a. Students create graphs of four polynomials and approximate their roots. Sample graphs of each function are given below.

1.

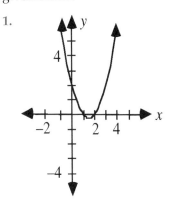

real roots:
$x = 1$, $x = 2$

2.

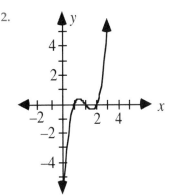

real roots:
$x = 1, 2$, and 3

3.

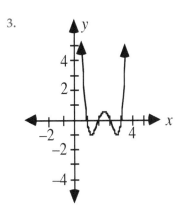

real roots:
$x = 1, 2, 3$, and 4

4.

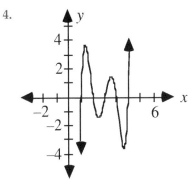

real roots:
$x = 1, 2, 3, 4$, and 5

b. These polynomial functions can be written in factored form because all of their roots are real numbers.

   1. $y = (x - 1)(x - 2)$

   2. $y = (x - 1)(x - 2)(x - 3)$

   3. $y = (x - 1)(x - 2)(x - 3)(x - 4)$

   4. $y = (x - 1)(x - 2)(x - 3)(x - 4)(x - 5)$

c. Adding a constant to a function of the form $f(x) = (x - c_1)(x - c_2) \cdots (x - c_n)$ translates the graph vertically.

d–e. Students should discover that a graph of a polynomial function of degree n that does not intersect the x-axis n times cannot be expressed in factored form using only first-degree factors. **Note:** Students will be introduced to imaginary roots in later modules. However, you might wish to discuss them with your students at this time.

The following sample graphs show vertical translations of the original functions in Part **a** by 2 units, along with the approximate real roots, if any.

1. 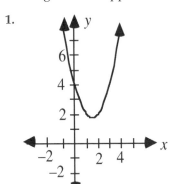   real roots:
   none

2. 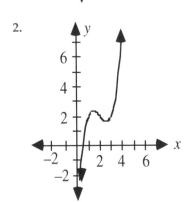   real roots:
   $x \approx 0.5$

3. 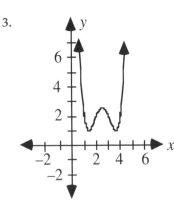   real roots:
   none

4. 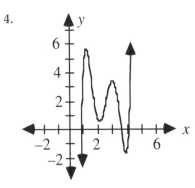   real roots:
   $x \approx 0.9, 4.3,$ and 4.9

Discussion 2

a. If the linear function $f(x) \; mx + b$ has a non-zero value of m, translating the function vertically will change the value of the root but not the number of roots. If $m = 0$, the function has no zeros unless $b = 0$.

b. Sample response: No. Translating a function only affects the function's position, not its degree.

c. Sample response: No. The translated functions cannot be expressed as a product of first-degree factors. The value of c in factors of the form $(x - c)$ are determined by the points where the graph crosses the x-axis. Although they have the same degree, the translated graphs cross the x-axis fewer times than the original functions.

d. 1. The number of real roots of a polynomial function in factored form is equal to its degree.
   2. Sample response: No. The maximum number of real roots is equal to the degree of the polynomial function. The actual number of real roots can vary.

e. Although the degree of a polynomial sometimes can be determined by the shape of its graph, this is not always true. In most cases, the graph can be used to identify only the least possible degree of the polynomial.

f. 1. Sample response: Based on the number of times the function must cross the x-axis, the function has 5 real roots. This would indicate a minimum degree of 5.
   2. Sample response: No. Polynomial functions of a higher degree could model the set of points, as could pieces of several functions of lower degrees.

Warm-Up

1. **a.** $f(x) = (x - 5)^2$
   b. $f(x) = x^2 + 1.6$
   c. $f(x) = (x + 3)^2 - 1$
2. **a.** Answers will vary. The function should have two factors of the form $(x - c)$ that are raised to even powers. Sample response:
   $$f(x) = (x - 1)^2(x - 4)^2.$$
   b. Answers will vary. The function should have two factors of the form $(x - c)$ with exactly one of them raised to an odd power. Sample response:
   $$f(x) = (x - 1)^3(x - 4)^2.$$

e. What can you tell about the degree of a polynomial by examining its graph?

f. 1. What degree of polynomial function would you recommend to a drafter trying to fit a curve to the following set of points? Explain your response.

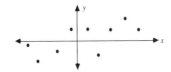

2. Is this the only degree that the drafter could use? Explain your response.

Warm-Up

1. Determine a function of the form $f(x) = a(x - c)^2 + d$ that represents each of the following changes to the function $f(x) = x^2$.

   a. a translation 5 units to the right

   b. a translation 1.6 units up

   c. a translation 3 units to the left and 1 unit down

2. a. Determine a polynomial function with two zeros whose range is the set of non-negative real numbers.

   b. Determine a polynomial function with two zeros whose range is the set of real numbers.

Assignment

4.1 Examine the graphs of $f(x) = (x - 2)^n$ for $n = 1, 2, 3, 4, 5, 6$. Describe any patterns you observe.

4.2 a. Determine a polynomial function with a degree greater than 3 that has exactly two distinct real roots and whose range does not include all real numbers.

   b. Determine a polynomial function with a degree greater than 3 that has exactly three distinct real roots and whose range includes all real numbers.

4.3 a. Create a function whose y-values increase over a portion of the interval [–5, 5] for x and decrease over the rest of the interval.

   b. Create a function whose y-values decrease as x increases from –5 to 5.

Assignment

Problems suitable for use as assessment items are identified by an asterisk (*).

4.1 Sample response: When $n = 1$, $f(x)$ is a line that intercepts the x-axis at 2 and the y-axis at –2. When n is even, the graph is tangent to the x-axis at $x = 2$ and the range is the set of non-negative real numbers. The general shape of the graph of $f(x) = (x - 2)^n$, when n is even, is illustrated below.

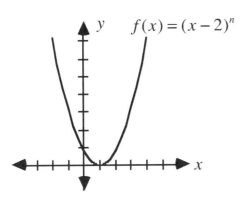

When n is odd and $n \geq 3$, the graph intersects the x-axis at $x = 2$ and the range is the set of real numbers. The general shape of the graph of $f(x) = (x - 2)^n$, when n is odd and $n \geq 3$, is illustrated below.

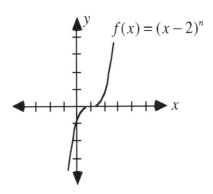

4.2 a. Answers will vary. Students should find a polynomial function of even degree with exactly two distinct real roots. This can be done by finding a polynomial in factored form with an even number of distinct real roots greater than 2 and translating it vertically until the graph crosses the x-axis exactly two times. Sample response:

$$f(x) = (x + 4)(x + 2)(x - 2)(x - 1) + 6$$
$$= x^4 + 3x^3 - 8x^2 - 12x + 22$$

   b. Answers will vary. Students should find a polynomial function of odd degree with exactly three distinct real roots. This can be done by finding a polynomial in factored form with an odd number of distinct real roots greater than 3 and translating it vertically until the graph crosses the x-axis exactly three times. Sample response:

$$f(x) = (x + 4)(x + 2)(x - 2)(x - 1)(x - 1) + 4$$
$$= x^5 + 2x^4 - 11x^3 - 4x^2 + 28x - 12$$

4.3 a. Sample response: Any function of the form $f(x) = -(x - b)^n$, where $-5 < b < 5$ and n is even, will satisfy these conditions.

   b. Any function of the form $f(x) = -(x - b)^n$, where n is odd, will satisfy these conditions.

4.4 **a.** Sample response: The letter U in the following diagram was defined by the functions $y = 0.8x^6 + 0.2$ for x in $[-1.15, 1.15]$, $y = 0.1x^{14}$ for x in $[-1.24, 1.24]$, and $y = 2.05$ for x in $[1.15, 1.24]$ and $[-1.24, -1.15]$.

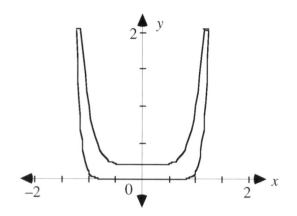

b. Sample response: The design from Part **a** more closely resembles the printed letter. This design uses even-degree polynomials of a high degree to create a flattened outline at the bottom of the U.

* 4.5 **a.** Answers may vary. Some students may indicate the "peaks" and "valleys" of the curve, because these regions contain no more than two turning points. The sample sketch below shows the points where a drawing program spliced the cubic curves together.

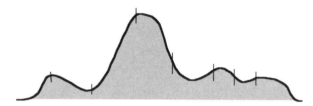

b. Sample response: A collection of cubics is easier to manipulate than a single higher-degree polynomial. It is also easier to determine several equations, each modeling some of the points, than it is to find a single equation that models all of the points.

✳ ✳ ✳ ✳ ✳

4.6 **a.** By examining the graph, students should observe that the y-values increase as x increases in the intervals $(-3.56, 0.40)$ and $(3.18, \infty)$.

b. By examining the graph, students should observe that the y-values decrease as x increases in the intervals: $(-\infty, -3.56)$ and $(0.40, 3.18)$.

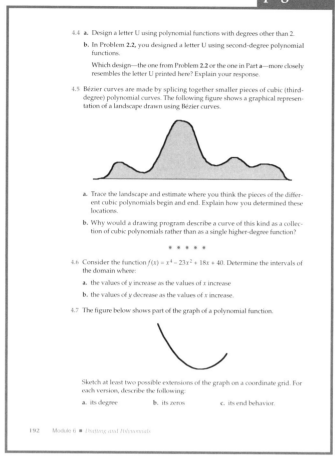

4.4 **a.** Design a letter U using polynomial functions with degrees other than 2.

  b. In Problem **2.2**, you designed a letter U using second-degree polynomial functions.

   Which design—the one from Problem **2.2** or the one in Part **a**—more closely resembles the letter U printed here? Explain your response.

4.5 Bézier curves are made by splicing together smaller pieces of cubic (third-degree) polynomial curves. The following figure shows a graphical representation of a landscape drawn using Bézier curves.

  a. Trace the landscape and estimate where you think the pieces of the different cubic polynomials begin and end. Explain how you determined these locations.

  b. Why would a drawing program describe a curve of this kind as a collection of cubic polynomials rather than as a single higher-degree function?

✳ ✳ ✳ ✳ ✳

4.6 Consider the function $f(x) = x^4 - 23x^2 + 18x + 40$. Determine the intervals of the domain where:

  a. the values of y increase as the values of x increase

  b. the values of y decrease as the values of x increase.

4.7 The figure below shows part of the graph of a polynomial function.

  Sketch at least two possible extensions of the graph on a coordinate grid. For each version, describe the following:

   a. its degree   **b.** its zeros   **c.** its end behavior.

4.7 It is possible to argue that the complete graph is a polynomial of any degree greater than or equal to 2. Sample response:

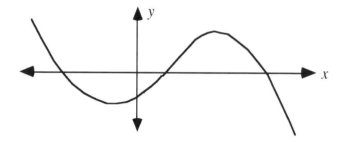

a. The sample graph shown appears to have degree 3.

b. There are three zeros: two positive and one negative.

c. Sample response: The end behavior approaches positive infinity for small values of x. It approaches negative infinity for large values of x.

Summary Assessment

The diagram below shows three versions of a capital letter W, along with the names of their respective fonts. The boundaries of each letter were described using polynomials. Design your own capital letter W using polynomials. In your report, include a list of each polynomial function used and its corresponding domain.

New York   Times   Customized Font

---

teacher note

An additional assessment, for use at your discretion, appears in the Teacher Resources for this module.

Summary Assessment

Answers will vary. Students may use two fourth-degree equations to define the boundaries of the letter W, because some fourth-degree polynomials have three "turning points"—for example, $x^2(x + 3)^2$ and $0.25(x - 1)^2(x + 4)^2 - 7$. Others may use linear equations. The sample below was created by experimenting with a graphing utility. It is composed of a quadratic (the inside edge), a cubic (the outside edge), horizontal lines, and the reflections of all these polynomials in the y-axis. Appropriate values for the domains were found by tracing curves to find the points of intersection. The letter is defined by the following functions:

- $y = 2(x + 1)(x + 3)$ defined over the domain $[-4.36, 0)$
- $y = 2(x - 1)(x - 3)$ defined over the domain $[0, 4.36)$
- $y = 0.15(x + 0.5)(x + 4)(x + 10)$ defined over the domain $[-7.55, 0]$
- $y = -0.15(x - 0.5)(x - 4)(x - 10)$ defined over the domain $(0, 7.55]$
- $y = 9.15$ defined over the domain $[-7.55, -4.36)$ and $[4.36, 7.55]$

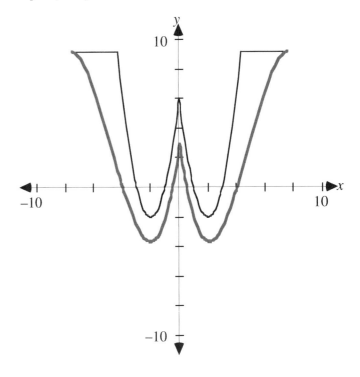

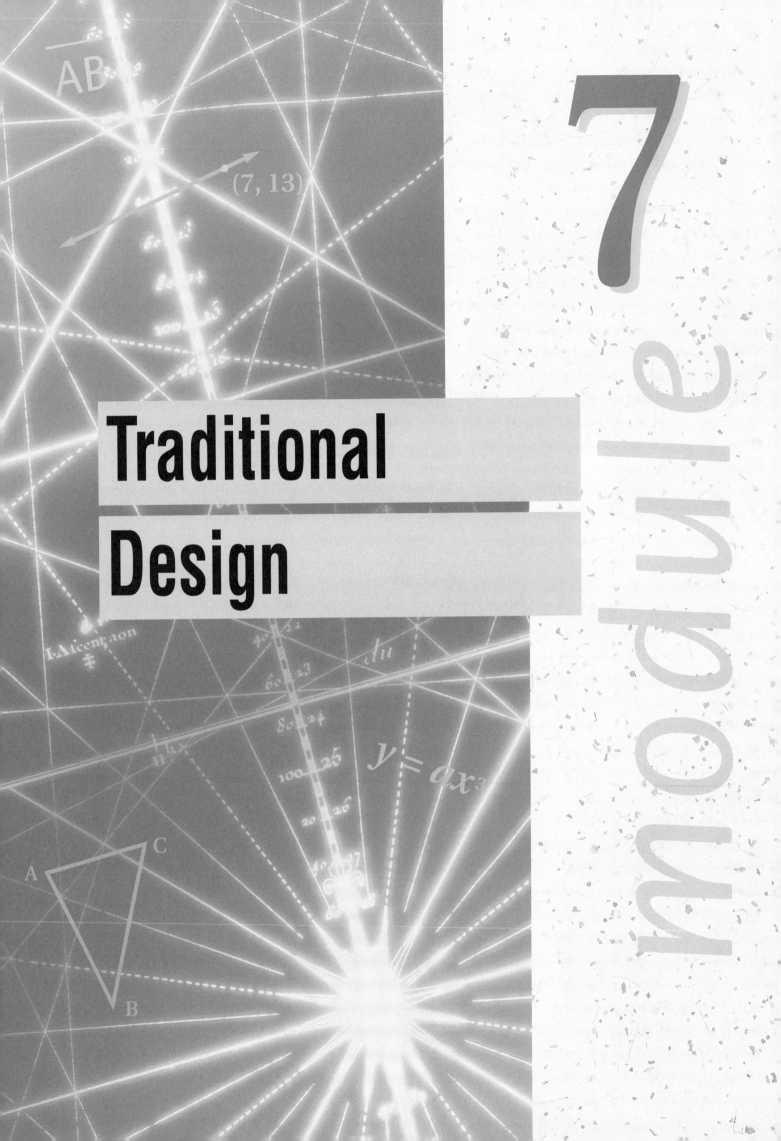

Traditional Design

Overview

Overview

This module uses traditional American Indian art to examine basic geometric principles. Students use the lone-star quilts of the Assiniboine and Sioux tribes to explore parallel and perpendicular lines. They then use the medicine wheels of the Northern Cheyenne to explore properties of tangents and secants in relation to a circle. Finally, they use Navajo sand paintings to explore transformations.

Introduction:	Students develop paper-folding methods to construct angle bisectors, perpendicular bisectors, parallel lines, and midpoints.
Activity 1:	Students investigate the properties of a rhombus and the relationships defining vertical angles, corresponding angles, and alternating angles.
Activity 2:	Students explore the properties of tangents and secants on a circle.
Activity 3:	Students explore dilations and classify the appropriate transformations as isometries.

Objectives

In this module, students will:

✳ use paper-folding constructions to examine angle bisectors, perpendicular lines, parallel lines, and midpoints (Introduction)

✳ explore properties of angles formed by parallel lines and a transversal (1)

✳ explore geometric rep tiles (1)

✳ examine properties of parallelograms (1)

✳ identify properties of chords, tangents, and secants of a circle (2)

✳ examine congruent figures created by reflections, rotations, and translations (2, 3)

✳ examine similar figures created by dilations (3)

✳ classify transformations as isometries (3).

Prerequisites

For this module, students should know:

* the definition of supplementary angles
* line symmetry
* properties of a square
* properties of reflections, dilations, rotations, and translations
* the definition of congruent figures.

 Flashbacks, for use at your discretion, appear in the Teacher Resources for this module. These brief problem sets provide a review of some prerequisite skills for each activity.

Planning Guide

Activity	Materials	Technology	Time Line
Introduction	■ straightedge ■ protractor ■ template A	■ none	1 day
Activity **1**	■ straightedge ■ scissors ■ template B	■ geometry utility	2 days
Activity **2**	■ straightedge ■ template C ■ template D ■ template E ■ template F	■ geometry utility	3 days
Activity **3**	■ straightedge ■ protractor ■ template G ■ template H	■ geometry utility	2 days
Assessment Activities	■ straightedge ■ template I	■ none	3 days **Total: 11 days**

 teacher note

Blackline masters of the templates appear in the Teacher Resources for this module.

Template I is required to complete Problem **3** in the Module Assessment (not the Summary Assessment).

Introduction

Students develop paper-folding methods to construct angle bisectors, perpendicular lines, parallel lines, and midpoints.

Materials List

- template A (one copy per student; a blackline master appears in the Teacher Resources for this module)
- straightedge (one per student)
- protractor (one per student)

Student Outcomes

After completing the following exploration and discussion, students should be able to:

✳ recognize lines of symmetry

✳ use paper folding to construct angle bisectors, perpendicular bisectors, parallel lines, and midpoints.

Exploration

Each student will require a copy of template A to complete the exploration.

a. 1. Student papers should resemble the following diagram:

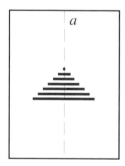

2. Each bar is divided in half by the crease.
3. The angles appear to be 90°.
4. Sample response: The line of symmetry is the perpendicular bisector of each bar in the symbol.

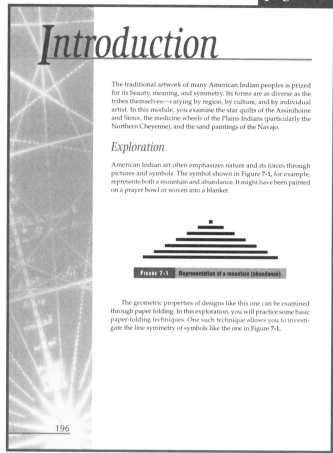

b. 1. Students should fold the paper so that the line of symmetry coincides with itself, creating a crease parallel to the bars. Student papers should resemble the following diagram:

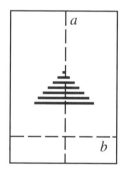

2. Student papers should resemble the following diagram:

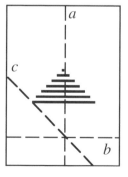

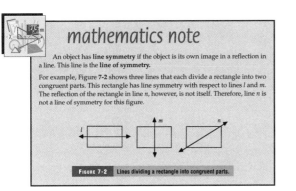

mathematics note

An object has **line symmetry** if the object is its own image in a reflection in a line. This line is the **line of symmetry**.

For example, Figure **7-2** shows three lines that each divide a rectangle into two congruent parts. This rectangle has line symmetry with respect to lines *l* and *m*. The reflection of the rectangle in line *n*, however, is not itself. Therefore, line *n* is not a line of symmetry for this figure.

FIGURE 7-2 Lines dividing a rectangle into congruent parts.

Complete Parts **a–c** using a reproduction of the symbol in Figure **7-1**.

a. 1. Fold your paper along the symbol's line of symmetry. Unfold the paper and label the resulting crease line *a*.

2. Measure the length of the bars on each side of crease *a*.

3. Measure the angles formed by line *a* and the bars in the symbol.

4. Make a conjecture about the relationship of the line of symmetry to the bars in the symbol.

b. 1. Fold the paper to form a line parallel to the bars in the symbol. Unfold the paper and label this crease line *b*.

2. Identify an angle formed by crease *a* and crease *b*. As shown in Figure **7-3** on the right, fold the paper so that one side of the angle coincides with its other side. Unfold the paper and label this crease line *c*.

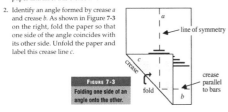

FIGURE 7-3
Folding one side of an angle onto the other.

Module 7 ■ *Traditional Design* 197

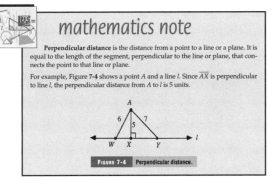

mathematics note

Perpendicular distance is the distance from a point to a line or a plane. It is equal to the length of the segment, perpendicular to the line or plane, that connects the point to that line or plane.

For example, Figure **7-4** shows a point *A* and a line *l*. Since $\overline{AX}$ is perpendicular to line *l*, the perpendicular distance from *A* to *l* is 5 units.

FIGURE 7-4 Perpendicular distance.

c. 1. Select a point on crease *c* and measure the perpendicular distance from this point to each side of the angle formed by creases *a* and *b*.

2. Measure the angles formed by creases *c* and *b* and the angles formed by creases *c* and *a*.

3. Make a conjecture about the relationship of crease *c* to the angle formed by creases *a* and *b*.

Discussion

a. Describe a paper-folding method that could be used to create each of the following:

1. an object's reflection in a line

2. a perpendicular bisector of a line segment

3. a bisector of an angle

4. a midpoint of a line segment.

b. Describe a paper-folding method that could be used to form a square from a rectangular sheet of paper.

c. 1. The two perpendicular distances should be equal.

2. The measure of each angle is 45°.

3. Sample response: Crease *c* is the bisector of an angle formed by creases *a* and *b*.

Discussion

a. 1. Sample response: An object can be reflected by folding along a line of reflection, then tracing to show the reflected image.

2. The perpendicular bisector of a segment can be found by folding one of the segment's endpoints onto the other.

3. The angle bisector can be found by folding one side of an angle so that it coincides with the other side of the angle. (See Figure **7-3** in the student edition.)

4. The midpoint of a line segment can be found by creating a perpendicular bisector. The intersection of the perpendicular bisector and the segment is the midpoint.

b. As shown in the following diagram, a square can be formed from a rectangular sheet of paper by creating the angle bisector of one of the 90° corners. The part of the paper that is not doubled can then be cut off, leaving a square.

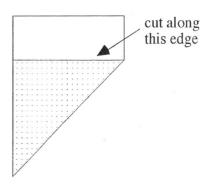

cut along this edge

ACTIVITY 1

Students use the design of a star quilt to review the properties of angles formed from parallel lines cut by a transversal. They also examine the properties of a rhombus and explore how to create geometric rep tiles.

Materials List

- straightedge (one per student)
- pair of scissors (one per student)
- copy of template B (for Problem **1.2,** one per student; a blackline master appears in the Teacher Resources for this module)

Technology

- geometry utility (optional)

Student Outcomes

After completing the following discussions and exploration, students should be able to:

✳ describe the geometric properties of a rhombus

✳ identify vertical angles, corresponding angles, and alternate angles and describe their properties

✳ identify similar polygons.

Discussion 1

a. Other than the eight-pointed star, students should recognize some parallelograms—including rhombi—in the design. They also might mention other shapes, such as the octagon that can be made by connecting the star's eight outer vertices.

b. **1.** A parallelogram—specifically, a rhombus—is the basic shape used to construct the star.

    2. A rhombus is a parallelogram with congruent sides. **Note:** You might want students to discuss the properties of parallelograms as well.

ACTIVITY 1

For hundreds of years, some American Indian families marked important events in the lives of their children by giving gifts. These gifts were not intended for the individual child, however, but for some other admired person. In this tradition, gift giving demonstrated the deep pride that a family felt for its children.

    Today, the Assiniboine and Sioux tribes of northeastern Montana preserve this tradition through the star quilt ceremony. Each star quilt represents many hours of painstaking labor. It is a great honor both to give away a star quilt and to receive one. Star quilt ceremonies usually are held at community gatherings, particularly athletic events. For example, the family of a basketball player or cheerleader might make a quilt to present between games at a state tournament. The person to receive the quilt might be a coach, an admired member of the community, or a player from another team.

    The family often wraps the quilt around the shoulders of the chosen recipient while introductions are made and the audience stands respectfully. This ceremony is a powerful medium for reflecting the values, attitudes, pride, and identity of the presenting family.

    Although there are many kinds of star quilts, all of them have the lone star as their primary focus. Figure 7-5 shows one example of a lone star pattern.

FIGURE 7-5   Lone star quilt pattern.

Discussion 1

a. Identify some of the geometric shapes you recognize in the lone star pattern in Figure 7-5.

b. 1. What basic shape do you think was used to construct the star?

    2. Describe the properties of this shape.

Exploration

In this exploration, you use paper folding to investigate the properties of the basic shape in the lone star pattern.

a. Fold and cut a standard sheet of paper to form a square. If no crease has been formed along a diagonal of the square, use another fold to create one.

b. As shown in Figure 7-6a, use paper folding to bisect an angle formed by a side of the square and the creased diagonal. Using the same vertex—and without unfolding the paper—repeat this step for the adjacent angle, as shown in Figure 7-6b. Do not unfold this shape.

a.   b.

FIGURE 7-6   Folding in the sides of a square.

c. Repeat Parts **a** and **b** using the opposite vertex of the original square, as shown in Figure 7-7. The resulting shape is a **rhombus.**

FIGURE 7-7   Folding at the opposite vertex.

d. 1. By carefully examining the folds made in creating this rhombus, determine and record the measures of its interior angles.

2. Predict the relationship that occurs between opposite angles of a rhombus.

e. Turn the rhombus over so that the previous folds are not visible. Fold it along the shorter diagonal. Unfold it, fold along the longer diagonal, and then unfold again. Make a conjecture concerning the diagonals of this rhombus.

f. 1. Find the midpoint of each side of the rhombus.

2. Using a straightedge, draw the line that contains the midpoints of two opposite sides. Identify the shapes formed by these lines and the sides of the rhombus.

3. Draw the line that contains the midpoints of the other pair of opposite sides.

g. Identify the four shapes formed by the lines in Part f and the sides of the rhombus.

h. Record the measure of each angle of the shapes you identified in Part g. **Note:** Save the folded rhombus for use in Discussion 2 and in the assignment.

mathematics note

Two polygons are **similar** if there is a one-to-one correspondence between their vertices so that corresponding sides are proportional and corresponding angles are congruent.

For example, Figure **7-8** shows two triangles, the approximate lengths of their sides, and the approximate measures of their angles.

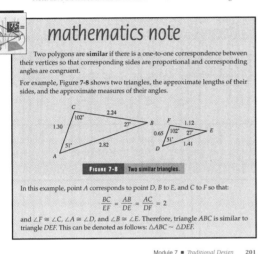

FIGURE 7-8 Two similar triangles.

In this example, point A corresponds to point D, B to E, and C to F so that:

$$\frac{BC}{EF} = \frac{AB}{DE} = \frac{AC}{DF} = 2$$

and $\angle F \cong \angle C$, $\angle A \cong \angle D$, and $\angle B \cong \angle E$. Therefore, triangle ABC is similar to triangle DEF. This can be denoted as follows: $\triangle ABC \sim \triangle DEF$.

teacher note

In the following exploration, students should discover these properties of a rhombus: opposite angles are congruent, the diagonals are perpendicular bisectors of each other, and the diagonals bisect the angles.

Although students also may complete this construction using a geometry utility, this activity is designed to reflect the historical methods used by quiltmakers.

To allow for broader generalizations in student conjectures, you may vary the dimensions of the paper used by each group.

Exploration

Students use paper folding to form a rhombus and explore some of its properties.

a. A square can be formed from a rectangular sheet of paper by creating the angle bisector of one of the 90° corners. The part of the paper that is not doubled is then cut off. (See Part **b** of the discussion in the introduction.)

b. Student papers should resemble the shape shown in Figure **7-6b** of the student edition.

c. As shown in Figure **7-7**, the resulting shape is a rhombus.

d. 1. Students should not have to use protractors to measure these angles. The measure of each of the two smaller angles of the rhombus is the sum of two angles whose measures are:

$$\frac{1}{2}\left(\frac{1}{2} \bullet 90°\right) = 22.5°$$

The sum is therefore 45°. The adjacent angles of the rhombus are supplementary to these 45° angles. Thus, each has a measure of 135°.

2. The opposite angles of a rhombus (and, in general, a parallelogram) are congruent.

e. The diagonals of the rhombus are perpendicular bisectors of each other. As seen from the construction of this rhombus, the diagonals also bisect the interior angles.

f. 1. The midpoint of a line segment can be found by folding one of the segment's endpoints onto the other to create the segment's perpendicular bisector. The intersection of the perpendicular bisector and the segment is the midpoint.

2. Two congruent parallelograms are formed. Student papers should resemble the diagram below.

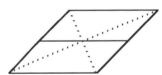

3. Student papers should resemble the following diagram.

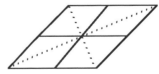

g. Four smaller congruent rhombi are formed, each similar to the original rhombus.

h. The measures of the interior angles of the smaller rhombi are the same as those of the original rhombus: 45° and 135°.

Discussion 2

a. Sample response: Yes, the shapes are similar to the original rhombus. The corresponding sides are proportional and the corresponding angles are congruent. **Note:** You might wish to ask students what information is necessary to determine if two rhombi are similar. If one angle of a rhombus is congruent to one angle of another rhombus, then the two rhombi are similar.

b. The two parallelograms are congruent. Because they are formed by joining the midpoints of opposite sides of a rhombus, the corresponding sides are congruent and the corresponding angles are congruent.

c. 1. Sample response: My conjecture was that opposite angles of a rhombus are congruent. This is supported by my measurements of the opposite angles and by the measurements of others in the class.

   2. Sample response: The diagonals are perpendicular bisectors of each other. When I folded the rhombus, each portion of the diagonal coincided with the other portion, indicating that the diagonal was bisected. I found, by measuring, that each angle formed by the intersection of the diagonals was 90°, making the diagonals perpendicular.

d. 1. Sample response: If two interior angles of a rhombus (and, in general, a parallelogram) are opposite angles, then the angles are congruent. If two interior angles of a rhombus are adjacent angles, then the angles are supplementary.

   2. Sample response: One way to show congruence is to tear off the angles from the paper models and match them. Another way is to measure.

      One way to show supplementary angles is to tear off the angles and place them together at the vertices. The non-adjacent sides will form a straight line.

      Note: All of these methods are demonstrations. To prove that these relationships are true, students must work with congruent figures.

e. 1. The measures of angles 1 and 3 are equal.

   2. The measures of angles 2 and 4 are equal. Angles 2 and 4 also have the same positional relationship as angles 1 and 3 because they are two non-adjacent angles formed by two intersecting lines.

   3. Vertical angles are two non-straight, non-adjacent angles formed by two intersecting lines.

   4. Students should identify many pairs of vertical angles. In the diagram below, these pairs include $\angle AOB$ and $\angle EOF$, $\angle BOD$ and $\angle FOH$, $\angle COD$ and $\angle GOH$, $\angle AOD$ and $\angle EOH$.

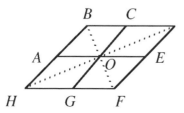

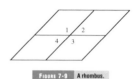

Discussion 2

a. Are the new shapes that you identified in Part **g** of the exploration similar to the original rhombus created in Part **c**?

b. Describe the relationship between the two parallelograms formed in Part **f** of the exploration.

c. 1. Compare the conjecture that you made in Part **d** of the exploration concerning the opposite angles of a rhombus with others in your class. What evidence do you have to support your conjecture?

   2. Compare the conjecture that you made in Part **e** of the exploration concerning the diagonals of a rhombus with others in your class. What evidence do you have to support this conjecture?

d. Recall that a **conditional statement** is one that can be written in if-then form.

   1. Use conditional statements to describe the relationships that exist among the interior angles of a rhombus.

   2. What methods could you use to demonstrate these relationships?

e. After connecting the midpoints of opposite sides in Part **f** of the exploration, your paper rhombus should have resembled the diagram in Figure **7-9**.

FIGURE 7-9 A rhombus.

   1. Angles 1 and 3 are **vertical angles**. What is the relationship between the measures of these angles?

   2. Does another pair of angles in Figure **7-9** have this same relationship?

   3. What characteristics do you think might define a pair of vertical angles?

   4. Using the rhombus that you created in the exploration, identify several pairs of vertical angles formed by crease lines.

f. Connecting the midpoints of opposite sides in Part **f** of the exploration created new, smaller shapes similar to the original rhombus. If you repeat this process on the smaller rhombi, what is the result?

teacher note

In Part **f** of Discussion **2**, you might wish to ask students to draw the lines described on their rhombi before answering the question.

f. The result will resemble the diagram below. Each smaller rhombus is divided into four congruent rhombi. Each of these rhombi is similar to the original rhombus and to the four intermediate rhombi from which they were formed.

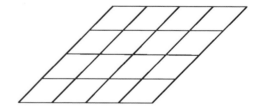

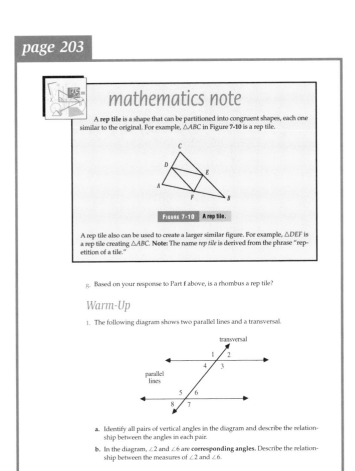

mathematics note

A **rep tile** is a shape that can be partitioned into congruent shapes, each one similar to the original. For example, △ABC in Figure 7-10 is a rep tile.

FIGURE 7-10 A rep tile.

A rep tile also can be used to create a larger similar figure. For example, △DEF is a rep tile creating △ABC. **Note:** The name *rep tile* is derived from the phrase "repetition of a tile."

g. Based on your response to Part f above, is a rhombus a rep tile?

Warm-Up

1. The following diagram shows two parallel lines and a transversal.

a. Identify all pairs of vertical angles in the diagram and describe the relationship between the angles in each pair.

b. In the diagram, ∠2 and ∠6 are **corresponding angles**. Describe the relationship between the measures of ∠2 and ∠6.

Warm-Up

1. **a.** There are four pairs of vertical angles: ∠1 and ∠3, ∠4 and ∠2 , ∠5 and ∠7, and ∠6 and ∠8. The two angles in each pair are congruent.

   b. Pairs of corresponding angles formed along a transversal of parallel lines are congruent.

g. Sample response: Yes, because the original rhombus is divided into congruent rhombi, each similar to the original. **Note:** The self-similar nature of rep tiles is a feature common to many fractals. You may use this opportunity to introduce fractals through Sierpinski's triangle. (Students will examine Sierpinski's triangle in a research project in the Level 2 module, "Take It to the Limit.")

teacher note

To demonstrate their understanding of the definitions for corresponding angles, alternate interior angles, and alternate exterior angles, students should complete Problem **1** of the Warm-Up before proceeding to the assignment.

After students complete Problem **1h,** you might wish to discuss the fact that both the alternate interior angles and the alternate exterior angles formed when two non-parallel lines are cut by a transversal are *not* congruent.

c. There are four pairs of corresponding angles: ∠1 and ∠5, ∠2 and ∠6, ∠4 and ∠8, and ∠3 and ∠7.

d. Sample response: Corresponding angles are in the same relative position relative to parallel lines cut by a transversal. **Note:** Students should observe that a pair of corresponding angles can be above the parallel and on the same side of a transversal, or below the parallel and on the same side of the transversal. You might wish to discuss the possibility of calling angles "corresponding" even if the lines are not parallel. In this case, however, the angles are not congruent.

e. The measures of the two angles are equal.

f. The measures of the two angles are equal.

g. There are two pairs of alternate interior angles: ∠4 and ∠6, and ∠3 and ∠5. There are two pairs of alternate exterior angles: ∠1 and ∠7, and ∠2 and ∠8.

h. Sample response: Alternate interior angles are between the parallel lines and on opposite sides of a transversal. Alternate exterior angles are outside the parallel lines and on opposite sides of a transversal. With parallel lines, the respective pairs of angles are congruent.

2. a. ∠S ≅ ∠K; ∠Z ≅ ∠M; ∠D ≅ ∠P

b. $\dfrac{SD}{KP} = \dfrac{SZ}{KM} = \dfrac{ZD}{MP}$

teacher note

To complete Problem **1.2,** each student will need a copy of template B. A blackline master appears in the Teacher Resources for this module.

Assignment

Problems suitable for use as assessment items are identified by an asterisk (*)

1.1 a. Angle 1 and angle 3 are vertical angles. Angle 1 and angle 2 are supplementary angles. Angles 1 and 4 are also supplementary angles.

b. Sample response: Angles 1 and 5 are congruent because they are corresponding angles of two parallel lines cut by a transversal. Likewise, angles 1 and 13 are corresponding angles.

Angle 1 has the same measure as angle 9 because angle 9 and angle 5 are corresponding angles, or because angle 1 and angle 3 are vertical angles, while angle 3 and angle 9 are opposite angles of the rhombus.

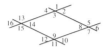

c. Identify as many other sets of corresponding angles as possible.

d. Suggest a general definition for corresponding angles.

e. In the diagram, ∠4 and ∠6 are **alternate interior angles.** Describe the relationship between the measures of ∠4 and ∠6.

f. In the diagram, ∠2 and ∠8 are **alternate exterior angles.** Describe the relationship between the measures of ∠2 and ∠8.

g. Identify as many pairs of alternate interior and alternate exterior angles as possible.

h. Suggest how alternate interior and alternate exterior angles might have received their names.

2. The following statement is true: △SZD ~ △KMP.

a. Describe the relationship between each pair of corresponding angles.

b. Use proportions to describe the relationship between each pair of corresponding sides.

Assignment

1.1 Consider the following rhombus with its sides extended.

a. Determine the relationship that exists between ∠1 and each of the remaining angles at that vertex.

b. Explain why the measure of ∠1 is equal to the measure of ∠5, ∠13, and ∠9.

c. What is the minimum number of angles that you must measure to determine the measures of all 16 angles in the diagram?

d. Suppose that none of the sides of the figure were parallel. How would this change your response to Part **c**?

1.2 a. Because making a star quilt requires many hours of work, quilters often use certain cutting and sewing techniques to simplify the task. To make the lone star in Figure **7-5,** for example, quilters generally start by sewing long strips of material together as shown on the next page.

c. Sample response: You have to measure only one angle to determine the measures of all of the angles at one vertex. Given the angles at one vertex, you then can determine the measures of all 16 angles in the diagram. Therefore, the measures of all the angles can be found if you measure just one angle.

d. Sample response: It would be necessary to measure four angles, one angle at each vertex.

* 1.2 a. Students may use lined notebook paper to help them draw sets of parallel lines. If the lines are perpendicular to the quilt strips, then the figures created are rectangles.

Suppose that you drew a set of parallel lines on this material so that each line was perpendicular to the strips. Describe the geometric figures that would be formed by the lines and strips.

b. On a copy of the diagram above, draw a set of parallel lines that are not perpendicular to the strips of material. Describe what kind of geometric figures are obtained.

c. The lone star pattern in Figure **7-5** has eight evenly spaced "points." What is the measure of the central angle for each of these points?

d. By cutting the quilt material along a set of parallel lines such as those in Part **b**, then shifting each new strip by one color, a quilter can create the following arrangement of rhombi. Describe how to draw this set of parallel lines. Verify your method using a copy of the diagram in Part **b**.

e. Imagine that you are stitching the strips created in Part **d** to make a lone star quilt. As you sew, the quilt starts to curl and buckle. Describe what might be causing this problem, and what you might do to correct it.

1.3 One way of classifying quadrilaterals is by the number of parallel sides. When characterized in this manner, a trapezoid can be defined as a quadrilateral with at least one pair of parallel sides. In the same fashion, a parallelogram can be defined as a trapezoid with two pairs of parallel sides.

b. If the parallel lines are not perpendicular to the quilt strips, then the figures created are parallelograms.

c. $360° / 8 = 45°$

d. Sample response: The quilter should draw a set of parallel lines that form 45° angles with the strips. To form rhombi, these lines must be spaced the same distance apart as the vertical strips.

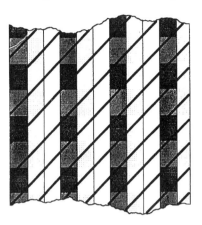

Cutting along these parallel lines would create strips of rhombi. These new strips of material then could be shifted up or down one color and sewn to create the desired pattern. The eight large rhombi then could be cut from this new pattern. **Note:** Students should simulate this process using the paper template, scissors, and tape.

e. Sample response: The stitching might have been neither straight nor parallel. If the lines of stitches are not parallel, there is no guarantee that the corresponding angles will be congruent. As a result, the quilt may start to buckle or curl. To correct this, the seams would have to be taken out and re-sewn.

1.3 Student responses should resemble the following diagram:

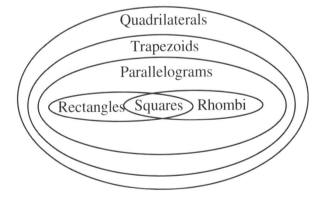

1.4 **a.** Sample drawing:

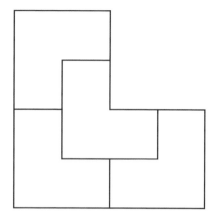

b. Sample response: I started with a triangle, found the midpoints of the sides, and connected them. This formed segments parallel to the corresponding sides of the original triangle and, in turn, four smaller triangles similar to the original. They are similar using the measures of corresponding and alternate interior angles, and the sum of the measures of the angles of a triangle.

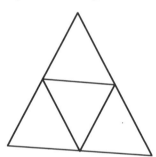

I then rotated the original triangle 180° about the midpoint of a side so that the original and the image formed a parallelogram. To make the quilt pattern, I used groups of parallelograms in the same way that the rhombus is used in the lone star quilt in Figure **7-5.**

1.5 Student responses may include some of the following methods.

1. Show that both pairs of opposite sides are the same length.
2. Show that both pairs of opposite sides are parallel.
3. Show that the diagonals bisect each other.
4. Show that both pairs of opposite angles are congruent.
5. Show that one pair of opposite sides is parallel and congruent.

1.6 **a.** ∠3, ∠6, ∠8, ∠9, ∠11, ∠14, ∠16
   b. ∠4, ∠5, ∠7, ∠10, ∠12, ∠13, ∠15

Create a copy of the following Venn diagram. Using the definitions described above, label each region in the diagram with one of the following classifications: quadrilaterals, parallelograms, trapezoids, rectangles, squares, rhombi.

1.4 **a.** Make a copy of the figure below. Draw line segments on the figure to create a rep tile. *Hint:* Begin by examining the midpoints of the edges.

b. Design a rep tile that could be used in a quilt pattern. Describe the roles of angles and parallel lines, if any, in your design.

* * * * *

1.5 Describe at least three ways in which you could determine if a quadrilateral is a parallelogram.

1.6 In the diagram below, lines *a* and *b* are parallel, while lines *c* and *d* are parallel.

a. Identify all of the angles that are congruent to ∠1.
b. Identify all of the angles that are congruent to ∠2.

206   Module 7 ■ *Traditional Design*

ACTIVITY 2

The medicine wheels of the Northern Cheyenne and other Plains peoples are both beautiful and symmetrical. Almost every aspect of each wheel—its symbols, color, and design—holds a special significance for the person who creates it.

In the past, simple wheels were built by placing small stones or pebbles on the ground. One pattern for such a wheel is shown in Figure 7-11. Each stone represented one of the many things in the universe. For example, an individual stone might have represented an animal, an individual person, or a nation.

Medicine wheels also were painted on personal shields. These shields were made from a variety of animal hides—including buffalo, bear, deer, coyote, weasel, and mouse—and often were decorated with eagle plumes or tassels of animal fur. The designs and symbols on each wheel held deep personal meaning for the bearer. Figure 7-12 shows a medicine wheel with two **concentric circles** (circles that have the same center), a set of evenly spaced quadrilaterals, and a Cheyenne design in the middle.

FIGURE 7-11
Medicine wheel formed with pebbles.

FIGURE 7-12 A Cheyenne medicine wheel.

In this activity, you use some geometric properties of a circle to create your own medicine wheel.

Module 7 ■ *Traditional Design*   207

---

mathematics note

A **rotation** is a transformation that pairs one point C, the center, with itself and every other point P with a point P' that lies on a circle with center C such that $m\angle PCP'$ is the magnitude of the rotation.

Counterclockwise rotations about a point are denoted by positive degree measures. Clockwise rotations are represented by negative degree measures.

In Figure 7-13, for example, $\triangle P'Q'R'$ is the image of $\triangle PQR$ under a 90° rotation about point C.

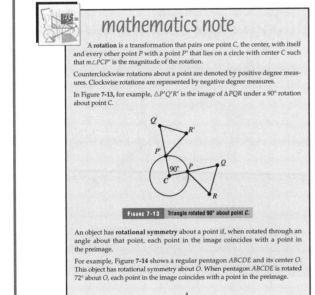

FIGURE 7-13 Triangle rotated 90° about point C.

An object has **rotational symmetry** about a point if, when rotated through an angle about that point, each point in the image coincides with a point in the preimage.

For example, Figure 7-14 shows a regular pentagon $ABCDE$ and its center O. This object has rotational symmetry about O. When pentagon $ABCDE$ is rotated 72° about O, each point in the image coincides with a point in the preimage.

FIGURE 7-14 A regular pentagon and its center.

208   Module 7 ■ *Traditional Design*

ACTIVITY 2

Students use medicine wheel designs to explore properties of tangents and secants. They also use the properties of a circle to create their own medicine wheels.

Materials List

■ copy of template C (for Problem **2.5,** one per student)
■ copy of template D (for Discussion **2,** one per student)
■ copy of template E (for Problem **2.3,** one per student)
■ copy of template F (for Problem **2.4,** one per student)
■ straightedge

teacher note

Blackline masters of the templates appear in the Teacher Resources for this module.

Technology

■ geometry utility

Student Outcomes

After completing the following discussions and exploration, students should be able to:

✳ identify the properties of chords, secants, and tangents to a circle

✳ construct perpendicular bisectors and tangent lines

✳ describe the geometric relationship between a preimage and its image under a rotation

✳ determine if a figure has rotational symmetry

✳ verify that the intersection of the perpendicular bisectors of two chords is the center of a circle.

Discussion 1

a. The medicine wheel displays rotational and line symmetries.

b. A clockwise rotation of 270° produces the same image as a counterclockwise rotation of 90°. In general, a clockwise rotation of $k°$ is equivalent to a counterclockwise rotation of $(n \cdot 360° - k)$ for any integer n.

c. In a rotation, the image and the preimage are congruent.

d. Sample response: Half of the symbol in the center could be constructed and reflected to create the other half. The larger circle is a dilation of the smaller one with center at the center of the circle. The quadrilaterals between the two concentric circles are all rotational images of another about the center. Each feather along the bottom of the wheel might be considered a translated image of the feather on the far right.

Exploration

Students use a geometry utility to investigate properties of chords, secants, and tangents. (This exploration also can be completed with a compass and straightedge.)

a. For best results, the diameter of the circle should be at least two-thirds the width of the screen.

b. 1. See sample drawing given in Step **3** below.
   2. Predictions may vary.
   3. Sample drawing:

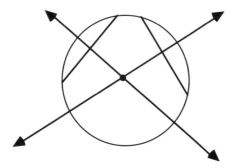

   4–5. Students should observe that the perpendicular bisectors of chords intersect at the center of the circle.

Discussion 1

a. Disregarding the tassels and beads, what types of symmetry do you observe in the medicine wheel in Figure **7-12**?

b. What clockwise rotation would produce the same result as a counterclockwise rotation of 90°?

c. In a rotation, what is the geometric relationship between an image and its preimage?

d. In the Level 2 module "Crazy Cartoons," you explored three other types of transformations: reflections, dilations, and translations. Explain how you could use transformations to reconstruct this medicine wheel—including tassels and beads—on a geometry utility.

Exploration

In this exploration, you investigate the properties of segments and lines that intersect a circle.

a. Using a geometry utility, draw a circle whose diameter is approximately two-thirds the width of the screen.

b. 1. A **chord** is a line segment joining any two points on a circle. Draw two chords of your circle.

   2. Predict where the perpendicular bisectors of the two chords will intersect. Draw a point at that location.

   3. Construct the perpendicular bisectors of the chords. Mark the intersection point (if different from the location predicted in Step 2).

   4. Drag the endpoints of the chords to change their sizes and locations. Record your observations.

   5. Change the size of the circle. Record your observations.

c. 1. Draw a new circle and construct a diameter.

   2. Identify the intersection points of the diameter and the circle.

   3. Construct a line through one of the points of intersection.

   4. Measure an angle at the intersection of the diameter and the line constructed in Step **3**.

   5. Adjust the angle constructed in Step **3** until its measure is 90°.

   6. Record your observations.

Module 7 ■ *Traditional Design*   **209**

c. Students should observe that when the angle has a measure of 90°, the line intersects the circle at a single point and therefore is a tangent line. The final sketch should resemble the following:

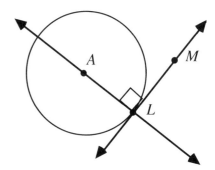

mathematics note

A **secant** of a circle is a line that intersects a circle in two points.

A **tangent** of a circle is a line, segment, or ray in the plane of the circle that intersects the circle in exactly one point and is perpendicular to a radius at that point. This intersection is the **point of tangency**.

For example, Figure 7-15 shows circle O with secant $\overleftrightarrow{AB}$, tangent $\overleftrightarrow{BC}$, and B, a point of tangency.

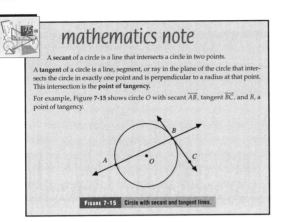

FIGURE 7-15 Circle with secant and tangent lines.

Discussion 2

a. 1. What is the measure of the angle between a diameter of a circle and a tangent to that circle whose point of tangency is the endpoint of the diameter?

2. Suppose that a secant does not contain the center of a circle. If a tangent to the circle is then drawn as in Figure 7-14, what can be said about the measure of an angle formed by this secant and tangent?

b. Describe how to use paper folding to find a line tangent to a circle.

c. What is true about two tangents whose points of tangency are opposite endpoints of a diameter? Explain your response.

d. Figure 7-16 shows a fragment of American Indian pottery. Before beginning reconstruction of the circular plate, a museum curator might first make a sketch of the original artifact, including its center. Using your observations from the exploration, describe how to find the center of this circular plate.

FIGURE 7-16
Pottery fragment.

teacher note

Before discussing Part **d** below, you might wish to distribute copies of template D (one per student; a blackline master appears in the Teacher Resources for this module).

Discussion 2

a. 1. 90°
   2. The angle cannot measure 90°.

b. Sample response: A line tangent to a circle can be created by first folding a circle onto itself through a line containing the center of the circle. This fold represents a secant containing a diameter. Next, without unfolding the first fold, fold the crease onto itself where the first fold intersects the circle. This second fold creates a tangent line perpendicular to a diameter, through the point of tangency.

c. Sample response: The tangents are parallel. Two lines in the same plane perpendicular to the same line must be parallel to each other because alternate interior angles are congruent.

d. Sample response: The center of the circular plate can be found by drawing two chords and their perpendicular bisectors as shown in the sketch below. The intersection of the perpendicular bisectors is the center of the circle.

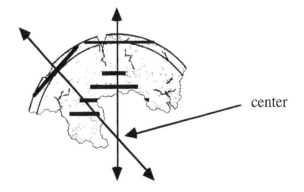

center

e. Sample response: Fold to create two chords on the circle. Fold to create the perpendicular bisector of each chord. The intersection of the perpendicular bisectors is the center of the circle.

f. The point of intersection of the perpendicular bisectors is the point equidistant from the four endpoints of the two chords. The center of a circle is the point that is equidistant from all points on the circle.

g. The altitude of an isosceles triangle is the perpendicular bisector of the base.

Warm-Up

1. Sample response: The rotational symmetry for the square in Part **a** is 90° about its center, for the pentagon in Part **b** is 72°, and for the circle in Part **c** is any degree measure. The lines of symmetry for the square and pentagon are shown below. Any line passing through the center of a circle is a line of symmetry.

a.

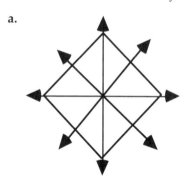

b.

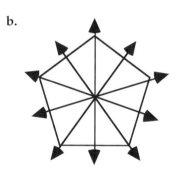

2. **a.** A chord is a segment, not a line.
   b. A radius must contain point *C*, the center of the circle.
   c. A secant must contain two points of the circle.
   d. A secant is a line, not a line segment.

e. Describe how to use paper folding to find the center of a circle.

f. The perpendicular bisector of a chord is the set of points in the plane equidistant from the ends of the chord. This means that for any point *C* in Figure **7-17** below, *AC* = *BC*.

FIGURE 7-17 Chord *AB* and its perpendicular bisector.

How does this verify that the intersection of the perpendicular bisectors of two chords is the center of the circle?

g. In Figure **7-17**, △*ABC* is isosceles and $\overline{CF}$ is an altitude. What is the relationship between the altitude of an isosceles triangle and its base?

Warm-Up

1. Describe the line and rotational symmetry, if any, for each shape in Parts **a–c**.

   a.   b.   c.

2. Use the following diagram to complete Parts **a–d** below.

   a. Why is $\overleftrightarrow{BG}$ not a chord?   b. Why is $\overline{AG}$ not a radius?
   c. Why is $\overrightarrow{FD}$ not a secant?   d. Why is $\overline{AG}$ not a secant?

Assignment

2.1 **a.** Using appropriate technology, construct a point *A* on a circle and a tangent to the circle at that point.

b. Continue the construction from Part **a** to create a circle inscribed in quadrilateral *XYZW*, as shown in the diagram below. Describe the process you used to complete the drawing.

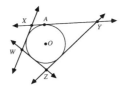

2.2 The diagram below shows two drawings of a medicine wheel. The drawing on the right represents the design of the wheel without the feathers, arrows, and shading of the drawing on the left.

a. Recreate the drawing on the right using a geometry utility. Describe the techniques you used.

b. 1. Does the drawing that you created in Part **a** have line symmetry? Explain your response.

2. Does it have rotational symmetry? Explain your response.

212   Module 7 ■ *Traditional Design*

---

teacher note

Each student will need a copy of template E to complete Problem **2.3,** a copy of template F to complete Problem **2.4,** and a copy of template C to complete Problem **2.5.** Blackline masters appear in the Teacher Resources for this module.

Assignment

Problems suitable for use as assessment items are identified by an asterisk (*)

2.1 a–b. Student methods will vary, depending on the technology used. Sample response: To draw each tangent, the radius containing both the point of the tangency and the center of the circle is constructed first. The tangent is then constructed as the line perpendicular to the radius and containing the point of tangency.

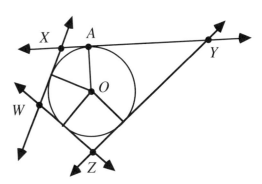

* **2.2 a.** The following sample response refers to the labeled points in the diagram below: First, I constructed the circle with the larger radius. Then I constructed a point *B* on the circle. Point *F* was constructed by transforming *B* using a rotation of 60° around center *A*. Four more points were constructed using the same type of transformation for a total of six points. These form the vertices of a hexagon.

Next, I constructed the six sides of the hexagon (such as $\overline{BF}$) and the midpoints of each side (such as *C*). Then I drew the three segments connecting opposite pairs of midpoints (such as $\overline{CE}$). Finally, I constructed the circle with center *A* and radius $\overline{CA}$.

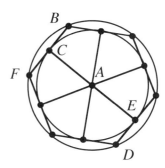

b. 1. The drawing has symmetry with respect to six lines: three that pass through the center of the circles and a pair of opposite vertices of the hexagon (such as *B* and *D* in the sample diagram above); and three that pass through the center of the circles and a pair of midpoints of the sides of the hexagon (such as *C* and *E* in the diagram above).

2. The drawing has rotational symmetry around the center of the circles for any rotation of *n* • 60°, where *n* is an integer.

* **2.3 a–b.** Students should find the center of the circle by constructing the perpendicular bisectors of at least two chords. Sample drawing:

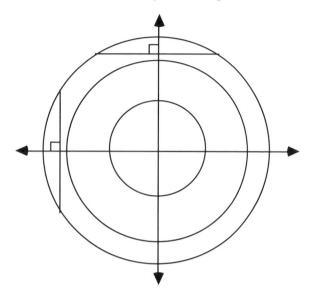

c. Selections will vary. Your school already might have a mascot or symbol.

d–e. Encourage students to be creative. They might want to display their wheels as a class.

2.4 a. Sample response: The center of the circle must be on the perpendicular bisector of $\overline{CC'}$ because all points contained on it are equidistant from C and C'.

b. Sample response: Draw the perpendicular bisector of $\overline{CC'}$ and the perpendicular bisector of $\overline{BB'}$. Their point of intersection is the center of rotation O.

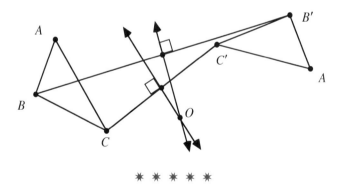

✳ ✳ ✳ ✳ ✳

2.5 a. Students should observe that the two pieces are congruent. Some might want to cut the star along the line to compare pieces. **Note:** Students are not limited to existing lines in the design. They may draw any line that passes through the center of the star.

b. The two pieces have 180° rotational symmetry about the center of the star. They may also have symmetry about the line.

2.3 **a.** The diagram below shows the outline of a medicine wheel.

Using a copy of this diagram, find the center of the circle. Use the center to construct two smaller, concentric circles on the wheel.

b. Describe how you found the center of the circle.

c. Personal medicine wheels often display the symbols of an individual or clan. What symbols could you use to represent yourself, your class, or your school?

d. Using the three circles drawn in Part **a**, create a medicine wheel that combines chords, tangents, and at least one traditional American Indian symbol in a design that radiates from the center.

e. Describe how you used each required component in your design.

2.4 The following illustration shows △*ABC* and its image under a rotation, △*A'B'C'*.

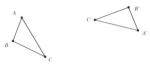

Any two corresponding points on the image and the preimage, such as *C'* and *C*, are contained on a circle whose center is also the center of rotation. The center of the circle is not shown in the illustration below.

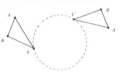

a. Explain why the center of the circle must be contained on the perpendicular bisector of $\overline{CC'}$.

b. Using a copy of the diagram, determine the center of rotation. Describe the method you used.

✳ ✳ ✳ ✳ ✳

2.5 Obtain a copy of the lone star design from your teacher.

a. Draw a line that passes through the center of the star. If you cut the star along this line, how would the two pieces be related?

b. Describe any symmetries that would exist between the two pieces.

c. Would your observations in Parts **a** and **b** hold true for any line that passes through the center of the star? Explain your response.

d. Summarize your responses to Parts **a–c** in a paragraph.

2.6 **a.** In the following diagram, $\overline{CD}$ and $\overline{BE}$ both contain *A*, the center of the circle. What other geometric term describes these chords?

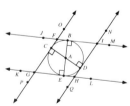

b. In the diagram above, $\overleftrightarrow{FI}$ and $\overleftrightarrow{GH}$ are tangent to the circle at *B* and *E*, respectively, and $\overleftrightarrow{FG}$ and $\overleftrightarrow{IH}$ are tangent to the circle at *C* and *D*, respectively.

1. Explain why $\overleftrightarrow{FI}$ and $\overleftrightarrow{GH}$ are parallel.

2. Is there another set of parallel lines in the diagram? Explain your response.

c. 1. Recreate the diagram on a geometric utility.

2. Measure ∠*KGP*, ∠*CGE*, ∠*KGC* and ∠*CFB*.

3. Any two of the angles listed in Step **2** can be used to illustrate a special angle relationship. Identify several of these relationships.

d. Identify all pairs of congruent angles formed by $\overleftrightarrow{IH}$, $\overleftrightarrow{FI}$ and $\overleftrightarrow{GH}$. Describe the relationship that exists between the angles in each pair.

e. Make a conjecture about the lengths of $\overline{FI}$, $\overline{IH}$, $\overline{HG}$, and $\overline{GF}$. Confirm your conjecture by measuring these lengths.

f. Do you believe *GFIH* is a rhombus? Explain your response.

2.7 As you learned in the Level 1 module "Reflect on This," when a light ray reflects off a flat mirror, the incoming angle is congruent to the outgoing angle. For example, the diagram below shows a light ray reflecting off a flat mirror at an angle of 22°.

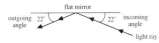

When light reflects off a curved mirror, the incoming angle also is congruent to the outgoing angle. In this case, the angles are measured with respect to the tangent at the point of reflection. For example, the following diagram shows a light ray reflecting off a curved mirror at an angle of 70°.

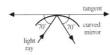

2.6 a. Both chords include the center of the circle; therefore they are diameters of the circle.

b. 1. Sample response: Because $\overleftrightarrow{FI}$ and $\overleftrightarrow{GH}$ are tangent to the circle at *B* and *E*, respectively, the measures of $\angle JBA$ and $\angle LEA$ are both 90°. Because these two angles are congruent, they are alternate interior angles of the two parallel lines $\overleftrightarrow{FI}$ and $\overleftrightarrow{GH}$.

2. Using a similar argument to the one given above, students can show that $\overleftrightarrow{FG}$ and $\overleftrightarrow{IH}$ are parallel.

c. Although angle measures may vary among constructions, students should observe that $\angle KGP \cong \angle CGE$ and $\angle KGC \cong \angle CFB$. Sample response: $\angle KGP$ and $\angle CGE$ are vertical angles; $\angle KGC$ and $\angle CFB$ are alternate interior angles; and $\angle KGP$ and $\angle KGC$ are supplements.

d. See the table at the bottom of the page for a sample response.

e. Sample response: All four segments are congruent. Allowing for rounding errors, measurement supports this conjecture.

f. Sample response: Yes, *GFIH* is a rhombus because the lengths of $\overline{FI}$, $\overline{IH}$, $\overline{HG}$, and $\overline{GF}$ are the same, $\overline{FI}$ is parallel to $\overline{HG}$, and $\overline{IH}$ is parallel to $\overline{GF}$.

c. The two pieces will have 180° rotational symmetry about the center of the star for any line that passes through the center. If the line does not pass through the center and one of the outer vertices of the star, the pieces will not have symmetry with respect to the line.

d. Sample response: A line that passes through the center of the lone star design divides the star into two pieces that are the same size and the same shape. The two pieces are identical in design and are related by 180° rotational symmetry about the center of the star. Only those lines that pass through the center and one of the outer vertices of the star are lines of symmetry.

Vertical Angles	Alternate Interior and Exterior Angles	Corresponding Angles
$\angle BID \cong \angle NIM$	$\angle BID \cong \angle IHL$	$\angle NIM \cong \angle DHL$
$\angle MID \cong \angle BIN$	$\angle MID \cong \angle DHE$	$\angle NIB \cong \angle DHE$
$\angle EHQ \cong \angle DHL$	$\angle NIB \cong \angle LHQ$	$\angle MID \cong \angle LHQ$
$\angle EHD \cong \angle QHL$	$\angle NIM \cong \angle EHQ$	$\angle BID \cong \angle EHQ$

2.7 **a.** They are congruent isosceles triangles.

    b. 1. The two smaller angles are congruent. For example, consider the two angles formed by $\overline{CB}$. Because $\overline{CB}$ is a radius, it is perpendicular to the tangent at B. The incoming angle and outgoing angle are congruent. The sum of the incoming angle and $\angle ABC$ is 90°, as is the sum of the measures of the outgoing angle and $\angle DBC$. Therefore, $\angle ABC \cong \angle DBC$. A similar argument can be made at each of the other vertices.

    2. angle bisector

  c. Sample response: The outgoing angle at point B and $\angle BDA$ are alternate interior angles, where $\overleftrightarrow{BD}$ is a transversal. Both angles measure 60°, so the incoming ray and the tangent at point D must be parallel.

Research Project

Students have many choices for both culture and historical period. Besides the examples listed in the student edition, several movements in modern and contemporary art make dramatic use of geometric shapes and lines.

Consider a mirror whose cross section is a portion of a circle with center at point C. As shown in the following illustration, points A, B, and D are on circle C. A light ray travels from A to B with an incoming angle of 60°, reflects off the mirror at B, reflects again off the mirror at D, then passes back through A.

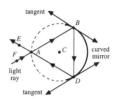

a. If segments are drawn from C to each vertex of △ABD in the diagram above, three triangles are formed: △ACB, △ACD, and △BCD. What type of triangles are these?

b. 1. Each segment described in Part **a** cuts an interior angle of △ABD into two smaller angles. What is the relationship between these two smaller angles? Explain your response.

    2. What term can be used to identify each of these segments?

c. Why must the outgoing light ray at point D be parallel to the tangent to the circle at point B?

Research Project

Geometric designs appear in the art of many cultures and historical periods. Byzantine mosaics, for example, contain many polygonal designs and symmetries. Celtic knot designs are two-dimensional representations of three-dimensional patterns. And many well-known Renaissance painters used similarity and line perspective to portray landscapes and the human form.

    Choose a culture and historical period. Research the use of geometric shape and design in the art of that time and place. Write a paper discussing your findings.

ACTIVITY 3

The art of the Navajo people of the southwestern United States is rich in symbolism and meaning. Navajo sand paintings, for example, are an important component of traditional healing rituals. The sand paintings themselves are done with five sacred, symbolic colors and usually represent a particular character in tribal legend. Figure 7-18 shows one sand painting design recreated on a geometry utility.

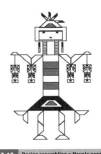

FIGURE 7-18 Design resembling a Navajo sand painting.

Discussion 1

a. Where does symmetry appear to play a part in the design in Figure 7-18?

b. Describe the two basic geometric figures used in the design.

c. Where does similarity appear to play a part in the design?

Module 7 ■ *Traditional Design* 217

ACTIVITY 3

Students use Navajo sand paintings—along with similar triangles—to explore dilations.

teacher note

A brief assessment of the mathematical content in Activities **1, 2,** and **3,** for use at your discretion, appears in the Teacher Resources for this module.

Materials List

■ template G (for Problem **3.1,** one copy per student)

■ template H (for Problem **3.2,** one copy per student)

teacher note

Blackline masters of the templates appear in the Teacher Resources for this module.

Technology

■ geometry utility

Student Outcomes

After completing the following discussions and exploration, students should be able to:

✳ construct a dilated image from a given preimage

✳ determine the scale factor for a given dilation

✳ recognize reflections, rotations, and translations as isometries

✳ construct reflections, translations, dilations, and rotations of a figure

✳ construct compositions of transformations.

Discussion 1

a. Sample response: Ignoring the feathers on the head, the design appears to have a vertical axis of symmetry. Some individual parts of the sand painting also display line symmetry.

b. This design was constructed using two basic figures: rectangles and trapezoids.

c. Many of the geometric shapes that make up the sand painting are similar to each other. For example, the trapezoids that make up the headdress are similar to each other and to the trapezoids that make up the hands, the arms, and the feet. These trapezoids are also similar to ones that form the garment worn around the waist of the figure, the design on the garment, and the tassels on the edge of the garment. The parallelograms that form the feathers in the headdress are similar to those that are found in the legs.

Exploration

In this exploration, students use similar triangles to explore the properties of dilations.

a. Sample drawing:

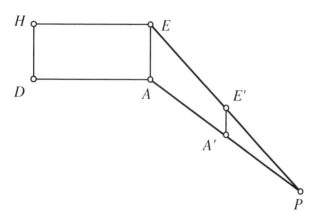

b. Because corresponding sides are proportional and corresponding angles are congruent, $\triangle PEA \sim \triangle PE'A'$.

c. Students complete a sketch of the image of *HEAD* under a dilation with center at *P*.

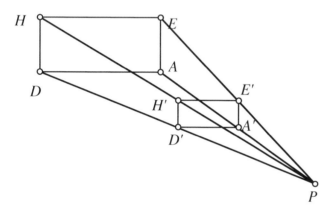

d. Dilations of polygons yield similar polygons. Angle measures and parallelism are preserved.

e. Sample response: Only the location of the image changes; its size stays the same.

f. Sample response: The lengths of the sides of the preimage, *HEAD*, would be reduced by a scale factor of 1/4 in the image, instead of 1/2.

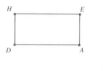
page 218

Exploration

In this exploration, you examine one shape from the design in Figure **7-18** and investigate how that shape can be transformed to create other parts of the design.

a. **1.** On a geometry utility, construct a rectangle to represent the head of the figure in the design. Label the vertices of the rectangle *HEAD*, as shown in Figure **7-19** below.

    2. Create a point *P* outside the rectangle to serve as a center of dilation.

FIGURE 7-19   A rectangle with center of dilation.

    3. Construct $\triangle PEA$.

    4. Find the midpoints of $\overline{PE}$ and $\overline{PA}$. Label these points E' and A'.

    5. Construct $\overline{E'A'}$.

b. Verify that $\triangle PE'A'$ is similar to $\triangle PEA$.

c. Using the same techniques as in Part **a**, construct $\overline{D'A'}$, $\overline{H'D'}$, and $\overline{E'H'}$ to create rectangle $H'E'A'D'$.

d. Rectangle $H'E'A'D'$ is a **dilation** of rectangle *HEAD* with center at point *P* and a scale factor of $H'E'/HE$. Describe the properties of the preimage that are preserved in a dilation.

e. Move point *P* to several other locations on your screen. Record your observations.

f. In Parts **a** and **c**, you used the midpoints of segments to construct rectangle $H'E'A'D'$.

    Predict what would happen if you repeated this process using points 1/4 the distance from *P* to each vertex of rectangle *HEAD*.

Discussion 2

a. **1.** What is the scale factor for the dilation in Part **d** of the exploration?

    2. What would be the scale factor for the dilation suggested in Part **f** of the exploration?

Discussion 2

a. **1.** The scale factor is 0.5.

    2. The scale factor would be 0.25.

b. Describe how changing the location of the center of dilation in Part e affected the resulting image.

c. Describe how you could use a dilation to create an image larger than the preimage.

d. A transformation that produces an image congruent to the preimage is an **isometry**. Which of the following transformations—reflections, rotations, dilations, and translations—can be classified as isometries? Explain your responses.

Warm-Up

1. The two triangles below are similar. Find the values of a and b.

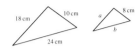

2. The two quadrilaterals below are similar. Determine the values of a, b, and c.

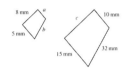

3. Identify the angle of rotation for each of the following transformations.

a.

b.

---

b. Changing the location of the center of dilation changes only the location of the image; it does not change the dimensions of the image.

c. Sample response: The image is larger than the original if the scale factor is greater than 1. For instance, in Part **b** of the exploration, E' would be on $\overrightarrow{PE}$ but E would be between P and E'.

d. Reflections, rotations, and translations are isometries because congruence is preserved. Although the measures of angles and the ratios between adjacent sides are preserved under dilations, they are not necessarily isometries. The preimage and image are congruent under a dilation only if the scale factor is 1.

Warm-Up

1. $a = 14.4$ cm; $b = 19.2$ cm

2. $a = \dfrac{10}{3}$ mm; $b = \dfrac{32}{3}$ mm; $c = 24$ mm

3. a. approximately $99°$
   b. approximately $145°$

teacher note

To complete Problems **3.1** and **3.2,** students will need copies of templates G and H, respectively. Blackline masters appear in the Teacher Resources for this module.

Assignment

Problems suitable for use as assessment items are identified by an asterisk (*).

* **3.1** Sample response:

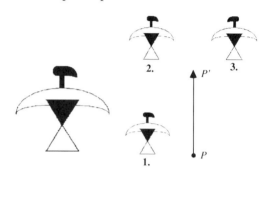

* **3.2** **a.** The line of reflection can be found by constructing the perpendicular bisector of a segment whose endpoints are corresponding points on the image and preimage (or by paper folding).

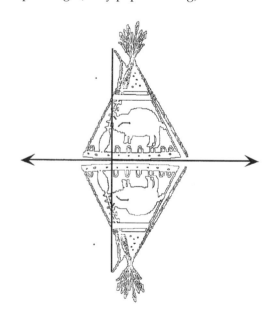

Assignment

3.1 **a.** Using the template supplied by your teacher, find the images of several points of the following figure under the transformations described below.

1. a dilation with center at point *P* and a scale factor of 1/2
2. a translation by the vector $\overline{PP'}$ of the image in Step **1**
3. a reflection in $\overline{PP'}$ of the image found in Step **2**
4. a 90° clockwise rotation, with center at point *P,* of the image found in Step **3**

b. Sketch the remainder of each image in Part **a.**

3.2 The Blackfeet tribe of the American Northwest sometimes painted symbols and designs on their tipis. In the diagram below, the tipi in the upper left-hand corner, labeled **T,** is the preimage. Use a copy of the diagram to complete Parts **a–e.**

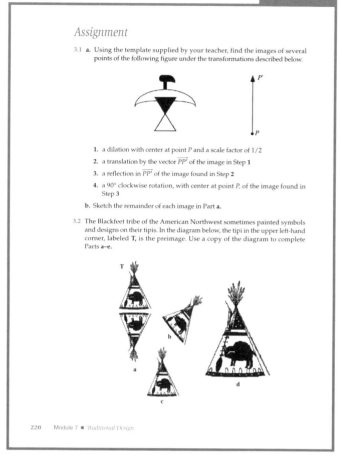

220   Module 7 ■ *Traditional Design*

b. The center of rotation can be found by determining the perpendicular bisectors of two segments whose endpoints are corresponding points on the image and preimage. The intersection of the perpendicular bisectors is the center of rotation.

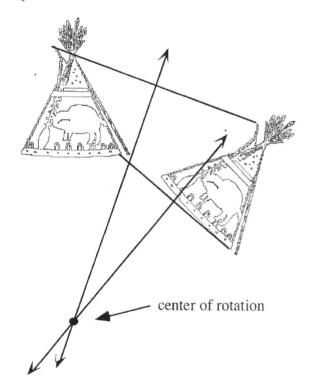

center of rotation

a. Image **a** is a reflection of **T**. Draw the line of reflection.

b. Image **b** is a transformation of **T** using a rotation. Find the center of rotation.

c. Image **c** is a translation of **T**. Draw a vector to represent the translation.

d. Image **d** is a dilation of **T**. Find the center of dilation and identify the scale factor.

e. When more than one transformation is performed on a figure, the result is a **composition of transformations**.

The preimage **T** also can be transformed to the image **c** by a composition of transformations involving two reflections. Draw two lines of reflection that could be used to perform this composition.

3.3 Navajo sand paintings frequently represent legendary characters. The following design is associated with Big Thunder.

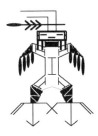

a. Create your own design for a sand painting using transformational geometry. (You may use a geometry utility.)

b. Write a paragraph describing how you used transformations to create your design.

* * * * *

c. The vector may be indicated by connecting any point and its image, in the direction from the preimage to the image.

d. The center of dilation can be found at the intersection of two lines connecting corresponding points on the image and preimage. The scale factor is approximately 2.

center of dilation

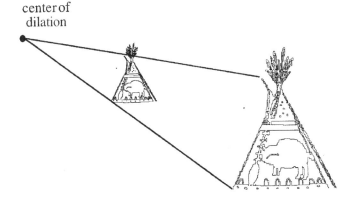

e. Two possible reflection lines are perpendicular to a line connecting any point and its image. The distance between the reflection lines is half the distance between the point and its image.

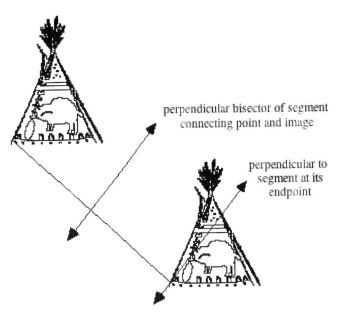

perpendicular bisector of segment connecting point and image

perpendicular to segment at its endpoint

3.3 a. To help students consider possible designs, you may provide some reference materials.

b. You might prefer to ask students to give oral presentations.

* * * * *

3.4 The table at the bottom of the page provides sample descriptions for each figure.

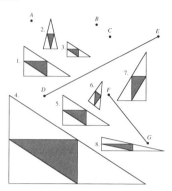

3.4 The following diagram shows eight numbered figures. Some of these figures are the images of figure 1 under transformations involving the labeled points and segments.

If possible, describe the transformation used to produce each numbered image, with figure 1 as its preimage. Each description should respond to the questions listed below:

a. Is the transformation an isometry?

b. Is the image similar to the preimage?

c. Which labeled points or lines were used in the transformation?

d. If the transformation includes a dilation, what is the approximate scale factor?

e. If the transformation includes a rotation, what is the approximate angle of rotation?

f. If the transformation includes a translation, what is the approximate magnitude and direction of the translation vector?

Figure	Description of Transformation
2.	Not an isometry and not similar. Not an obvious type of transformation.
3.	Not an isometry, but similar. Dilation using C as the center. Scale factor appears to be 0.5.
4.	Not an isometry, but similar. Dilation using A as the center. Scale factor appears to be 3.
5.	An isometry and therefore also similar. A translation by a vector equivalent to the vector from F to G, with a length of approximately 4.3 cm, in a direction which can be described as about 300°, or a bearing of about 150°, or approximately southeast.
6.	Not an isometry, but similar. Two transformations: first a dilation identical to figure 3, then a reflection in the line containing $\overline{DE}$.
7.	An isometry and therefore also similar. A rotation of 90° about point B.
8.	Not an isometry and not similar. Not an obvious type of transformation.

Summary Assessment

1. The people of Florida's Seminole tribe are known for their patchwork designs. Beginning in the 1880s, they used hand-cranked sewing machines to stitch their patterns. Although there are many variations in Seminole patchwork, each one is started by sewing strips of fabric together as shown in the diagram below.

   a. How could these strips of fabric be cut and sewn to create the following pattern?

   b. Describe the method you developed in Part **a** in a paragraph. Include specific directions to complete the task and use geometric terms to explain why your method works.

2. A symbol often used by the Hopi people resembles the five-pointed star (or pentagram) shown below.

   a. Use appropriate technology to create a pentagram like the one above.

   b. Dilate the pentagram by a scale factor of your choice.

   c. Explain why the corresponding sides of the image and preimage are parallel.

---

teacher note

An additional assessment, for use at your discretion, appears in the Teacher Resources for this module.

Summary Assessment

1. a. Sample response: Parallel lines could be cut as shown in the sketch below. The resulting strips can be shifted one color and re-sewn.

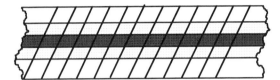

   b. Answers will vary. Cutting the fabric along parallel lines creates congruent corresponding angles. Re-aligning the new strips along the parallels creates the pattern of parallelograms.

2. a–b. Sample sketch:

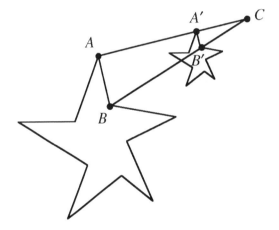

   c. The following sample response refers to the labeled points in the diagram above: Because the transformation is a dilation, $\triangle ABC \sim \triangle A'B'C$. Therefore, $\angle BAC \cong \angle B'A'C$. Because these are corresponding angles, $\overline{AB}$ is parallel to $\overline{A'B'}$. A similar argument could be used for every pair of corresponding sides.

3. a. The center of rotation can be found by constructing the perpendicular bisectors of segments connecting corresponding points on the image and preimage, as shown below.

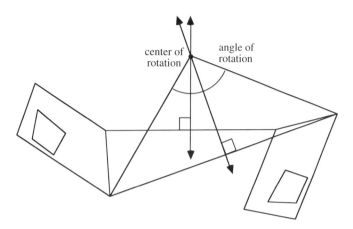

b. Sample sketch:

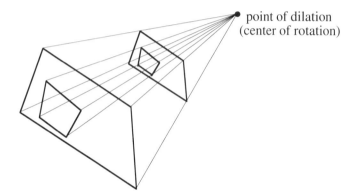

point of dilation (center of rotation)

3. The Navajo symbol for a medicine man's eye represents wisdom. The eye symbol on the right-hand side of the diagram below is the image of the one on the left under a rotation.

a. Using a copy of this diagram, find the center of rotation. Describe the procedure you used to locate the center.

b. Using the center found in Part **a**, dilate the preimage by a scale factor of 1/2.

And the Survey Says ...

module 8

Overview

In this module, students explore methods of sampling. They examine potential sources of bias and experiment with different types of sampling. Histograms are used to represent data and to predict characteristics of a population. Confidence statements and margins of error are introduced as methods for interpreting the results of a survey.

Activity 1:	Students explore the effects of biased sampling methods on attempts to characterize a population.
Activity 2:	Students use different types of sampling techniques, including stratified sampling and systematic sampling.
Activity 3:	Students explore sampling as a tool for describing a population. Using frequency histograms, they investigate the distribution of sample proportions.
Activity 4:	Students determine the maximum standard deviation of all possible sample proportions for samples of a given size and use this value to describe the interval for a confidence statement.

Objectives

In this module, students will:

* use a variety of sampling techniques (1, 2)

* predict the characteristics of a population based on samples (1, 2, 3)

* explore the role that biases play in sampling (1, 2)

* use histograms to estimate probabilities and make predictions (3)

* investigate how sample size affects a survey's reliability (4)

* explore confidence statements and margins of error (4).

Prerequisites

For this module, students should know:

* how to calculate population mean and population standard deviation

* how to create frequency tables

* how to construct histograms.

 Flashbacks, for use at your discretion, appear in the Teacher Resources for this module. These brief problem sets provide a review of some prerequisite skills for each activity.

Planning Guide

Activity	Materials	Technology	Time Line
Activity **1**	▪ paper bags ▪ dry beans	▪ none	1 day
Activity **2**	▪ graph paper ▪ template of town map	▪ spreadsheet ▪ random number generator	2 days
Activity **3**	▪ graph paper ▪ paper bags ▪ dry beans ▪ markers (optional)	▪ statistics package ▪ spreadsheet ▪ programmable calculator (optional)	3 days
Activity **4**	▪ none	▪ statistics package ▪ spreadsheet ▪ graphing utility ▪ programmable calculator (optional)	2 days
Assessment Activities	▪ none	▪ statistics package ▪ spreadsheet ▪ programmable calculator (optional)	3 days **Total: 11 days**

teacher note

The exploration in Activity **1** calls for two varieties of dry beans that are significantly different in size, such as kidney beans and lentils. The exploration in Activity **3** requires beans of different colors but similar sizes, such as kidney beans and pinto beans. (You may substitute other objects that satisfy these criteria.)

A blackline master of the template appears in the Teacher Resources for this module.

Introduction

You might wish to ask students to discuss some recent opinion polls.

ACTIVITY 1

Using a population of two different kinds of beans, students explore the effects of biased sampling methods on attempts to characterize a population. **Note:** This activity introduces students to some terms used throughout the module: *population, parameter, sample, statistic, census,* and *bias.*

Materials List

- two varieties of dry beans that are significantly different in size (about 150 beans per group)
- paper bags or other opaque containers (one per group)

teacher note

Each population should consist of a total of about 150 beans of two different sizes—for example, kidney beans and lentils. (The actual proportion of the smaller beans to larger beans is unimportant.)

Student Outcomes

After completing the following exploration and discussion, students should be able to:

✳ distinguish between a population and a sample

✳ distinguish between parameters and statistics

✳ recognize some potential sources of bias in a sampling technique

✳ use data collected from samples to characterize a population.

Introduction

Opinion polls have become a familiar feature of American life. You read about them in magazines and newspapers, and hear them discussed on radio and television. Such surveys are administered by a number of different polling organizations. Some—like Gallup, Roper, and Harris—are independent companies. Others, like the New York Times and CBS, are members of the news media themselves.

The pollsters question you about everything from religion to politics, from your views on health care to your preferred brand of toothpaste. The information they obtain has many applications. A candidate for the U.S. Senate might use polls to plan a campaign strategy. A Hollywood producer might use audience surveys to edit an upcoming movie. A cookie manufacturer might use consumer taste preferences to target a profitable new market.

How do polling organizations discover the likes and dislikes of a nation of more than 250 million? Fortunately for the pollsters, reliable results can be obtained by surveying only about 1500 people—a small percentage of the entire population. Why is this sample big enough? This module will help you answer that question.

ACTIVITY 1

Whether you watch television, listen to the radio, or read newspapers, what you get from the news often comes in the form of statistics. Statistics arise from the collection of data. In the case of opinion polls, information is collected by surveying small samples of the entire population. In this activity, you investigate some methods pollsters use to determine whom to survey and examine some of the factors that might prevent a sample from representing the entire population.

228

---

mathematics note

A **population** is a group of all objects, individuals, or observations about which information is to be gathered. A quantity that describes a population is a **parameter**.

A **sample** is a portion of the population. A quantity that describes a sample is a **statistic**.

A **bias** is a factor that prevents a sample from representing the entire population.

A **census** is the collection of data about an entire population.

For example, a pollster's study of voter preferences for an upcoming presidential election might describe the responses from all registered voters as a *population*. The percentage of voters who intend to vote for a particular candidate is a *parameter*.

A *sample* of the population might include 1500 registered voters who answered their home telephones on a Monday morning. The percentage of those surveyed who intend to vote for a particular candidate is a *statistic*.

Most working people are not home on weekday mornings. Their exclusion would constitute a *bias* of this sample, because these people would not have a chance of being selected. To perform a *census* of the population, the polling organization would have to question every registered voter in the country—a nearly impossible task.

Exploration

In this exploration, you describe the characteristics of a population of beans based on the data obtained from samples. **Note:** Do not examine the contents of your container before beginning the exploration.

a. 1. Shake the container containing the population of beans.
   2. Take a small handful of beans from the container. This is one sample of the population.
   3. Record the percentage of each kind of bean in the sample.
   4. Return the sample to the container and mix it thoroughly with the other beans.

b. Repeat Part **a** four more times.

c. Based on the data collected in your five samples, predict the percentage of each kind of bean in the entire population.

d. Take a census of the beans. Determine the percentage of each kind of bean in the population. Compare the actual percentages to your predictions in Part **c**.

Exploration

a. When students take samples by the handful, the size difference in the two kinds of beans creates a bias in favor of the larger beans.

b. The following sample data was collected using a population of 30% kidney beans and 70% lentils.

Sample	Kidney Bean	Lentils
1	77%	23%
2	60%	40%
3	57%	43%
4	38%	63%
5	64%	36%
Mean	59%	41%

c. Answers will vary. Students may use the mean percentages from their five samples to predict the population percentages. (See sample data given in Part **b.**)

d. This actual proportions of beans in the population might differ considerably from student predictions.

Discussion

a. 1. The percentages of each type of bean determined in the census are parameters.

   2. The percentages of each type of bean in a sample (and the means of these percentages) are statistics.

b. Sample response: The data collected by sampling predicted a higher percentage of the larger beans and a lower percentage of the smaller beans than are actually in the population.

c. The sampling method—in combination with the difference in the size of the beans—creates bias. When sampling by the handful, larger beans have a better chance of being selected because smaller ones tend to slip through the fingers.

d. Students should suggest sampling techniques that give each bean the same chance of being selected. For example, using a cup to select the sample might help to reduce the bias in favor of the larger beans.

e. Real-life surveys often ignore segments of the population through biased sampling. For example, telephone surveys eliminate anyone who does not own a phone. If conducted during normal business hours, they also might eliminate people who do not work at home. Other polls solicit voluntary responses and therefore count only those people with strong opinions. Because many magazines target specific audiences, their polls are limited to a select readership. Polls taken on downtown streets or in shopping malls exclude large segments of the general population. The wording of questions, especially regarding sensitive topics, also may bias a survey.

f. Because of the descriptive adjectives used to praise the eagle and belittle the bison, this survey question is biased in favor of the eagle. To reduce bias, the question may be rephrased as follows: "Would you prefer the eagle or the bison as the school mascot, or do you have no opinion?"

Warm-Up

1. A population is the entire set of objects or observations about which information is being gathered. A sample is a subset of the population.

2. A parameter is a number that describes a characteristic of a population. A statistic is a number that describes a characteristic of a sample.

3. a. The population is the 2380 Washington High School students.

   b. Students should describe methods that survey every student in the school population. Sample response: Send a person to poll every first-period class in the school. Check records for any students without a first-period class and find them in the next available class.

Discussion

a. 1. Which values in the exploration are parameters?

   2. Which values are statistics?

b. How did the results of the census compare with your predictions based on five samples?

c. Describe any biases in the selection process that might have prevented samples from accurately representing the entire population.

d. How could you eliminate bias in this sampling method?

e. What kinds of bias could affect a real-life survey?

f. Consider the following survey question, "Would you prefer the powerful and graceful eagle or the clumsy bison as the school mascot?" How could you reword this question to minimize possible bias?

Warm-Up

1. Describe the difference between a population and a sample.

2. Describe the difference between a parameter and a statistic.

3. Washington High School has 2380 students: 500 seniors, 597 juniors, 626 sophomores, and 657 freshmen. Elections for student government are coming up next month. To predict who the next student body president might be, the school newspaper has asked you to take a preliminary poll.

   a. What is the population for this poll?

   b. Describe how to conduct a census of the population.

   c. Describe one method for sampling the population.

   d. What advantages or disadvantages are there to the sampling method you described in Part c?

Assignment

1.1 Some television programs offer their audiences a chance to express opinions on everything from favorite rock videos to favorite presidential candidates. Viewers typically dial a phone number to register their votes. Is such a survey biased? If so, describe the biases that might exist. If not, explain why not.

1.2 To help determine consumer preferences, an electronics company conducts a poll in a shopping mall. The pollsters stand outside a department store and ask all the people who pass by if they own a video recorder. Describe any biases that this sample might contain.

230   Module 8 ■ *And the Survey Says . . .*

c. Answers will vary. Three sample responses are listed below.

   1. Choose the first person who walks into the cafeteria at lunch time and every 10th person after that.

   2. Select all the sophomores in one homeroom class.

   3. Write a computer program to generate random numbers that correspond with student ID numbers. Sample those students whose ID numbers match the computer-generated numbers.

d. The following list describes some advantages and disadvantages to the sample responses in Part **c**.

   1. This type of sample is easy to administer. However, every student might not eat lunch in the cafeteria. The students who don't will be excluded from the sample.

   2. This type of sample is also easy to administer. But because all students other than sophomores are excluded, in addition to all other students not in that homeroom, the sample is extremely biased.

   3. Because every student has an equal chance of being selected, this method produces a random sample. It might take some time and effort, however, to write a computer program that will generate appropriate numbers.

1.3 In 1936, incumbent Franklin Delano Roosevelt was campaigning against Alf Landon for the presidency of the United States. Shortly before the election, pollsters for the *Literary Digest* conducted a survey. They sent postcard ballots to people selected at random from a list of automobile registrations and from a telephone directory. Their results indicated that Landon would win the election. That prediction was incorrect. In a landslide victory, Franklin Roosevelt won all but two states—Maine and Vermont.

   a. What biases in the poll might have caused the incorrect prediction?

   b. How might the pollsters have obtained a more accurate picture of the nation's preferences?

1.4 Jordan is conducting a survey of music preferences at his school using the following questionnaire:

   Which of the following music types do you prefer?

   (1) rock and roll   (2) alternative
   (3) country and western (4) classical
   (5) heavy metal   (6) other

   To obtain a sample of 50 people, he polls 20 students in his mathematics class, 20 friends and acquaintances sitting nearby at lunch, and 10 fellow band members at an after-school practice session.

   a. Is Jordan's sample representative of the entire school population?

   b. Describe any biases that might exist in his survey question or sampling techniques.

   c. Suggest how Jordan could change the sampling method to minimize bias.

* * * * *

1.5 According to pollster George Gallup, "Nothing is so difficult, nor so important, as the selection and wording of questions." In fact, poor word choice and misleading questions have biased many surveys. Write a survey question that introduces bias due to its own wording and explain the cause of that bias.

1.6 For an article in the school paper, Susanne wants to survey students on a proposal to open the campus for lunch. This has been a hot topic for weeks. If the school board approves the proposal, the lunch period will be lengthened from 30 minutes to 45 minutes, which in turn will add 15 minutes to the end of the day. She plans to ask the following question:

   "Do you want to have an open campus for the lunch period in order to go anywhere you want instead of being confined to the school cafeteria?"

   a. What do you think is Susanne's opinion on this proposal?

   b. Write a question that shows a bias for the opposing view.

   c. Write a question on this proposal that minimizes bias.

Assignment

Problems suitable for use as assessment items are identified by an asterisk (*).

1.1 Answers will vary. Such surveys do not provide random samples for several reasons. Many dial-in surveys charge a small fee for the call, which creates bias against those unwilling to pay. Often, only those people who have strong opinions about the topic will call. The most significant bias, of course, is against people who are not watching the program.

1.2 Responses may vary. This type of survey does not give everyone in the population an equal chance to be in the sample. The polling method excludes those who do not visit shopping malls. Of those who are questioned, several members of the same household might answer affirmatively, although each individual does not own a separate video recorder.

1.3 a. In 1936, many people did not own a car or a telephone. A significant portion of the voting population therefore was excluded from the survey.

   b. The pollsters should have designed a survey that gave every registered voter an equal chance of being selected. (**Note:** George Gallup did an accurate poll for this election, and his career as a pollster blossomed.)

* 1.4 a. Sample response: No. Jordan's survey does not necessarily provide a representative sample of the population, since it contains only his classmates and friends. **Note:** You might wish to point out that, although a random sample also may not necessarily provide a representative sample of a population, the manner in which it was selected is unbiased.

   b. Jordan's survey question appears to be relatively free of bias. Some students may argue, however, that the question is biased towards rock and roll, since this category is listed first.

      Since music preferences tend to be similar among friends, his survey technique introduces a bias against the preferences of other students in the school.

   c. To minimize bias in the sampling method, students may suggest that Jordan randomly select 50 people from a list of the entire school population.

❋ ❋ ❋ ❋ ❋

1.5 Sample response: In a survey on providing housing for the homeless, the following question would be biased in favor of a "yes" response: "If some friends of yours suddenly became homeless, would you want them to be provided with housing?" By including the clause about friends, the question creates bias. Most people would not want to have friends in such a desperate situation. If the question was rewritten as follows—"Would you vote for a bond issue to provide housing for the homeless?"—the number of affirmative answers might change dramatically.

1.6 a. Sample response: Because of her use of the word *confined,* Susanne appears to favor the proposal.

   b. Sample response: "Do you want to have open campus for the lunch period even though it would lengthen the school day by 15 minutes?"

   c. Sample response: "Are you in favor of or against an open campus lunch, or do you have no opinion?"

Research Project

a. Student summaries should include a description of the population, the sample size, and the sampling technique, and a discussion of potential bias in the survey.

b. Students might need some guidance on possible topics and on the format of their presentations. You might wish to consult a history teacher for suggestions.

This activity focuses on different types of sampling techniques, including stratified sampling and systematic sampling.

teacher note

A brief assessment of the mathematical content in Activities 1 and 2, for use at your discretion, appears in the Teacher Resources for this module.

Materials List

- template of town map (one per student; a blackline master appears in the Teacher Resources for this module)

Technology

- statistics package
- random number generator

Student Outcomes

After completing the following exploration and discussion, students should be able to:

✳ use different types of sampling techniques, including simple random sampling, stratified sampling, and systematic sampling

✳ identify and discuss the possible biases involved in various types of sampling techniques.

Research Project

Select and complete one of the projects described below.

a. Find a report of an interesting survey in a magazine or newspaper. Write a summary of its results, including a description of the population, the sample size, and the sampling method. Identify potential sources of bias in the survey and suggest how these biases might have been avoided.

b. Identify a poll or survey (other than the one mentioned in Problem **1.3**) that produced an incorrect prediction. Describe some of the biases that might have caused the mistake. Present your findings to the class.

To design reliable surveys, many polling organizations work hard to remove biases from both their samples and their survey questions. At the same time, however, they also must try to control the costs of administering the poll. Selecting an appropriate sampling method can help achieve all of these goals. In this activity, you examine several sampling methods that can reduce polling costs, simplify administration, and minimize bias.

Exploration

The map in Figure **8-1** shows a small town located at the intersection of two highways. The town is divided into 40 different districts, each identified by a number. On this map, the area of each district indicates its population (1 square unit represents 100 people).

FIGURE 8-1 **Population of a town, by district.**

232   Module 8 ■ *And the Survey Says . . .*

a. Select a sample of 4 of the 40 districts from the map in Figure **8-1**.

    1. Determine the population of each district in your sample.

    2. Using only your sample, predict the mean number of people per district for the entire town.

    3. Using only your sample, estimate the population of the entire town.

b. Determine the population of the entire town. Compare the actual value with your prediction in Part **a**.

mathematics note

A **simple random sample** is selected so that each member of the population has the same chance of being included in the sample.

For example, consider a population of students in a classroom. To obtain a simple random sample of this population, each student's name could be written on an identical slip of paper. The slips of paper could then be placed into a bowl, mixed thoroughly, and drawn one at a time.

c. 1. Randomly generate four different integers in the interval [1, 40]. Use these integers to identify four districts on the map in Figure **8-1**.

    2. Use this sample to predict the mean number of people per district.

    3. Use this sample to estimate the population of the entire town.

mathematics note

Stratified sampling requires that a population be divided into parts. Each part is a **stratum** (plural, **strata**). To produce a stratified sample, simple random samples are taken from each stratum. These samples do not necessarily have to be the same size.

For example, differences in age could determine the strata of a voting population. To select a stratified sample of this population, a polling organization might survey groups of people with ages 18–28 years, 29–45 years, 46–60 years, and 61 years or older.

Systematic sampling is accomplished by collecting data from every *n*th unit of a population after randomly choosing a starting point.

For example, a systematic sample of the customers in a shopping mall could be obtained by selecting every fifth person, beginning with the first person who enters after 10:00 A.M.

Exploration

The exploration provides hands-on activities that allow students to examine different sampling techniques. **Note:** Students sample from a map of a town divided into districts. This is a much simplified version of an actual district map. Typical voting districts or precincts often have irregular boundaries (and populations that are not multiples of 100).

a. Allowing students to select their own samples can illustrate the need for sampling techniques that eliminate unintentional biases. Students often choose one small, one large, and two medium-sized districts. This creates bias, because after one small district is chosen, for example, the other small districts do not have an equal chance of being selected in the sample. Students also might tend to choose only rectangular districts, which creates bias against those with other shapes.

    1. The populations of individual districts vary from 100 to 600 people.

    2. Answers will vary. Many students will calculate the mean population of the four districts in their sample. The actual mean is 207.5.

    3. Estimates will vary. Students may multiply the mean number of people per district by the total number of districts (40), multiply the number of people in their four samples by 10, or devise other methods.

b. The actual population of the town is 8300.

c. Student results will vary. A random sample of districts 25, 40, 39, and 32 results in the following mean population per district:

$$\frac{200 + 300 + 100 + 200}{4} = 200$$

This corresponds with a population estimate of $200 \cdot 40 = 8000$.

d. 1. Answers will vary. Some students may group districts by size and select one at random from each subgroup. Others may group districts by location or district number. For example, the two highways divide the town into four regions. Each region could be considered a stratum.

2. Using the method in Part **1,** the following four districts might be selected: 4, 15, 21, and 37. For this sample, the mean population per district is:

$$\frac{300 + 200 + 300 + 400}{4} = 300$$

This corresponds with a population estimate of $300 \cdot 40 = 12,000$.

e. 1. Sample response: Starting with region 5, select every 10th region after that. The sample contains regions 5, 15, 25, and 35.

2. The mean population per district for the sample described in Step **1** is:

$$\frac{200 + 200 + 200 + 200}{4} = 200$$

This corresponds with a population estimate of $200 \cdot 40 = 8000$.

Discussion

a. Because different samples can be selected using the same method, identical sampling techniques do not necessarily produce identical results. The class data should illustrate this point.

b. An intuitive sampling method will not guarantee that every district has the same chance of being selected.

Because each district has the same chance of inclusion in a simple random sample, this method has no apparent bias.

Depending on how strata are determined or on how samples are selected from each stratum, bias might or might not appear in a stratified sampling method.

A systematic sampling method might introduce bias through the selection of the starting point and the value of *n.*

c. The sampling method based on intuition allows the most bias. Simple random sampling has the least potential for bias because every district has an equal chance of being selected.

Warm-Up

1. **a.** This method does not produce a simple random sample because everyone in the school might not eat in the cafeteria and because it selects only those who arrive early.

b. This method produces a simple random sample because every student has an equal chance of selection.

d. 1. Devise a stratified sampling method to obtain a sample of four districts from the map in Figure **8-1.**

2. Use your stratified sample to predict the mean number of people per district and to estimate the population of the entire town.

e. 1. Devise a systematic sampling method to obtain a sample of four districts from the map in Figure **8-1.**

2. Use your systematic sample to predict the mean number of people per district and to estimate the population of the entire town.

Discussion

a. Compare your results in the exploration with those of others in your class.

Is it reasonable to expect population estimates made using the same sampling technique to be similar? Why or why not?

b. You used four different sampling methods in the exploration: sampling based on intuition, simple random sampling, stratified sampling, and systematic sampling. Where might bias occur in each of these methods?

c. Which method has the most potential for bias? Which has the least potential for bias? Explain your responses.

Warm-Up

1. Parts **a–f** each describe a sampling method. Identify those that produce a simple random sample. If a method does not produce a simple random sample, explain why this occurs.

a. Select the first 20 students who enter the cafeteria for lunch.

b. Assign a number to each student in the school, then use a random number generator to select 20 students.

c. Assign a number to each student in the school, then use a random number generator to select 10 boys and 10 girls.

d. Write all student identification numbers on identical slips of paper, place the slips in a bin, mix them up, and select 20 from the bin.

e. Select the first person who walks into a pep assembly and every 10th person thereafter.

f. Select only those students whose school identification numbers end with a 0.

2. Which of the sampling methods described in Problem **1** represent stratified sampling? Which represent systematic sampling?

234 Module 8 ■ *And the Survey Says . . .*

c. This method produces a simple random sample of boys and a simple random sample of girls, but not a simple random sample of students, because selections depend on gender. This is an example of stratified sampling by gender.

d. This method produces a simple random sample because every student has an equal chance of selection.

e. This method does not produce a simple random sample because it is biased against students who do not attend the pep assembly. This is an example of systematic sampling.

f. This method produces a simple random sample only if student ID numbers are issued randomly (and some ID numbers end with 0).

2. Because it creates subgroups by gender, the method described in Part **e** represents stratified sampling. Because it selects every *n*th unit of the population, starting with the first student, the method described in Part **e** represents systematic sampling

Assignment

2.1 Identify the type of sampling method used in each setting below. Justify your responses.

   a. At a battery factory, finished batteries travel along a conveyor belt to the packaging area. Before the batteries are packaged, an employee selects every 200th battery for testing.

   b. At a bingo parlor, numbers are written on Ping-Pong balls and placed in a rotating bin. The caller reaches into the bin and blindly selects one ball at a time.

   c. A politician running for city council divides the city into 48 different regions. She randomly selects 30 people from each region, then visits each one to discuss their concerns.

2.2 **a.** The editors of a school paper want to survey student preferences for an upcoming election. The school has 400 students. Suggest one way to obtain a sample of 20 students from this population using each of the following methods:

   1. simple random sampling

   2. stratified sampling

   3. systematic sampling

   b. Identify potential sources of bias in each sampling technique you suggested in Part **a.**

2.3 Identify an issue of concern at your school. Devise a method of surveying student opinion on this issue.

   a. Describe your poll in a paragraph, including a list of survey questions and an explanation of your sampling technique.

   b. Describe both some advantages and some disadvantages of the method you devised.

2.4 Write a paragraph describing a situation in which a biased sample could be used to influence people. Identify the source of bias and suggest why this influence might be considered misleading.

* * * * *

2.5 Consider a district that contains 1400 registered voters, 748 of which are women. Describe how you could obtain a sample of 100 registered voters from this population using each of the following methods:

   a. systematic sampling   **b.** simple random sampling

   c. stratified sampling

Module 8 ■ *And the Survey Says . . .*   235

Assignment

Problems suitable for use as assessment items are identified by an asterisk (*)

2.1 **a.** The sampling is systematic. Each nth item of the population is selected for testing.

   b. The sampling is random. Each Ping-Pong ball has the same probability of being selected.

   c. The sampling is stratified. The area was first divided into regions (strata). People from each region were then selected randomly.

* 2.2 **a.** **1.** Sample response: Write the names of all students on identical slips of paper, put the slips into a bin, mix them thoroughly, and draw out 20 slips.

   2. Sample response: Select five names at random from each of the four classes: seniors, juniors, sophomores, and freshmen.

   3. Sample response: Select the first person who walks into the next school-wide assembly and every 10th person after that, until you have selected 20 people.

   b. The following answers correspond with the sample responses given in Part **a.**

   1. Because this is a simple random sample, where each name has the same chance of being selected in the sample, there is little potential for bias.

   2. Some bias might occur in the stratified approach since each student is not selected independently. The proportions of students from each class in the sample might not reflect their proportions in the population. **Note:** When the sample sizes are proportional to the sizes of the strata, this type of stratified sampling is known as *proportional sampling*.

   3. This method selects from only those students who attend the assembly. (Also, if fewer than 200 students attend, it will not provide the desired sample size.)

2.3 Answers will vary. Students should not feel compelled to use simple random samples. Depending on the purposes of the survey, a different method—such as stratified sampling—could eliminate other biases, even though it does not produce a simple random sample. In a survey of dating preferences, for example, it might be appropriate to guarantee equal participation by males and females and by each class.

2.4 Sample response: For a magazine article on public attitudes about hunting, a group that seeks to ban hunting might sample only an urban population. Because many urban residents may have only limited experience with hunting, the sample would not accurately represent the views of the population as a whole.

* * * * *

2.5 **a.** Sample response: Starting with the 2nd voter on the list, select every 14th voter.

   b. Sample response: Randomly generate 100 integers in the interval [1,1400] and select voters corresponding to these numbers.

   c. Sample response: Because 53% of the population is female, randomly select 53 female voters and 47 male voters.

2.6 **a.** The proposed method will not provide a simple random sample, because only the potential buyers who request a test drive are sampled.

b. Sample response: One advantage of the proposed method is that the sample would be easy to collect. This might make it more cost-effective for the manufacturer. One disadvantage is that the sample is biased against potential buyers who do not ask for a test drive.

In this activity, students explore sampling as a tool for describing a population. Using frequency histograms, they investigate the distribution of sample proportions.

Materials List

- two varieties of dry beans of different colors but similar sizes (approximately 150 beans per group)

- paper bags or other opaque containers (one per group)

- markers (optional; one per group)

teacher note

The two types of beans should be distinguishable by color but not by size—for example, kidney beans and pinto beans. As an alternative, students may place a clearly discernible mark on 40% of the beans. Objects other than beans also may be used if they are of similar size and shape and can be classified into two distinct groups.

Technology

- statistics package

- spreadsheet (optional)

- programmable calculator (optional)

2.6 A car manufacturer is conducting a marketing study. The proposed sampling method consists of interviewing customers who request test drives at a dealership.

a. Will this sampling method produce a simple random sample of all potential car buyers?

b. Describe the advantages and disadvantages of the proposed method.

ACTIVITY 3

Amelia and Bernadette are both running for president of Washington High School. Two weeks before election time, the school newspaper surveyed the entire school population of 2380 students. According to the results of this census, 40% of the students favored Amelia, 30% preferred Bernadette, 20% were undecided, and 10% did not plan to vote.

With the election approaching quickly, Amelia felt that she had a comfortable lead. A week after the census, however, she took a strong stand in favor of an unpopular dress code. Concerned that Amelia might have lost some support, her campaign staff surveyed a random sample of 25 students. Of those polled, only 8 students planned to vote for Amelia.

Now Amelia is worried. Do the results of this most recent poll mean that her support has slipped to 8/25 or 32%? Her campaign manager points out that these are the findings of only one sample. Another sample might show completely different results.

"But if that's true," says Amelia, "what's the use of taking any samples at all?" Before drawing any conclusions, Amelia and her friends decide to investigate the sampling process.

Exploration

If 40% of Washington High students plan to vote for Amelia, how likely is it for a random sample of 25 students to show only 32% support? In this exploration, you use simulations to model the results of such samples.

a. The percentage of a population with a given characteristic is a **population proportion**. Create a population of beans in which 40% have a distinguishing characteristic other than size or shape.

In this model, the marked beans represents students who planned to vote for Amelia. The remaining 60% represents students who did not indicate that they planned to vote for Amelia.

teacher note

In Part **f** of the exploration, students use technology to simulate sampling. If a statistics package that allows sampling using binomial trials is not available, students may use a spreadsheet or a programmable calculator.

For example, the following program was written for Texas Instruments' TI-89 and Voyage 200 calculators. It stores the results of each sample as an element of a list in the variable "listl." (Each student should input a different seed number before running the program.)

SAMPLING—A program for the TI-89 and Voyage 200

```
: Sampling( )
: Prgm
: C1rIO:DelVar listl
: Input "Known Percentage?", p
: Input "Number of samples?", n
: Input "Sample size?", s
: 0 → c
: For i,l,n
: Disp "Sample number", i
: For j,l,s
: rand(100) → r
: If r<p Then
: c+l → c
: EndIf
: EndFor
: int(100 * (c/s) + 0.5) → listl[i]
: 0 → c
: Disp "Percent marked:", list1[i]
: EndFor
: EndPrgm
```

Other calculators might require a slightly different program. For example, the following program was written for Texas Instruments' TI-84.

SAMPLING—A program for the TI-84

```
PROGRAM: SAMPLING
: C1rList L₁
: Input "KNOWN PERCENT",P
: Input "NUMBER OF SAMPLES",N
: Input "SAMPLE SIZE",S
: 0 → C
: For (I,1,N)
: Disp "SAMPLE NUMBER",I
: For (J,1,S)
: rand 100 → R
: If R<P
: C+1 → C
: End
: int (100 * (C/S) + 0.5) → L₁(I)
: 0 → C
: Disp "PERCENT MARKED",L₁(I)
: End
```

To use a spreadsheet to simulate sampling from a population in which 40% have a particular characteristic, complete the following steps.

- Enter "1" in the first 40 rows in column 1.

- Enter "0" in the next 60 rows in column 1.

- Enter random numbers in each of the first 100 rows of column 2.

- Sort the random numbers, allowing each value in column 1 to follow its corresponding random number.

- To select a sample of size n, find the sum of the values in the first n rows of column 1. This sum represents the number of individuals in the sample with the given characteristic.

The spreadsheet below shows how this method was used to simulate a sample of size 10 from such a population.

0	0.97677807	
0	0.94181197	
0	0.9394662	sum = 4
1	0.91934078	
1	0.91402806	
0	0.88979734	
0	0.87726297	
1	0.85729261	
1	0.82452538	
0	0.80195173	
⋮	⋮	

Student Outcomes

After completing the following exploration and discussion, students should be able to:

✳ use a simulation to explore sampling techniques

✳ use frequency histograms to investigate the distribution of sample proportions

✳ recognize the effect of increasing the number of samples on the distribution of sample proportions

✳ recognize the effect of increasing the sample size on the distribution of sample proportions.

Exploration

This exploration is intended for small groups. In Part **e,** the class will combine their data to obtain a larger pool of samples.

a. Students do not need to create a population of 2380 beans. Approximately 150 beans are sufficient, if the population proportion is 40%.

b. In a simple random sample of 25 beans from this population, about how many would you expect to be marked?

c. The percentage of a sample with a given characteristic is a **sample proportion**. Take a random sample of 25 beans from the container. Record the percentage of marked beans in the sample, then return the sample to the container and mix the beans thoroughly.

d. Repeat Part **c** nine more times, for a total of 10 samples.

e. 1. Combine the results of your 10 samples with the results of the rest of your class and sort the data from least to greatest.

2. Determine the mean of the sample proportions.

3. Display the class data in a histogram, using intervals with a width of 4%. Represent the percentage of marked beans on the *x*-axis and the frequency on the *y*-axis.

4. Find the percentage of sample proportions that are less than or equal to 32%.

f. 1. Use technology to simulate Parts **a–d** of the exploration. Generate as many samples as the technology allows, not to exceed the number of samples in the class data from Part **e**.

2. Determine the mean of the sample proportions.

3. Create a histogram of the data using the same intervals as the histogram in Part **e**.

Discussion

a. What patterns did you observe in the two histograms created in the exploration?

b. How does the mean of the sample proportions compare with the population proportion?

c. 1. If the population proportion had been 52% instead of 40%, how would the histograms have been affected?

2. What would the histograms have looked like if twice as many samples had been taken?

d. 1. In the class data, what percentage of the sample proportions were less than or equal to 32%?

2. Given this percentage, should Amelia be concerned about a loss of student support? Explain your response.

e. How might you change the sampling method described in Part **c** of the exploration to obtain a more accurate characterization of the population?

b. Because 40% of 25 is 10, it would be reasonable to expect about 10 beans to be marked.

c–d. Sample data:

Sample	Percentage of Marked Beans
1	48
2	32
3	36
4	48
5	48
6	60
7	56
8	48
9	40
10	36

e. 1. Sorting the data should simplify the task of determining the number of sample proportions that fall within a given interval.

2. The mean of the sample proportions should be close to the population proportion of 40%.

3. Sample histogram for class data:

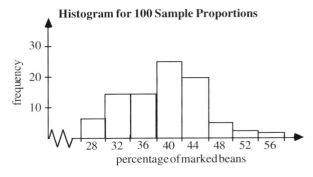

Histogram for 100 Sample Proportions

4. In the sample data shown above, 23% of the sample proportions are less than or equal to 32%.

f. The results of a simulation using technology should be reasonably close to the results obtained using a population of beans.

Discussion

a. Sample response: Both graphs have peaks near the mean of the sample proportions, then gradually taper off on each side.

b. The mean of the sample proportions should be close to 40%, the population proportion.

c. 1. Sample response: The histograms would be similar in shape, but would be centered about the population proportion of 52%.

2. If twice as many samples were taken, the histogram still would be centered about the mean and would have the same basic shape.

d. Students should observe that the percentage of sample proportions less than or equal to 32% provides an estimate of the probability of obtaining such a sample from a population in which the population proportion is 40%.

1. Responses will vary. In one simulation of 90 samples of size 25, 23% were less than or equal to 32%. In another simulation, 26% were less than or equal to 32%.

2. Sample response: The simulation models a situation in which Amelia is preferred by 40% of student voters. The selected sample showed only 32% support for her candidacy. Because the simulated samples indicate that obtaining a sample with 32% support from a population with 40% support is unlikely, Amelia should not be concerned.

e. To obtain a more accurate characterization of the population, students may suggest increasing the sample size.

Warm-Up

1. **a.** approximately 529 hot dogs
   b. 1500/3700 ≈ 41%
2. The population proportion is the percentage of the population with a specific characteristic. The sample proportion is the percentage of the sample with a specific characteristic.

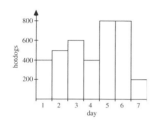

Warm-Up

1. The following histogram shows the number of hot dogs sold by a vendor each day for 7 days.

   a. Find the mean number of hot dogs sold per day.

   b. Calculate the percentage of hot dogs sold on or before day 3.

2. Describe the difference between a population proportion and a sample proportion.

Assignment

3.1 For your community to build a new swimming pool, 51% of the voting population must approve its construction. Before hiring an architect, the local council decided to assess community support by surveying a random sample of 25 voters. Of those surveyed, 9 people indicated that they would vote for the new pool.

To determine what conclusions they could draw from this sample, the council used a computer simulation to collect numerous samples of size 25 from a population in which 51% favored a proposal. The following histogram shows the results of this simulation.

teacher note

Problem **3.3** asks students to simulate 300 samples of 5 rolls of a fair die, counting the number of sixes obtained in each sample. The table below shows some formulas that could be used in a spreadsheet simulation. The following calculator programs also can be used to perform this simulation.

Roll	6 rolled?	number of 6s
	0=no, 1=yes	per sample
=INT(6*RAND())+1	=IF(A3=6,1,0)	=SUM(B3:B7)
=INT(6*RAND())+1	=IF(A4=6,1,0)	
=INT(6*RAND())+1	=IF(A5=6,1,0)	
=INT(6*RAND())+1	=IF(A6=6,1,0)	
=INT(6*RAND())+1	=IF(A7=6,1,0)	
=INT(6*RAND())+1	=IF(A8=6,1,0)	=SUM(B8:B12)
=INT(6*RAND())+1	=IF(A9=6,110)	
=INT(6*RAND())+1	=IF(A10=6,1,0)	
=INT(6*RAND())+1	=IF(A11=6,1,0)	
=INT(6*RAND())+1	=IF(A12=6,1,0)	
=INT(6*RAND())+1	=IF(A13=6,1,0)	=SUM(B13:B17)
=INT(6*RAND())+1	=IF(A14=6,1,0)	

PROB33—A program for the TI-84

```
PROGRAM: PROB33
: ClrHome
: Disp "PLEASE WAIT..."
: 0→B:0→C:0→D: 0→E:0→F: 0→G
: For(A,1,300)
: 0→W
: For(V,1,5)
: randInt(1,6)→Q
: If Q=6:W+1→W
: End
: If W=0:B+1→B
: If W=1:C+1→C
: If W=2:D+1→D
: If W=3:E+1→E
: If W=4:F+1→F
: If W=5:G+1→G
: End
: Disp "0 6'S",B
: Pause
: Disp "1 6'S ",C
: Pause
: Disp "2 6'S",D
: Pause
: Disp "3 6'S",E
: Pause
: Disp "4 6'S",F
: Pause
: Disp "5 6'S",G
```

prob33( )—A program for the TI-89 and Voyage 200

```
: prob33( )
: Prgm
: ClrHome
: Disp "PLEASE WAIT..."
: 0→B:0→C:0→D: 0→E:0→F: 0→G
: For(A,1,300)
: 0→W
: For(V,1,5)
: rand(6)→Q
: If Q=6:W+1→W
: EndFor
: If W=0:B+1→B
: If W=1:C+1→C
: If W=2:D+1→D
: If W=3:E+1→E
: If W=4:F+1→F
: If W=5:G+1→G
: EndFor
: Disp "0 6'S",B
: Pause
: Disp "1 6'S ",C
: Pause
: Disp "2 6'S",D
: Pause
: Disp "3 6'S",E
: Pause
: Disp "4 6'S",F
: Pause
: Disp "5 6'S",G
: EndPrgm
```

Assignment

Problems suitable for use as assessment items are identified by an asterisk (*)

* **3.1 a.** Of those surveyed, 36% (9 of 25) indicated that they would vote for the pool.

  b. There are 300 samples in the simulation.

  c. The mean percentage of "yes" votes may be estimated by dividing the sum of the products of each frequency and its corresponding percentage by the total number of samples. The mean of the sample proportions in the simulation is about 52%.

  d. Sample response: The architect should not be hired. The simulation models a population that would just barely pass the proposal. The town's single sample of 25 voters revealed only 36% support, which is at the extreme low end of the simulated samples from a population with 51% support. The town's sample is very unlikely to have come from a population with enough votes to pass the proposal.

3.2 a. Sample response: Because 10% of the population will not vote, Amelia must obtain a majority of the remaining 90%. Therefore, she would need approximately 46% to win.

  b. The following sample histogram shows the results of 90 samples of size 25 taken from a population with an assumed parameter of 46%.

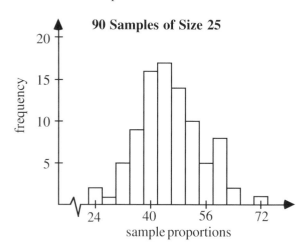

90 Samples of Size 25

  c. In the histogram in Part **b,** 8 of the 90 samples, or approximately 9%, have a sample proportion of less than 32%.

  d. Sample response: If Amelia actually has 46% support, the probability of selecting a sample of 25 students with 8 or fewer in favor of Amelia is fairly small. Amelia's chances of winning the election are not encouraging. Because there were a large number of undecided voters in the census, however, Amelia still has a chance of winning.

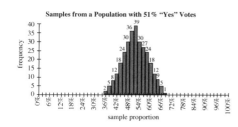

3.3 A group of friends is playing a board game. In this game, players use a six-sided die to determine the number of spaces that they may move around the board. Because 4 of the first 5 players have each rolled a six, the group suspects that the die may not be fair.

a. Create a simulation to model the roll of a fair die. Use the simulation to obtain 300 samples of size 5 and determine the number of sixes in each sample.

b. Create a histogram to display the results of the simulation.

c. Use the histogram to estimate the probability of obtaining a six in 4 out of 5 rolls with a fair die.

d. Do you think that the die in the board game is fair? Explain your response.

ACTIVITY 4

Amelia was relieved to know that her popularity might not have slipped. With 20% of voters still undecided and the election just a few days off, she felt that she still had a chance to win.

Her campaign staff, however, was beginning to have some doubts. In their previous survey of 25 students, only 32% had indicated that they would vote for Amelia. What if they had surveyed a sample of 100 students? What would a 32% rating have meant then?

As the staff discussed these questions, they realized that selecting a random sample of size 25 from the Washington High population could result in many different combinations of students. In fact, for a population of 2380, there are about 10^{60} different samples of size 25. Some of these samples would reflect an accurate picture of Amelia's support, while others might give misleading information. How could they possibly be confident in their results?

The campaign staff paid a visit to their mathematics teacher. She told them that even though they could never survey all the possible samples, they could still obtain a reasonable estimate of Amelia's chances in the election using the mean and standard deviation of all possible sample proportions.

3.3 **a–b.** The following histogram shows the results for 300 samples of size 5 for a simulation of a fair die.

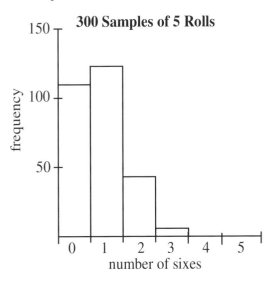

300 Samples of 5 Rolls

c. Answers will vary. Using the sample data shown in Parts **a** and **b,** the estimated probability is 0, because 4 sixes in 5 rolls did not occur in the 300 samples. **Note:** The theoretical probability of rolling a six 4 out of 5 times with a fair die is approximately 0.3%.

d. Sample response: No. The die does not appear to be fair. Although rolling a six 4 out of 5 times is possible, it is very unlikely. It is not clear if the die is fair or not fair. Theoretically (see answer to Part **c**), only 1 sample in 300 would show this outcome. The simulation produced 0 such results.

ACTIVITY 4

In this activity, students determine the maximum standard deviation of all possible sample proportions for samples of any size. They then use this value to describe the interval for a confidence statement.

teacher note

A brief assessment of the mathematical content in Activities **3** and **4,** for use at your discretion, appears in the Teacher Resources for this module.

Materials List

■ none

Technology

■ graphing utility
■ spreadsheet
■ statistics package
■ programmable calculator (optional)

Student Outcomes

After completing the following explorations and discussions, students should be able to:

✷ identify the effects of sample size on the standard deviation of all possible sample proportions

✷ calculate the maximum standard deviation of all possible sample proportions for samples of a given size using the formula

$$\sigma = \sqrt{\frac{p(1-p)}{n}}$$

✷ use standard deviation to determine intervals and make a confidence statement that includes a margin of error.

teacher note

To save time in Exploration **1**, you may ask some students to complete Parts **a** and **b**, some to complete Part **c**, and some to complete Part **d**.

Students may use the same simulations as in Activity **3** to model this situation.

mathematics note

The mean of all possible sample proportions for samples of size *n* equals the population proportion *p*.

Standard deviation is a measure of the spread in a data set. For a population consisting of all possible sample proportions for a given sample size, the standard deviation can be calculated using the following formula:

$$\sigma = \sqrt{\frac{p(1-p)}{n}}$$

where *p* is the population proportion and *n* is the sample size. For example, if 40% of Washington High students support Amelia, the population proportion *p* is 0.4. For samples of size 20, the standard deviation of all possible sample proportions is:

$$\sigma = \sqrt{\frac{0.4(1-0.4)}{20}} \approx 0.11 = 11\%$$

Exploration 1

In this exploration, you investigate the effects of sample size on the standard deviation of all possible sample proportions for samples of a given size.

a. Assume that 40% of the Washington High student population still supports Amelia.

  1. Use a simulation to obtain 90 samples of size 25 from this population. Record the proportion of favorable votes in each sample.
  2. Sort the data from least to greatest.
  3. Create a histogram of the sample proportions.

b. Using the formula given in the mathematics note, calculate the standard deviation of all possible sample proportions for the simulation in Part **a**.

  1. Determine the percentage of sample proportions from Part **a** that lie within 1 standard deviation of the population proportion.
  2. Determine the percentage of sample proportions that lie within 2 standard deviations of the population proportion.

c. Repeat Parts **a** and **b** using a sample size of 50.

d. Repeat Parts **a** and **b** using a sample size of 100. **Note:** Save this data for use in Exploration 2.

Exploration 1

a. 1. Using a statistics package that allows binomial simulations, students should generate 90 samples of size 25, with a probability of success of 0.40. (See teacher note in Activity 3 if this technology is not available.)

   2. Sorting the data should simplify the task of determining the percentage of sample proportions that fall within 1 or 2 standard deviations of the population proportion.

   3. Sample histogram:

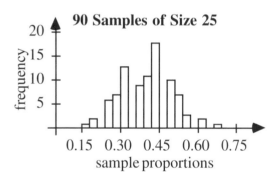

b. 1. Using the formula given in the mathematics note, the standard deviation of all possible sample proportions is:

$$\sqrt{\frac{0.4(1-0.4)}{25}} \approx 0.098$$

or about 9.8%.

In the sample data shown in Part **a,** 69% of the sample proportions were contained in the interval [30.2,49.8].

   2. In the sample data shown in Part **a,** 98% of the sample proportions were contained in the interval [20.4,59.6].

c. The following histogram shows the results of 90 samples of size 50.

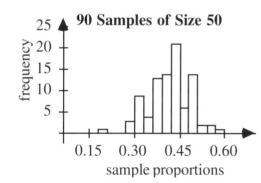

Using the formula given in the mathematics note, the standard deviation of all possible sample proportions is:

$$\sqrt{\frac{0.4(1-0.4)}{50}} \approx 0.069 = 6.9\%$$

For the sample data shown above, 69% of the sample proportions were contained in the interval [33.1,46.9], and 98% were contained in the interval [26.2,53.8].

Discussion 1

a. Compare your histogram from Part **a** of Exploration **1** with the class histogram from Activity **3**.

b. Describe how changing the sample size affected each of the following:

   1. the shape of the histograms

   2. the standard deviation of all possible sample proportions

   3. the interval that represents values within 1 standard deviation of the population proportion.

c. Statisticians have found that, for reasonably large sample sizes, approximately 68% of sample proportions fall within 1 standard deviation of the population proportion, while approximately 95% fall within 2 standard deviations of the population proportion.

   1. How do these values compare with the percentages you found in Exploration **1**?

   2. What do these percentages indicate about the results of a single sample?

d. If the campaign staff found that 32% of a sample of 100 students planned to vote for Amelia, what should they conclude? Explain your response.

Exploration 2

As election day approaches, the number of undecided voters grows smaller and smaller. Some choose Amelia, while others throw their support to Bernadette. Amelia's campaign staff decides to take one last poll, this time with a larger sample size.

   One thing worries them, however. In the two weeks that have passed since the school-wide census, the proportion of students who favor Amelia almost certainly has changed. The campaign staff knows that no matter what the level of her support, the sample proportion is likely to be within 2 standard deviations of the population proportion. The hard part involves calculating this standard deviation, because its formula depends on knowing the population proportion.

   Without knowing the actual population proportion, how could they draw a reliable conclusion from their sample? In this exploration, you determine how confident you can be in the results of a single sample.

a. The formula for the standard deviation of all possible sample proportions, where *p* is the population proportion and *n* is the sample size, is shown below:

$$\sigma = \sqrt{\frac{p(1-p)}{n}}$$

d. The following histogram shows the results of 90 samples of size 100.

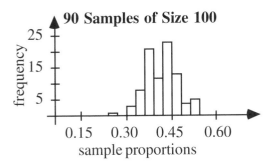

90 Samples of Size 100

Using the formula given in the mathematics note, the standard deviation of all possible sample proportions is:

$$\sqrt{\frac{0.4(1-0.4)}{100}} \approx 0.049 = 4.9\%$$

For the sample data shown above, 68% of the sample proportions were contained in the interval [35.1,44.9], and 94% were contained in the interval [30.2,49.8].

Discussion 1

a. The histograms should display approximately the same mean of the sample proportions (40%), although their shapes may vary.

b. 1. As the sample size increases, the sample proportions tend to be closer to the mean.

   2. As the sample size increases, the standard deviation of all possible sample proportions decreases.

   3. As the sample size increases, the interval that represents values within 1 standard deviation of the population proportion becomes narrower.

c. 1. For a sample size of 25, the percentages may vary. They should be relatively close—approximately 68% and 95%—for the larger sample sizes.

   2. Sample response: They indicate an estimated probability that the sample proportion will be within 1 or 2 standard deviations of the population proportion.

d. Answers will vary. For a sample size of 100, a sample proportion of 32% is more than 1 standard deviation from the population proportion. In the sample data given in Exploration **1,** only 5% of the samples yielded a proportion of 32% or less. This suggests that Amelia should be very concerned about her support, since the sample is not likely to have come from a population in which 40% favored her.

Exploration 2

In this exploration, students use the formula for the standard deviation of all possible sample proportions to examine the maximum standard deviation for a given sample size. This value is a conservative estimate of the standard deviation of all possible sample proportions for a situation in which the actual population proportion is unknown.

a. 1. Sample graph:

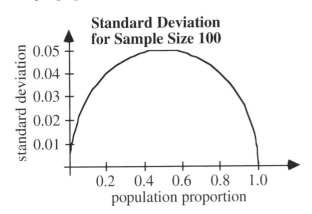

Standard Deviation for Sample Size 100

2. Students may use the trace function on a graphing utility to find that the maximum standard deviation is 0.05.

3. The population proportion that corresponds with the maximum standard deviation is 0.5.

b. After repeating Part **a** for other sample sizes, students should conjecture that the maximum standard deviation always occurs when the population proportion is 0.5. As the sample size increases, the maximum standard deviation decreases.

c–d. Students add and subtract 5% from each sample proportion to obtain 90 intervals, then determine how many of these intervals contain the known population proportion of 40%.

e. The percentage of intervals that contain the population proportion should be close to 68%.

f. For a sample size of 100, 2 • MSD = 10%. The percentage of intervals that contain the population proportion should be near 95%.

Discussion 2

a. The domain of the function is $0 \le p \le 1$, the range is $0 \le \sigma \le 0.05$.

b. Sample response: I would be more confident predicting that the population proportion is within 2 MSDs of the sample proportion. According to the results of the simulation, about 95% of those intervals contained the known population proportion.

c. Sample response: It is important to use the maximum standard deviation because this value describes the largest possible interval, thereby reducing the chance of error.

d. Sample response: Because the width of the intervals depends on the MSD, and the MSD is calculated using the formula $0.5/\sqrt{n}$, increasing the sample size would make the intervals narrower, and decreasing the sample size would make the intervals wider.

e. Sample response: I would be more confident in predicting the population proportion using the larger sample size. For a sample size of 100, the MSD is 5%. This means that the sample proportion would be within 10% of the true proportion about 95% of the time.

For a sample size of 400, the MSD is $0.5/\sqrt{400}$ or 2.5%. The value of 2 MSDs is 2(2.5%) or 5%. This means that the sample proportion would be within 5% of the true proportion about 95% of the time.

1. Graph this equation for a sample size of 100 ($n = 100$).

2. Use the graph to determine the largest possible standard deviation for a sample size of 100.

3. What population proportion corresponds with this maximum standard deviation?

b. Repeat Part **a** for some other sample sizes. Use your results to make a general statement about the maximum standard deviation for any sample size.

c. In Part **d** of Exploration **1**, you simulated 90 samples of size 100 from a population with a known population proportion of 40%.

Add and subtract 1 maximum standard deviation (MSD) from each of these sample proportions to obtain 90 intervals. For example, given a sample proportion of 34%, the corresponding interval would be:

$$[34 - \text{MSD}, \ 34 + \text{MSD}]$$

d. Determine the number of intervals from Part **c** that contain the population proportion (40%).

e. Combine your results from Part **d** with those of the rest of the class. Determine the percentage of intervals that contain the population proportion.

f. Repeat Parts **c–e** using twice the maximum standard deviation (2 • MSD).

Discussion 2

a. Describe the domain and range of the following function, when $n = 100$:

$$\sigma = \sqrt{\frac{p(1-p)}{n}}$$

b. Would you be more confident in predicting that an unknown population proportion is within 1 MSD of a sample proportion, or within 2 MSDs of a sample proportion? Explain your response.

c. In Part **c** of Exploration **2**, why do you think it was important to use the maximum standard deviation to determine each interval?

d. How do you think that changing the sample size would affect these intervals?

e. Would you be more confident in predicting an unknown population proportion using a sample size of 100 or a sample size of 400? Explain your response.

mathematics note

The **maximum standard deviation** of all possible sample proportions occurs when the population proportion $p = 0.5$. The value of 2 maximum standard deviations for all possible sample proportions equals:

$$2 \cdot \sigma = 2 \cdot \sqrt{\frac{0.5(1 - 0.5)}{n}} = \frac{2 \cdot 0.5}{\sqrt{n}} = \frac{1}{\sqrt{n}}$$

A **confidence statement** declares that a population parameter lies within a specific range of values. Given the value of 2 maximum standard deviations calculated above, the following confidence statement can be made, where n is the sample size: "It is highly likely that the population proportion is within $1/\sqrt{n}$ of the sample proportion."

For example, consider a random sample of 1500 registered voters. Of those surveyed, 700 plan to vote for candidate A. In this case, the sample proportion is 700/1500 or 47%. The value of 2 maximum standard deviations is $1/\sqrt{1500}$ or 2.6%. Therefore, the following confidence statement can be made: "It is highly likely that the proportion of the population who plan to vote for candidate A is within the interval [44.4%, 49.6%]."

The interval within which a parameter is likely to fall is often reported using a **margin of error.** Identifying a margin of error that is twice the maximum standard deviation provides an interval that is highly likely to contain the population proportion.

For example, the results of the survey described above might be reported as follows: "At the time of our poll, it was estimated that 47% of registered voters preferred candidate A, with a margin of error of 2.6%."

f. 1. When using the maximum standard deviation to identify a margin of error, how is the margin of error affected by the size of the sample?

   2. How is it affected by the size of the population?

g. Why do you think that a pollster would be willing to predict the outcome of a national election based on a random sample of only 1500 registered voters?

Warm-Up

1. Determine the standard deviation for each of the following situations.

   a. The population proportion is 55% and the sample size is 81.

   b. The population proportion is 90% and the sample size is 16.

   c. The population proportion is 40% and the sample size is 60.

f. 1. When the margin of error is twice the maximum standard deviation, it decreases as the sample size increases.

   2. Because the maximum standard deviation of all possible sample proportions is not affected by the size of the population, neither is the margin of error.

g. Using a value of twice the maximum standard deviation, the margin of error for a sample size of 1500 is approximately 2.6%. Therefore, the pollster can be confident that the statistic is within 2.6% of the parameter.

Warm-Up

1. a. $\sigma \approx 0.055$
    b. $\sigma \approx 0.075$
    c. $\sigma \approx 0.063$

2. **a.** 0.1

   b. ≈ 0.115

   c. ≈ 0.04

3. **a.** ≈ 0.56

   b. ≈ 0.033

   c. Sample response: The margin of error is approximately 3.3%. It is highly likely that between 52.7% and 59.3% of voters will vote for candidate A.

Assignment

Problems suitable for use as assessment items are identified by an asterisk (*).

4.1 **a.** For a sample size of 400, the maximum standard deviation of all possible sample proportions is 2.5%. Therefore, it is highly likely that the proportion of the population that will vote for Amelia is between 44% and 54%.

   b. Sample response: Because 10% of the student body does not intend to vote, Amelia only needs the support of 46% of the population to win. Because it is very likely (about 95% probability) that the population proportion falls within the 44% to 54% interval, her prospects are very good, but not guaranteed.

4.2 Sample response: A confidence statement should not be made about this survey. The ratio of 4 to 5 does not give any indication of sample size.

4.3 Sample response: A margin of error of ±3% means that Senator Rodriguez is likely to receive somewhere between 51% and 57% of the vote. Although Senator Rodriguez is not assured of reelection, a victory is likely because the poll predicts a majority of at least 51% (54 – 3) with a high level of confidence.

* 4.4 The margin of error for a sample of size 1500 is $1/\sqrt{1500} \approx 0.026$, which is less than 3%.

* 4.5 Sample response: The margin of error for a sample of 100 is about 10%. Amelia only needs votes from 46% of the population to win, so her election is highly likely.

✳ ✳ ✳ ✳ ✳

4.6 The value of twice the maximum standard deviation of all possible sample proportions for $n = 40$ is:

$$2 \cdot \sigma = 2 \cdot \sqrt{\frac{0.5 \cdot (1 - 0.5)}{40}} = \frac{1}{\sqrt{40}} \approx 0.16$$

Using this value to determine the margin of error, the population proportion is likely to fall in the interval $[0.67, 0.99]$.

4.7 The value of twice the maximum standard deviation of all possible sample proportions for $n = 25$ is:

$$1/\sqrt{25} = 0.2$$

This value corresponds with a margin of error of 20%.

---

2. Find the value of 2 maximum standard deviations for each of the following sample sizes.

   a. 100

   b. 75

   c. 600

3. In a random sample of 900 registered voters, 500 plan to vote for candidate A.

   a. What is the sample proportion in this situation?

   b. Determine the value of 2 maximum standard deviations.

   c. Write a confidence statement for this situation, including the margin of error.

Assignment

4.1 On the day before the election, Amelia's campaign staff surveyed a random sample of 400 students. Of those polled, 49% favored Amelia.

   a. Write a confidence statement describing the true proportion of Amelia's supporters.

   b. If you were Amelia's campaign manager, what would you say about her chances of winning the election? Explain your response.

4.2 A television commercial made the following claim: "Our survey shows that 4 out of 5 dentists prefer sugarless gum for their patients who chew gum." Can you make a confidence statement about this proportion? If so, make one. If not, explain why not.

4.3 A poll taken the day before a congressional election reported the following results: "Senator Rodriguez currently has 54% of the vote. The poll's margin of error is ±3%." Is Senator Rodriguez assured of re-election? Explain your response.

4.4 For its annual election survey, one polling organization selects a random sample of 1500 registered voters. Using twice the maximum standard deviation of all possible sample proportions, will the survey's margin of error be more or less than three percentage points? Explain your response.

4.5 The editors of the Washington High newspaper surveyed a random sample of 100 students on the morning of the election. Of those surveyed, 56 planned to vote for Amelia. What predictions can you make about the election? Justify your response.

* * * * *

4.6 To assess customer satisfaction with its new checkout system, a supermarket surveyed a random sample of 40 shoppers. Of those surveyed, 83% were happy with the new system. In what interval is the actual proportion of satisfied customers likely to fall? Explain your response.

4.7 As part of its quality control process, a car dealership surveyed a random sample of 25 customers. Of those surveyed, 73% expressed satisfaction with the service they received. Using twice the maximum standard deviation of all possible sample proportions, what is the margin of error for this survey? Explain your response.

Summary Assessment

Imagine that you are a quality control specialist for a light bulb manufacturer. Your job involves testing bulbs to make sure that the production line is working properly. When the equipment is functioning as designed, the proportion of defective bulbs is less than 5%. Since the factory produces many thousands of bulbs each day, you must use a sampling technique to estimate the actual proportion.

1. Design a practical method of sampling light bulbs so that the sample proportions provide a reliable estimate of the population proportion.

2. Use technology to create a simulation of the sampling process. Display the results in a histogram.

3. Determine the margin of error for a sample proportion obtained using your method.

4. Describe how you would respond to a sample proportion of 6.2% defective bulbs obtained using your method.

teacher note

An additional assessment, for use at your discretion, appears in the Teacher Resources for this module.

Summary Assessment

1. Answers will vary. Sample response: To sample the bulbs, I would use a systematic sampling method. Assuming that about 10,000 bulbs are produced per day, I would select every 250th bulb. This would create an approximate sample size of 40, which would be practical and efficient in terms of time and money.

2. The following histogram shows the results of 100 samples of size 40 from a population in which $p = 0.05$:

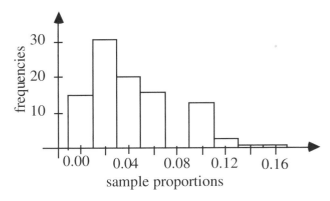

3. Using the value of twice the maximum standard deviation of all possible sample proportions, the margin of error for a sample size of 40 is:

$$\frac{1}{\sqrt{40}} \approx 0.158$$

4. Sample response: Judging from the results of the simulation, the experimental probability of obtaining a sample with at least 6% defective bulbs from a population in which $p = 0.05$ is about 35%.

    Given a sample proportion of 6.2%, the population proportion is highly likely to be contained in the interval [0,22.0%]. Because this interval is very wide, I would take another sample of the day's production using a larger sample size. If this sample also resulted in a proportion of defective bulbs greater than 5%, I would check to make sure that the equipment was running properly.

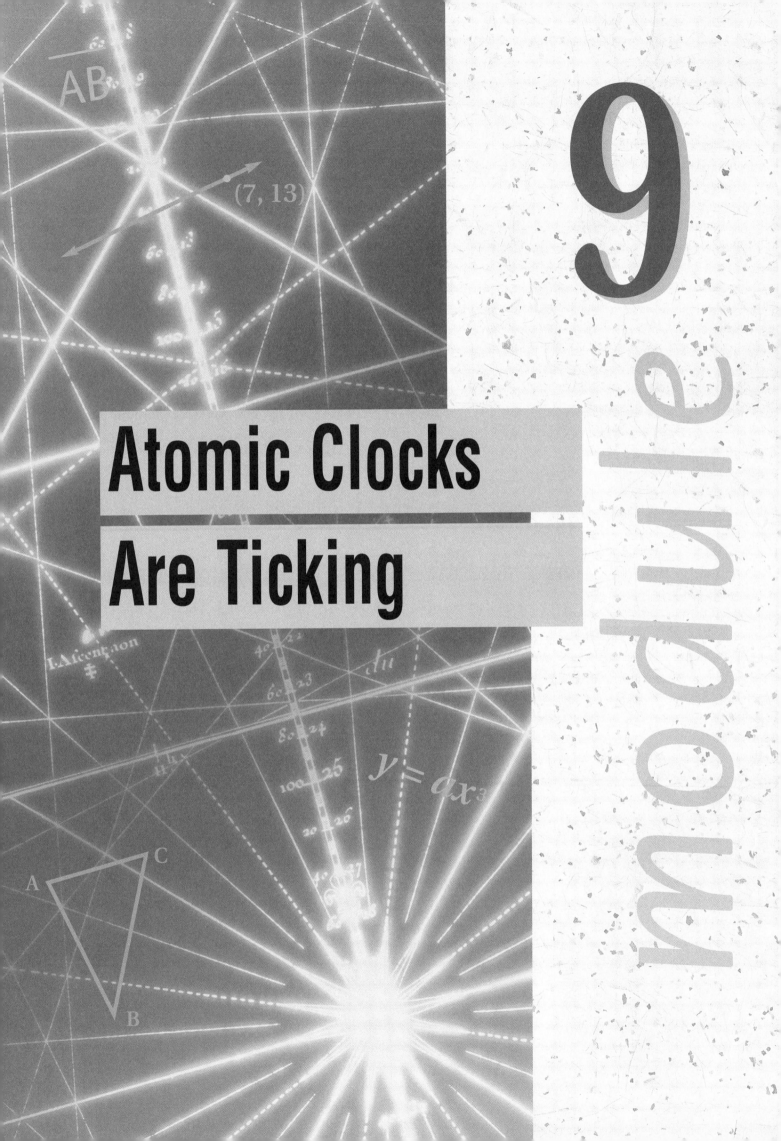

Atomic Clocks Are Ticking

9 module

Overview

Teacher EditionThis module uses radioactive decay and carbon dating to develop models of exponential decay and examine negative and fractional exponents. Exponential equations are solved graphically and by guess-and-check using a calculator.

Activity 1: Students simulate radioactive decay using marked chips in a pizza box. They use an exponential equation in the form $f(x) = a \cdot b^x$ to model the data.

Activity 2: Students use a spreadsheet to investigate properties of exponents. They also investigate rational exponents.

Activity 3: Students apply their knowledge of exponents to problems involving radioactive decay and half-life.

Objectives

In this module, students will:

* use simulations to model real-world events (1, 3)
* use exponential functions of the form $f(x) = a \cdot b^x$ to model exponential decay (1, 2, 3)
* examine the relationship between rational exponents and roots (2)
* develop properties of exponents (2)
* identify equivalent exponential expressions (2)
* examine the relationship between negative and positive exponents (2, 3)
* solve simple exponential equations with like bases (2, 3).

Prerequisites

For this module, students should know:

* how to calculate percent change
* how to interpret an exponential expression
* how to model exponential growth using equations of the form $y = a \cdot b^x$
* how to perform arithmetic with numbers expressed in scientific notation
* how to use a spreadsheet.

Flashbacks, for use at your discretion, appear in the Teacher Resources for this module. These brief problem sets provide a review of some prerequisite skills for each activity.

Planning Guide

Activity	Materials	Technology	Time Line
Activity **1**	■ chips or disks ■ graph paper ■ boxes with lids	■ graphing utility ■ spreadsheet	2 days
Activity **2**	■ none	■ graphing utility ■ spreadsheet	3 days
Activity **3**	■ graph paper ■ dice (optional)	■ graphing utility ■ spreadsheet	3 days
Assessment Activities	■ none	■ graphing utility	3 days **Total: 11 days**

Introduction

The opening narrative introduces students to carbon dating. As the module progresses, students eventually gain a more accurate understanding of radioactive decay. In the summary assessment, students will use Professor Cordova's data to determine the age of charcoal found in the cave.

Note: Students should not perceive radioactive decay as the "death" of an atom. A radioactive atom typically emits a small particle (or particles) from the nucleus—resulting in a new nucleus with a different number of protons. The decay of an atom of carbon-14, for example, produces an atom of nitrogen.

In this activity, students use equations of the form $y = a \cdot b^x$ to model data collected during a simulation of radioactive decay. In this simulation, each shake of the container represents a half-life. **Note:** In Activity **3,** students use a simulation that produces half-life values which are not whole units.

Materials List

- chips or disks (32 per group)
- flat boxes with lids (one per group)

teacher note

To conduct the exploration, each group will require 32 chips (such as poker chips) that can be marked on one side. As an alternative, you may use pennies as chips.

Pizza boxes work well for containers. Local pizza parlors may donate boxes for educational use or provide them at a minimal cost.

Technology

- graphing utility
- spreadsheet (optional)

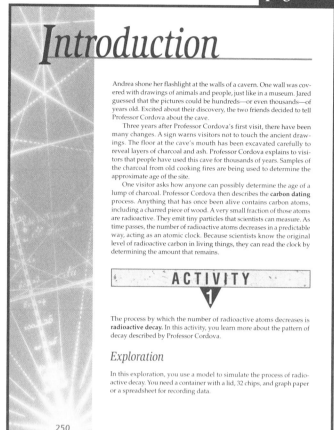

Introduction

Andrea shone her flashlight at the walls of a cavern. One wall was covered with drawings of animals and people, just like in a museum. Jared guessed that the pictures could be hundreds—or even thousands—of years old. Excited about their discovery, the two friends decided to tell Professor Cordova about the cave.

Three years after Professor Cordova's first visit, there have been many changes. A sign warns visitors not to touch the ancient drawings. The floor at the cave's mouth has been excavated carefully to reveal layers of charcoal and ash. Professor Cordova explains to visitors that people have used this cave for thousands of years. Samples of the charcoal from old cooking fires are being used to determine the approximate age of the site.

One visitor asks how anyone can possibly determine the age of a lump of charcoal. Professor Cordova then describes the **carbon dating** process. Anything that has once been alive contains carbon atoms, including a charred piece of wood. A very small fraction of those atoms are radioactive. They emit tiny particles that scientists can measure. As time passes, the number of radioactive atoms decreases in a predictable way, acting as an atomic clock. Because scientists know the original level of radioactive carbon in living things, they can read the clock by determining the amount that remains.

ACTIVITY 1

The process by which the number of radioactive atoms decreases is **radioactive decay.** In this activity, you learn more about the pattern of decay described by Professor Cordova.

Exploration

In this exploration, you use a model to simulate the process of radioactive decay. You need a container with a lid, 32 chips, and graph paper or a spreadsheet for recording data.

250

Student Outcomes

After completing the following exploration and discussion, students should be able to:

✳ recognize patterns of exponential decay

✳ use equations of the form of $f(x) = a \cdot b^x$ to model exponential decay

✳ determine which values of r in an equation of the form $f(x) = a(1 + r)^x$ indicate exponential growth and which values indicate exponential decay

✳ express roots of a number using fractional exponents in the form $1/n$, where n is a natural number

✳ design a simulation that models a decay rate of $1/2$.

Read Parts **a–g** before beginning the exploration. The chips represent radio-active atoms. Predict how the number of chips will change during the simulation. Record your prediction, then begin.

a. Put a mark on one side of all 32 chips and place them in the container.

b. Close the lid, then shake the container.

c. Open the container and remove each chip with a mark showing.

d. Count the number of chips remaining.

e. Record both the number of chips remaining and the shake number. (After shake 0, there are 32 chips.)

f. Repeat Parts **b–e** until no chips remain in the container.

g. Graph the data. Plot the shake number along the *x*-axis and the number of chips remaining along the *y*-axis. **Note:** Save your data for use in the assignment.

Discussion

a. Describe any patterns you observed in your data or graph.

b. What similarities or differences are there among the patterns found by the class?

c. What fraction of the previous number of chips would you expect to remain after each shake?

d. What happens to any number representing a population when it is multiplied by a factor between 0 and 1?

mathematics note

An equation of the form $f(x) = a \bullet b^x$ is an exponential function. The function can be used to describe a pattern of **exponential growth** or **exponential decay**.

When this equation describes the growth or decay in a population, a represents the size of the initial population. The value of b is the sum of two percentages: 100 (representing the initial population) and r (representing the rate of growth or decay). The variable x represents number of time periods, and $f(x)$ represents the total population after x time periods.

In this case, the exponential function will be of the form $f(x) = a(1 + r)^x$. In exponential growth, r is positive and represents the **growth rate**. In exponential decay, r is negative and represents the **decay rate**.

Exploration

Students should recall the simulation of exponential growth from the Level 1 module, "Skeeters Are Over-running the World."

Note: Students should save their data for use in the assignment.

a–f. Students simulate the process of radioactive decay. It should take from 4 to 7 shakes to remove all the chips. Sample data:

Shake	No. of Chips Remaining
0	32
1	15
2	12
3	8
4	3
5	1
6	1
7	0

g. A graph of the sample data appears below.

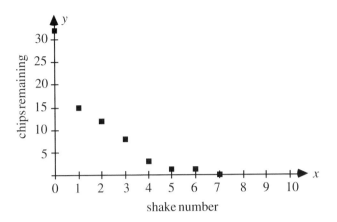

teacher note

In Parts **d** and **e** of the discussion, students are introduced to values of b less than 1 and greater than 0 in equations of the form $f(x) = a \bullet b^x$, and negative values for r in equations of the form $f(x) = a(1 + r)^x$.

When discussing the mathematics note, it is important to emphasize that 19% is the decay rate or the percent decrease, and 81% is the percent remaining. You might wish to remind students of this fact periodically.

Discussion

a. Sample response: The number of remaining chips appears to decrease more slowly as the shake number increases.

b. Answers will vary. Sample response: The general shapes of the graphs are the same, with the number of chips decreasing as the shake number increases. However, different numbers of shakes were required to remove all the chips, and the graphs vary in steepness.

c. Because the probability of a chip landing with the mark up is 1/2, students should expect half of the chips to be removed and half to remain.

d. When a positive number is multiplied by a factor between 0 and 1, the number decreases.

e. 1. Sample response: The value of y represents the worth of the machine at the end of half a year, or 6 months.

   2. Sample response: The value of y represents the worth of the machine at the end of one-third of a year, or 4 months.

f. Answers will vary, depending on the calculator used.

   1. Sample response: Type "0.81^(1/2)" then press the enter button.

   2. Sample response: Type "0.81^(1/3)" then press the enter button.

g. Students should realize that the value of $(0.81)^{1/2}$ is the square root of 0.81, or 0.9.

h. Students should conjecture that because an exponent of $1/2$ in the expression $(0.81)^{1/2}$ represents the square root, an exponent of $1/3$ in the expression $(0.81)^{1/3}$ represents the cube root of 0.81. This can be verified by cubing the value reported by the calculator for $(0.81)^{1/3}$.

i 1. If the equation models exponential growth, then $b > 1$.

   2. If the equation models exponential decay, then $0 < b < 1$.

For example, the value of business equipment often depreciates exponentially. If the value of a machine originally worth $1000 decreases by 19% each year, the equation that models its depreciation is $y = 1000(1 - 0.19)^x$ or $y = 1000(0.81)^x$. In this case, x represents the number of years since the machine was purchased and y represents the value of the machine after x years. The graph in Figure 9-1 shows the depreciation of this machine over a 10-year period.

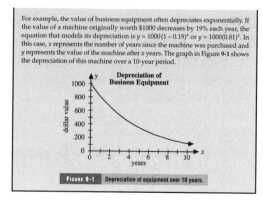

FIGURE 9-1 Depreciation of equipment over 10 years.

e. Given the example outlined in the previous mathematics note, how would you interpret the value of y in each of the following equations?

   1. $y = 1000(0.81)^{1/2}$ 2. $y = 1000(0.81)^{1/3}$

f. Describe how you could use a calculator to find the value of each of the following expressions.

   1. $(0.81)^{1/2}$ 2. $(0.81)^{1/3}$

g. What is the mathematical meaning of $(0.81)^{1/2}$?

h. From your response to Part **g**, what do you think is the mathematical meaning of $(0.81)^{1/3}$? Verify your response.

mathematics note

The roots of a number can be represented using exponents of the form $1/n$, where n is a natural number. If the nth root of a exists, it can be represented as follows:

$$\sqrt[n]{a} = a^{1/n}$$

For example, $\sqrt[4]{64} = 64^{1/4}$, $\sqrt[5]{32} = 32^{1/5}$, and $\sqrt{16} = 16^{1/2}$.

page 253

i. In the equation $y = a \bullet b^x$, $b = 1 + r$.

1. What are the possible values of b when the equation models exponential growth?
2. What are the possible values of b when the equation models exponential decay?

Warm-Up

1. Evaluate each of the following expressions:
   - **a.** $125^{1/3}$
   - **b.** $81^{1/4}$
   - **c.** $343^{1/3}$
   - **d.** $\sqrt[10]{1024}$
2. Each of the following exponential functions models a pattern of growth or decay. Determine the value of r in each case.
   - **a.** $f(x) = 229 \bullet 0.44^x$
   - **b.** $g(x) = 750 \bullet 1.10^x$
   - **c.** $h(x) = 99.95 \bullet 3^x$
   - **d.** $y(x) = 82 \bullet 0.7^x$
3. Evaluate each function in Problem **2** for the values below.
   - **a.** $x = 3$
   - **b.** $x = 0.5$
   - **c.** $x = 1/3$

Assignment

1.1 Use the data you collected in the exploration to complete Parts **a–e.**

a. Find the **percent decrease** in the population after each shake. For example, if there are 17 chips remaining after shake 1, the percent decrease can be found using the following ratio:

$$\frac{32 - 17}{32} = \frac{15}{32} \approx 0.47 = 47\%$$

b. **1.** Determine the mean of the percents of decrease for all shakes.

2. Considering the theoretical probability of a chip landing with the marked side up, what would you expect this mean to be? Explain your response.

Module 9 ■ *Atomic Clocks Are Ticking* 253

Warm-Up

1. **a.** 5
   b. 3
   c. 7
   d. 2
2. **a.** –0.56
   b. 0.10
   c. 2
   d. –0.3
3. **a.** $f(x) \approx 19.5$; $g(x) \approx 998.25$; $h(x) \approx 2698.65$; $y(x) \approx 28.1$
   b. $f(x) \approx 151.9$; $g(x) \approx 786.6$; $h(x) \approx 173.1$; $y(x) \approx 68.6$
   c. $f(x) \approx 174.2$; $g(x) \approx 774.2$; $h(x) \approx 144.2$; $y(x) \approx 72.8$

Assignment

Problems suitable for use as assessment items are identified by an asterisk (*).

1.1 a. The table below shows the percent decrease after each shake for the sample data given in the exploration:

Shake	No. of Chips Remaining	Percent Decrease
0	32	
1	15	47%
2	12	20%
3	8	33%
4	3	63%
5	1	67%
6	1	0%
7	0	100%

b. 1. Answers will vary. The mean of the percents of decrease for the sample data shown above is 47%.

2. Sample response: I would expect the mean of the percents of decrease to be close to 50%, because each chip has a 50% chance of having its mark showing.

c. Sample response: The mean of the percents of decrease can be used as the rate of decay, which is also a percentage, because they measure the same thing.

d. Answers will vary. For the sample data, the rate of decay is –0.47. In this case, $b = 1 – 0.47 = 0.53$.

e. Since the initial population is 32, the equation that models the data is $y = 32 \cdot (0.53)^x$.

1.2 A completed table is shown at the bottom of the page.

1.3 $5.02 \cdot 10^{22} / 1 \cdot 10^{12} \approx 5 \cdot 10^{10}$ atoms

1.4 Using an equation of the form $y = a \cdot b^x$, the initial population a is $4 \cdot 10^{14}$ chips, b is 0.5, and the number of shakes x is 3. Solving for y gives $5 \cdot 10^{13}$ or 50 trillion chips.

Students also may solve this problem as follows: After the first shake, the number of chips is $(4 \cdot 10^{14})/2 = 2 \cdot 10^{14}$; after the second shake, the number of chips is $(2 \cdot 10^{14})/2 = 1 \cdot 10^{14}$; after the third shake, the number of chips is $(1 \cdot 10^{14})/2 = 5 \cdot 10^{13}$.

1.5 Sample response: To find the number of atoms in the previous year, multiply by 2: $3.8 \cdot 10^{13}(2) = 7.6 \cdot 10^{13}$ atoms. **Note:** Some students may substitute –1 for x in the equation $y = (3.8 \cdot 10^{13})(0.5^x)$ to calculate an answer. Negative exponents are introduced in Activity **2**.

1.6 Sample response: Starting with $1 \cdot 10^{12}$ and repeatedly multiplying by 0.5 for each decade, it would take 10 decades before the number of atoms was less than $1 \cdot 10^9$ (one billion).

* 1.7 a. Because $b > 1$, this equation models exponential growth. In this case, $1.055 = 1 + r$ or $r = 0.055$. As x increases, the graph increases gradually at first, then dramatically.

b. Because $0 < b < 1$, this equation models exponential decay. In this case, $0.50 = 1 + r$ or $r = –0.50$. As x increases, the graph decreases dramatically at first, then gradually.

c. Because $0 < b < 1$, this equation models exponential decay. In this case, $0.75 = 1 + r$ or $r = –0.25$. As x increases, the graph decreases dramatically at first, then gradually.

✳ ✳ ✳ ✳ ✳

---

c. Describe the relationship between the rate of decay and the mean of the percents of decrease.

d. Use the mean from Part **b** to determine the value of b, where $b = 1 + r$.

e. Write an equation of the form $y = a \cdot b^x$ that models the exponential decay of the population of chips.

1.2 Complete the following table.

	Initial Population	Rate of Growth or Decay	Model Equation of the Form $y = a \cdot b^x$
a.	500	8%	
b.			$y = 20,000 \cdot (0.89)^x$
c.	100	–32%	

1.3 A 1-g sample of carbon contains $5.02 \cdot 10^{22}$ atoms, of which 1 out of every 1 trillion ($1 \cdot 10^{12}$) is radioactive. How many radioactive atoms are there in this sample?

1.4 Suppose that you began the exploration in Activity **1** with $4 \cdot 10^{14}$ chips. Predict the number of chips remaining after the third shake. Explain your reasoning.

1.5 An object contains $3.8 \cdot 10^{13}$ radioactive atoms. The annual rate of decay is 0.5. Estimate the number of radioactive atoms that the object contained in the previous year. Describe how you found your solution.

1.6 A sample contains $1 \cdot 10^{12}$ radioactive atoms that decay at the rate of 50% every decade. How many decades will it take for the number of radioactive atoms to be less than 1 billion? Explain your reasoning.

1.7 Each of the equations below models a pattern of either exponential decay or exponential growth. For each equation, complete the following steps.

■ Identify whether the equation models growth or decay.

■ Determine the value of r.

■ Use appropriate technology to graph the function.

■ Describe the basic shape of the graph.

a. $y = 350 \cdot (1.055)^x$

b. $y = 100 \cdot (0.50)^x$

c. $y = 5000 \cdot (0.75)^x$

✳ ✳ ✳ ✳ ✳

254   Module 9 ■ *Atomic Clocks Are Ticking*

	Initial Population	Rate of Growth or Decay	Model Equation of the Form $y = a \cdot b^x$
a.	500	8%	$y = 500 \cdot (1.08)^x$
b.	20,000	–11%	$y = 20,000 \cdot (0.89)^x$
c.	100	–32%	$y = 100 \cdot (0.68)^x$

238   Module 9 ■ *Atomic Clocks Are Ticking*

1.8 The balance of an interest-bearing account also can be modeled by an exponential equation. For example, consider an initial deposit of $1000 at an annual interest rate of 8%. The interest earned each year is deposited in the account at the end of the year.

a. Assuming that no withdrawals or deposits are made, write an equation that models the account balance after *x* years.

b. What is the account balance at the end of 5 years?

c. 1. Create a graph that shows the increase in the account balance over the next 20 years.

   2. Using the graph, estimate how many years it will take for the initial deposit to double.

d. If you deposited $1000 in an account of this type, what would the account balance be when you are 65 years old?

1.9 The following graph shows the change in a town's population over a 20-year period.

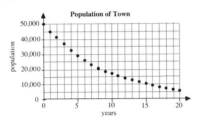

a. What was the town's initial population?

b. About how many years did it take for the population to decrease by half?

c. Judging from the graph, what was the population at year 15?

d. Using the method described in Problem **1.2**, determine the mean of the percents of decrease in the population over the 20-year period.

e. 1. Find an equation of the form $y = a \cdot b^x$ that models this data, where *y* represents population and *x* represents years.

   2. Use this equation to verify your response to Part **c**.

1.8 a. The total amount of money in the account after *x* years may be modeled by the equation:

$$y = 1000 \cdot (1 + 0.08)^x = 1000 \cdot (1.08)^x.$$

b. The account balance after 5 years is:

$$y = 1000 \cdot (1.08)^5 = \$1469.33.$$

c. 1. Sample graph:

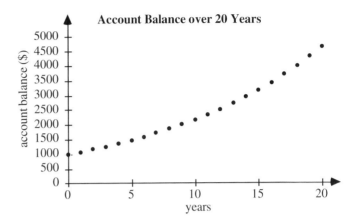

  2. The account balance will reach $2000 in about 9 years.

d. Answers may vary. For a 16-year-old student, the account balance may be calculated as follows: $y = 1000 \cdot (1.08)^{49} \approx \$43,\!427.42.$

1.9 a. The town's initial population was 50,000.

b. The population decreased to 25,000 between year 6 and year 7.

c. The population at year 15 is about 11,000.

d. Answers may vary slightly. The rate of decrease is 10% per year.

e. 1. Sample response: $y = 50,\!000 \cdot (0.90)^x.$

  2. The estimated value from the graph and the approximate value from the equation should be reasonably close. Using the sample equation given above, $y = 50,\!000 \cdot (0.90)^{15} \approx 10,\!295.$

ACTIVITY 2

In this activity, students use negative values for x in equations of the form $y = a \cdot b^x$ to represent periods of time before the present. This allows them to explore negative exponents and continue their investigation of carbon dating.

Materials List

- none

Technology

- spreadsheet
- graphing utility

Student Outcomes

After completing the following explorations and discussions, students should be able to:

✳ describe the relationships among $(1/2)^x$, $1/2^x$, 2^{-x}, and 2^x

✳ compare the graphs of $y = 2^x$ and $y = 2^{-x}$

✳ write equivalent exponential expressions using positive and negative exponents

✳ multiply exponential expressions containing like bases

✳ divide exponential expressions containing like bases

✳ raise an exponential expression to a power

✳ convert exponential expressions with rational exponents to the equivalent radical form

✳ evaluate selected exponential expressions with rational exponents

✳ solve simple exponential equations with like bases.

ACTIVITY 2

In living plants and animals, only about 1 in every $1 \cdot 10^{12}$ carbon atoms is radioactive. When a plant or animal dies and new carbon is no longer absorbed or metabolized, these radioactive carbon atoms decay. When determining the age of an artifact using carbon dating, scientists can estimate the number of radioactive carbons remaining. This number, along with carbon's known rate of decay, allows scientists to determine the age of the sample.

Given carbon's rate of decay and the number of radioactive atoms present at a particular time, it is also possible to calculate the number of radioactive atoms at any time in the past. Such calculations may require the use of negative exponents.

In this activity, you examine other ways to represent the model of exponential decay from the exploration in Activity 1.

Exploration 1

a. Create a spreadsheet with the headings shown in Table 9-1 below. Complete the table for values of x from 4 to –4, where x is an integer.

TABLE 9-1 ■ Spreadsheet for Exploration 1

x	2^x	$(1/2)^x$	$1/2^x$	2^{-x}
4	16	0.0625		
3	8			
2				
⋮				
–2				
–3				
–4				

b. Describe any patterns you observe in the spreadsheet.

c. 1. Create a scatterplot of the values of 2^{-x} versus the values of x.

   2. On the same coordinate system from Step 1, create a scatterplot of the values for 2^x versus the values for x.

Exploration 1

a. Sample spreadsheet:

x	2^x	$(1/2)^x$	$1/2^x$	2^{-x}
4	16	0.0625	0.0625	0.0625
3	8	0.125	0.125	0.125
2	4	0.25	0.25	0.25
1	2	0.5	0.5	0.5
0	1	1	1	1
–1	0.5	2	2	2
–2	0.25	4	4	4
–3	0.125	8	8	8
–4	0.0625	16	16	16

b. Sample response: The entries in the $(1/2)^x$, $1/2^x$, and 2^{-x} columns are the same. Because $1/2^x$ is the reciprocal of 2^x, then $(1/2)^x$ and 2^{-x} are also reciprocals of 2^x.

Discussion 1

a. Based on your results in Table **9-1**, what is the value of 2^0?

b. Describe the relationship among the following expressions: $(1/2)^x$, $1/2^x$, and 2^{-x}.

c. What is the relationship between 2^x and each of the other expressions in Table **9-1**?

d. In the Level 1 module "Are You Just a Small Giant," you learned that

$$\left(\frac{a}{b}\right)^n = \frac{a^n}{b^n}$$

where n is a non-negative integer and $b \neq 0$. From your spreadsheet, it appears that

$$\left(\frac{1}{2}\right)^x = \frac{1}{2^x}$$

Are these two relationships in conflict? Explain your response.

e. Describe some other ways to represent the quantity 2^{-3}.

f. How do the graphs from Part **c** of the exploration compare?

mathematics note

If a is a nonzero real number, then $a^0 = 1$.

If a is a nonzero real number and n is an integer, then

$$a^{-n} = \frac{1}{a^n}$$

For example, $2^{-3} = 1/2^3$ and $3^4 = 1/3^{-4}$. This relationship is also true when $a \neq 0$ and n is a real number.

g. Describe how to express each of the following using a negative exponent:
   1. 2^3
   2. $a \cdot b^2$

h. Describe how to express each of the following without using a negative exponent:
   1. 2^{-3}
   2. $a \cdot b^{-2}$

Discussion 1

a. $2^0 = 1$

b. The expressions $(1/2)^x$, $1/2^x$, and 2^{-x} are equal.

c. Sample response: The value of 2^x is the reciprocal of the value of each of the other expressions.

d. Sample response: There is no conflict. Because $1^x = 1$ for any value of x,

$$(1/2)^x = 1^x/2^x = 1/2^x.$$

e. Sample response:

$$2^{-3} = \frac{1}{2^3} = \left(\frac{1}{2}\right)^3 = \frac{1}{8} = 0.125$$

f. Sample response: The graphs are reflections of each other in the y-axis.

g. 1. Using negative exponents, 2^3 can be expressed as $(1/2)^{-3}$ or $1/2^{-3}$.

   2. Using negative exponents, $a \cdot b^2$ can be expressed as $a \cdot (1/b)^{-2}$, $a \cdot 1/b^{-2}$, or a/b^{-2}.

h. 1. Without using negative exponents, 2^{-3} can be expressed as $(1/2)^3$ or $1/2^3$.

   2. Without using negative exponents, $a \cdot b^{-2}$ can be expressed as $a \cdot (1/b)^2$, $a \cdot 1/b^2$, or a/b^2.

c. Sample graph:

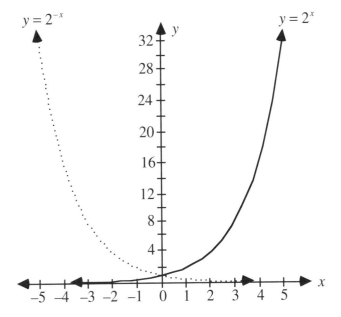

Exploration 2

a–e. Students use a spreadsheet to experiment with various values for b, x, and y in the expressions b^{x+y}, b^{x-y}, $b^{x\cdot y}$, $b^x \cdot b^y$, b^x/b^y, and $(b^x)^y$.

They should observe the following relationships: $b^x \cdot b^y = b^{x+y}$, $(b^x)^y = b^{x\cdot y}$, and $b^x/b^y = b^{x-y}$.

Discussion 2

a. Sample response: Yes, the relationships $b^x \cdot b^y = b^{x+y}$, $(b^x)^y = b^{x\cdot y}$, and $b^x/b^y = b^{x-y}$ appear to be true for all values tested.

b. 1. Sample response: This equation indicates that $4^{-5} \cdot 4^x = 4^{-5+x}$. This means that $-5 + x = 10$, so $x = 15$.

   2. Sample response: This equation indicates that $(4^{-5})^x = 4^{-5x}$. This means that $-5x = 10$, so $x = -2$.

c. Sample response: This equation indicates that $(5^3)^x = 5^{3\cdot x}$. This means that $3x = 1$, so $x = 1/3$.

d. 1. $16^{0.25} = 16^{25/100} = 16^{1/4} = \sqrt[4]{16} = 2$

   2. $16^{3/4} = (\sqrt[4]{16})^3 = (2)^3 = 8$

Exploration 2

In this exploration, you examine some properties of integer exponents that can help you determine rates of decay.

a. Create a spreadsheet with headings like those in Table 9-2 below. The spreadsheet should be created so that the values you select for b, x, and y in the first three cells of each row are used to complete the rest of the entries in that row.

TABLE 9-2 ■ Spreadsheet for Exploration 2								
b	x	y	b^{x+y}	b^{x-y}	$b^{x\cdot y}$	$(b^x)^y$	$b^x \cdot b^y$	b^x/b^y

b. Select values for b, x, and y and enter them in the appropriate columns. Note the values generated in the remaining columns. Describe any relationships you observe.

c. Change any combination of the values of b, x, and y. Determine if your observations from Part **b** hold true for these new values.

Discussion 2

a. Compare your observations with those of others in the class. Do the generalizations you made seem to hold true for all examples?

mathematics note

When two exponential expressions containing the same base are multiplied, their product is the base raised to a power equal to the sum of the exponents. For natural numbers m and n,

$$a^m \cdot a^n = \overbrace{a \cdot a \cdots a}^{m \text{ terms}} \cdot \overbrace{a \cdot a \cdots a}^{n \text{ terms}}$$

$$= \overbrace{a \cdot a \cdots a}^{m+n \text{ terms}} = a^{m+n}$$

This result also is true for any real numbers m and n when $a > 0$.

For example, $3^{-2} \cdot 3^4 = 3^{-2+4} = 3^2 = 9$.

When an exponential expression is raised to a power, the result equals the base in the original expression raised to the product of the powers. For natural numbers m and n,

$$\left(a^m\right)^n = \overbrace{a^m \cdot a^m \cdots a^m}^{n \text{ terms}} = a^{m\cdot n}$$

This result is also true for any real numbers m and n when $a > 0$.

For example, $(3^{-2})^3 = 3^{-2\cdot 3} = 3^{-6} = 1/729$.

When two exponential expressions containing the same base are divided, their quotient is the base raised to a power equal to the exponent of the dividend minus the exponent of the divisor. For natural numbers m and n,

$$\frac{a^m}{a^n} = a^m \cdot \frac{1}{a^n} = a^m \cdot a^{-n} = a^{m+(-n)} = a^{m-n}$$

This result also is true for any real numbers m and n when $a > 0$.

For example, $3^7/3^4 = 3^{7-4} = 3^3 = 27$.

b. Explain how you could use the relationships described in the mathematics note above to find the value of x in each of the following:

   1. $4^{-5} \cdot 4^x = 4^{10}$

   2. $(4^{-5})^x = 4^{10}$

c. What value of x satisfies the equation $(5^3)^x = 5^1$? Describe how you identified this value.

d. What number do you think is represented by each of the following expressions?

   1. $16^{0.25}$

   2. $16^{3/4}$

mathematics note

When $a \geq 0$, a rational exponent in the form m/n can be represented as follows, where m/n is in lowest terms:

$$a^{m/n} = (a^{1/n})^m = (\sqrt[n]{a})^m = \sqrt[n]{a^m}$$

For example, $8^{0.4} = 8^{4/10} = 8^{2/5} = (8^{1/5})^2 = (\sqrt[5]{8})^2 \approx 2.30$.

e. The number of radioactive atoms in a sample at a given time can be modeled by the equation $y = 64 \cdot 0.67^{4.3}$. What does 4.3 represent in this situation?

f. Describe another way to represent the expression $b^{4.3}$.

g. Because 2/6 = 1/3, one might incorrectly believe that $(-8)^{2/6} = (-8)^{1/3}$.

   1. Express $(-8)^{2/6}$ and $(-8)^{1/3}$ in as many different forms as you can. Evaluate each expression and compare the results.

   2. According to the mathematics note above, the relationship below is true only when the exponent m/n is in lowest terms.
   $$a^{m/n} = \sqrt[n]{a^m}$$
   Using $(-8)^{2/6}$ and $(-8)^{1/3}$ as examples, explain why you think this condition is necessary.

Warm-Up

1. Evaluate the following expressions.
   a. 7^{-2}
   b. $81^{-1/4}$
   c. $\dfrac{1}{6^{-3}}$

2. Rewrite each expression below using a positive exponent.
   a. $x^{-1/2}$
   b. $\sqrt[7]{x}$
   c. $\dfrac{1}{x^{-9}}$
   d. $\dfrac{1}{\sqrt[5]{32}}$
   e. $\dfrac{1}{x^{-3/5}}$

3. Simplify each of the following expressions.
   a. $(x^5)^2$
   b. $(x^4)^{-6}$
   c. $(x^9)^{1/3}$

4. a. Rewrite the expression $(1/3)^3$ using an integer as the base.
   b. Rewrite the expression $(1/a)^b$ using a as the base, where $a \neq 0$.
   c. Rewrite the expression $(3/5)^2$ without using parentheses.

Note: Some forms of technology might give results that are inconsistent with this sample response. For example, some calculators might report that $(-8)^{2/6} = -2$.

2. Sample response: When the rational exponent is not in lowest terms, raising a base to that power might be undefined or might give conflicting values. **Note:** Another way of approaching this topic is to consider the rational exponent as a decimal. This works well when the decimal is terminating. If the decimal is non-terminating, however, one must consider the corresponding limit.

Warm-Up

1. a. $1/49$
   b. $1/3$
   c. 216

2. a. $\dfrac{1}{x^{1/2}}$
   b. $x^{1/7}$
   c. x^9
   d. $1/32^{1/5}$
   e. $x^{3/5}$

3. a. x^{10}
   b. x^{-24}
   c. x^3

4. a. 3^{-3}
   b. a^{-b}
   c. $\dfrac{3^2}{5^2} = \dfrac{9}{25}$

e. Sample response: In this case, 4.3 represents the number of units of time that have passed since the initial level of radioactivity was measured.

f. Sample responses:

$$b^{4.3} = b^4 \cdot b^{0.3} = b^4 \cdot b^{3/10} = b^4 \cdot (\sqrt[10]{b})^3$$

$$\text{or } b^{4.3} = b^{43/10} = (\sqrt[10]{b})^{43}$$

g. 1. Sample response:

$$(-8)^{2/6} = \sqrt[6]{(-8)^2} = \sqrt[6]{64} = 2$$

$$(-8)^{2/6} = (\sqrt[6]{-8})^2 = \text{undefined}$$

$$(-8)^{2/6} = ((-8)^2)^{1/6} = 2$$

$$(-8)^{2/6} = ((-8)^{1/6})^2 = \text{undefined}$$

$$(-8)^{1/3} = \sqrt[3]{(-8)^1} = -2$$

$$(-8)^{1/3} = (\sqrt[3]{-8})^1 = -2$$

$$(-8)^{1/3} = ((-8)^1)^{1/3} = -2$$

$$(-8)^{1/3} = ((-8)^{1/3})^1 = -2$$

d. $(5/3)^{-2}$

e. $(3/4)^2$

Assignment

Problems suitable for use as assessment items are identified by an asterisk (*).

2.1 a. 1. In 2 years, 1/4 of the radioactive atoms will remain.

   2. Because $x = 0$ indicates that no time has passed, the number of atoms would remain the same.

   3. Two years earlier, the number of radioactive atoms was four times the present number.

   b. Sample response: The –2 indicates that you are calculating the number of atoms that were present two years earlier.

2.2 a. Sample response: This represents the number of bacteria present after 4 min.

   b. Sample response: This represents the number of bacteria present 4 min before the initial population was counted.

   c. The expression can be rewritten as $32 \cdot (1/2^4)$ or $32 \cdot (1/2)^4$.

2.3 a. Sample response: $y = 32 \cdot 2^{-x}$.

   b. Some students may solve this problem by graphing $y = 32 \cdot (1/2)^x$ and using the trace feature on their graphing utility. Some may write 32 as 2^5 and use the properties of exponents; others may choose to use a spreadsheet.

   1. 2 shakes

   2. 4 shakes

   3. –1 shakes

   4. –2 shakes

   5. 0 shakes

2.4 Sample response:

$$\left(\frac{a}{b}\right)^{-x} = \frac{a^{-x}}{b^{-x}} = \frac{1/a^x}{1/b^x} = \frac{b^x}{a^x} = \left(\frac{b}{a}\right)^x$$

d. Rewrite $(3/5)^2$ using a negative exponent.

e. Rewrite $(4/3)^{-2}$ using a positive exponent.

Assignment

2.1 The number of radioactive atoms in a sample decays at a rate of 50% per year and can be modeled by an equation of the form $y = a \cdot b^x$.

   a. Determine the proportion of the original number of radioactive atoms that remain for each of the following values of x:

   1. 2   **2.** 0   **3.** –2

   b. In this situation, what does $x = -2$ represent?

2.2 The equation $y = 32 \cdot 2^x$ models the number of bacteria present in a population after x minutes.

   a. In this situation, what does the expression $32 \cdot 2^4$ represent?

   b. Given this same population of bacteria, what does the expression $32 \cdot 2^{-4}$ represent?

   c. Write the expression in Part **b** without using a negative exponent.

2.3 a. In Activity **1**, you modeled the number of chips remaining after x shakes using the equation $y = 32 \cdot (1/2)^x$. Write an equivalent equation using a negative exponent.

   b. Use the equation $y = 32 \cdot (1/2)^x$ to predict the shake number at which each of the following populations of chips would remain:

   1. 8 chips

   2. 2 chips

   3. 64 chips

   4. 128 chips

   5. 32 chips.

2.4 The two relationships below were described in Part **d** of Discussion **1** and in the mathematics note after Part **a** of Discussion **2**, respectively:

$$\left(\frac{a}{b}\right)^n = \frac{a^n}{b^n} \quad \text{and} \quad a^{-m} = \frac{1}{a^m}$$

Use these relationships to show that the following relationship is true, where $a \neq 0$ and $b \neq 0$.

$$\left(\frac{a}{b}\right)^{-x} = \left(\frac{b}{a}\right)^x$$

2.5 A fragment of animal bone originally contained $5.12 \cdot 10^{14}$ radioactive carbon atoms. Now it contains only $3.2 \cdot 10^{13}$ radioactive carbons.

    a. Given a rate of decay of 50% for each interval of time, represent this situation in an equation of the form $y = a \cdot b^x$.

    b. Determine the age of the artifact.

2.6 a. How does a change in the initial population affect the graph of the equation $y = a \cdot b^x$?

    b. How does a change in the rate of decay affect the graph of the equation $y = a \cdot b^x$?

2.7 The equation $y = 4000 \cdot (17/20)^x$ models the decay of radioactive atoms in an object. In a paragraph, describe the situation represented by this equation.

2.8 To solve the equation $64 = x^3$ for x, both sides of the equation can be raised to the exponent $1/3$, as follows:

$$64 = x^3$$
$$(64)^{1/3} = (x^3)^{1/3}$$
$$64^{1/3} = x$$

    a. Explain why $(x^3)^{1/3}$ can be replaced with x.

    b. Find the value of x in the equation $64^{1/3} = x$.

2.9 Solve each of the following equations for x and describe how you obtained your solutions.

    a. $x^6 = 729$

    b. $x^{0.125} = 2$

    c. $10^5 \cdot x = 10^{1/6}$

2.10 Each of the following equations is a model of exponential growth or decay in the form $y = a \cdot b^x$. For each one, determine the value of b, explain whether it models growth or decay, and identify the rate.

    a. $1024 = 64 \cdot b^4$

    b. $13 = 10 \cdot b^3$

    c. $1.6 \cdot 10^{13} = 5.0 \cdot 10^{14}(b^5)$

    d. $107 = 1000 \cdot b^{10}$

* * * * *

---

* **2.5 a.** Using $5.12 \cdot 10^{14}$ for a and $(1 - 0.5)$ for b, the equation is: $3.2 \cdot 10^{13} = 5.12 \cdot 10^{14} \cdot (0.5)^x$.

    b. Sample response: The equation $3.2 \cdot 10^{13} = 5.12 \cdot 10^{14} \cdot (0.5)^x$ can be simplified to $0.0625 = (0.5)^x$, or $1/16 = (1/2)^x$. In this case, $x = 4$. The radioactive atoms in the artifact began decaying 4 intervals of time ago.

2.6 a. Sample response: Changing the initial population changes the value of a, which in turn changes the y-intercept. The graph appears less steep as the value of a approaches 0. **Note:** Although the graph no longer models decay, it curves downward when the value of a becomes negative and appears steeper as a continues to decrease. When $a = 0$, the graph of $y = a \cdot b^x$ is the horizontal line $y = 0$.

    b. Sample response: Because $b = 1 + r$, changing the rate of decay changes b. For values of b between 0 and 1, the graph becomes less steep for values closer to 0. When b is 0, the graph coincides with the x-axis. When b is 1, the curve coincides with the line $y = a$. **Note:** Although the graph no longer models decay, it curves upward and to the right instead of upward and to the left for values of b greater than 1. When b is less than 0, the graph alternates between positive and negative values.

* **2.7** Sample response: The equation indicates that the initial number of radioactive atoms in the object was 4000. The rate of decay is $-3/20$. This means that 15% of the radioactive material decays in each time interval.

2.8 a. $(x^3)^{1/3} = x^{3 \cdot 1/3} = x^1 = x$

    b. $x = 4$

2.9 a. Sample response: In this case, $x = 3$. This can be found by raising both sides of the equation to a power of $1/6$.

$$\left(x^6\right)^{1/6} = 729^{1/6}$$
$$x^{6 \cdot 1/6} = 729^{1/6}$$
$$x = 729^{1/6} = 3$$

    b. Sample response: In this case, $x = 256$. This can be found by raising both sides of the equation to the 8th power.

$$x^{0.125} = 2$$
$$x^{1/8} = 2$$
$$\left(x^{1/8}\right)^8 = 2^8$$
$$x = 256$$

    c. Sample response:

$$10^5 \cdot x = 10^{16}$$
$$x = 10^{16}/10^5$$
$$= 10^{16-5} = 10^{11}$$

2.10 a. Because $b = 2$, $r = 1$. Because r is positive, this equation models a pattern of exponential growth.

    b. Because $b \approx 1.1$, $r \approx 0.1$. Because r is positive, this equation models a pattern of exponential growth.

    c. Because $b \approx 0.5$, $r \approx -0.5$. Because r is negative, this equation models a pattern of exponential decay.

    d. Because $b \approx 0.8$, $r \approx -0.2$. Because r is negative, this equation models a pattern of exponential decay.

✳ ✳ ✳ ✳ ✳

2.11 a. Sample scatterplot:

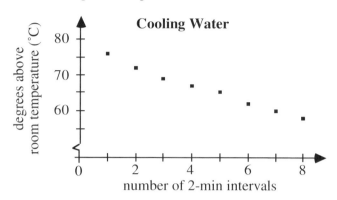

b. The mean of the percents of decrease in temperature is approximately 4.1% per 2-min interval.

2-min Interval	Degrees above Room Temperature (°C)	Percent Decrease
1	74	
2	70	5.1%
3	67	4.4%
4	65	3.1%
5	63	3.2%
6	60	5.0%
7	58	3.4%
8	56	3.6%

c. Using the rate of decay from Part **b,** one equation that could be used to model the data is $77(0.959)^x$, where x represents the number of 2-min intervals. Students may find the value of a in their models by trial and error or by examining residuals for various values. **Note:** The regression equation for the data is $y \approx 76(0.962)^x$.

d. Using their model from Part **c,** students can estimate the room temperature by subtracting the value of the function at $x = 0$ from 100°C. Using the equation $y = 77(0.959)^x$, the approximate room temperature is 23°C.

e. Sample response: The exponential equation would not be a good model to predict temperatures before the water is poured because the function increases without bound as x decreases. This would indicate that the water continually increases in temperature as the time prior to pouring the liquid increases.

2.12 The equation $y = 5 \bullet (1 - 0.5)^3$ is equivalent to $y = 5 \bullet (2)^{-3}$. The equation $y = 5 \bullet (2)^3$ is equivalent to $y = 5 \bullet (1/2)^{-3}$. The equation $y = 5 \bullet (2)^{1/3}$ is equivalent to $y = 5 \bullet (0.5)^{-1/3}$.

2.11 The table below shows some data collected while a container of boiling water cooled to room temperature.

Number of 2-min Intervals Elapsed	Degrees above Room Temperature (°C)
1	74
2	70
3	67
4	65
5	63
6	60
7	58
8	56

a. Create a scatterplot of the data.

b. Find the mean of the percents of decrease in the temperature for these 2-min intervals.

c. Using the mean from Part b as a rate, write an equation of the form $y = a \bullet b^x$ that models the data.

d. When the water was first poured, its temperature was 100°C. Use this fact and your model to estimate the temperature of the room.

e. Should your equation from Part c be used to make predictions about the temperature of the water several minutes before the time frame given in the table? Explain your response.

2.12 Identify the equation in column B that is equivalent to each equation in column A.

Column A	Column B
$y = 5 \bullet (1 - 0.5)^3$	$y = 5 \bullet (1/2)^{-3}$
$y = 5 \bullet (2)^3$	$y = 5 \bullet (0.5)^{-1/3}$
$y = 5 \bullet (2)^{1/3}$	$y = 5 \bullet (2)^{-3}$

All living organisms contain carbon atoms. A relatively small proportion of these carbon atoms are unstable. Over time, these unstable atoms, known as carbon-14 atoms, decay. The time required for one-half of the carbon-14 atoms in a given sample to decay is the **half-life.**

Carbon-14 has a half-life of 5730 years. Other unstable atoms have half-lives that range from fractions of seconds to billions of years. For example, the half-life of carbon-11 is about 21 min, and the half-life of uranium-238 is 4.5 billion years. These unstable atoms rarely have half-lives that are exactly 1 unit of time. In the following exploration, you modify models of exponential decay to include half-lives that are not whole numbers.

Exploration

Although a typical artifact might contain trillions of radioactive atoms, in this exploration, you again consider a sample that has only 32 unstable atoms.

a. Create a table with headings like those in Table **9-3.** Round 0 represents the time when the number of radioactive atoms in the sample is 32.

TABLE 9-3 ▪ Radioactive Atom Simulation

Round	Number of Radioactive Atoms
0	32
1	
2	
⋮	
9	
10	

b. Suppose the rate of decay is 1/6. This means each radioactive atom has 1 chance in 6 of decaying.

1. To model a rate of decay of 1/6, randomly generate an integer from 1 to 6 for each radioactive atom remaining in the sample. The last entry in the second column of Table **9-3** represents the number of radioactive atoms remaining in the sample.

For example: In Round 1, generate a list of 32 random integers because 32 is the last entry in the second column of Table **9-3**.

264   Module 9 ▪ *Atomic Clocks Are Ticking*

This activity focuses on solving equations of the form $y = a \cdot b^x$ for x.

teacher note

A brief assessment of the mathematical content in Activities **1, 2,** and **3,** for use at your discretion, appears in the Teacher Resources for this module.

Materials List

■ graph paper

■ numbered dice (or other random number generator; one per group)

Technology

■ graphing utility

■ spreadsheet (optional)

Student Outcomes

After completing the following exploration and discussion, students should be able to:

✳ use a random number generator to simulate a pattern of exponential decay

✳ model exponential decay using equations of the form $y = a \cdot b^x$

✳ determine the half-life of a radioactive element by solving an equation of the form $1 = 2b^x$ for x.

Exploration

a–c. The simulation requires students to use an appropriate random number generator. It should take about four rounds to reach the first half-life. Although students might need more than 10 rounds to remove all the atoms, 10 is sufficient to show the existing patterns. Sample data:

Round	Number of Radioactive Atoms
0	32
1	29
2	25
3	19
4	16
5	15
6	12
7	10
8	9
9	8
10	6

d. A graph of the sample data appears in Part **e** below.
e. 1. $y = 32 \cdot (5/6)^x$
   2. Sample graph:

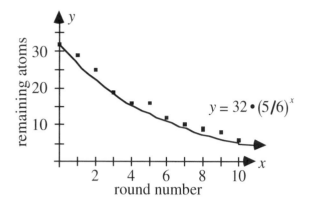

$$y = 32 \cdot (5/6)^x$$

f. 1. Sample response: The half-life is about 4 rounds.
   2. Students may examine the graph to find the inter-section of $y = 16$ and $y = 32 \cdot (5/6)^x$ or use the trace feature to estimate the value of x when $y = 16$. Students also could use a guess-and check-method to solve $16 = 32 \cdot (5/6)^x$ for x.

teacher note

In Part **d** of the discussion, students are introduced to a comparative equation, $50 = 100b^x$, that can be used to identify half-life. You might wish to point out that any two values with a ratio of 1 to 2 can be used in place of 50 and 100.

Discussion

a. Sample response: Because the probability of decay in the simulation is 1/6, about 5/6 of the atoms should remain after each round.
b. The half-life in this exploration is about 4 rounds. The half-life for the simulation in Activity **1** was 1 round (or shake).
c. 1. Because $a = 32$ and $b = 1 - (1/6) = 5/6$, an appropriate model is $y = 32(5/6)^x$.
   2. Sample response: The value of a in both simulations is 32. The value of b in Activity **3** is 5/6; it was 1/2 in Activity **1**. The value of r in Activity **3** is $-1/6$; it was $-1/2$ in Activity **1**.
d. Sample response: In this case, 100 represents the initial population and 50 represents one-half the initial population. If b is known, then x would be the time when half of the initial population remains. This is by definition the half-life.

2. Count the number of times that the integer 1 appears in the list. Reduce the quantity of radioactive atoms in the sample by this number.
3. Record the remaining number of radioactive atoms in the second column of Table **9-3**. This ends the round. The number recorded represents the number of radioactive atoms that remain in the sample.
c. Repeat Part **b** for 10 rounds, or until no radioactive atoms remain.
d. Create a scatterplot of the data. Represent the round number on the x-axis and the number of radioactive atoms on the y-axis.
e. 1. What equation of the form $y = a \cdot b^x$ would you expect to model this simulation?
   2. Graph this equation on the coordinate system from Part **d**.
f. 1. Use the data to estimate the half-life, in number of rounds, of these radioactive atoms.
   2. Use your equation from Part **e** to determine the half-life of the atoms.

Discussion

a. What fraction of the number of atoms did you expect to remain after each round? Explain your response.
b. How does the half-life of the atoms in this simulation compare with the half-life of the atoms in the simulation in Activity **1**?
c. 1. Describe how you determined a model equation of the form $y = a \cdot b^x$ in Part **e** of the exploration.
   2. How does this equation compare with the one that modeled the simulation in Activity **1**?
d. One method of identifying the half-life uses an equation of the form $50 = 100b^x$, where the value of b is known. In this situation, why does the value of x represent the half-life?

Warm-Up

1. a. Find a value for x when $3^x = 9$.
   b. Find a value for x when $3^x = 27$.
   c. If the equation $3^x = 16$ has a solution, between what two whole numbers must x lie?
   d. Use a guess-and-check method to find x to the nearest hundredth.
   e. Find x to the nearest hundredth when $2.5^x = 20$.

Warm-Up

1. **a.** $x = 2$
   b. $x = 3$
   c. Sample response: The value of x must be between 2 and 3.
   d. $x \approx 2.52$
   e. $x \approx 3.27$

2. Use technology to find a value of x so that $256^x = 4$. Express this value as a decimal and as a fraction.

3. Find the value of x in each of the following equations to the nearest hundredth.

   a. $5^x = 100$

   b. $7^x = 81$

   c. $12^x = 60$

   d. $169^x = 13$

   e. $64^x = 14$

   f. $2^x = 0.15$

Assignment

3.1 A sample originally contained $1.05 \cdot 10^{11}$ radioactive atoms, which have been decaying at a rate of 0.00003 atoms/year.

   a. Write an equation of the form $y = a \cdot b^x$ to model this situation.

   b. The number of radioactive atoms currently in the sample is $2.3 \cdot 10^{10}$. Use your model to estimate the age of the sample.

3.2 In the exploration in this activity, you conducted a simulation with 32 radioactive atoms and a rate of decay of 1/6. This situation can be modeled by the exponential equation $y = 32 \cdot (5/6)^x$.

The half-life is the time required for the number of radioactive atoms to decrease to 16. Substituting this value into the model equation yields $16 = 32 \cdot (5/6)^x$. Use this equation to estimate the half-life.

3.3 a. Each of the following equations models the radioactive decay of a substance over time, where x represents years. Determine the half-life for each substance and describe the methods you used.

   1. $y = 4000(0.61)^x$

   2. $y = 5.3 \cdot 10^7(0.61)^x$

   3. $y = 0.61^x$

   b. Considering your responses to Part **a**, how does the initial number of radioactive atoms appear to affect the half-lives of substances with the same rate of decay?

3.4 Kim is a doctor in the Department of Nuclear Medicine at the county hospital. She uses radioactive tracers to detect disease or injury in her patients. When comparing levels of radioactivity in the tracers, Kim designates the initial

2. $x = 0.25$ or $1/4$

3. a. 2.86

   b. 2.26

   c. 1.65

   d. 1/2

   e. 0.63

   f. −2.41

Assignment

Problems suitable for use as assessment items are identified by an asterisk (*).

3.1 a. $y = 1.05 \cdot 10^{11} \cdot (0.99997)^x$

   b. The sample is about 51,000 years old. To find a solution, students may graph the equation or use a guess-and-check method. Sample graph:

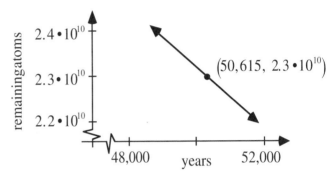

3.2 The half-life is approximately 3.80 rounds. See Part **f2** of the exploration for solution methods.

3.3 a. In all three cases, the problem can be solved by substituting $a/2$ for y. The value of x can then be found by guess-and-check using a calculator. Students also may graph each equation, trace until the y-value equals $a/2$, then record the corresponding x-value. (Students are not expected to use logarithms.)

   In each case, the half-life is about 1.4 time intervals.

   b. Sample response: Since all three equations have the same value for b, they must also have the same rate of decay. Because the half-life is the same in all three cases, the initial number of radioactive atoms does not appear to affect the half-life.

*3.4 **Note:** Radioactive tracers are useful in a number of applications, including engineering, biochemistry, and medicine. Iodine-131 and technetium-99m are two radioactive isotopes used in nuclear medicine.

a. $y = 100 \cdot 0.8^x$

b. Sample graph:

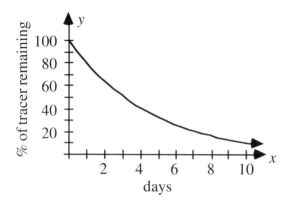

c. The half-life occurs when $y = 50\%$. From the graph, this takes place after about 3 days.

d. Sample response: Using the equation $y = 100 \cdot (0.8)^x$ and an exponent of -2, the newly manufactured sample's radioactivity was about 156% of the sample that Kim received.

3.5 **a.** $b = 0.5^{1/125} \approx 0.946$; $r \approx -5.39\%/\text{hour}$

b. $b = 0.5^{1/57.3} \approx 0.988$; $r \approx -1.20\%/\text{century}$

*3.6 **a.** $b^5 = 0.50$; $b \approx 0.87$

b. $r \approx -0.13 \approx -13\%/\text{year}$

c. Substituting 0.87 for b and 93 for y in the comparative equation $y = 100b^x$ gives $93 = 100(0.87)^x$. Solving this equation for x, the sample is about 0.5 years old.

*3.7 **a.** The percentage of radioactivity remaining after each hour is equal to the value of b in the equation $50 = 100 \cdot (b)^6$. Solving this equation for b gives $b \approx 0.89$.

b. $y \approx 100(0.89)^x$

c. Because 45 min equals 0.75 hours, students should write the equation $y = 100(0.89)^{0.75}$. This yields a value of approximately 92% for y.

d. After about 20 hours, 10% of the tracer will remain. This can be calculated by solving the equation $10 = 100(0.89)^x$ for x.

level as 100%. Later measurements are then recorded as percentages of that level. Using this method, radioactive decay can be modeled by equations of the form $y = 100 \cdot b^x$. When $y = 50$, the value of x equals the half-life.

a. In one case, Kim has monitored the radioactivity of a tracer at the same time each day for two consecutive days. The second day's radioactivity is 80% of the first day's. Write an equation of the form $y = 100 \cdot b^x$ to model this situation, where x represents time in days.

b. Create a graph of the model for the next 10 days.

c. Estimate the half-life of the tracer.

d. Kim received the radioactive tracer 2 days after it was manufactured. If the rate of decay is constant, what was the radioactivity of the tracer when it was first produced? Explain your response.

3.5 The comparative equation $50 = 100 \cdot b^x$ can be used to calculate the value of b for a given half-life. Determine the value of b and identify the rate of decay for each of the following half-lives:

a. 12.5 hours

b. 57.3 centuries

3.6 Imagine that you are examining a sample that contains radioactive atoms with a half-life of 5.0 years.

a. The radioactive decay of these atoms can be modeled by the equation $y = 100 \cdot b^x$ where x represents time in years. What is the value of b in this equation?

b. What is the radioactive material's rate of decay?

c. If the level of radioactivity remaining is 93% of the original level, how old is the sample you are examining? Explain your response.

3.7 Adrian's foot has bothered him since Wednesday. The X-rays taken on Friday looked normal, but his doctor suspects a possible stress fracture. On Monday, the doctor will inject a radioactive tracer to help detect the site of the fracture. The tracer has a half-life of 6.0 hr.

a. What percentage of the tracer's radioactivity remains after each hour?

b. Write an equation of the form $y = 100 \cdot b^x$, where x represents hours, to model the decay of this tracer.

c. After the tracer has been in Adrian's body for 45 min, the doctor will scan Adrian's foot for signs of radioactivity. What percentage of the tracer is left in his body at this time?

d. How many hours will pass before only 10% of the tracer remains?

e. The radioactive tracer was manufactured 3 hr before it was injected into Adrian. How much more radioactive was the tracer at the time of its manufacture?

3.8 As mentioned in the introduction to Activity **3**, the half-life of carbon-14 is 5730 years. Use an equation of the form $y = a \cdot b^x$ to determine the rate of decay for carbon-14 per century. *Hint*: If the initial amount of carbon-14 is 100%, the amount remaining after 57.3 centuries is 50%.

* * * * *

3.9 One of your classmates has conducted a simulation like the one described in Activity **3**. Instead of randomly generating integers from 1 to 6 however, she generated integers from 1 to 20, inclusive, and removed an atom for each multiple of 5 that appeared in the list.

   a. What fraction of the atoms would you expect to remove after each round? Explain your response.

   b. What fraction of the atoms would you expect to remain in the container after each round?

   c. A scatterplot of the data from your classmate's simulation is shown below. Use it to estimate the half-life of the substance.

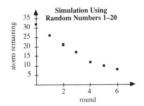

   d. Find an equation of the form $y = a \cdot b^x$ that models the data.

3.10 The Trojan Nuclear Power Plant near Portland, Oregon, was shut down in 1992. One of the waste products of its operation was radioactive strontium-90. Strontium-90 is extremely hazardous to people and other living things. Its half-life is 28.0 years. As an environmental engineer, you must design leak-proof containers to hold strontium-90 until less than 1% of its radio-activity remains.

   a. What percentage of a sample of strontium-90's initial radioactivity remains after 1 year?

---

e. The time 3 hours prior to the injection may be represented by $x = -3$. Solving the equation $y = 100(0.89)^{-3}$ for y yields approximately 142. This means that the tracer was 42% more radioactive at the time of manufacture.

3.8 Sample response: Because 5730 years is 57.3 centuries, the comparative equation $50 = 100(b)^{57.3}$ can be used to find the rate of decay in centuries. Solving for b yields $b = 0.5^{1/57.3} \approx 0.988$. Because $b = 1 + r$, the rate of decay is about -0.012 or -1.2% per century.

✳ ✳ ✳ ✳ ✳

3.9 a. Sample response: There are four multiples of 5 in the numbers from 1 to 20, therefore the probability of generating a multiple of 5 is $4/20$ or $1/5$. The number of atoms removed should be approximately $1/5$ of the atoms remaining in the box from the previous round.

   b. $4/5$

   c. The half-life is about 3 rounds.

   d. $y = 32 \cdot (0.8)^x$

3.10 a. Approximately 97.6% of the initial radioactivity remains after 1 year. This can be calculated by finding the value of b using the known half-life of strontium-90:

$$50 = 100 \cdot (b)^{28}$$

$$0.5^{1/28} = b$$

$$0.976 \approx b$$

b. Solving the equation $1 = 100(0.976)^x$ for x, it will take about 190 years for the level of radioactivity to drop below 1%.

c. Solving the equation $y = 100(0.976)^{-5}$ for y yields about 113. This means that the material was approximately 13% more radioactive 5 years ago.

d. **Note:** In the following sample graph, the labels on the x-axis were generated by adding the year 2002 to the value of x. Students should add the present year to x.

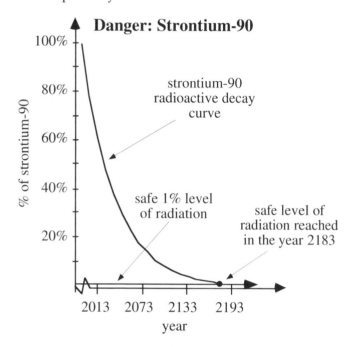

Danger: Strontium-90

strontium-90 radioactive decay curve

safe 1% level of radiation

safe level of radiation reached in the year 2183

2013 2073 2133 2193

year

% of strontium-90

3.11 **a.** To find the growth rate, students should solve the following equation for b:

$$0.65 = 0.25 \cdot b^{24}$$

$$b = \sqrt[24]{2.6}$$

$$b \approx 1.04$$

$$r \approx 4\%$$

b. The following sample equation models the price of the candy bar where x represents the number of years after 1972:

$$y = 0.25 \cdot (1.04)^x$$

c. Solving the equation $0.10 = 0.25 \cdot (1.04)^x$ for x yields approximately -23.4. This corresponds with the year 1948.

d. Solving the equation $1.00 = 0.25 \cdot (1.04)^x$ for x yields approximately 35.3. This corresponds with the year 2008.

b. How many years will it take for a sample of strontium-90 to have less than 1% of its present radioactivity?

c. If some of the plant's strontium-90 was buried in temporary storage containers 5 years ago, how much more radioactive was this material at the time of its burial?

d. To inform the public of the radioactivity present in the new, leak-proof containers, your firm has decided to attach a warning label to each one. Design a label that includes a graph showing the percentage of radioactivity remaining as a function of the year.

3.11 In 1972, a candy bar cost $0.25. In 1996, the same candy bar sold for $0.65.

a. Assuming that the cost of the candy bar grew exponentially, determine the annual rate of growth.

b. Write an equation that could be used to model the cost of the candy bar in a given year.

c. Use your equation to estimate the year in which the candy bar cost only $0.10.

d. Predict the year in which the candy bar will cost $1.00.

Summary Assessment

Professor Cordova found many layers of charcoal in the fire pit near the mouth of Andrea and Jared's cave. Each layer contained a different percentage of the carbon-14 activity of living trees. Her data is shown in the table below. Layer 1 was taken from the top of the pit; layer 11 was taken from the bottom.

Layer	Percentage of Carbon-14 Radioactivity
1	91.6
2	83.3
3	81.6
4	78.5
5	75.0
6	71.2
7	65.4
8	47.4
9	42.9
10	39.9
11	32.1

1. Professor Cordova believes humans have occupied this site for no more than 12,000 years. Given that the half-life of carbon-14 is about 57.3 centuries, the rate of decay is approximately 0.012. Find the approximate age of each layer of charcoal.

2. Near the cave, Professor Cordova found what appears to be a mammoth bone. Mammoths became extinct about 11,500 years ago. What percentage of carbon-14 radioactivity would you expect to find in this artifact? Explain your reasoning.

3. As trees grow, new carbon-14 is absorbed only by the outermost ring of the trunk. The amount of carbon-14 radioactivity in the inner rings decays as if the wood were actually dead. Because of this phenomenon, the age of trees can be determined by carbon dating.

   a. To verify her carbon-dating procedure, Professor Cordova decides to test a newly fallen tree near the cave. The outermost ring of the tree has 112% of the carbon-14 radioactivity of the innermost ring. Use this information to estimate the age of the tree.

   b. The age of a tree also can be found by counting the growth rings in the trunk, one ring for each year of life. The rings of the tree indicate that it was about 940 years old. How does your estimate in Part a compare with this value?

---

teacher note

An additional assessment, for use at your discretion, appears in the Teacher Resources for this module.

Summary Assessment

1. Students can solve this problem efficiently by using the trace function on a graphing calculator. Professor Cordova's maximum estimate of 12,000 years (120 centuries) should give students an idea of the appropriate domain. Using the value of b found in Problem **3.8**, students may use the equation $y = 100(0.988)^x$. (See table at the bottom of the page.)

2. Because 11,500 years is about two half-lives ago, about 25% of the original carbon-14 should remain. This solution also can be found by substituting 115 for x in the equation $y = 100(0.988)^x$.

3. a. Using the comparative equation $y = 100b^x$ and the value of b for carbon-14 found in Problem **3.8**, $112 = 100(0.988)^x$. Solving for x, $x \approx -9.4$ centuries. The negative sign indicates that the carbon-14 in the innermost ring has been decaying 940 years longer than the carbon-14 in the outermost ring.

   b. The age of the tree using carbon dating is the same as the age determined by counting the rings.

Layer	% Radioactive C-14	Age (in centuries)
1	91.6	7.3
2	83.3	15.1
3	81.6	16.8
4	78.5	20.0
5	75.0	23.8
6	71.2	28.1
7	65.4	35.2
8	47.4	61.8
9	42.9	70.1
10	39.9	76.1
11	32.1	94.1

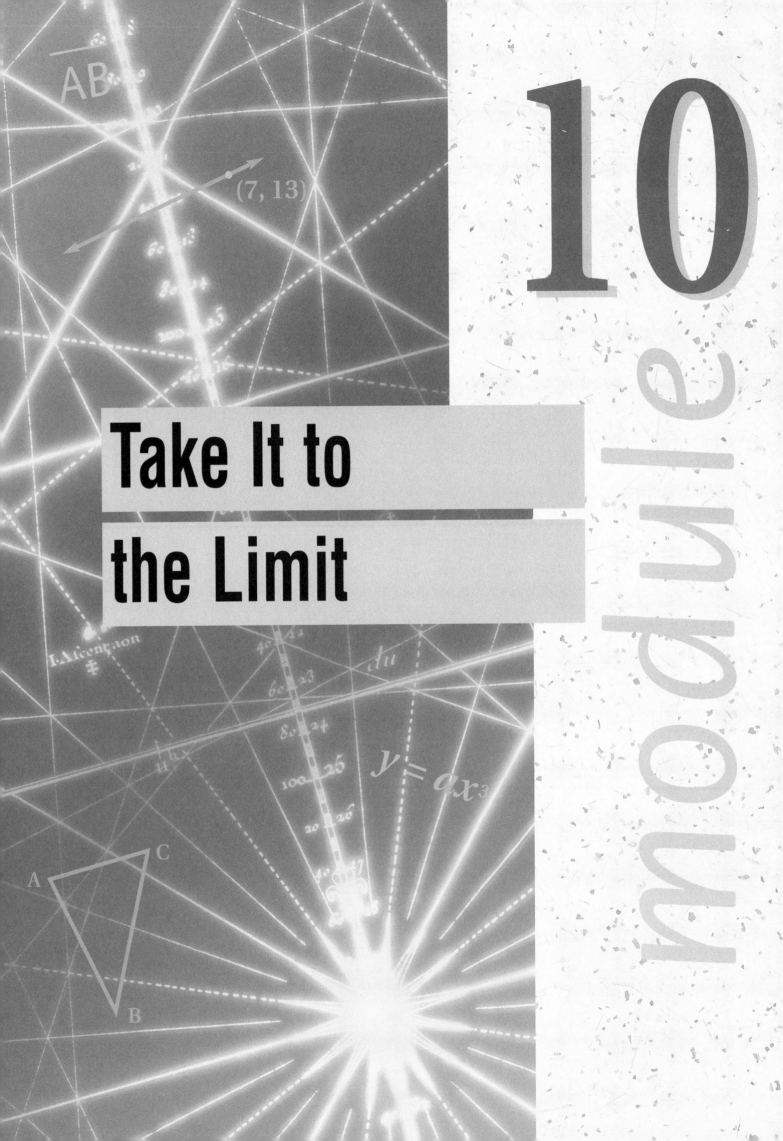

Take It to the Limit

Overview

In this module, students explore arithmetic and geometric sequences and series. They are introduced to limits through infinite geometric sequences and series.

Activity 1: Students explore arithmetic and geometric sequences. They write recursive and explicit formulas, then use explicit formulas to determine the number of terms in a sequence.

Activity 2: Students investigate finite arithmetic series. They write formulas to find the sum of a finite arithmetic sequence and to determine the number of terms in a series.

Activity 3: Students investigate finite geometric series. They write formulas to find the sum of a finite geometric sequence and to determine the number of terms in a series.

Activity 4: Students explore the idea of a limit for an infinite sequence, both graphically and numerically.

Objectives

In this module, students will:

* identify sequences as arithmetic, geometric, or neither (1, 2, 3)

* write recursive formulas for arithmetic and geometric sequences (1)

* write explicit formulas for arithmetic and geometric sequences (1, 2, 3, 4)

* determine the number of terms in a finite arithmetic sequence (1, 2)

* determine the number of terms in a finite geometric sequence (1, 3)

* write formulas for finite arithmetic series (2)

* write formulas for finite geometric series (3)

* investigate the limit of an infinite sequence both graphically and numerically (4)

* determine the sum of the terms of an infinite geometric sequence in which $-1 < r < 1$, where r represents the common ratio (4)

* compare sequences that approach limits and those that do not (4).

Prerequisites

For this module, students should know:

* how to interpret subscript notation

* how to use interval notation

* how to find explicit and recursive formulas for simple arithmetic and geometric sequences.

 Flashbacks, for use at your discretion, appear in the Teacher Resources for this module. These brief problem sets provide a review of some prerequisite skills for each activity.

Planning Guide

Activity	Materials	Technology	Time Line
Introduction and Activity **1**	▪ none	▪ spreadsheet ▪ symbolic manipulator	3 days
Activity **2**	▪ none	▪ spreadsheet ▪ symbolic manipulator	2 days
Activity **3**	▪ graph paper	▪ spreadsheet ▪ symbolic manipulator	2 days
Activity **4**	▪ none	▪ geometry utility ▪ graphing utility ▪ spreadsheet ▪ symbolic manipulator	2 days
Assessment Activities	▪ none	▪ geometry utility ▪ spreadsheet ▪ symbolic manipulator	3 days **Total: 12 days**

teacher note

Throughout this module, students are asked to generate and evaluate sequences and series. Once students demonstrate the ability to generate sequences by hand, you may allow them to explore the capabilities of available technology.

For example, Texas Instruments' TI-84, TI-89, or Voyage 200 calculators can define a sequence using its explicit formula and the "seq( )" command. Using this feature, "seq(1/x,x,1,10)" generates a list of the first 10 unit fractions: {1/1, 1/2, 1/3, . . . , 1/10}. The command "sum(seq(1/x,x,1,10))" gives the sum of this sequence. **Note:** To view exact values, select "Frac" under the Math menu on the TI-84. On the TI-89 and Voyage 200, select "Exact" under the Mode menu.

Introduction

In this introduction, students review arithmetic and geometric sequences along with explicit and recursive formulas.

Student Outcomes

After completing the following discussion, students should be able to:

✳ describe sequences as arithmetic or geometric

✳ describe recursive notation to define simple sequences

✳ identify common differences and common ratios

✳ describe the differences between recursive and explicit formulas.

Discussion

a. 1. This is an arithmetic sequence. The first term is 7 and the common difference is 6. The next term is 31.

2. This is a geometric sequence. The first term is 162 and the common ratio is 1/3. The next term is 2.

3. Sample response: This is a sequence of figures. Each figure is a set of dots forming a right triangle with n dots on each leg and on the hypotenuse, where n is the figure number. The next figure is:

4. This is a geometric sequence. The first term is –7 and the common ratio is –7. The next term is –16,807.

5. This is a sequence of closed intervals. The left-hand value of the interval is always 2, and the right-hand value is $2 + (1/n)$, for $n = 1, 2, 3, 4, \ldots$. The next interval is [2, 2.2].

6. This is a Fibonacci sequence. The first two terms are 4 and 5. Each successive term is the sum of the previous two terms. The next term is 37.

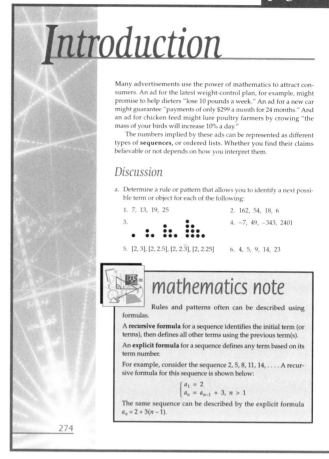

Introduction

Many advertisements use the power of mathematics to attract consumers. An ad for the latest weight-control plan, for example, might promise to help dieters "lose 10 pounds a week." An ad for a new car might guarantee "payments of only $299 a month for 24 months." And an ad for chicken feed might lure poultry farmers by crowing "the mass of your birds will increase 10% a day."

The numbers implied by these ads can be represented as different types of **sequences**, or ordered lists. Whether you find their claims believable or not depends on how you interpret them.

Discussion

a. Determine a rule or pattern that allows you to identify a next possible term or object for each of the following:

1. 7, 13, 19, 25

2. 162, 54, 18, 6

3.

4. –7, 49, –343, 2401

5. [2, 3], [2, 2.5], [2, 2.3̄], [2, 2.25]

6. 4, 5, 9, 14, 23

mathematics note

Rules and patterns often can be described using formulas.

A **recursive formula** for a sequence identifies the initial term (or terms), then defines all other terms using the previous term(s).

An **explicit formula** for a sequence defines any term based on its term number.

For example, consider the sequence 2, 5, 8, 11, 14, ... A recursive formula for this sequence is shown below:

$$\begin{cases} a_1 = 2 \\ a_n = a_{n-1} + 3, \; n > 1 \end{cases}$$

The same sequence can be described by the explicit formula $a_n = 2 + 3(n-1)$.

274

b. If possible, determine a recursive formula for each sequence in Part **a.**

c. If possible, determine an explicit formula for each sequence in Part **a.**

mathematics note

In an **arithmetic sequence**, every term after the first is formed by adding a constant value, the **common difference**, to the preceding term.

For example, the sequence 2, 7, 12, 17, 22 is a finite arithmetic sequence with a common difference of 5.

In a **geometric sequence**, every term after the first is formed by multiplying the preceding term by a constant value, the **common ratio**.

For example, the sequence 2, 10, 50, 250, 1250 is a finite geometric sequence with a common ratio of 5.

d. 1. Which of the ordered lists in Part **a** can be represented by an arithmetic sequence?

   2. Which can be represented by a geometric sequence?

e. Describe how to find the common difference for an arithmetic sequence.

f. Describe how to determine the common ratio for a geometric sequence.

In this activity, you use formulas for arithmetic and geometric sequences to create and interpret sequential patterns.

mathematics note

The recursive formula for an arithmetic sequence, where d is the common difference, n is the term number, and a_n is the nth term, is:

$$\begin{cases} a_1 = \text{first term} \\ a_n = a_{n-1} + d, \ n > 1 \end{cases}$$

The explicit formula for such a sequence is $a_n = a_1 + d(n-1)$.

---

b. A sample formula for each sequence shown below.

1. $\begin{cases} a_1 = 7 \\ a_n = a_{n-1} + 6 \ \text{for} \ n > 1 \end{cases}$

2. $\begin{cases} a_1 = 162 \\ a_n = a_{n-1}(1/3) \ \text{for} \ n > 1 \end{cases}$

3. Although it is not possible to write a recursive formula for the sequence of figures, the number of dots in each figure can be described as follows:

$$\begin{cases} a_1 = 1 \\ a_n = a_{n-1} + n, \ n > 1 \end{cases}$$

4. $\begin{cases} a_1 = -7 \\ a_n = -7a_{n-1} \ \text{for} \ n > 1 \end{cases}$

5. A recursive formula for the right-hand value in each interval is shown below:

$$\begin{cases} a_1 = 3 \\ a_n = a_{n-1} - \dfrac{1}{n(n-1)} \ \text{for} \ n > 1 \end{cases}$$

6. $\begin{cases} a_1 = 4 \\ a_2 = 5 \\ a_n = a_{n-2} + a_{n-1} \ \text{for} \ n > 2 \end{cases}$

c. A sample formula for each sequence shown below.

1. $a_n = 7 + 6(n-1)$ for $n \geq 1$

2. $a_n = 162(1/3)^{n-1}$ for $n \geq 1$

3. Although it is not possible to write an explicit formula for the sequence of figures, the number of dots in each figure can be described as follows:

$$a_n = \frac{n(n+1)}{2}$$

4. $a_n = -7(-7)^{n-1}$ for $n \geq 1$

5. An explicit formula for the right-hand value in each interval is shown below:

$$b_n = 2 + \frac{1}{n}, \ n > 1$$

6. Determining an explicit formula for this sequence is beyond the scope of this module.

d. 1. The sequence in Step **1** is arithmetic.

   2. The sequences in Steps **2** and **4** are geometric.

e. Sample response: The common difference of an arithmetic sequence can be found by subtracting any term from the following term.

f. Sample response: The common ratio of a geometric sequence can be found by dividing any term by the previous term.

This activity continues the review of arithmetic and geometric sequences, and recursive and explicit formulas. **Note:** These concepts were introduced in the Level 1 module "From Rock Bands to Recursion."

Materials List

■ none

Technology

■ spreadsheet (optional)

■ symbolic manipulator (optional)

Student Outcomes

After completing the following exploration and discussion, students should be able to:

✳ identify sequences that are arithmetic, geometric, or neither

✳ identify the common difference in an arithmetic sequence

✳ identify the common ratio in a geometric sequence

✳ write recursive formulas for arithmetic and geometric sequences

✳ write explicit formulas for arithmetic and geometric sequences.

Exploration

This exploration is designed for groups of four students. To ensure equal participation, each student should create a sequence, and each group should pass in a consistent clockwise or counterclockwise rotation.

The following responses describe a sample game.

a. The first student creates an arithmetic sequence with a common difference of –2 and a first term of 20. The student writes down the first five terms—20, 18, 16, 14, 12—and passes the sheet of paper to the second student.

b. The second student identifies the sequence as arithmetic and writes this below the first five terms. The student then writes the following rule: "To make this sequence, start with 20 and add –2 (or subtract 2) every time to get the next term."

c. The third student uses this algorithm to write the recursive formula

$$\begin{cases} a_1 = 20 \\ a_n = a_{n-1} + (-2) \text{ for } n \geq 1 \end{cases}$$

and the explicit formula $a_n = 20 + (-2)(n-1)$ for $n \geq 1$.

d. The fourth student uses these formulas to write the first five terms of the sequence: 20, 18, 16, 14, 12.

e. The first student compares the sequence written by the fourth student with the original sequence. (If the terms do not match, the group should examine the paper and identify the source of the mistake.)

Discussion

a. Responses will vary.

b. Sample response: For arithmetic sequences, the difference between consecutive terms must be the same. For geometric sequences, the ratio of any two successive terms must be the same. A sequence that does not have a common ratio or a common difference between successive terms is neither arithmetic nor geometric.

The recursive formula for a geometric sequence, where r is the common ratio ($r \neq 0$), n is the term number, and g_n is the nth term, is:

$$\begin{cases} g_1 = \text{first term} \\ g_n = rg_{n-1}, \ n > 1 \end{cases}$$

The explicit formula for such a sequence is $g_n = g_1 r^{n-1}$.

Exploration

In this exploration, you use your knowledge of sequences to play a game. Read Parts **a–e** before beginning play.

a. To play this game, each person creates a sequence based on a specific rule or pattern. The first five terms of the sequence are written near the top of a sheet of paper. The paper is then passed to a second person.

b. After examining the first five terms, the second person identifies the sequence as *arithmetic, geometric,* or *neither.* The second person writes this identification on the sheet of paper below the sequence.

Using complete sentences, the second person then writes a rule for the sequence, folds the paper so that only the rule shows, and passes it to a third person.

c. Using only the rule written by the second person, the third person writes both a recursive formula and an explicit formula (if possible) for the sequence.

The third person then folds the paper so that only the two formulas are visible, and passes it to a fourth person.

d. Using only the formulas written by the third person, the fourth person writes the first five terms of the sequence on the paper, then passes it back to the sequence's original creator.

e. The creator unfolds the paper and checks to see that the new sequence matches the original five terms. If the two sequences do not match, any discrepancies are identified and recorded.

Discussion

a. Did the sequence found in Part **d** of the exploration match the original five terms of your sequence? If not, explain why the two patterns differed.

b. Describe how to determine whether a sequence is arithmetic, geometric, or neither.

c. Consider a sequence whose first three terms are 1, 2, 3. Describe a rule which allows the next three terms to be:

1. 4, 5, 6

2. 5, 8, 13

3. 6, 11, 20

d. Given the first three terms of an arithmetic sequence, must the next three terms follow the same pattern? Explain your response.

Warm-Up

1. Write the first five terms of the sequence defined by each of the following explicit formulas:

   a. $k_n = 9 - 3(n - 1)$

   b. $k_n = -5(1.3)^{n-1}$

2. Determine the number of terms in each of the following sequences. *Hint:* Find an explicit formula for the sequence, then solve the formula for the term number n.

   a. $11, 13, 15, \ldots, 99$

   b. $20, 16, 12.8, \ldots, 6.5536$

   c. $7, 10.5, 14, \ldots, 357$

   d. $3, 6, 12, \ldots, 3072$

Assignment

1.1 Complete Steps 1–3 for each sequence in Parts a–e below.

1. Identify the next two terms in the sequence.

2. Write an explicit or recursive formula, if one exists, that describes each pattern. If such a formula does not exist, write a description of the pattern you used to identify the next two terms.

3. Explain whether the sequence is arithmetic, geometric, or neither.

a. $1, 3, 7, 15, 31, \ldots$

b. $-50, 10, -2, 2/5, \ldots$

c. $1, 4, 7, 10, \ldots$

d. $2\frac{1}{2}, 2\frac{1}{3}, 2\frac{1}{4}, 2\frac{1}{5}, \ldots$

e. $6, -6, 6, -6, 6, -6, \ldots$

c. 1. If the sequence is arithmetic with a common difference of 1, the next three terms will be 4, 5, 6.

2. If the next term in the sequence is the sum of the two previous terms, then the next three terms will be 5, 8, 13.

3. If the next term in the sequence is the sum of the previous three terms, then the next three terms will be 6, 11, 20.

d. Sample response: Yes. Because the sequence is defined as arithmetic, then there must be a common difference and the next three terms would follow the same pattern.

Warm-Up

1. a. The first five terms are 9, 6, 3, 0, −3.

   b. The first five terms are −5, −6.5, −8.45, −10.985, −14.2805.

2. a. $99 = 11 + 2(n - 1) \Rightarrow n = 45$

   b. $6.5536 = 20(0.8)^{n-1} \Rightarrow n = 6$

   c. $357 = 7 + 3.5(n - 1) \Rightarrow n = 101$

   d. $3072 = 3(2)^{n-1} \Rightarrow n = 11$

Assignment

Problems suitable for use as assessment items are identified by an asterisk (*)

* 1.1 a. 1. Two possible terms are 63, 127.

   2. The explicit formula is $a_n = 2^n - 1$ for $n \geq 1$. The recursive formula is:

   $$\begin{cases} a_1 = 1 \\ a_n = a_{n-1} + 2^{n-1} \text{ for } n > 1 \end{cases}$$

   3. The sequence is neither arithmetic nor geometric.

   b. 1. Two possible terms are $-2/25, 2/125$.

   2. The explicit formula is $g_n = -50(-1/5)^{n-1}$ for $n \geq 1$. The recursive formula is:

   $$\begin{cases} g_1 = -50 \\ g_n = (-1/5)\, g_{n-1} \text{ for } n > 1 \end{cases}$$

   3. The sequence is geometric.

   c. 1. Two possible terms are 13, 16.

   2. The explicit formula is $a_n = 1 + 3(n - 1)$ for $n \geq 1$. The recursive formula is:

   $$\begin{cases} a_1 = 1 \\ a_n = a_{n-1} + 3 \text{ for } n > 1 \end{cases}$$

   3. This is an arithmetic sequence.

   d. 1. Two possible terms are $2\frac{1}{6}, 2\frac{1}{7}$.

   2. The explicit formula is:

   $$a_n = 2 + \frac{1}{n + 1} \text{ for } n \geq 1$$

   The recursive formula is:

   $$\begin{cases} a_1 = 2\frac{1}{2} \\ a_n = a_{n-1} - \frac{1}{n(n + 1)} \text{ for } n > 1 \end{cases}$$

   3. This sequence is neither arithmetic nor geometric.

   e. 1. Two possible terms are 6, −6.

   2. The explicit formula is $a_n = 6(-1)^{n-1}$ for $n \geq 1$. The recursive formula is:

   $$\begin{cases} a_1 = 6 \\ a_n = -1(a_{n-1}) \text{ for } n > 1 \end{cases}$$

   3. This sequence is geometric.

1.2 a. Any geometric sequence with a common ratio of 1 is also an arithmetic sequence with a common difference of 0. For example, the following sequence is both arithmetic and geometric:

$$\pi, \pi, \pi, \pi, \pi, \ldots$$

b. An explicit formula for the sample sequence given in Part **a** is $a_n = \pi + 0(n-1)$ for $n \geq 1$.

c. An explicit formula for the sample sequence given in Part **a** is $g_n = \pi \bullet (1)^{n-1}$ for $n \geq 1$.

1.3 a. The common difference can be found by solving the following equation:

$$93 = 13 + d(50 - 1)$$
$$d = 80/49$$

b. The common ratio can be found by solving the equation below:

$$192 = 12 \bullet r^{5-1}$$
$$r = \pm 2$$

c. The common difference is 3 and the number of terms is 18.

d. The common ratio is 5 and the number of terms is 10.

1.4 Sample response: The dog's mass would be 43.2 kg. If the dog's loss of mass is actually an arithmetic sequence, then the dog would lose 0.9 kg per month for 12 months—a total of 10.8 kg. Depending on the size of the animal, this might not be reasonable. The veterinarian would not let the dog's mass fall below a healthy level.

1.5 a. Sample response: If the mass of a chick is 36 g when hatched, and it gains 10% of its mass each day for 8 weeks, then its daily mass is a geometric sequence with the following formula: $g_n = 36 \bullet 1.1^{n-1}$. After 56 days, the chick's mass would be about 6.8 kg.

b. This is probably not reasonable. Students might know from experience that the mass of a broiler chicken is typically under 2 kg. According to most poultry growers, the mass of an 8-week-old chicken should be about 43 times its mass at birth, or about 1548 g.

c. The advertiser should claim a 7% daily mass gain.

1.2 a. Write the first five terms of a sequence that is both arithmetic and geometric. Explain why your sequence fits in both categories.

b. Write an explicit formula for your sequence when it is considered an arithmetic sequence.

c. Write an explicit formula for your sequence when it is considered a geometric sequence.

1.3 a. If the first term of an arithmetic sequence is 13 and the 50th term is 93, what is the common difference? Describe the process you used to solve this problem.

b. If the first term of a geometric sequence is 12 and the fifth term is 192, what is the common ratio? Describe the process you used to solve this problem.

c. If the first term of an arithmetic sequence is 11, the second term is 14, and the last term is 62, what is the common difference? How many terms are there in this sequence?

d. If the first term of a geometric sequence is 4, the second term is 20, and the last term is 7,812,500, what is the common ratio? How many terms are there in this sequence?

1.4 Obesity in pets can cause joint problems, and it is related to arthritis and other diseases. In some cases, veterinarians might recommend specially formulated pet foods to help control this condition. One such product claims that it can "help your pet lose 0.9 kg a month." Imagine that a veterinarian has prescribed this diet for a dog with a mass of 54 kg. What would you expect the mass of the dog to be at the end of 12 months? Explain your reasoning.

1.5 In its ad for chicken feed, a supplier promises a 10% daily gain in mass. A newly hatched chick has an approximate mass of 36 g. When the chicken reaches 8 weeks of age, it is considered a marketable broiler.

a. Consider the chicken's mass as a geometric sequence. If the ad's claim is true, what will the chicken's mass be after 8 weeks?

b. Do you think your answer to Part **a** is reasonable? Explain your response.

c. After 56 days on the advertised feed, a broiler chicken has a mass of 1487 g. What percentage daily gain in mass should the advertiser claim? Explain your response.

1.6 As the term number n becomes increasingly large, predict what will happen to a geometric sequence with a common ratio:

a. between −1 and 0   **b.** between 0 and 1

c. less than −1   **d.** greater than 1.

* * * * *

1.6 The following sample responses assume that the first term is positive.

a. If the common ratio is between −1 and 0, then the sequence will alternate between positive and negative terms and will get progressively closer to 0.

b. If the common ratio is between 0 and 1, then the sequence will get progressively closer to 0.

c. If the common ratio is less than −1, then the sequence will alternate between positive and negative terms. The absolute value of the terms will get progressively larger.

d. If the common ratio is greater than 1, the terms of the sequence will get progressively larger.

✳ ✳ ✳ ✳ ✳

1.7 Cut out a square of paper that measures 16 cm on each side.

   a. **1.** Fold the paper in half.

      2. Record the fold number, the number of layers created by the fold, and the area of the top surface.

   b. Repeat Part **a** as many times as you can.

   c. Write both explicit and recursive formulas for the area of the top surface after n folds.

   d. Write both explicit and recursive formulas for the number of layers after n folds.

   e. What value does the area of the top surface appear to approach as the number of folds increases?

   f. What value does the number of layers appear to approach as the number of folds increases?

1.8 In Problem **1.7**, you folded the paper in half at each stage. After seven or eight folds, you probably noticed that continued folding became nearly impossible. Instead of folding the paper at each stage, suppose you cut it in half and stacked the cut sheets.

   a. How big would the original sheet of paper have to be for the area of the top surface of the stack to be 1 cm^2 after 50 cuts?

   b. After 50 cuts, how tall would the stack of paper be? Give your estimate in kilometers and describe how you arrived at your response.

1.9 Describe the pattern for each of the following sequences. If possible, identify the sequence as arithmetic, geometric, or neither. If the sequence is arithmetic, find the common difference. If it is geometric, find the common ratio.

   a. $1, 1, 2, 3, 5, 8, \ldots, k_n$

   b. $\begin{cases} k_1 = 2 \\ k_n = k_{n-1}(1.05), \ n > 1 \end{cases}$

   c. $k_n = 2000 - (1000)(n - 1)$

   d. $\begin{cases} k_1 = 0 \\ k_n = k_{n-1} + (n - 1), \ n > 1 \end{cases}$

   e. $3, 3/2, 1, 3/4, 3/5, \ldots, k_n$

1.10 For each sequence in Problem **1.9**, describe what happens to the terms as n becomes increasingly large.

---

* 1.7 **a–b.** Students generate sequences by paper folding.

   c. The explicit formula for the area of the top surface (in cm^2) is $g_n = 128 \cdot (0.5)^{n-1}$ for $n \geq 1$. The recursive formula for the area of the top surface is:

$$\begin{cases} g_1 = 128 \\ g_n = g_{n-1} \cdot 0.5 \ \text{for} \ n > 1 \end{cases}$$

   d. The explicit formula for the number of layers is $g_n = 2 \cdot 2^{n-1}$ for $n \geq 1$. The recursive formula for the number of layers is:

$$\begin{cases} g_1 = 2 \\ g_n = g_{n-1} \cdot 2 \ \text{for} \ n > 1 \end{cases}$$

   e. As the number of folds increases, the area of the top surface appears to approach 0 cm^2.

   f. As the number of folds increases, the number of layers becomes larger and larger.

1.8 **a.** The sheet of paper would have to have an area of about $5.6 \cdot 10^{14}$ cm^2. Its dimensions would be about $2.4 \cdot 10^7$ cm (or 240 km) on each side.

   b. Answers will vary, depending on the thickness of the paper. If a single layer were 0.1 mm thick, the height of the stack after 50 cuts would be about $1.1 \cdot 10^8$ km.

1.9 **a.** This is a Fibonacci sequence with the first two terms equal to 1. It is neither arithmetic nor geometric.

   b. This is a geometric sequence with a common ratio of 1.05 and a first term of 2.

   c. This is an arithmetic sequence with a common difference of −1000 and a first term of 2000.

   d. This sequence $(0, 1, 3, 6, 10, 15, 21, \ldots)$ is neither arithmetic nor geometric. The pattern can be described by the recursive formula.

   e. This sequence is neither arithmetic nor geometric. The first term is 3/1. In each successive term, the numerator remains constant at 3 and the denominator increases by 1.

1.10 **a.** The terms increase without bound.

   b. The terms increase without bound.

   c. The terms decrease without bound.

   d. The terms increase without bound.

   e. The terms approach 0.

ACTIVITY 2

This activity introduces students to finite arithmetic series and their expanded form.

teacher note

A brief assessment of the mathematical content in Activities **1** and **2**, for use at your discretion, appears in the Teacher Resources for this module.

Materials List

■ none

Technology

■ spreadsheet (optional)

■ symbolic manipulator (optional)

Student Outcomes

After completing the following exploration and discussion, students should be able to:

✳ calculate sums of finite arithmetic sequences using the definition of an arithmetic series

✳ determine a formula for a finite arithmetic series using paired sums

✳ write formulas to calculate finite arithmetic series

✳ determine the number of terms in a finite arithmetic sequence, given the nth term

✳ describe the sums of infinite arithmetic sequences.

teacher note

In Part **d** of the exploration, students develop a formula for the sum of the first n terms of an arithmetic sequence. This requires several steps with numerous algebraic manipulations. You might wish to guide the entire class through this process.

ACTIVITY 2

Carl Friedrich Gauss (1777–1855) was one of the most productive and influential mathematicians of the 19th century. He made many important mathematical discoveries while still a student at the University of Göttingen.

Even as a child, Gauss showed a remarkable skill with numbers—in particular with the set of natural numbers {1, 2, 3, 4, . . .}. According to mathematical lore, one day his teacher asked the class to add all the natural numbers from 1 to 100. Students were instructed to place their slates on the table when finished. To the surprise of the teacher, young Gauss placed his slate on the table after only a few moments.

mathematics note

The indicated sum of the terms of a finite sequence is a **finite series**. A finite series of n terms, denoted S_n, may be written in expanded form as follows:

$$S_n = a_1 + a_2 + a_3 + \cdots + a_n$$

where a_n represents the nth term of the sequence.

The sum of the terms of an arithmetic sequence is an **arithmetic series**. For example, the finite arithmetic sequence shown below has seven terms:

$$2,\ 4,\ 6,\ 8,\ 10,\ 12,\ 14$$

The sum of those terms, in expanded form, is the following arithmetic series:

$$S_7 = 2 + 4 + 6 + 8 + 10 + 12 + 14 = 56$$

To find the sum of the first 100 natural numbers, Gauss used a method involving a finite series. For example, the sum of the first 100 numbers can be written as the arithmetic series S_{100}:

$$S_{100} = 1 + 2 + \cdots + 99 + 100$$

This series can also be written in reverse order, as shown below.

$$S_{100} = 100 + 99 + \cdots + 2 + 1$$

These two series can then be added as follows:

$$S_{100} = 1 + 2 + \cdots + 99 + 100$$
$$S_{100} = 100 + 99 + \cdots + 2 + 1$$
$$2S_{100} = 101 + 101 + \cdots + 101 + 101$$

The resulting equation contains 100 terms of 101, therefore the sum of the two equations can be written as:

$$2S_{100} = 100(101)$$

Solving this equation for S_{100}, the sum of the first 100 natural numbers can be found as follows:

$$S_{100} = \frac{100(101)}{2} = 5050$$

Exploration

a. 1. Use a method like Gauss's to find the sum of the first 1000 natural numbers.

2. Generalize this method to find the sum of the first n natural numbers.

b. Use a similar method to find the sum of the first 50 even natural numbers.

c. Consider an arithmetic sequence with a first term of 2 and a common difference of 4. Find the sum of the first 75 terms of this sequence. *Hint:* Determine the 75th term of the sequence before trying to find the sum.

d. Consider an arithmetic sequence of n terms with a first term a_1 and a common difference d.

1. Using a_1 and d, write expressions for the second, third, and fourth terms of the sequence.

2. Using a_1 and d, write expressions for the nth term of the sequence and the three terms preceding the nth term.

3. Find the sum of the first n terms of this arithmetic sequence.

mathematics note

The sum of the terms of a finite arithmetic sequence with n terms and a common difference d can be found using the following formula:

$$S_n = \frac{n}{2}[2a_1 + (n-1)d] = \frac{n}{2}(a_1 + a_n)$$

where a_1 is the first term of the sequence and a_n is the nth term.

Exploration

a. 1. Sample response:

$$S_{1000} = 1 + 2 + \cdots + 999 + 1000$$
$$S_{1000} = 1000 + 999 + \cdots + 2 + 1$$
$$2S_{1000} = 1001 + 1001 + \cdots + 1001 + 1001$$

Because there are a total of 1000 terms of 1001:

$$S_{1000} = \frac{1000 \cdot 1001}{2} = 500,500$$

2. Sample response:

$$S_n = n + (n-1) + \cdots + 2 + 1$$
$$S_n = 1 + 2 + \cdots + (n-1) + n$$
$$2S_n = (n+1) + (n+1) + \cdots + (n+1) + (n+1)$$

Because there are a total of n terms of $(n+1)$:

$$S_n = \frac{n \cdot (n+1)}{2}$$

b. Sample response:

$$S_{50} = 2 + 4 + \cdots + 998 + 100$$
$$S_{50} = 100 + 998 + \cdots + 4 + 2$$
$$2S_{50} = 102 + 102 + \cdots + 102 + 102$$

Because there are a total of 50 terms of 102:

$$S_{50} = \frac{50 \cdot (102)}{2} = 2550$$

c. Using the explicit formula for an arithmetic sequence, $a_{75} = 2 + (75 - 1) \cdot 4 = 298$. Given this value, students should use a method like the one employed in Parts **a** and **b**:

$$S_{75} = 2 + 6 + \cdots + 294 + 298$$
$$S_{75} = 298 + 294 + \cdots + 6 + 2$$
$$2S_{75} = 300 + 300 + \cdots + 300 + 300$$

Because there are a total of 75 terms of 300:

$$S_{75} = \frac{75 \cdot (300)}{2} = 11,250$$

d. 1. $a_2 = a_1 + d, \ a_3 = a_1 + 2d, \ a_4 = a_1 + 3d$

2. $a_n = a_1 + (n-1) \cdot d, \ a_{n-1} = a_1 + (n-2) \cdot d,$
$a_{n-2} = a_1 + (n-3) \cdot d, \ a_{n-3} = a_1 + (n-4) \cdot d$

3. Using a method like the one employed in Parts **a** and **b**:

$$S_n = a_1 + [a_1 + d] + \cdots + [a_1 + (n-2)d] + [a_1 + (n-1)d]$$
$$S_n = [a_1 + (n-1)d] + [a_1 + (n-2)d] + \cdots + [a_1 + d] + a_1$$
$$2S_n = [2a_1 + (n-1)d] + [2a_1 + (n-1)d] + \cdots + [2a_1 + (n-1)d] + [2a_1 + (n-1)d]$$

Because there are a total of n terms of $[2a_1 + (n-1)d]$:

$$S_n = \frac{n \cdot [2a_1 + (n-1)d]}{2} = na_1 + \frac{n \cdot [(n-1)d]}{2}$$

Discussion

a. The equation below

$$S_n = \frac{n}{2}[2a_1 + (n-1) \bullet d]$$

can be expanded as follows:

$$S_n = \frac{n}{2}[a_1 + a_1 + (n-1) \bullet d]$$

Because $a_n = a_1 + (n-1) \bullet d$, students can make the following substitution:

$$Sn = \frac{n}{2}(a_1 + a_n)$$

b. The sequences in Parts **a** and **b** are arithmetic sequences because there is a common difference between consecutive terms.

c. **1.** Sample response: The sum of the first 100 even numbers should be twice the sum of the first 100 natural numbers because:

$$2 + 4 + 6 + \cdots + 200 = 2(1 + 2 + 3 + \cdots + 100)$$
$$= 2(5050) = 10,100$$

2. The sum of the first 100 multiples of k can be found as follows:

$$k + 2k + 3k + \cdots + 99k + 100k = k(1 + 2 + 3 + \cdots + 99 + 100)$$
$$= k\frac{100(101)}{2} = 5050k$$

d. Sample response: If the common difference is positive, the sum of the infinite arithmetic series will increase without bound. If the common difference is negative, the sum of the infinite arithmetic series will decrease without bound.

Warm-Up

1. **a.** Sample response:

$$k + 2k + 3k + \cdots + (n-1)k + nk = k(1 + 2 + 3 + \cdots + (n-1) + n)$$
$$= k\frac{n(n+1)}{2}$$

b. The sum can be found as follows:

$$\frac{3(600)(600+1)}{2} = 540,900$$

2. **a.** The first term of the sequence is 3.
b. The common difference is 4.

For example, consider the sequence 7, 11, 15, . . . , 59. The number of terms in this arithmetic sequence can be found using the general form of the explicit formula, $a_n = a_1 + (n-1)d$. In this case, $a_1 = 7$, $a_n = 59$, and $d = 4$. By substituting as shown below, the equation can be solved for n, the number of terms.

$$59 = 7 + (n-1)4$$
$$59 = 7 + 4n - 4$$
$$56 = 4n$$
$$14 = n$$

Because $n = 14$, the sum of those terms, S_{14}, can be found as follows:

$$S_{14} = \frac{14}{2}(7 + 59) = 462$$

Discussion

a. Verify that the following two expressions are equivalent:

$$S_n = \frac{n}{2}[2a_1 + (n-1)d] \qquad S_n = \frac{n}{2}(a_1 + a_n)$$

b. Consider the sequences whose terms you added in Parts **a** and **b** of the exploration. Are these sequences arithmetic, geometric, or neither?

c. **1.** Multiplying the first 100 natural numbers by 2 produces the first 100 even natural numbers. Describe how to find the sum of this set of numbers.

2. Multiplying the first 100 natural numbers by k produces the first 100 multiples of k. Describe how to find the sum of this set of numbers.

d. Suppose that the following arithmetic series continued indefinitely:

$$S = a_1 + a_2 + a_3 + \cdots + a_n + \cdots$$

What do you think the sum of the series would be?

Warm-Up

1. Find the sum of the first 2000 natural numbers.

2. Consider the arithmetic sequence 3, 7, 11, . . . , 451.

a. What is the first term of the sequence?

b. What is the common difference?

c. How many terms are there in the sequence?

d. What is the sum of the terms of the sequence?

3. Find the sum of each of the following sequences.

   a. $21, 29, 37, 45, \ldots, 109$ b. $7, 14, 21, 28, \ldots, 126$

Assignment

2.1 Write a formula to find the sum of the first n even natural numbers.

2.2 a. Generalize your response to Part c of the discussion to find a formula for the sum of the first n multiples of k.

   b. Use your formula from Part a to find the sum of the first 600 multiples of 3.

2.3 Can Gauss's method be used to find the sum of a geometric sequence? Explain your response.

2.4 To attract customers, a car dealership displays the following advertisement.

New Car for Only $11,111.00	
Starting at $206.26 a Month!*	
***36-month Lease**	
Refundable Security Deposit	$ 150.00
Down Payment	$ 1,000.00
First Month's Payment	$ 206.26
Cash Due at lease Inception	$ 1,356.26

a. Do the monthly payments described in this ad form an arithmetic sequence? Explain your response.

b. Does the total amount paid over the term of the loan form an arithmetic series? Explain your response.

c. According to this ad, how much money will the buyer pay over the entire 36-month period?

d. Explain any discrepancies you observe between the amount determined in Part c and the advertised price of $11,111.00.

2.5 Consider a weekly newspaper with 15,000 subscribers. During the next year, the paper plans to increase its number of subscribers by 50 every week. If this plan succeeds, what will be the total number of newspapers delivered for the entire year?

* * * * *

c. Using the explicit formula for an arithmetic sequence:

$$451 = 3 + 4(n - 1)$$
$$113 = n$$

d. The sum is the finite arithmetic series $3 + 7 + 11 + \cdots + 451$. Using the formula for an arithmetic series:

$$S_{113} = \frac{113}{2}(3 + 451) = 25,561$$

3. a. $s_{12} = 780$

   b. $s_{18} = 1197$

Assignment

Problems suitable for use as assessment items are identified by an asterisk (*).

2.1 The sum of the first n even numbers can be found as follows:

$$S_n = \frac{n}{2}(2 + 2n)$$
$$= \frac{n}{2} \cdot 2(1 + n)$$
$$= n(n + 1)$$

2.2 Student methods may vary. Using the formula from Part a of the exploration:

$$S_n = \frac{n(n+1)}{2} = \frac{2000(2000+1)}{2} = 2,001,000$$

2.3 Sample response: No, because the sum of each pair of numbers is not constant. For example, given the sequence 32, 16, 8, 4, 2, 1, the sums of the pairs are 33, 18, 12, 18, and 33.

* 2.4 a. Sample response: The monthly payments may be considered an arithmetic sequence where the first term is $206.26 and the common difference is $206.26.

   b. Sample response: Yes. Because the payments themselves form an arithmetic sequence, their indicated sum forms an arithmetic series.

   c. The lessee pays $150.00 + $1000.00 + (36 • $206.26) or $8575.36, of which $150.00 is refunded at the end of the lease.

   d. Sample response: The difference of $2535.64 may be the cost to purchase the car at the end of the lease.

2.5 The number of newspapers delivered each week forms an arithmetic sequence where $a_1 = 15,000$ and $d = 50$. Using the formula for an arithmetic series:

$$S_{52} = \frac{52}{2}(2 \bullet 15,000 + 51 \bullet 50) = 846,300$$

✳ ✳ ✳ ✳ ✳

2.6 a. The first three terms are $-2, 3, 8$.

b. $a_{150} = -2 + 5(149) = 743$

c. $S_{150} = \dfrac{150}{2}(-2 + 743) = 55{,}575$

2.7 a. $S_{41} = \dfrac{41}{2}(5 + 120) = 2562.5$

b. Using the general formula for an arithmetic sequence, solve $120 = 5 + 40d$ and the common difference is 2.875.

c. The second and third terms of the sequence are 7.875 and 10.75.

In this activity, students develop an algorithm for finding the sum of the terms of a finite geometric sequence.

Materials List

■ graph paper (two sheets per student)

Technology

■ spreadsheet

■ symbolic manipulator (optional)

Student Outcomes

After completing the following exploration and discussion, students should be able to:

✳ calculate sums of finite geometric sequences

✳ write formulas to find finite geometric series

✳ determine the number of terms in a finite geometric series, given the nth term.

Exploration

a. The number of messages sent in the first stage is $2 \bullet 3 = 6$.

b. The second group sends $6 \bullet 3 = 18$ messages.

c. The number of messages sent at the third stage is 54, at the fourth stage is 162, and at the fifth stage is 486.

d. $g_n = 6 \bullet 3^{n-1}$

2.6 Consider a sequence described by the explicit formula $a_n = -7 + 5n$, for $n \geq 1$.

  a. Write the first three terms of the sequence.

  b. Find a_{150}.

  c. Find S_{150}.

2.7 Consider an arithmetic sequence with a first term of 5 and a 41st term of 120.

  a. Find the sum of the first 41 terms of this sequence.

  b. Identify the common difference of the sequence.

  c. Write the second and third terms of the sequence.

A C T I V I T Y 3

Have you ever received an e-mail from a friend warning you about a computer virus? Such warnings usually urge you to forward them to all the names in your address book.

What happens if the warning is a hoax? What are the consequences for the computer servers that route these e-mail messages?

Exploration

Imagine that you have just heard about Red Ant, a computer virus that destroys all the data stored on an infected hard drive. Worried that Red Ant could wreak havoc on your school network, you immediately e-mail a warning to two friends.

  a. Each of your two friends forwards the warning to three other people. What is the total number of messages sent by your two friends?

  b. Each of the people to whom your friends sent warnings forwards the message to three others. What is the total number of messages sent by this second group?

  c. Assume that every recipient continues to forward the message to three others. Record the total number of messages sent at each of the next three stages.

  d. Write an explicit formula for the geometric sequence formed by the number of messages sent at each stage, beginning with Part a.

mathematics note

The indicated sum of the terms of a geometric sequence is a **geometric series**. For example, the finite geometric sequence below has five terms.

$$2, 6, 18, 54, 162$$

The sum of those terms, in expanded form, is the following finite geometric series:

$$S_5 = 2 + 6 + 18 + 54 + 162 = 242$$

e. Write the expanded form of the geometric series that represents the total number of messages sent after 20 stages. List at least three terms at the beginning of the series and three terms at the end of the series. Use an ellipsis to indicate the middle terms.

Set the series equal to S_{20} and call this "equation 1."

f. When a geometric series has many terms, determining its sum by simple addition can be time-consuming. Use the following steps to determine the total number of messages sent.

1. Multiply both sides of equation 1 by the common ratio of the sequence. Call the result "equation 2."

2. Subtract equation 1 from equation 2.

3. Solve the resulting equation for S_{20}.

g. A geometric series with n terms, where g_1 is the first term and r is the common ratio, also can be represented in the following expanded form:

$$S_n = g_1r^0 + g_1r^1 + g_1r^2 + \cdots + g_1r^{n-3} + g_1r^{n-2} + g_1r^{n-1}$$

Use the process described in Part f above to simplify this expression.

Discussion

a. If every recipient continues to forward the message to three others, how many messages will be sent at the 200th stage? Is this a reasonable expectation? Why or why not?

b. What are some possible consequences of unrestrained e-mail forwarding?

e. The following geometric series (equation 1) represents the total number of warnings sent:

$$S_{20} = 6 + 18 + 54 + \cdots + 6 \bullet 3^{17} + 6 \bullet 3^{18} + 6 \bullet 3^{19}$$

f. 1. Multiplying both sides of the equation above by 3 yields equation 2:

$$3S_{20} = 18 + 54 + 162 \cdots + 6 \bullet 3^{18} + 6 \bullet 3^{19} + 6 \bullet 3^{20}$$

2. Subtracting equation 1 from equation 2 as shown below:

$$3S_{20} = 18 + 54 + \ldots + 6 \bullet 3^{17} + 6 \bullet 3^{18} + 6 \bullet 3^{19} + 6 \bullet 3^{20}$$
$$-(S_{20} = 6 + 18 + 54 + \ldots + 6 \bullet 3^{17} + 6 \bullet 3^{18} + 6 \bullet 3^{19})$$
$$2S_{20} = 6 \bullet 3^{20} - 6$$

3. Solving for S_{20}, the number of messages is:

$$S_{20} = \frac{6 \bullet 3^{20} - 6}{2} = 10,460,353,200$$

g. Student answers may vary, but the general formula should appear as follows:

$$S = \frac{g_1r^n - g_1}{r - 1} = \frac{g_1(r^n - 1)}{r - 1}$$

Discussion

a. Sample response: If every recipient continues to forward the warning to three others, the 20th stage would consist of almost 21 billion messages. This is not reasonable, because it far exceeds the earth's population.

b. Sample response: The number of e-mail messages can quickly overload servers. Whenever you receive an e-mail warning, you should verify its legitimacy before sending it to others.

c. Answers may vary, but the general formula should appear as follows:

$$S = \frac{g_1 r^n - g_1}{r - 1} = \frac{g_1(r^n - 1)}{r - 1}$$

Note: Some students might have obtained the equivalent form shown below (found by multiplying both the numerator and the denominator by –1):

$$S = \frac{g_1(1 - r^n)}{1 - r}$$

d. Sample response: If r equals 1, the denominator in the formula is 0. This makes the value of the fraction undefined.

e. 1. Sample response: $S_n = 4_1 + 4_2 + \cdots + 4_{n-1} + 4_n$

   2. Sample response: If r is 1, then each term is equal to the first term, and the sequence is arithmetic with a common difference of 0. The sum of n terms can be found as follows: $S_n = n \bullet g_1$.

f. 1. Sample response: These are equivalent by using the distributive property and factoring out g_1.

   2. Sample response: These are equivalent by factoring out r from $g_1 r^n$ and substituting g_n for $g_1 r^{n-1}$

g. Sample response: Use the first three terms to calculate r, then substitute g_1, r, and g_n in the formula given in Part **f2** of the discussion.

Warm-Up

1. **a.** The variable g_1 is the first term.

   b. The variable r is the common ratio.

   c. The variable n is the number of terms.

---

mathematics note

The sum of the terms of a finite geometric sequence with n terms and a common ratio r can be found using the following formula:

$$S_n = \frac{g_1 r^n - g_1}{r - 1}$$

where g_1 is the first term of the sequence and $r \neq 1$.

For example, consider the geometric sequence 2, 6, 18, 54, 162. In this case, $n = 5$, $r = 3$, and $g_1 = 2$. Using the formula given above, the sum of the sequence can be found as follows:

$$S_5 = \frac{2(3)^5 - 2}{3 - 1} = 242$$

c. How does the formula given in the mathematics note above compare with the one you found in Part **g** of the exploration?

d. Why must r not equal 1 in the formula given in the mathematics note?

e. 1. Describe a geometric series S_n where $r = 1$.

   2. Find a formula for the geometric series S_n where $r = 1$.

f. Describe how to demonstrate that this formula for a geometric series

$$S_n = \frac{g_1 r^n - g_1}{r - 1}$$

is equivalent to each of the following expressions. *Hint:* $g_1 r^{n-1} = g_n$.

1. $S_n = \frac{g_1(r^n - 1)}{r - 1}$ 2. $S_n = \frac{g_n r - g_1}{r - 1}$

g. Given the first three terms and the last term of a geometric series, how could you determine the sum?

Warm-Up

1. One formula for finding the sum of a geometric series is given below.

$$S_n = \frac{g_1 r^n - g_1}{r - 1}$$

   a. What does g_1 represent?

   b. What does r represent?

   c. What does n represent?

d. Use the formula to find the sum of a geometric series with 10 terms whose first term is 5 and whose common ratio is a.

2. a. Determine the sum of the terms of a geometric sequence in which $g_1 = 3.5$, $r = 0.6$, and $n = 17$.

b. Determine the sum of the terms of a geometric sequence in which $g_1 = 10$, $r = 10$, and $n = 10$.

3. Find each of the sums below.

a. $20 + 16 + 12.8 + \cdots + 6.5536$ **b.** $3 + 6 + 12 + \cdots + 3072$

Assignment

3.1 Identify each of the following series as arithmetic, geometric, or neither and find the sum.

a. $11 + 13 + 15 + 17 + 19 + 21 + 23 + \cdots + 99$

b. $2 + (-3) + (-8) + \cdots + (-28)$

c. $2\frac{1}{2} + 2\frac{1}{3} + 2\frac{1}{4} + \cdots + 2\frac{1}{7}$ **d.** $\frac{1}{2} + \frac{1}{4} + \frac{1}{8} + \frac{1}{16} + \frac{1}{32}$

3.2 The Greek philosopher, Zeno of Elea, used paradoxes to demonstrate the difficulties of dividing time and space into an infinite number of parts. The following situation is similar to one of Zeno's paradoxes.

Imagine a race between the legendary Greek hero, Achilles, and a tortoise. Achilles can run 10 times faster than the tortoise, so he gives the tortoise a 10-m head start. During the time it takes Achilles to run the first 10 m, the tortoise travels a distance of 1 m. Because of its head start, the tortoise still leads, but now by only 1 m.

During the time it takes Achilles to make up that 1 m, the tortoise travels 0.1 m. While Achilles runs that 0.1 m, the tortoise travels 0.01 m. As Achilles runs 0.01 m, the tortoise moves another 0.001 m. Imagine that this pattern continues for each successive interval of time. **Note:** As the race continues, the intervals of time used to analyze the situation become smaller and smaller.

a. If the tortoise has traveled a distance of 1.11111 m, how many time intervals have elapsed since the start of the race?

b. Find the distance covered by Achilles when the tortoise has traveled a distance of 1.11111 m. Describe the process you used.

c. Compare the distance traveled by Achilles in Part **a** with the total distance traveled by the tortoise, including its 10-m head start. Did Achilles catch the tortoise? Explain your response.

d. If the race continues in this fashion, do you think Achilles will ever catch the tortoise? Explain your response.

Module 10 ■ *Take It to the Limit* **287**

d. $s_{10} = \dfrac{5a^{10} - 5}{a - 1} = \dfrac{5(a^{10} - 1)}{a - 1}$

2. a. $S_{17} = \dfrac{(3.5)(0.6)^{17} - 3.5}{0.6 - 1} \approx 8.75$

b. $S_{10} = \dfrac{(10)(10)^{10} - 10}{10 - 1} = 11,111,111,110$

3. a. $S = \dfrac{(6.5536)(0.8) - 20}{0.8 - 1} \approx 73.79$

b. $S = \dfrac{(3072)2 - 3}{2 - 1} = 6141$

teacher note

Students must complete Problem **3.3** before proceeding to Problem **3.4**.

Assignment

Problems suitable for use as assessment items are identified by an asterisk (*)

3.1 a. This is an arithmetic series.

$$S_{45} = \frac{45}{2}(11 + 99) = 2475$$

b. This is an arithmetic series.

$$S_7 = \frac{7}{2}(2 + (-28)) = -91$$

c. This series is neither arithmetic nor geometric, so neither formula can be used to find the sum.

$$S_6 = \frac{1903}{140} \approx 13.59$$

d. This is a geometric series.

$$S_5 = \frac{\frac{1}{2} \bullet \left(\frac{1}{2}\right)^5 - \frac{1}{2}}{\frac{1}{2} - 1} = \frac{31}{32} \approx 0.97$$

* 3.2 a. Sample response: When the tortoise has run 1.11111 m, six time intervals have elapsed since the start.

$$1.11111 = 1 + 0.1 + 0.01 + 0.001 + 0.0001 + 0.00001$$

b. Sample response: To determine the total distance Achilles covered, I could multiply the distance covered by the tortoise by 10, or use the formula for a finite geometric series:

$$S_6 = \left(\frac{10(0.1)^6 - 10}{0.1 - 1}\right) = 11.1111$$

c. Sample response: No, with its 10-m head start, the tortoise is 11.11111 m from Achilles' starting point. After six time intervals, Achilles has only traveled 11.1111 m. He is still 0.00001 m behind.

d. Students may respond in a number of different ways. Some possible responses are given below:

- No, because the tortoise would always be some distance ahead of Achilles, even though that distance is getting smaller and smaller.

- Yes, because the lead of the tortoise will become so small that it will be impossible to determine if the tortoise is ahead.

- Yes, because if Achilles travels 10 m/sec, in 2 sec, he will cover 20 m while the tortoise—who travels 1/10 as fast, or 1 m/sec—will have moved only 12 m (including the 10-m head start). Therefore, at some time during the first 2 sec, Achilles must pass the tortoise.

- Yes, because the total distance traveled by both Achilles and the tortoise appears to approach a maximum of $11\frac{1}{9}$ m.

Module 10 ■ *Take It to the Limit* **271**

* 3.3 **a.** Using the formula for the sum of a geometric series, the total number of wheat kernels in the reward is:

$$S_{64} = \frac{1 \cdot 2^{64} - 1}{2 - 1} \approx 1.8 \cdot 10^{19}$$

b. The wheat would cover approximately

$$2.4 \cdot 10^8 \text{ km}^2.$$

c. The wheat would be 24 layers thick.

3.4 Using the formula for the sum of a geometric series, the total number of wheat kernels in the reward is:

$$S_{64} = \left(\frac{1(3)^{64} - 1}{3 - 1} \right) \approx 1.72 \cdot 10^{30}$$

This is enough wheat to cover the United States with approximately 2.3 trillion layers. **Note:** This is a good opportunity to compare the magnitudes of numbers like 2^{64} and 3^{64}.

* 3.5 **a.** The first six terms of the sequence are illustrated below:

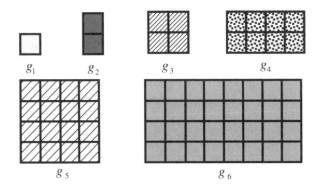

b. 1. Sample response:

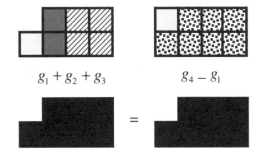

$$g_1 + g_2 + g_3 \qquad g_4 - g_1$$

2. Sample response:

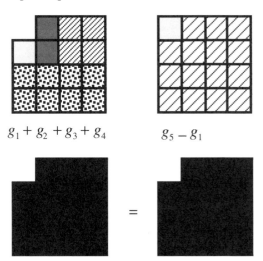

$$g_1 + g_2 + g_3 + g_4 \qquad g_5 - g_1$$

Demonstrate a similar property for each of the following:

1. the sum of the first three terms

2. the sum of the first four terms

3. the sum of the first five terms.

c. Generalize the pattern for the sum of the first n terms of the sequence.

d. Show how the formula you obtained in Part **c** is related to the general formula for a finite geometric series.

* * * * *

3.6 Consider a ball bouncing as shown in the figure below.

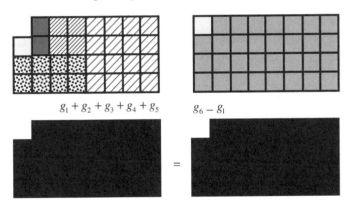

On the first bounce, the ball reaches a height of 6.00 m. On the second bounce, the ball reaches a height of 4.80 m. On the third bounce, the ball reaches a height of 3.84 m.

a. Assuming that this pattern continues, determine a geometric sequence that models the height of the ball on each bounce.

b. Write the expanded form of the geometric series for the first n terms of the sequence.

c. Determine the value of the geometric series for each of the following:

1. the first 10 terms
2. the first 20 terms
3. the first 30 terms
4. the first 40 terms.

d. 1. What value does the geometric series appear to approach?

2. What does this value represent?

3.7 A tree in a tropical rain forest grows 9 m in one year, 6 m in the next year, and 4 m in the following year.

a. Assuming that this pattern continues, write a geometric series that models the tree's growth for 5 years.

b. What is the common ratio?

c. Given that the tree's initial height was 4 m, use a geometric series to determine the height of the tree after:

1. 10 years
2. 20 years
3. 30 years

d. What value does the height of the tree appear to approach?

---

3. Sample response:

$$g_1 + g_2 + g_3 + g_4 + g_5 \qquad g_6 - g_1$$

$$=$$

c. Sample response: The sum of the terms is equal to the difference between the term following the last term of the series and the first term of the series, or $g_1 + g_2 + g_3 + \cdots + g_n = g_{n+1} - g_1$.

---

d. Sample response: The sum of a geometric series can be found using the formula:

$$S_n = \frac{g_n r - g_1}{r - 1}$$

In this series r is 2. By substituting 2 for r, the formula becomes:

$$S_n = \frac{g_n(2) - g_1}{2 - 1}$$

or $S_n = g_n(2) - g_1$. Because $g_n r$ represents the term following g_n, g_{n+1} can be substituted for $g_n(2)$. The result is $S_n = g_{n+1} - g_1$.

✳ ✳ ✳ ✳ ✳

3.6 **a.** The geometric sequence is: $6, 4.8, 3.84, \ldots, 6(0.8)^{n-1}$.

b. $S_n = 6 + 4.8 + 3.84 + \cdots + 6(0.8)^{n-1}$.

c. 1. $S_{10} = \dfrac{6(0.8)^{10} - 6}{0.8 - 1} \approx 26.78$ m

2. $S_{20} = \dfrac{6(0.8)^{20} - 6}{0.8 - 1} \approx 29.65$ m

3. $S_{30} = \dfrac{6(0.8)^{30} - 6}{0.8 - 1} \approx 29.96$ m

4. $S_{40} = \dfrac{6(0.8)^{40} - 6}{0.8 - 1} \approx 30.00$ m

d. 1. The geometric series appears to approach 30 m.

2. Sample response: The number is the sum of all the heights that the ball reaches.

3.7 **a.** $S_5 = 9 + 6 + 4 + \dfrac{8}{3} + \dfrac{16}{9}$ or

$$S_5 = 9 + 9\left(\frac{2}{3}\right)^1 + 9\left(\frac{2}{3}\right)^2 + 9\left(\frac{2}{3}\right)^3 + 9\left(\frac{2}{3}\right)^4$$

b. The common ratio is 2/3.

c. 1. The height of the tree is:

$$4 + S_{10} = 4 + \frac{9\left(\frac{2}{3}\right)^{10} - 9}{\frac{2}{3} - 1} \approx 30.53 \text{ m}$$

2. The height of the tree is:

$$4 + S_{20} = 4 + \frac{9\left(\frac{2}{3}\right)^{20} - 9}{\frac{2}{3} - 1} \approx 30.99 \text{ m}$$

3. The height of the tree is:

$$4 + S_{30} = 4 + \frac{9\left(\frac{2}{3}\right)^{30} - 9}{\frac{2}{3} - 1} \approx 31.00 \text{ m}$$

d. The height appears to approach 31 m. This value represents the maximum height of the tree.

ACTIVITY 4

In this activity, students are introduced to limits, sequences that approach limits, and sequences that do not approach limits.

teacher note

A brief assessment of the mathematical content in Activities **3** and **4,** for use at your discretion, appears in the Teacher Resources for this module.

Materials Required

- none

Technology

- graphing utility
- spreadsheet
- geometry utility
- symbolic manipulator (optional)

Student Outcomes

After completing the following exploration and discussion, students should be able to:

✳ investigate the limit of an infinite geometric sequence, if it exists, both graphically and numerically

✳ determine the sum of the terms of an infinite geometric sequence in which $-1 < r < 1$, where r represents the common ratio

✳ compare sequences that approach limits and those that do not.

Exploration

a. Students create a sequence by connecting the midpoints of sides of successive triangles. See Figure **10-1** in student edition.

b. See sample table at the bottom of page 275.

c. **1.** See table given in Part **b.**

ACTIVITY 4

Paradoxes are statements that seem contrary to common sense, yet somehow may be true. Zeno of Elea used the race between Achilles and the tortoise, for example, to support his argument that time could not be split into an infinite number of parts.

Because it is difficult to describe an infinite number, problems involving infinity have intrigued mathematicians for centuries. In this activity, you begin an informal investigation of some problems involving infinite processes.

Exploration

a. 1. Using a geometry utility, create a triangle large enough to fill the screen. Label the vertices *A, B,* and *C.*

2. Locate the midpoint of each side of the triangle and label them *D, E,* and *F,* respectively. Connect these points to form △*DEF.*

3. Connect the midpoints of the sides of △*DEF* to form △*GHJ.*

4. Repeat this process to form △*KLM.* Your drawing should now resemble the one shown in Figure **10-1.**

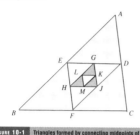

FIGURE 10-1 Triangles formed by connecting midpoints of sides.

2. Sample scatterplot:

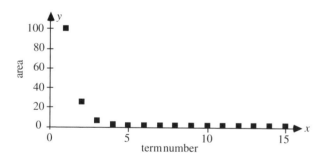

d. **1.** See table given in Part **b.**

2. Sample scatterplot:

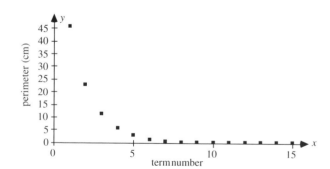

b. Create a spreadsheet with headings like those in Table **10-1** and complete the first four rows.

TABLE 10-1 ■ *Data for Sequence of Triangles*

Term No.	Name of Triangle	Area	Perimeter	Area of △ —— Area of Previous △	Perimeter of △ —— Perimeter of Previous △
1	△ABC			none	none
2	△DEF				
3	△GHI				
4	△KLM				
⋮					
15					

c. 1. Use the ratios of areas developed in Part **b** to extend the spreadsheet for 15 triangles.

 2. Create a scatterplot of area versus term number.

d. 1. Use the ratios of perimeters developed in Part **b** to extend the spreadsheet for 15 triangles.

 2. Create a scatterplot of perimeter versus term number.

e. 1. Use the data for the areas of the triangles to find each of the following sums: $S_1, S_2, S_3, \ldots, S_{10}$.

 For example, if the area of △ABC is 100 cm^2, the area of △DEF is 25 cm^2, and the area of △GHI is 6.5 cm^2, then $S_1 = 100$, $S_2 = 100 + 25 = 125$, and $S_3 = 100 + 25 + 6.5 = 131.5$.

 2. Create a scatterplot of the sum versus the number of terms.

f. Find the sums S_{20}, S_{30}, S_{50}, and S_{100} using the formula below:

$$S_n = \frac{g_1(r^n - 1)}{r - 1}$$

Discussison

a. 1. Considering the four triangles from Part **a** of the exploration, what do you notice about the areas of consecutive triangles?

 2. What do you notice about the perimeters of consecutive triangles?

b. 1. If your spreadsheet columns containing areas and perimeters could be extended indefinitely, what value would the areas appear to approach?

 2. What value would the perimeters appear to approach?

e. 1. The following table shows the sums for the sample triangle used in Parts **a** and **b** (rounded to the nearest hundredth).

Sum	Area (cm^2)
S_1	100.20
S_2	125.25
S_3	131.51
S_4	133.07
S_5	133.47
S_6	133.57
S_7	133.59
S_8	133.60
S_9	133.60
S_{10}	133.60

Term No.	Name of Triangle	Area (cm^2)	Perimeter (cm)	Area of △ —— Area of Previous △	Perimeter of △ —— Perimeter of Previous △
1	△ABC	100.2	45.7	none	none
2	△DEF	25.05	22.9	0.25	0.5
3	△GHI	6.3	11.4	0.25	0.5
4	△KLM	1.6	5.7	0.25	0.5
5	⋮	0.4	2.9	0.25	0.5
6		9.8E–2	1.4	0.25	0.5
7		2.4E–2	7.1E–1	0.25	0.5
8		6.1E–3	3.6E–1	0.25	0.5
9		1.5E–3	1.8E–1	0.25	0.5
10		3.8E–4	8.9E–2	0.25	0.5
11		9.6E–5	4.5E–2	0.25	0.5
12		2.4E–5	2.2E–2	0.25	0.5
13		6.0E–6	1.1E–2	0.25	0.5
14		1.5E–6	5.6E–3	0.25	0.5
15		3.7E–7	2.8E–3	0.25	0.5

2. Sample graph:

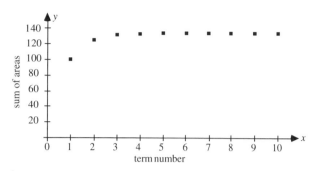

f. The following table shows the sums for the sample triangle used in Parts **a** and **b** (rounded to the nearest hundredth).

Sum	Area (cm²)
S_{20}	133.60
S_{30}	133.60
S_{50}	133.60
S_{100}	133.60

Discussion

a. 1. The area of each triangle is 1/4 the area of the previous triangle.

 2. The perimeter of each triangle is 1/2 the perimeter of the previous triangle.

b. 1. Sample response: The area would approach 0 but never actually reach it.

 2. Sample response: The perimeter would approach 0 but never actually reach it.

c. Sample response: When finding a limit, you can choose a prescribed accuracy however small you wish. This prescribed accuracy sets up boundaries above and below the conjectured limit. If all the terms after a certain term lie within the boundaries we picked, no matter how small, we know what the limit is, as the number of terms increases indefinitely.

d. Sample response: My answers are consistent with the graphs. The perimeters and areas appear to approach 0 after only a few terms.

e. 1. Sample response: From the spreadsheet, the perimeter of each triangle after the 13th one is within 1/100 of 0.

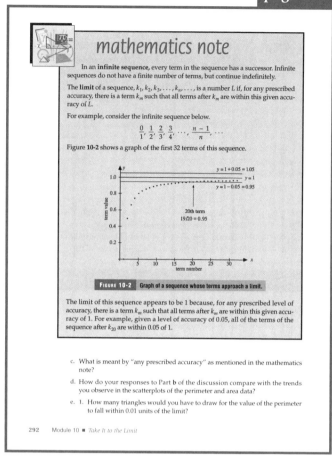

FIGURE 10-2 Graph of a sequence whose terms approach a limit.

c. What is meant by "any prescribed accuracy" as mentioned in the mathematics note?

d. How do your responses to Part **b** of the discussion compare with the trends you observe in the scatterplots of the perimeter and area data?

e. 1. How many triangles would you have to draw for the value of the perimeter to fall within 0.01 units of the limit?

page 293

2. How many triangles would you have to draw for the value of the area to fall within 0.01 square units of the limit?

f. In Part **f** of the exploration, you used the following formula to find sums for larger values of n, where $r = 1/2$.

$$S_n = \frac{g_1(r^n - 1)}{r - 1}$$

1. Describe what happens to the value of $(1/2)^n$ as n gets very large.

2. Describe what happens to the value of the formula below as n gets very large.

$$S_n = \frac{g_1 \cdot ((1/2)^n - 1)}{(1/2) - 1}$$

g. Consider the following formula for a geometric series where $-1 < r < 1$.

$$S_n = \frac{g_1(r^n - 1)}{r - 1}$$

1. Describe what happens to the value of r^n as n increases indefinitely.

2. Describe what happens to the formula for S_n as n increases indefinitely.

h. Consider the following formula for a geometric series where $r \leq -1$ or $r > 1$.

$$S_n = \frac{g_1(r^n - 1)}{r - 1}$$

1. Describe what happens to the value of r^n as n increases indefinitely.

2. Describe what happens to the formula for S_n as n increases indefinitely.

mathematics note

The sum of the terms of an infinite geometric sequence in which $-1 < r < 1$ can be found using the following formula:

$$S = \frac{g_1(-1)}{r - 1} = \frac{g_1}{1 - r}$$

For example, consider the infinite geometric series below:

$$27 + 9 + 3 + 1 + \cdots$$

In this case, $g_1 = 27$ and $r = 1/3$. The sum of the terms can be found as follows:

$$S = \frac{27}{1 - (1/3)} = \frac{27}{2/3} = 40.5$$

---

2. Sample response: From the spreadsheet, the area of each triangle after the 7th one is within $1/100$ of 0.

f. 1. As n increases indefinitely, the value of $(1/2)^n$ approaches 0.

2. As n increases indefinitely, the formula approaches the following expression:

$$S = \frac{g_1 \cdot (0 - 1)}{\frac{1}{2} - 1} = \frac{g_1 \cdot -1}{-\frac{1}{2}} = \frac{g_1}{\frac{1}{2}} = 2g_1$$

g. 1. As n increases without bound, the value of r^n (for $-1 < r < 1$) approaches 0.

2. As n increases without bound, the formula approaches the following expression:

$$S = \frac{g_1 \cdot (0 - 1)}{r - 1} = \frac{g_1 \cdot -1}{r - 1} = \frac{g_1}{1 - r}$$

h. 1. If $r \leq -1$, then $|r^n|$ increases indefinitely as n increases, while r^n alternates between positive and negative values. If $r > 1$, then r^n increases indefinitely as n increases.

2. Sample response: The formula is affected in the same manner as r^n.

Warm-Up

1. **a.** Sample response: These terms do not appear to have a limit. As the term number increases, the value of the term appears to increase without bound.

    b. Sample response: These terms appear to have a limit of 0. As the term number increases, the value of the term approaches 0.

    c. Sample response: These terms appear to have a limit of 100 because all the terms are the same.

2. **a.** 1/4

    b. 0

    c. 7

3. Since $r = 0.2$ and $g_1 = 98$, the sum can be found as follows:

$$S = \frac{98}{1 - 0.2} = 122.5$$

Warm-Up

1. Each graph in Parts **a–c** below shows a scatterplot of the first 10 terms of a sequence. As the number of terms increases indefinitely, which of the sequences appears to have a limit? Explain your responses.

    a.
    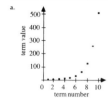

    b.
    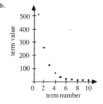

    c.

2. Consider the following infinite geometric sequence:

$$2, \frac{1}{2}, \frac{1}{8}, \frac{1}{32}, \ldots$$

    a. What is the common ratio?

    b. What does the limit appear to be?

    c. After how many terms of the sequence are all successive terms within 0.001 of the limit?

3. Determine the sum of the terms of the infinite geometric sequence below:

$$98, \ 19.6, \ 3.92, \ \ldots$$

294   Module 10 ■ *Take It to the Limit*

4. Which of the following infinite sequences, if any, appears to have a limit? Explain your reasoning in each case. If any sequence has a limit, determine the sum of that sequence.

    a. 512, 602, 692, 782, 872, . . .   **b.** 400, 200, 100, 50, 25, . . .

    c. 14, 3, –8, –19, –30, . . .   **d.** 6, 18, 54, 162, 486, . . .

    e. 15, 4.5, 1.35, 0.405, 0.1215, . . .

Assignment

4.1 Using a spreadsheet, enter the sequence 1, 2, 3, 4, . . . , 50 in column A. In column B, enter the geometric sequence with a first term of 1 and a common ratio of 10.

    a. Suppose that the values in column A represent the term numbers of a sequence and the values in column B represent the term values. As the term number increases indefinitely, do the values in column B appear to approach a limit?

    b. Determine the ratio of each term in column B to the preceding term. Enter these values in column C.

    c. Suppose that the values in column A represent the term numbers of a sequence and the values in column C represent the term values. As the term number increases indefinitely, do the values in column C appear to approach a limit?

    Verify your response by finding a term such that all terms after it are within 0.01 of the limit.

    d. Determine the reciprocal of each term in column B and enter these values in column D.

    e. Suppose that the values in column A represent the term numbers of a sequence and the values in column D represent the term values. As the term number increases indefinitely, do the values in column D appear to approach a limit?

    Verify your response by finding a term such that all terms after it are within 0.005 of the limit.

    f. Determine the ratio of each term in column D to the preceding term. Enter these values in column E.

    g. Suppose that the values in column A represent the term numbers of a sequence and the values in column E represent the term values. As the term number increases indefinitely, do the values in column E appear to approach a limit?

    Verify your response by finding a term such that all terms after it are within 0.001 of the limit.

---

4. a. This is an increasing arithmetic sequence. It has no limit.

    b. This geometric sequence has a common ratio less than 1 and approaches a limit of 0. The sum is 800.

    c. This is a decreasing arithmetic sequence. It has no limit.

    d. This is an increasing geometric sequence with a common ratio of 3. It has no limit.

    e. This geometric sequence has a common ratio less than 1 and approaches a limit of 0. The sum is 21.43.

Assignment

Problems suitable for use as assessment items are identified by an asterisk (*)

4.1 Sample spreadsheet:

A	B	C	D	E
1	1		1	
2	10	10	0.1	0.1
3	100	10	0.01	0.1
4	1000	10	0.001	0.1
5	10000	10	0.0001	0.1
6	100000	10	0.00001	0.1
7	1000000	10	0.000001	0.1
8	10000000	10	0.0000001	0.1
9	100000000	10	0.00000001	0.1
10	1000000000	10	1E–09	0.1
⋮	⋮	⋮	⋮	⋮
45	1E+44	10	1E–44	0.1
46	1E+45	10	1E–45	0.1
47	1E+46	10	1E–46	0.1
48	1E+47	10	1E–47	0.1
49	1E+48	10	1E–48	0.1
50	1E+49	10	1E–49	0.1

    a. The values in column B are increasing and do not appear to approach a limit. **Note:** Some students might respond that they approach infinity. You might wish to remind them that, although we often talk about positive and negative infinity, infinity is not an actual number.

    b. The ratio of consecutive terms is 10.

    c. The limit of the sequence is 10. After the first term, each successive term is within 0.01 of 10.

    d. See sample spreadsheet above.

    e. The terms appear to approach 0. After the fifth term, each successive term is within 0.005 of 0.

    f. The ratio of consecutive terms is 0.1.

    g. The limit of the sequence is 0.1. After the first term, each successive term is within 0.001 of 0.1.

h. 1. Sample graph:

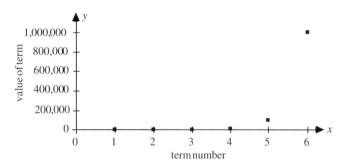

2. Sample graph:

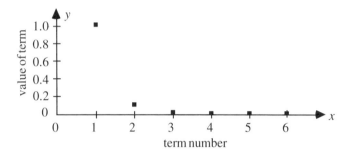

3. Sample response: As the number of terms increases, the scatterplot of column B is increasing and does not approach a limit. As the number of terms increases, the scatterplot of column D is decreasing and appears to approach a limit of 0.

4.2 Sample spreadsheet:

A	B	C	D	E
1	–1		–1	
2	–10	10	–0.1	0.1
3	–100	10	–0.01	0.1
4	–1000	10	–0.001	0.1
5	–10000	10	–0.0001	0.1
6	–100000	10	–0.00001	0.1
7	–1000000	10	–0.000001	0.1
8	–10000000	10	–0.0000001	0.1
9	–100000000	10	–1E–08	0.1
⋮	⋮	⋮	⋮	⋮
48	–1E+47	10	–1E–47	0.1
49	–1E+48	10	–1E–48	0.1
50	–1E+49	10	–1E–49	0.1

a. The terms in column B are decreasing negatively and do not appear to approach a limit.

b. The ratio of consecutive terms is 10.

c. The limit of the sequence is 10. After the first term, all terms are within 0.01 of 10.

d. See sample spreadsheet.

e. The terms appear to approach 0. After the fourth term, all terms are within 0.005 of 0.

f. The ratio of consecutive terms is 0.1.

g. The limit of the sequence is 0.1. After the first term, all terms are within 0.001 of 0.1.

h. 1. Create a scatterplot of the term value versus the term number for the first six terms of the sequence in column B.

    2. Create a scatterplot of the term value versus the term number for the first six terms of the sequence in column D.

    3. Describe the differences you observe in the two scatterplots.

4.2 Repeat Problem **4.1** using a geometric sequence with a first term of –1 and a common ratio of 10 in column B.

4.3 Use a geometry utility to construct a square. Connect the midpoints of the sides to form a quadrilateral. Repeat the process two more times.

    a. Justify that your original figure is a square.

    b. What type of quadrilateral is each of the other three figures in your drawing? Explain your response.

    c. Find the areas and perimeters of the four quadrilaterals.

    d. 1. Calculate the ratio of the area of each quadrilateral to the area of the next larger one. What pattern do you observe in these ratios?

        2. In the exploration in this activity, the ratio of the areas of consecutive triangles was 1:4. How does this ratio compare with the ratio of the areas of consecutive squares?

    e. The ratio of the perimeters of consecutive triangles in the exploration was 1:2. How does this ratio compare with the ratio of the perimeters of consecutive squares?

    f. 1. If you continued to construct quadrilaterals as described above, what would happen to the sequence of areas?

        2. What would happen to the sequence of perimeters?

4.4 Consider the intervals described by the following expression, where n is the term number:

$$\left[3, \, 3 + \frac{1}{n}\right]$$

    a. Use this expression to write the first four terms of the sequence.

    b. As n increases indefinitely, does the sequence appear to approach a limit? Explain your response.

h. 1. Sample graph:

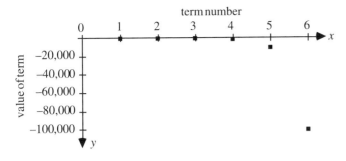

2. Sample graph:

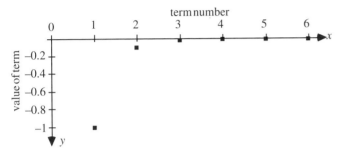

3. Sample response: As the number of terms increases, the scatterplot of column B is decreasing and does not approach a limit. As the number of terms increases, the scatterplot of column D is increasing and appears to approach a limit of 0.

* **4.3** In the sample construction at the bottom of the page, polygon 1 is *ABEC*, polygon 2 is *GHJK*, polygon 3 is *LMNP* and polygon 4 is *QRST*.

a. Answers may vary. Students should show that the figure is equilateral and that all angles are right angles.

b. Sample response: Each of the other three figures is a square. The four sides of each one are the same length and the four angles in each are right angles.

c. Answers will vary, depending on the size of the original square.

d. 1. Students should observe that the ratio of consecutive areas is 1/2.

2. The ratio of the areas of consecutive squares is not the same as the ratios of the areas of the consecutive triangles.

e. Sample response: The ratio of the perimeters is $\sqrt{2}/2 \approx 0.707$, which is not the same as the ratios of the perimeters for the triangles.

f. 1. The sequence of areas approaches 0.

2. The sequence of perimeters approaches 0.

4.4 a. Sample response: $[3, 4], [3, 3.5], [3, 3.\bar{3}], [3, 3.25]$.

b. Sample response: As *n* increases, the limit appears to be the interval $[3, 3]$, which is equivalent to 3.

Area(Polygon 1) = 50.28 square cm
Area(Polygon 2) = 25.14 square cm
Area(Polygon 3) = 12.57 square cm
Area(Polygon 4) = 6.29 square cm

Area(Polygon 4)/Area(Polygon 3) = 0.50
Area(Polygon 3)/Area(Polygon 2) = 0.50
Area(Polygon 2)/Area(Polygon 1) = 0.50

Perimeter(Polygon 1) = 28.36 cm
Perimeter(Polygon 2) = 20.06 cm
Perimeter(Polygon 3) = 14.18 cm
Perimeter(Polygon 4) = 10.03 cm

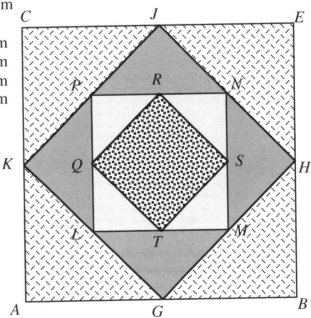

4.5 a. $r = 1/10$

b. The limit of the sequence appears to be 0.

c. After the third term, all the following terms are within 0.001 of 0.

d. $\dfrac{6}{10}, \dfrac{66}{100}, \dfrac{666}{1000}, \dfrac{6666}{10,000}, \dfrac{66,666}{100,000}, \dfrac{666,666}{1,000,000}$

e. The limit of the sequence of sums appears to be 2/3. **Note:** You might wish to discuss other infinitely repeating decimals whose limits are exact values, such as $0.\overline{33} = 1/3$.

✷ ✷ ✷ ✷ ✷

4.6 Students may use a spreadsheet to investigate this situation.

a. 250, 250 + 0.10(250), 250 + 0.10(250 + 0.10(250)), 250 + 0.10(250 + 0.10(250 + 0.10 (250))) or 250, 275, 277.5, 277.75

b. 277.5 mg

c-d. Sample response: By the middle of the third day (after five tablets), the amount of medication in the body approaches a limit of approximately 277.8 mg.

Number of Tablets	Amount of Medication in Body (mg)
0	250
1	275
2	277.5
3	277.75
4	277.775
5	277.7775
6	277.778
7	277.778
8	277.778

4.7 $\dfrac{5}{11} = 0.\overline{45} = \dfrac{45}{100} + \dfrac{45}{10,000} + \dfrac{45}{1,000,000} + \cdots$

4.8 a. $g_1 = 0.27, g_2 = 0.0027, g_3 = 0.000027, g_4 = 0.00000027$

b. The sum of the infinite geometric sequence can be found as follows:

$$S = \dfrac{0.27}{1 - 0.01} = \dfrac{0.27}{0.99} = \dfrac{27}{99} = \dfrac{3}{11}$$

4.5 Consider the following infinite geometric sequence:

$$\frac{6}{10}, \frac{6}{100}, \frac{6}{1000}, \frac{6}{10,000}, \ldots$$

a. What is the common ratio?

b. What does the limit of the sequence appear to be?

c. After how many terms of the sequence are all successive terms within 0.001 of the limit?

d. Find the sums $S_1, S_2, S_3, \ldots, S_6$ and write them as a sequence. *Hint:* $S_1 = 6/10$ and

$$S_2 = \frac{6}{10} + \frac{6}{100} = \frac{66}{100}$$

e. If the sequence of sums continues indefinitely, what limit does it appear to approach?

✷ ✷ ✷ ✷ ✷

4.6 While recovering from surgery, a patient takes a 250-mg pain relief tablet every 12 hours for 2 weeks. At the end of 12 hours, 10% of the medication remains in the body.

a. Write a sequence that describes the amount of medication in the body right after taking the first tablet, the second tablet, the third tablet, and the fourth tablet.

b. How much medication is there in the body on the morning of the second day (after the patient takes the third tablet)?

c. What appears to be the limit of the amount of medication in the body?

d. On what day does the amount of medication become close to this limit?

4.7 Express 5/11 as an infinite series.

4.8 a. Write the first four terms of the infinite geometric sequence in which $g_1 = 0.27$ and $r = 0.01$.

b. What is the sum of the infinite geometric series formed by the sequence in Part **a**?

Research Project

The idea of figures inside figures has intrigued many artists and mathematicians. To explore this idea in more detail, choose either Part **a** or **b** below.

a. Waclaw Sierpinski, a Polish mathematician, experimented with triangles like those described in the exploration in Activity **4**. Starting with a large triangle, he created a new triangle by connecting the midpoints of the sides of the original triangle. Sierpinski then removed the interior triangle and created new triangles using the midpoints of the sides of the three remaining triangles. He repeated this process over and over, removing the interior triangle each time, and examining the areas and the perimeters of all the remaining triangles.

Explore Sierpinski's triangle for yourself using a geometry utility, a graphing calculator, or graph paper.

b. Create a rectangle that is not a square. Construct consecutive quadrilaterals within the rectangle by connecting the midpoints of the sides. Explore the patterns created by the ratios of consecutive areas and consecutive perimeters of the quadrilaterals.

Research Project

a. One good resource for students is Peitgen, et al., *Fractals for the Classroom*. The authors provide many references to Sierpinski and describe how to produce these triangles using graphing calculators or dot paper.

b. When students construct these figures, they should observe that the first quadrilateral is a parallelogram (a rhombus), but not a rectangle. The second quadrilateral is a rectangle. This alternating pattern continues. The ratio of the areas of consecutive rectangles is a constant, while the ratio of the areas of consecutive parallelograms is a different constant.

teacher note

An additional assessment, for use at your discretion, appears in the Teacher Resources for this module.

Summary Assessment

1. Students may use different methods to analyze this situation. The area added to the snowflake at each stage after stage 1 can be described by the geometric sequence below, where n is the stage number minus 1:

$$\frac{3}{9}, \quad \frac{3}{9}\left(\frac{4}{9}\right), \quad \frac{3}{9}\left(\frac{4}{9}\right)^2, \quad \cdots, \quad \frac{3}{9}\left(\frac{4}{9}\right)^{n-1}$$

Thus, the area of the snowflake at each stage is:

$$1 + S_n = 1 + \frac{3}{9} + \frac{3}{9}\left(\frac{4}{9}\right) + \frac{3}{9}\left(\frac{4}{9}\right)^2 + \cdots + \frac{3}{9}\left(\frac{4}{9}\right)^{n-1}$$

a. 1 unit^2

b. Using the expression shown above, where n is the stage number minus 1:

$$1 + S_1 = 1 + \frac{3}{9} = 1\tfrac{1}{3} \text{ units}^2$$

c. By combining the expression shown above, where n is the stage number minus 1, with the formula for an infinite geometric series in which $-1 < r < 1$:

$$1 + S_{14} = 1 + \frac{\left(\frac{3}{9}\right)\left(\frac{4}{9}\right)^{14} - \frac{3}{9}}{\frac{4}{9} - 1} \approx 1.60 \text{ units}^2$$

2. Sample response: The area of the snowflake approaches 1.6 units^2. The following graph shows how, after stage 5, all of the terms fall within 0.05 units of 1.6.

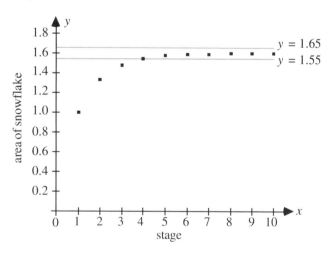

Summary Assessment

In 1906, Swedish mathematician Helge von Koch introduced a geometric figure that became known as the Koch curve. The Koch curve was later manipulated to create the Koch snowflake. The snowflake can be created with the following steps.

- Begin with an equilateral triangle. This is stage 1.
- Divide each edge of the figure into three equal segments.
- Use the middle segment of each edge to create an equilateral triangle, as shown in the diagram below. The resulting figure is stage 2.

stage 1   stage 2

- Continue dividing each edge of the figure into three equal segments and using the middle segment of each edge to create an equilateral triangle, as shown in the diagram below. The resulting figure is stage 3.

stage 2   stage 3

- To complete another stage, this process is repeated. When the process continues for an infinite number of stages, the figure becomes the Koch snowflake.

1. Assuming that the area of the original equilateral triangle is 1 unit^2, determine the area of the snowflake at each of the following stages:

  a. stage 1

  b. stage 2

  c. stage 15

2. If the process described above is continued, what does the area of the snowflake appear to approach? Explain your response.

Everyone Counts

11

module

Overview

The usefulness of combinatorics has expanded rapidly since the introduction of computers. Massive problems that once were unthinkable now can be solved quickly and efficiently with technology. For computers to accomplish these feats, however, programmers must have knowledge of counting algorithms.

In this module, students investigate the fundamental counting principle, permutations, and combinations. The setting for these investigations is a new shopping mall.

Activity 1:	Students develop the fundamental counting principle to determine the numbers of combinations available for different types of locks.
Activity 2:	Students review factorial notation and develop a formula for counting permutations (ordered arrangements) of items.
Activity 3:	Students develop the formula for combinations while investigating how to count numbers of possible committees that can be formed from a group.

Objectives

In this module, students will:

* use tree diagrams, lists, and charts to organize information and solve problems (1, 2)
* develop and use the fundamental counting principle (1)
* write and interpret factorial notation (2)
* develop and use a formula for permutations (2)
* develop and use a formula for combinations (3)
* apply the fundamental counting principle, permutations, and combinations to calculate simple probabilities (1, 2, 3).

Prerequisites

For this module, students should know:

* how to use tree diagrams
* a technique for generating Pascal's triangle
* how to determine simple probabilities.

 Flashbacks, for use at your discretion, appear in the Teacher Resources for this module. These brief problem sets provide a review of some prerequisite skills for each activity.

Planning Guide

Activity	Materials	Technology	Time Line
Activity **1**	■ combination locks ■ keys	■ none	3 days
Activity **2**	■ none	■ none	3 days
Activity **3**	■ template A	■ none	2 days
Assessment Activities	■ none	■ none	2 days **Total: 10 days**

 teacher note

A blackline master for template A appears in the Teacher Resources for this module.

Introduction

In this module, students encounter counting problems that could arise in the development of a mall. **Note:** The businesses named in the memo appear in assignment problems throughout the module.

ACTIVITY 1

In this activity, students review basic theoretical probability, factorial notation, and the fundamental counting principle. Tree diagrams and lists are used to organize information.

Note: Students may recall an informal introduction to the fundamental counting principle from the Level 1 module "Going in Circuits."

Materials List

■ rotary combination lock (optional; one per group)

■ pin-lock key (optional; one per student or group)

teacher note

You might wish to allow students to try to "crack" a rotary combination lock. This should illustrate the large number of possible combinations and encourage students to consider ways to count them systematically.

Student Outcomes

After completing the following exploration and discussion, students should be able to:

✳ use the fundamental counting principle

✳ apply their knowledge of the fundamental counting principle to determine simple probabilities.

Introduction

After months of intense work, real estate developer Nadia Nelson is exhausted but happy. All construction is complete and spaces have been leased to a dozen businesses. Riverside Mall is ready to open. As owner and manager of the mall, Nadia welcomes her new tenants with the following memo.

Nelson Real Estate Property Management

To: Members of the Riverside Store Managers' Association
From: Nadia Nelson
Re: Opening of Riverside Mall

Congratulations! Your businesses were selected for the mall after a survey of Riverside shoppers. I would like to welcome each of you to Riverside Mall.

Last Chance Beauty Parlor	Les Arts Magnifique
Kuzlowski's Pizza	Almost Human Pets
Riverside Read and Feed	Music Mania
Trendz Clothing	The Zone Sporting Goods
Toddler's Haven Toys	Planet Alpha Arcade
Zuzu's Petals and Gifts	Flix Theaters

Please keep me informed of all activities planned for the mall's grand opening. And if you have any questions, don't hesitate to contact me.

ACTIVITY 1

As part of the grand opening festivities, the managers' association is planning a promotion called "Crack the Safe." A large safe will be filled with merchandise contributed by each store. The shopper who manages to open the safe will take home all the prizes.

Nadia Nelson likes the idea, but wonders about the manner in which the promotion will be conducted. She expresses her concerns in another memo.

304

Nelson Real Estate Property Management

To: Members of the Store Managers' Association
From: Nadia Nelson
Re: "Crack the Safe" Promotion

I am excited about the "Crack the Safe" promotion. You have created an ingenious way to attract shoppers to the mall. I do have some questions, however. Three types of locks are available for the safe: rotary combination, keyed pin, and digital combination. Which type should we use? And how will we make sure that the promotion lasts for several days, yet gives shoppers a reasonable chance to win? Please send your recommendations for these challenges as soon as possible. Opening day is coming!

Exploration

a. As shown in Figure **11-1**, one type of rotary combination lock consists of a dial with 40 tick marks representing the numbers 0 through 39. The lock is opened by turning the dial to the right, then to the left, then back to the right, stopping each time at the corresponding number of a three-number code.

FIGURE 11-1 Rotary combination lock.

1. Estimate how many different three-number combinations are possible for this type of lock.

2. Using your estimate in Step **1**, determine the probability that a combination chosen at random will open the lock.

3. Develop a systematic plan to find the actual number of different combinations.

mathematics note

The **fundamental counting principle** states that if one event can occur in *h* ways, and for each of these ways a second event can occur in *k* ways, then the number of different ways in which the two events can occur is *h* • *k*.

For example, suppose a store sells soft drinks in 2 different sizes and 5 different flavors. In this situation, one event is the choice of size. The second event is the choice of flavor. Using the fundamental counting principle, there are 2 • 5 or 10 different selections from which to choose.

The fundamental counting principle can be extended to situations involving more than two events. For example, if the store also sells 4 different brands of soft drinks, each of which comes in 2 different sizes and 5 different flavors, the total number of possible selections is 2 • 5 • 4 or 40.

b. 1. Use the fundamental counting principle to determine the number of possible combinations.

2. Calculate the probability that any one combination will open the lock.

c. The second type of lock under consideration by the managers' association requires a key. Figure **11-2** shows a key for a standard pin lock. Depending on the manufacturer, such keys can have either 5 or 6 valleys. Each valley can have from 6 to 10 different depths.

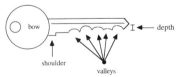

FIGURE 11-2 Key for a standard pin lock.

1. Draw a key with 5 valleys. Label these valleys with the letters A–E. If 6 different depths are available for each valley in this key, how many different keys are possible?

2. If 10 different depths are available for each valley in a key with 6 valleys, how many different keys are possible?

3. Using the number of keys found in Step **2**, determine the probability that a key chosen at random will open the mall contest lock.

Exploration

Students investigate rotary combination and keyed pin locks.

a. 1. Students should recognize that many combinations are possible. The actual number is 40 • 40 • 40 = 64,000.

2. Students should observe that the probability that a randomly selected combination will open the lock is:

$$\frac{1}{\text{total number of combinations}}$$

The actual probability is 1/64,000.

3. Answers will vary. Sample response: List the combinations in a sequenced pattern: 0–0–0, 0–0–1, 0–0–2, 0–0–3, . . . , 39–39–37, 39–39–38, 39–39–39.

b. 1. There are 40 • 40 • 40 = 64,000 possible combinations.

2. The probability that a randomly selected combination will open the lock is 1/64,000.

c. 1. Sample drawing:

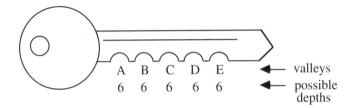

If 6 different depths are available for each of the 5 valleys, there are $6 • 6 • 6 • 6 • 6 = 6^5 = 7776$ possible keys.

2. The maximum number of keys is $10^6 = 1,000,000$.

3. The probability that a randomly selected key will open the lock is 1/1,000,000.

Discussion

a. 1. Answers will vary. Listing each combination in a sequenced arrangement of number patterns works well. Using this form, students may recognize a method of counting the total number of combinations.

2. Sample response: Yes, numbers in a lock combination can be repeated as one turns to the right or left.

3. Sample response: Because there are so many possibilities, it would be an enormous task to make a complete list of all of them.

b. Sample response: To increase the probability that the promotion will last a long time, use a pin key with 6 different valleys and 10 different depths. The probability of opening the lock on any one attempt is smaller than for the combination lock. This might be very expensive, however, because the mall would have to make a million keys or devise a computer program for a simulation.

c. Sample response: For a given lock, each person who tries has the same probability of opening the safe. Although it's possible that the first person will choose the right key or combination, it is highly unlikely because of the small probability for any combination.

Warm-Up

1. a. There are 2 • 3 or 6 different outfits.
b. Sample diagram:

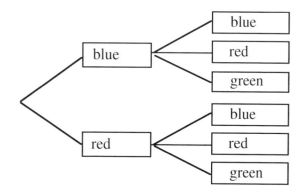

c. 1/6
2. There are 10 • 26 • 10 or 2600 different terms.
3. Using the fundamental counting principle, the number of possible radio stations is 2 • 26 • 26 • 26 = 35,152.

Assignment

Problems suitable for use as assessment items are identified by an asterisk (*).

1.1 a. There are 10 • 10 • 10 • 10 = 10⁴ = 10,000 possible combinations.
b. The probability that a combination chosen at random will open the lock is 1/10,000.

Discussion

a. 1. Describe the strategy that you devised in Part **a** of the exploration for determining the number of possible combinations for the lock.

2. Did your strategy consider combinations with repeated digits? Explain your response.

3. Why would it be impractical to use a tree diagram to determine the number of possibilities for the lock?

b. When a visitor to the mall opens the safe, the promotion is over. If you wanted the promotion to last as long as possible, which type of lock would you choose: rotary combination or keyed pin? Discuss the advantages and disadvantages of your choice.

c. Is it possible that the first person who tries to open the safe will be successful?

Warm-Up

1. A wardrobe contains 2 pairs of pants. One pair is red; the other is blue. The wardrobe also contains 3 different shirts: red, blue, and green.

a. How many different outfits can be formed from 2 pairs of pants and 3 shirts?

b. Draw a tree diagram to illustrate your response to Part **a**.

c. What is the probability that an outfit chosen at random from this wardrobe is all blue?

2. How many different 3-character terms can be formed if the first and third characters are numerals from 0 through 9 and the second character is a letter from the English alphabet?

3. In the United States, each radio station is identified by a set of 4 call letters. These call letters traditionally begin with either the letter K or the letter W. Assuming that the remaining 3 letters can be selected from any letter of the English alphabet, how many different sets of call letters can be created before a new naming system must be devised?

Assignment

1.1 The third type of lock being considered for the mall promotion is a digital combination lock. As illustrated on the right, one kind of digital combination lock features four electronic displays, each of which can show a number from 0 to 9. To enter a four-digit code, users press the buttons underneath the displays until the desired number is obtained.

a. Use the fundamental counting principle to determine the number of possible combinations.

b. Determine the probability that a combination chosen at random will open the lock.

1.2 Considering all three types of locks, which would you recommend for the mall's "Crack the Safe" promotion? Justify your choice.

1.3 In addition to selling books and espresso, the manager of Riverside Read and Feed plans to publish works by members of the local community. Before the store can publish its first book, the manager must apply for a Publisher Identifier number for the International Standard Book Number (ISBN).

In most industrialized nations, an ISBN is assigned to each published book. It consists of 10 digits divided into 4 different areas. The Group Identifier represents the language in which the book is written. The Publisher Identifier represents the publishing company. The Title Identifier represents the title of the book. The Check Digit is used to detect errors before shipping. A sample ISBN is shown below.

$$\underset{\substack{\text{Group}\\\text{Identifier}}}{0} - \underset{\substack{\text{Publisher}\\\text{Identifier}}}{679} - \underset{\substack{\text{Title}\\\text{Identifier}}}{41295} - \underset{\substack{\text{Check}\\\text{Digit}}}{6}$$

The Group Identifier and Check Digit each consist of 1 digit. The numbers of digits in the Publisher and Title Identifiers may vary, but must represent a total of 8 digits.

a. The manager of Riverside Read and Feed hopes to publish 20 books during her first year in business. What is the minimum number of digits needed in the Title Identifier? Explain your response.

b. Considering your response to Part **a**, how many different possibilities would the store have for its Publisher Identifier? Explain your response.

c. Do you think a large publishing company would want more or fewer digits designated for its Publisher Identifier? Justify your answer.

d. Suppose Riverside Read and Feed receives a three-digit Publisher Identifier. What is the maximum number of books it could publish?

1.4 Businesses often use the letters that correspond to a telephone number to help attract customers. The number for the Coiffure Salon, for example, is 244-4247, or BIG HAIR. As shown on the right, some older touch-tone telephones only have 24 letters on the keypad.

1	ABC 2	DEF 3
GHI 4	JKL 5	MNO 6
PRS 7	TUV 8	WXY 9
*	0	#

1.2 Answers will vary. Sample response: I would use the digital combination lock because the probability that a single combination will unlock it is 1/10,000. If 500 people enter the contest each day, the probability that the safe will be cracked on any given day is about 1/20. The probabilities of opening the other locks are too small and not practical if the contest is to have a winner in a reasonable period of time. **Note:** Because there is a small chance that more than one contestant in a day may select a particular combination, the actual probability in the sample response above is:

$$1 - \left(\frac{9,999}{10,000}\right)^{500} \approx 0.0488$$

* **1.3 a.** Sample response: A Title Identifier with 2 digits will allow the manager to publish 10^2 or 100 books.

b. Sample response: Because there are 8 digits shared between the Publisher and Title Identifiers, if 2 are designated for the Title Identifier, there are 6 available for the Publisher Identifier. Applying the fundamental counting principle, there are $10^6 = 1,000,000$ possibilities.

c. Sample response: A large publishing company that keeps many different books in print will want fewer digits for its Publisher Identifier so that it can have more digits for the Title Identifier. For example, with a two-digit Publisher Identifier, the company will have a million different possibilities for Title Identifier.

d. Sample response: Because there are 8 digits shared between the Publisher and Title Identifiers, if 3 are designated for the Publisher Identifier, there are 5 available for the Title Identifier. Applying the fundamental counting principle, there are $10^5 = 100,000$ possibilities.

*1.4 **a.** Sample response: The letters Q and Z are missing.

　　b. **1.** There are $24^3 = 13,824$ possible 3-letter prefixes.

　　　　2. There are $8^3 = 512$ possible 3-digit prefixes.

　　　　3. Sample response: There are fewer 3-digit prefixes because only 1 digit is assigned to each key. For example, on a telephone keypad, the prefixes ADG and ADH can be dialed using the same 3 digits.

　　c. If no letter may repeat, there are $24 \cdot 23 \cdot 22 = 12,144$ possible 3-letter prefixes.

✳ ✳ ✳ ✳ ✳

1.5 **a.** There are $26^3 = 17,576$ possible 3-letter prefixes.

　　b. If no letter may repeat, there are $26 \cdot 25 \cdot 24 = 15,600$ possible 3-letter prefixes.

1.6 **a.** There are $6^3 = 216$ possible arrangements.

　　b. The probability is $6/216 \approx 0.028 = 2.8\%$.

1.7 **a.** The number of possible license plates is $26^3 \cdot 10^3 = 17,576,000$.

　　b. The number of possible license plates is $10^4 \cdot 26^2 = 6,760,000$.

　　c. Sample response: Because the option described in Part **a** allows for more growth, it would be the better choice. **Note:** In 1994, the population of Alaska was about 606,000.

　　d. Sample response: The population of California in 1994 was about 31.4 million. Even if only half of these people owned cars, neither of the options would be acceptable.

Students explore counting situations in which repetition is not allowed. The formula for permutations is developed using the fundamental counting principle.

teacher note

A brief assessment of the mathematical content in Activities **1** and **2**, for use at your discretion, appears in the Teacher Resources for this module.

Materials List

■ none

a. Which letters are missing from the keypad?

b. The first 3 digits of a local telephone number represent its numerical prefix. In the past, the letters that correspond with these numbers also represented a prefix. For example, a resident of the Parkway neighborhood might have had the telephone number PAR-2374.

　1. Use the fundamental counting principle to determine how many 3-letter prefixes can be formed using the letters on this keypad.

　2. Using the number keys that also contain letters, how many 3-digit prefixes can be formed?

　3. Compare your answers to Parts **b1** and **b2**. Explain any differences you observe.

c. Suppose that no letter may be repeated in a prefix. In this case, how many 3-letter prefixes can be formed from the keypad?

✳ ✳ ✳ ✳ ✳

1.5 Most telephone keypads now display all 26 letters. To accommodate the extra letters, two buttons—the [7] and the [9]—correspond with 4 letters each.

　a. If letters may be repeated, how many 3-letter prefixes can be formed from this keypad?

　b. How many 3-letter prefixes can be formed if letters may not be repeated?

1.6 The toy store in the mall sells an imitation slot machine with 3 dials. Each dial contains the same sequence of 6 different symbols.

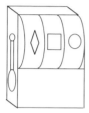

　a. How many different arrangements of 3 symbols are possible?

　b. What is the probability of getting the same symbol on all 3 dials?

Module 11 ■ *Everyone Counts*　309

1.7 In 1997, the state of Alaska used two different numbering and lettering systems for its automobile license plates.

a. One system used three letters followed by three digits. Assuming that all digits and letters may be repeated, how many different license plates are possible using this system?

b. The other system consisted of four digits followed by two letters. Assuming that all digits and letters may be repeated, how many different license plates are possible using this system?

c. Suppose that the state planned to use only one numbering and lettering system for the next 10 years. Which one would you recommend? Defend your choice.

d. Would either of these numbering and lettering systems work in the state of California? Write a paragraph explaining your response.

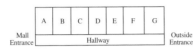

ACTIVITY 2

Excited by the initial success of Riverside Mall, Nadia Nelson has begun planning a new addition. As shown in Figure **11-3**, the new wing will house seven more shops.

| A | B | C | D | E | F | G |

Mall Entrance — Hallway — Outside Entrance

FIGURE 11-3 | Riverside Mall addition.

Exploration

Two business owners already are trying to reserve prime locations in the new wing. In this exploration, you help Ms. Nelson determine the number of different ways in which the stores can be arranged.

a. Draw a tree diagram to determine how many different ways the two businesses can be placed in the seven available locations.

b. Use the fundamental counting principle to verify your response to Part **a.**

310   Module 11 ■ *Everyone Counts*

teacher note

You might wish to wait until the assignment to introduce students to the $_nP_r$ button on their calculators. Students may better appreciate the capabilities of technology (and the corresponding formulas) after they have worked with large numbers.

In Part **g** of the exploration, students are asked to generalize their findings as a ratio in terms of n and r. You may conduct this process as a class endeavor.

Student Outcomes

After completing the following exploration and discussion, students should be able to:

✳ write and interpret factorial notation

✳ apply a formula for permutations

✳ apply their knowledge of permutations to determine simple probabilities.

Exploration

In this exploration, students use the fundamental counting principle to determine the number of ways in which distinct events can occur.

a–b. There are 7 • 6 = 42 arrangements, as shown in the tree diagram below.

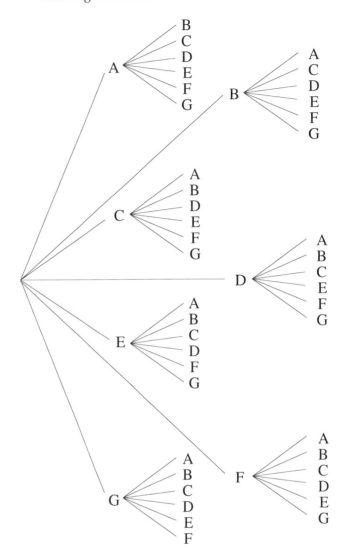

c. There are $5 \cdot 4 \cdot 3 \cdot 2 \cdot 1 = 5! = 120$ arrangements.

d. There are $(7 \cdot 6) \cdot (5 \cdot 4 \cdot 3 \cdot 2 \cdot 1) = 42 \cdot 120 = 5040$ arrangements.

e. 1. There are $7! = 7 \cdot 6 \cdot 5 \cdot 4 \cdot 3 \cdot 2 \cdot 1 = 5040$ arrangements.

   2. The number of arrangements is the same.

f. Sample response:

$$7 \cdot 6 = \frac{7 \cdot 6 \cdot 5 \cdot 4 \cdot 3 \cdot 2 \cdot 1}{5 \cdot 4 \cdot 3 \cdot 2 \cdot 1}$$

g. Sample response:

$$\frac{n(n-1)(n-2) \cdot \cdots \cdot 3 \cdot 2 \cdot 1}{(n-r)(n-r-1)(n-r-2) \cdot \cdots \cdot 3 \cdot 2 \cdot 1}$$

teacher note

In Part **d** of the discussion, students are expected to determine a formula for evaluating $P(n,r)$. After completing this discussion, you might wish to point out that the process described in Parts **a–d** of the exploration leads to the general equation

$$P(n,r) \cdot (n-r)! = n!,$$

which implies that

$$P(n, r) = \frac{n!}{(n-r)!}$$

the formula for the number of permutations of n things taken r at a time.

c. Once the first two stores have been placed, five spaces remain. Determine how many different arrangements are possible for the five stores that plan to rent these spaces.

d. Using the fundamental counting principle, determine the total number of possible arrangements if locations are assigned as described in Parts **a** and **c**.

e. 1. Determine the number of possible arrangements if locations are assigned to seven stores at one time.

   2. Compare this number with your response to Part **d**.

f. Using your responses to Parts **c** and **e**, write the number of arrangements that you determined in Part **a** as a ratio.

g. Use the process described in Parts **b–f** to write a ratio that represents the number of arrangements of r stores in n available spaces, given that $n > r$.

mathematics note

Factorial notation often is used to simplify the representation of the product of the positive integers from 1 to n. If n is a positive integer, then n **factorial** (denoted by $n!$) can be expressed as

$$n! = n \cdot (n-1) \cdot (n-2) \cdot \cdots \cdot 3 \cdot 2 \cdot 1$$

Zero factorial, or $0!$, is defined as 1.

For example, the number of possible arrangements of the letters A, B, and C can be found using the fundamental counting principle as follows: $3 \cdot 2 \cdot 1 = 6$. Using factorial notation, this can be represented as $3!$.

Discussion

a. The numerator of the fraction you wrote in Part **g** of the exploration can be expressed as $n \cdot (n-1) \cdot (n-2) \cdot \cdots \cdot 3 \cdot 2 \cdot 1$. How can this expression be written using factorial notation?

b. How could you use factorial notation to express the denominator of the fraction you wrote in Part **g** of the exploration?

c. How could you use factorial notation to describe the number of ways that r stores can be arranged in n available spaces?

Discussion

a. $n \cdot (n-1) \cdot (n-2) \cdot \cdots \cdot 3 \cdot 2 \cdot 1 = n!$

b. $(n-r)(n-r-1)(n-r-2) \cdot \cdots \cdot 3 \cdot 2 \cdot 1 = (n-r)!$

c. $n! / (n-r)!$

mathematics note

A **permutation** is an ordered arrangement of symbols or objects. The number of permutations of n different symbols or objects taken r at a time, denoted by $P(n,r)$, is given by the following formula:

$$P(n,r) = n(n-1)(n-2)\cdots(n-r+1) = \frac{n!}{(n-r)!}$$

Another commonly used notation for permutations is $_nP_r$.

For example, suppose that a license plate consists of 7 digits from 1 to 9 in which no digit can be repeated. The number of different license plates that can be made using this system is the number of permutations of 9 symbols taken 7 at a time, or $P(9,7)$. Using the formula given above,

$$P(9,7) = \frac{9!}{(9-7)!} = \frac{9!}{2!} = \frac{9 \bullet 8 \bullet 7 \bullet 6 \bullet 5 \bullet 4 \bullet 3 \bullet 2 \bullet 1}{2 \bullet 1}$$

$$= 9 \bullet 8 \bullet 7 \bullet 6 \bullet 5 \bullet 4 \bullet 3 = 181{,}440$$

d. In the formula for $P(n,r)$ given in the mathematics note, why is $n(n-1)(n-2)\cdots(n-r+1)$ equivalent to the following ratio?

$$\frac{n!}{(n-r)!}$$

e. The permutation of n objects arranged n at a time, $P(n,n)$, is $n!$. Use this fact and the formula for $P(n,r)$ to suggest a definition for $0!$.

Warm-Up

1. Substitute each of the values in Parts **a**–**c** for n in the following expression, then simplify.

$$\frac{n(n-4)}{n-1}$$

   a. 10   **b.** 3   **c.** −5

2. Use factorials to write an expression for each of the following:

   a. $P(12,4)$ **b.** $P(8,3)$ **c.** $P(8,7)$

3. Find the value of each of the following:

   a. $P(8,3)$ **b.** $P(8,4)$ **c.** $P(8,7)$ **d.** $P(8,8)$

4. Simplify the expression $n!/(n-1)!$ by first expanding the numerator and the denominator.

---

d. Sample response: The ratio $n!/(n-r)!$ can be written as follows:

$$\frac{n(n-1)(n-2) \bullet \cdots \bullet 3 \bullet 2 \bullet 1}{(n-r)(n-r-1)(n-r-2) \bullet \cdots \bullet 3 \bullet 2 \bullet 1}$$

Because $n > r$, there is some point where $(n-r)$ is one of the factors in $n!$ Therefore, $n!$ can be expressed as shown below:

$$n(n-1)\cdots(n-r+1)(n-r)(n-r-1)\cdots 3 \bullet 2 \bullet 1$$

Dividing the common factors leads to the following equation:

$$\frac{n!}{(n-r)!} = n(n-1)\cdots(n-r+1)$$

e. Sample response: Because $r = n$,

$$P(n,r) = P(n,n) = \frac{n!}{(n-n)!} = \frac{n!}{0!} = n!$$

Therefore, $0!$ must be defined as 1 if the formula is to hold true when $r = n$.

Warm-Up

1. **a.** $\dfrac{10(10-4)}{10-1} = \dfrac{20}{3}$

   b. $\dfrac{3(3-4)}{3-1} = -\dfrac{3}{2}$

   c. $\dfrac{-5(-5-4)}{-5-1} = -\dfrac{15}{2}$

2. **a.** $\dfrac{12!}{8!}$ or $\dfrac{12!}{(12-4)!}$

   b. $\dfrac{8!}{5!}$ or $\dfrac{8!}{(8-3)!}$

   c. $\dfrac{8!}{0!}$ or $8!$

3. **a.** $P(8,3) = 336$
   b. $P(8,4) = 1680$
   c. $P(8,7) = 40{,}320$
   d. $P(8,8) = 40{,}320$

4. $\dfrac{n!}{(n-1)!} = \dfrac{n(n-1)(n-2)\cdots(2)(1)}{(n-1)(n-2)\cdots(2)(1)} = n$

Assignment

Problems suitable for use as assessment items are identified by an asterisk (*).

2.1 **a.** Sample response: Yes, because a batting order is an ordered arrangement of players' names.

   b. 10! or 3,628,800

   c. $P(10, 3) = \dfrac{10!}{(10 - 3)!} = \dfrac{10!}{7!} = 720$

2.2 **a.** Sample response: The arrangement of songs on a tape is a permutation because the order is important.

   b. $P(11, 6) = \dfrac{11!}{(11 - 6)!} = \dfrac{11!}{5!} = 332,640$

   c. $P(5, 5) = \dfrac{5!}{(5 - 5)!} = \dfrac{5!}{0!} = \dfrac{5!}{1} = 5! = 120$

   d. $P(11, 11) = \dfrac{11!}{(11 - 11)!} = \dfrac{11!}{0!} = \dfrac{11!}{1} = 11! = 39,916,800$

   e. They are the same: $332,640 \cdot 120 = 39,916,800$.

   f. $P(11, 6) = \dfrac{P(11, 11)}{P(5, 5)}$

2.3 **a.** Because the order in which a ticket is drawn determines the prize, this is a permutation.

   $P(400, 3) = \dfrac{400!}{(400 - 3)!} = \dfrac{400!}{397!} = 63,520,800$

   b. Because two prizes have been given, only 398 tickets remain. The probability is 1/398 or about 0.0025.

Assignment

2.1 Before a game of slow-pitch softball, each team must submit a batting order—a list of 10 players that identifies the order in which they bat.

   a. Does a batting order represent a permutation? Explain your response.

   b. The Mall Misfits have 10 players on their team. How many different batting orders are possible?

   c. In how many ways can the first, second, and third batters be chosen from the group of 10 players?

2.2 Music Mania's sound technician is meeting with a local band to discuss the arrangement of songs on the band's upcoming demo tape.

   a. Explain why the arrangement of songs on a tape is a permutation.

   b. The demo tape will contain 11 songs, 6 on side A and 5 on side B. In how many ways can 6 of the songs be arranged on side A? Write your answer both as a number and in the form $P(n, r)$.

   c. After the songs for side A have been selected, in how many ways can the remaining 5 songs be arranged on side B? Write your answer both as a number and in the form $P(n, r)$.

   d. The band also plans to issue a compact disc (CD). A CD has only one "side." In how many ways can the 11 songs be arranged on a CD? Write your answer both as a number and in the form $P(n, r)$.

   e. Multiply your answers to Parts **b** and **c** and compare the product to your answer to Part **d**.

   f. Use your results from Parts **c** and **d** to write an equation for $P(11,6)$.

2.3 As part of the mall's grand opening, Almost Human Pets is holding a prize drawing. The first 400 visitors to the store each receive one ticket. At the end of the week, three ticket numbers will be drawn at random. The person who holds the first ticket drawn wins a St. Bernard. The person who holds the second ticket drawn wins a hamster. The person who holds the third ticket drawn wins a guppy.

   a. In how many ways can 3 winners be selected from the 400 ticket holders?

   b. After the St. Bernard and the hamster are given away, what is the probability that any one of the remaining ticket holders will win the guppy? Explain your response.

2.4 Each November, the citizens of Riverside hold elections for city council. The council has 3 members. In this year's election, 6 candidates, including all 3 incumbents, are vying for the 3 positions.

Although the candidates' names are supposed to be listed in random order on the ballot, the first 3 names on this year's ballot are all incumbents.

  a. In how many different ways can the 3 incumbents be listed in the first 3 positions on the ballot?

  b. In how many different ways can the 3 challengers be listed in the last 3 positions on the ballot?

  c. How many different ballot arrangements are possible if the incumbents appear in the first 3 positions and the challengers appear in the last 3 positions?

  d. How many different arrangements are possible if all 6 names are placed randomly on the ballot?

  e. Studies of voter behavior have shown that when there is no strong preference for candidates, those names that appear first on a ballot are more likely to be selected. One of the challengers complains that the ballot was "fixed" to favor the incumbents. Use probability to argue for or against this claim.

2.5 The Store Managers' Association has decided to use a rotary combination lock with 40 numbers for its "Crack the Safe" promotion. One manager suggests telling customers that the secret combination consists of 3 different numbers.

  a. Without this hint, how many 3-number combinations are possible?

  b. How many are possible with this hint?

  c. What percentage of the possible combinations is eliminated by the hint?

  d. How does having this hint affect the probability that someone will open the safe with one try? Explain your response.

* * * * *

2.6 Although the Riverside Mall has 12 stores, there are only 8 parking spaces reserved for store managers. If the 8 spaces are always full, in how many ways can they be occupied by the managers' cars?

2.7 In slow-pitch softball, a "rover" or "short fielder" is added to the traditional trio of outfielders. This results in a total of 10 positions on the field. Although Jean would accept any position on the Mall Misfits, he would like to play catcher.

  a. Before the season begins, 14 players try out for the Mall Misfits. In how many ways can the team fill the 10 positions, if there are no restrictions on who plays a given position?

  b. If Jean must play catcher, in how many ways can the remaining 9 positions be filled?

  c. If all 10 positions are filled at random, what is the probability that Jean will be the catcher?

* 2.4 **a.** $3! = 6$ ways

  b. $3! = 6$ ways

  c. $6 \bullet 6 = 36$ ways

  d. $6! = 720$ ways

  e. Sample response: Because there are only 36 ways out of 720 that the incumbents' names can appear in the first three positions on the ballot, the challenger's complaint is probably valid. The probability that such an arrangement will occur by chance is $36/720 = 0.05$.

* 2.5 **a.** $40 \bullet 40 \bullet 40 = 64{,}000$

  b. $P(40, 3) = \dfrac{40!}{(40-3)!} = \dfrac{40!}{37!} = 59{,}280$

  c. $\dfrac{64{,}000 - 59{,}280}{64{,}000} \approx 7.4\%$

  d. Sample response: This is a change of $4720/64{,}000 \approx 0.074$, or about 7.4%. The probability of guessing the correct combination increases from 1/64,000 to 1/59,280.

✳ ✳ ✳ ✳ ✳

2.6 $P(12, 8) = \dfrac{12!}{(12-8)!} = \dfrac{12!}{4!} = 19{,}958{,}400$

2.7 **a.** $P(14, 10) = \dfrac{14!}{(14-10)!} = \dfrac{14!}{4!} = 3{,}632{,}428{,}800$

  b. If Jean must play catcher, there are 13 people left to fill 9 positions:

$$P(13, 9) = \frac{13!}{(13-9)!} = \frac{13!}{4!} = 259{,}459{,}200$$

  c. 1/14 or about 0.071

Research Project

Students may prepare their reports in written form or as class presentations. Your local Social Security office should be a helpful source of information (ask for "Your Social Security Number," SSA Publication 05-10002). **Note:** Social security numbers are not assigned entirely at random. For example, the first three digits generally indicate the state of residence at the time the person applies.

Students explore counting situations in which repetition is not allowed and order does not matter. The exploration leads to the development of the formula for combinations without repetition.

teacher note

A brief assessment of the mathematical content in Activity **3,** for use at your discretion, appears in the Teacher Resources for this module.

Materials List

- template A (optional; a blackline master appears in the Teacher Resources for this module)

Student Outcomes

After completing the following exploration and discussion, students should be able to:

✳ use the formula for combinations

✳ apply their knowledge of combinations to calculate simple probabilities.

Research Project

Prepare a report on the system of numbering used by the U.S. Social Security Administration. Your report should include answers to the following questions:

a. How does the Social Security Administration assign numbers to individuals?

b. Can two people be assigned the same number?

c. How many different Social Security numbers are possible?

d. At current rates of population growth, are there enough numbers to last until the year 2020? until the year 2500?

As the winter holiday season approaches, Nadia Nelson begins thinking of ways to attract more shoppers to the mall. The decorations, she decides, should be both elaborate and eye-catching. To involve the store managers in the decorating process, she circulates the following memo.

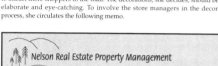

Nelson Real Estate Property Management

To: Members of the Store Managers' Association
From: Nadia Nelson
Re: Selection of Decorating Committee

Congratulations again! Although Riverside Mall has been open for only three months, business has exceeded all initial predictions. Just a reminder that the holidays will be here soon and we must begin planning the mall decorations. My hope is that these decorations will reflect the diversity of your membership and provide a strong enticement to holiday shoppers.

The decorations committee consists of three members. Five managers have volunteered to serve. According to the association bylaws, this committee must be selected randomly from all volunteers. The drawing will take place Tuesday evening at the association's regular meeting. See you there!

Exploration

The last names of the 5 volunteers for the decorating committee are Letasky, Milligan, Novotney, Oliphant, and Payne. In this exploration, the name of each volunteer will be represented by its first letter. For example, Letasky will be represented by the letter L.

a. In Activity **2**, you learned that the number of permutations of *n* distinct items taken *r* at a time is given by $P(n,r)$. Determine the number of permutations of 5 volunteers taken 3 at a time.

b. In this committee, the order of selection does not matter. In other words, a committee of Letasky, Oliphant, and Payne (LOP) is the same as a committee of Oliphant, Payne, and Letasky (OPL).

   1. List the 3-letter arrangements from Part **a** that include L, O, and P.

   2. Express this number of arrangements using permutation notation.

c. All the 3-letter arrangements that include L, O, and P can be considered as one committee. Similarly, all the 3-letter arrangements that include L, M, and O represent another committee. How many different 3-member committees can be selected from the 5 volunteers?

d. Use the fundamental counting principle and your responses to Parts **b** and **c** to write a product that equals the number of permutations of 5 letters chosen 3 at a time, or $P(5,3)$.

e. A collection of symbols or objects in which order is not important is called a **combination**. For example, the number of 3-member committees that can be selected from a group of 5 volunteers is the combination of 5 items taken 3 at a time. This can be written as $C(5,3)$.

   Write an equation that relates the permutation of 5 items taken 3 at a time to the combination of 5 items taken 3 at a time.

f. Write $C(5,3)$ in terms of $P(5,3)$ and $P(3,3)$.

Discussion

a. How did the selection process for the arrangements of stores in Activity **2** differ from the selection process for the decorating committee?

b. Explain why the permutation of 5 items taken 3 at a time is not appropriate for counting the number of committees of 3 from a group of 5.

c. What does the permutation of 3 items taken 3 at a time represent in this context?

d. As mentioned in Part **e** of the exploration, a combination is a collection of symbols or objects in which order is not important. Besides its mathematical definition, the word *combination* has several other meanings.

Exploration

a. The permutation of 5 distinct things taken 3 at a time is $P(5,3) = 60$.

b. 1. The 6 that include L, O, and P are: LOP, LPO, OLP, OPL, PLO, and POL.

   2. In permutation notation, $6 = P(3,3)$.

c. You might wish to distribute copies of template A to help students count the 10 different committees. They are: LMN, LMO, LMP, NLO, OMN, LNP, MPN, OMP, LOP, OPN. **Note:** Each column in the table at the bottom of the page represents a different committee of three.

d. Sample response: The number of permutations of 5 letters chosen 3 at a time is the product of the number of committees (10) and the number of permutations of 3 letters chosen 3 at a time:

$$P(5,3) = 10 \cdot P(3,3)$$

e. Sample response:

$$P(5,3) = C(5,3) \cdot P(3,3)$$

f. $C(5,3) = \dfrac{P(5,3)}{P(3,3)}$

Discussion

a. Sample response: When spaces were assigned to the stores, the order of the assignments made a difference in the arrangement of stores. In a committee, the order doesn't matter because all members are considered equal.

b. Sample response: Using a permutation would allow LOP and PLO to be different committees when, in fact, they are the same. In a combination, the duplicates are removed.

c. Sample response: The permutation of 3 things taken 3 at a time represents the different ways you can choose the same 3 people for a 3-member committee. The letters of each committee could be arranged in a total of 6 ways.

d. Sample response: In a combination for a lock, the order of the numbers is important and repetition is allowed. Neither of these facts fits the definition of a mathematical combination.

LMN	LMO	LMP	NLO	OMN	LNP	MPN	OMP	LOP	OPN
MLN	MLO	MLP	OLN	MON	PLN	PMN	PMO	OPL	NOP
NLM	OLM	PML	LNO	NOM	LPN	NPM	OPM	POL	PON
LNM	LOM	PLM	LON	ONM	NPL	PNM	POM	PLO	NPO
MNL	MOL	LPM	NOL	MNO	PNL	MNP	MOP	LPO	ONP
NML	OML	MPL	ONL	NMO	NLP	NMP	MPO	OLP	PNO

e. Sample response: By dividing both sides of the equation $P(n,r) = C(n,r) \cdot P(r,r)$ by $P(r,r)$, it follows that

$$C(n, r) = \frac{P(n, r)}{P(r, r)}$$

Warm-Up

1. In the formula for a combination, $r!$ represents the number of ways r items can be ordered in groups of r.

2. Sample response: This equation is true since both sides are equal to $C(n,r)$.

3. All of the statements are true. Sample justifications are given below.

a. $C(7, 2) = \dfrac{7!}{2!(7-2)!} = \dfrac{7!}{2!(5!)} = \dfrac{7!}{5!(2!)} = \dfrac{7!}{5!(7-5)!} = C(7, 5)$

b. $C(10, 6) = \dfrac{10!}{6!(10-6)!} = \dfrac{10!}{6!(4!)} = \dfrac{10!}{4!(6!)} = \dfrac{10!}{4!(10-4)!} = C(10, 4)$

c. $C(n, r) = \dfrac{n!}{r!(n-r)!} = \dfrac{n!}{(n-r)!r!} = \dfrac{n!}{(n-r)!(n-(n-r))!} = C(n, n-r)$

Earlier in this module, for example, you determined the number of different combinations possible for a digital lock. What two elements of the mathematical definition show that the *combination* in a combination lock is not a mathematical one?

mathematics note

The number of combinations of n different symbols or objects taken r at a time, denoted by $C(n,r)$, is given by the following formula:

$$C(n,r) = \frac{P(n,r)}{P(r,r)} = \frac{P(n,r)}{r!} = \frac{1}{r!} \cdot \frac{n!}{(n-r)!} = \frac{n!}{r!(n-r)!}$$

Two other common notations for combinations are $_nC_r$ and

$$\binom{n}{r}$$

For example, the number of combinations of 7 letters—A, B, C, D, E, F, and G—taken 3 at a time, can be found as shown below:

$$C(7,3) = \frac{P(7,3)}{P(3,3)} = \frac{7!}{3!(7-3)!} = \frac{7!}{3!(4!)} = \frac{7 \cdot 6 \cdot 5 \cdot 4 \cdot 3 \cdot 2 \cdot 1}{(3 \cdot 2 \cdot 1)(4 \cdot 3 \cdot 2 \cdot 1)} = 35$$

e. The process described in Parts **a–d** of the exploration leads to the general equation $P(n,r) = C(n,r) \cdot P(r,r)$. Describe how this equation can be used to find the formula for $C(n,r)$ given in the mathematics note.

Warm-Up

1. In the formula for a combination, what does $r!$ represent?

2. Is the following equation true or false? Justify your response.

$$\frac{n!}{r!(n-r)!} = \frac{P(n,r)}{r!}$$

3. Determine whether each of the following statements is true or false. Justify your responses.

a. $C(7,2) = C(7,5)$

b. $C(10,6) = C(10,4)$

c. $C(n,r) = C(n, n-r)$

4. Consider the set of numbers {1, 2, 3, 4, 5}.

    a. How many subsets of 3 numbers can be chosen from this set?

    b. How many of the possible subsets of 3 numbers include the number 5?

    c. How many of the possible subsets of 3 numbers do not include the number 5?

    d. How is the sum of your responses to Parts b and c related to your response to Part a?

    e. Generalize the relationship you described in Part d for subsets of r elements chosen from a set of n elements.

Assignment

3.1 Using the letters H, I, J, and K to represent four people, find the number of committees of 2 that can be selected from a group of 4. In other words, determine the combination of 4 items taken 2 at a time. Verify your response by listing the committees.

3.2 The narrators for the mall's daily radio ads are selected from a pool of 12 employees, one from each store. As part of management's efforts to build positive relationships among employees, new teams are chosen each day. Ideally, each employee should work with several different teams during the course of a year.

    a. What size teams would you recommend for the daily radio ads? Justify your response.

    b. James from the pet store and Alice from the flower and gift shop are friends. If the managers' association decides to use teams of 2 for the radio ads, how often can they expect to work as a team?

3.3 The mall's toy store, Toddler's Haven, plans to sell coloring kits that contain 4 crayons, each one a different color. The crayons are available in a total of 12 different colors. Should the store package every possible assortment of 4 crayons or create assortments as they are ordered? Explain your response.

3.4 One of the prizes in the "Crack the Safe" promotion was a deck of cards. Each card in the deck contained the description of an item from one of the stores. After randomly selecting 30 cards from the deck, the winner received each item described on those cards.

In one advertisement for the promotion, store managers claimed "There are more prize combinations possible than there are molecules of air in the mall!"

    a. The mall is a rectangular prism 50 m wide, 120 m long, and 5 m high. One cubic centimeter (1 cm^3) contains approximately $3 \cdot 10^{19}$ molecules of air. About how many molecules of air are there in the mall?

    b. If the managers' claim was true, what was the minimum number of cards in the deck?

Assignment

Problems suitable for use as assessment items are identified by an asterisk (*).

3.1 The number of committees of 2 possible from a group of 4 is $C(4,2) = 6$. Using the letters given, these are HI, HJ, HK, IJ, IK, and JK.

3.2 a. Answers will vary. Students may argue for groups of any size.

    b. There are 66 combinations of 2 employees chosen from a group of 12. James and Alice can expect to work together about every 2 months.

3.3 Sample response: Order is not important for the 4 crayons and there is no repetition, so this is a combination. There are $C(12,4)$ or 495 different assortments possible. It would not be reasonable to produce that many different kits. Toddler's Haven should create the kits as needed.

* 3.4 a. Sample response: The volume of the mall is

$$5000 \text{ cm} \bullet 12{,}000 \text{ cm} \bullet 500 \text{ cm} = 3 \bullet 10^{10} \text{ cm}^3$$

This means that it contains approximately

$$3 \bullet 10^{10} \text{ cm}^3 \left(\frac{3 \bullet 10^{19} \text{ molecules}}{1 \text{ cm}^3} \right) = 9 \bullet 10^{29} \text{ molecules of air}$$

    b. This problem asks "What is n such that $C(n,30) \geq 9 \bullet 10^{29}$?" Through trial and error, students should find $n \geq 135$. The minimum number of cards in the deck is 135.

4. a. $C(5,3) = 10$

    b. Because 5 must be one of the selected numbers, the remaining four numbers are chosen two at a time:

$$C(4, 2) = \frac{4 \bullet 3}{2 \bullet 1} = 6$$

    c. Because 5 cannot be one of the selected numbers, the remaining four numbers are chosen three at a time:

$$C(4, 3) = \frac{4 \bullet 3 \bullet 2}{3 \bullet 2 \bullet 1} = 4$$

    d. $C(5,3) = C(4,2) + C(4,3)$

    e. $C(n,r) = C(n-1, r-1) + C(n-1, r)$, where $r \neq 0$ and $r \neq n$

* 3.5 Responses will vary.

    a. There are 3 • 3 = 9 choices considering crust and size only.

    b. The number of choices of topping combinations can be found as follows:

$$C(10,0) + C(10,1) + C(10,2) + \cdots + C(10,10) = 1024.$$

    c. There are 9 • 1024 = 9216 different choices.

* 3.6 **a.** Row 10 of Pascal's triangle is:

$$1 \ \ 10 \ \ 45 \ \ 120 \ \ 210 \ \ 252 \ \ 210 \ \ 120 \ \ 45 \ \ 10 \ \ 1$$

    b. The sum of the terms in row 10 of Pascal's triangle is:

$$1 + 10 + 45 + 120 + 210 + 252 + 210 + 120 + 45 + 10 + 1 = 1024$$

    c. The numbers of combinations possible for the numbers of toppings are equivalent to the individual terms in row 10 of Pascal's triangle. In other words, $C(10,0) = 1$, $C(10,1) = 10$, $C(10,2) = 45$, and so on.

    d. This is the same result as obtained in Problem **3.5b.**

    e. Using $_nC_r$ notation, row 10 of Pascal's triangle is:

$$_{10}C_0 \quad _{10}C_1 \quad _{10}C_2 \quad _{10}C_3 \quad _{10}C_4 \quad _{10}C_5 \quad _{10}C_6 \quad _{10}C_7 \quad _{10}C_8 \quad _{10}C_9 \quad _{10}C_{10}$$

    f. Using $_nC_r$ notation, the first five rows are:

$$_0C_0$$
$$_1C_0 \quad _1C_1$$
$$_2C_0 \quad _2C_1 \quad _2C_2$$
$$_3C_0 \quad _3C_1 \quad _3C_2 \quad _3C_3$$
$$_4C_0 \quad _4C_1 \quad _4C_2 \quad _4C_3 \quad _4C_4$$

3.7 **a.** The sums of the terms in the first five rows of Pascal's triangle are:

Row 0: $1 = 2^0$
Row 1: $2 = 2^1$
Row 2: $4 = 2^2$
Row 3: $8 = 2^3$
Row 4: $16 = 2^4$

One possible formula is $2^{(\text{row number})}$ = sum of elements in row. **Note:** Although it is possible to prove that

$$\sum_{i=0}^{n} C(n,i) = 2^n$$

students are not expected to provide such a proof.

    b. Using the sample formula given above $2^{10} = 1024$.

3.5 Kuzlowski's Pizza offers 3 sizes of pizza, 3 types of crust, and 10 different toppings. Create an advertisement for Kuzlowski's that emphasizes the variety of pizzas available. Make your claims more believable by including the following:

    a. the number of choices possible considering crust and size only

    b. the number of combinations possible when choosing from 0 to 10 toppings [*Hint:* Find the number of ways that 0 toppings can be selected from 10, then the number of ways that 1 topping can be selected from 10, and so on. Assume that the order in which toppings are applied to a pizza does not matter.]

    c. the total number of pizza choices.

3.6 The figure below shows the first five rows of Pascal's triangle. Although this arithmetic number pattern was previously described by the Chinese mathematician Yenghui and the Persian poet Omar Khayyam, its common name honors the French philosopher Blaise Pascal (1623–1662).

    a. Extend the triangle until it includes row 10. **Note:** The uppermost row of Pascal's triangle is considered row 0.

    b. Find the sum of the terms in row 10.

    c. What is the relationship between the combinations possible for each number of toppings in Problem **3.5** and the individual terms in row 10 of Pascal's triangle?

    d. Describe how the sum of the terms in row 10 of Pascal's triangle is related to your response to Problem **3.5b.**

    e. Write row 10 of Pascal's triangle using combination notation.

    f. Write the first 5 rows of Pascal's triangle using combination notation.

3.7 **a.** Find the sum of the terms in each row of Pascal's triangle for at least the first 5 rows. Use your results to develop a formula for finding these sums.

    b. Use your formula from Part **a** to verify the sum of the terms of row 10 of Pascal's triangle from Problem **3.6b.**

Module 11 ■ *Everyone Counts* 319

---

c. Describe the significance of each number in your formula for the sum of the terms of row 10 of Pascal's triangle as it applies to pizzas and their toppings.

d. Explain why your formula is directly related to the fundamental counting principle.

* * * * *

3.8 a. Consider R = {1, 3, 8, 11}. List all the distinct subsets of R. **Note:** Each subset may contain zero to four elements.

b. How many distinct subsets of R exist?

c. Verify your answer to Part **b** by writing the number as a sum of combinations.

d. Predict a pattern for determining how many distinct subsets exist for a finite set.

3.9 Given 8 coplanar points, no 3 of which are collinear, how many different triangles can you draw?

3.10 In how many ways can a committee of 5 be selected from 20 people?

3.11 If 5 cards are dealt from an ordinary deck of 52 playing cards, how many different hands can occur?

3.8 **a.** The distinct subsets of R are: { }, {1}, {3}, {8}, {11}, {1, 3}, {1, 8}, {1, 11}, {3, 8}, {3, 11}, {8, 11}, {1, 3, 8}, {1, 3, 11}, {1, 8, 11}, {3, 8, 11}, and {1, 3, 8, 11}.

b. The number of distinct subsets of a 4-element set is 16.

c. $C(4,0) + C(4,1) + C(4,2) + C(4,3) + C(4,4) = 1 + 4 + 6 + 4 + 1 = 16$

d. The number of distinct subsets of a set with n elements is 2^n.

3.9 The number of triangles is $C(8,3) = 56$.

3.10 A committee of 5 can be selected from a group of 20 in $C(20,5) = 15,504$ ways.

3.11 The number of 5-card hands in a 52-card deck is $C(52,5) = 2,598,960$.

c. Using the sample formula above, 1024 represents the total number of pizzas that can be made using 10 toppings, 10 represents the number of available toppings, and 2 represents the choices for each topping (either put it on the pizza, or do not put it on the pizza).

d. Sample response: When buying a pizza with a choice of 10 toppings, each topping can either be chosen or not chosen. Thus, the problem can be modeled with the fundamental counting principle using 10 boxes to represent the 10 toppings. Each box contains a 2, representing the choices of whether or not the pizza has that topping. In other words, there are 10 factors of 2, or $2^{10} = 1024$ different pizzas.

✳ ✳ ✳ ✳ ✳

teacher note

An additional assessment, for use at your discretion, appears in the Teacher Resources for this module.

Summary Assessment

1. a. The number of different arrangements is 15! (over 1 trillion).
   b. This number is larger than many calculators will display or compute:

   $$(13 \bullet 2 + 16 \bullet 3)! = 74! \approx 3.3 \bullet 10^{107}.$$

2. a. Because there are 26 letters in the alphabet, it would require $26^2 = 676$ different mugs.
   b. Sample response: I disagree. The permutation of 26 items taken 2 at a time, or $P(26,2) = 650$. This does not allow for initials in which one letter appears twice, such as DD. So 26 more cups, or 676 cups, would have to be printed to accommodate the duplicate initials.
   c. Sample response: No, because using middle initials increases the number of possibilities to $26^3 = 17,576$. That is too many mugs for most stores to stock.

3. a. The number of ways is $C(800,20) \approx 3.8 \bullet 10^{39}$.
   b. Because there are 780 entries remaining, this second group can be selected in $C(780,30) \approx 1.2 \bullet 10^{54}$ ways.
   c. Because there are 750 entries remaining, the grand prize winner can be selected in $C(750,1) \approx 750$ ways.
   d. The probability that any single remaining entry will win is $1/750$.

Summary Assessment

1. Compact disc technology has changed dramatically in the past few decades. The first compact disc (CD) players accepted only one disc at a time and could play music only in the order in which it was recorded.

   a. Manufacturers soon provided an option that allowed users to hear songs in random order. Assuming all orders are possible and no songs are repeated, in how many ways could you play a CD with 15 songs?

   b. The next generation of CD players could hold more than one disc. Some early models allowed users to play up to 5 discs. Imagine that 2 of these 5 discs each contain 13 songs, while the other 3 discs each contain 16 songs. Assuming all orders are possible and no songs are repeated, in how many ways could you play all the selections on the 5 discs?

2. Riverside Read and Feed plans to stock coffee mugs personalized with first and last initials.

   a. How many different mugs would it take to stock every possible arrangement of initials?

   b. One employee argues that the store must order $P(26,2)$ mugs to cover every possible arrangement. Do you agree? Explain your response.

   c. Would you recommend that the store also stock mugs that include a middle initial? Explain your response.

3. As part of an advertising campaign, the Zone Sporting Goods sponsors a drawing. Each customer is allowed one entry in the drawing, and each entrant can win only one prize. A total of 800 people enter the drawing.

   a. Each of the first 20 winners receives the same prize: a discount coupon for 20% off all purchases made on the following Monday. In how many ways can these winners be selected?

   b. After the first 20 winners have been selected, each of the next 30 winners also receives an identical prize: 30% off all purchases made on the following Tuesday. In how many ways can these winners be selected?

   c. After the first 50 winners have been selected, a final drawing is made from the remaining entrants for a single grand prize: 50% off all purchases for the next year. In how many ways can the grand-prize winner be selected?

   d. Imagine that your name is entered in the drawing. You have waited patiently as the first 50 prizes were announced, without winning anything. What is the probability that you will win the grand prize?

So You Want to Build a House

AB

(7, 13)

$y = ax_3$

Overview

In this module, students investigate the planar geometric (Euclidean) system in the context of home construction. They explore triangle congruencies, the Pythagorean theorem, and properties of quadrilaterals. From these explorations, students develop conjectures that are then proved using the definitions, axioms, and theorems of the planar geometric system.

Introduction: Students examine the structural strength of various polygons, gaining some insight as to why triangles are the basic building blocks for construction.

Activity 1: Students determine the minimum information necessary to guarantee congruent triangles. They are introduced to Side-Side-Side (SSS) and Side-Angle-Side (SAS) as methods for proving triangles congruent.

Activity 2: Students are introduced to direct proof. They examine a variety of direct proofs concerning parallel lines and the associated angles. They also write explanations of various proofs of the Pythagorean theorem.

Activity 3: Students develop and prove the Angle-Side-Angle (ASA) and Angle-Angle-Side (AAS) triangle congruence theorems. They use these theorems to prove the relationship that exists in a triangle whose angles measure 30°, 60°, and 90°.

Activity 4: Students investigate characteristics of quadrilaterals, make conjectures, and use triangle congruence theorems to prove these conjectures. They then apply these newly proved theorems to home construction.

Objectives

In this module, students will:

* apply definitions, axioms, and theorems from a geometric system to a real-world context (1, 2, 3 ,4)

* investigate the Side-Side-Side (SSS) and Side-Angle-Side (SAS) triangle congruencies (1)

* identify included sides and angles (1)

* write congruence statements (1)

* write conditional statements in "if-then" form (2, 3)

* use direct proof as a method of establishing theorems in Euclidean geometry (2, 3)

* examine and write proofs (or explanations of proofs) of the Pythagorean theorem (2)

* investigate and prove some properties of quadrilaterals (4).

Prerequisites

For this module, students should know:

* the Angle-Angle-Angle (AAA) property of similarity
* how to determine when polygons are congruent
* how to name angles, segments, and polygons
* how to identify corresponding parts of similar and congruent polygons
* how to identify lateral faces of prisms
* how to name specific prisms
* the definition of corresponding, alternate interior, alternate exterior, and same-side interior angles formed by two lines and a transversal
* the Pythagorean theorem
* how to apply the distributive property of multiplication over addition with polynomials
* the definition of scale factor
* the relationship between scale factor and the ratio of areas of similar polygons
* the differences among various quadrilaterals.

 Flashbacks, for use at your discretion, appear in the Teacher Resources for this module. These brief problem sets provide a review of some prerequisite skills for each activity.

Planning Guide

Activity	Materials	Technology	Time Line
Introduction	■ index cards ■ tape ■ scissors	■ none	1 day
Activity 1	■ ruler ■ protractor	■ geometry utility	3 days
Activity 2	■ graph paper	■ geometry utility ■ symbolic manipulator	3 days
Activity 3	■ ruler ■ protractor	■ geometry utility	2 days
Activity 4	■ ruler ■ protractor ■ graph paper	■ geometry utility	2 days
Assessment Activities	■ ruler ■ protractor ■ graph paper	■ geometry utility	3 days **Total: 14 days**

 teacher note

This module is intended only as a first, informal look at geometric proof. Proof will be studied more formally in later modules, including "Prove It" (Level 3) and "Changing the Rules Changes the Game" (Level 4).

Introduction

Students build models of several different prisms to examine the structural strength of triangles, quadrilaterals, pentagons, and hexagons.

Materials List

- index cards (two per group)
- tape (four pieces per group)
- scissors (one pair per group)

Student Outcomes

After completing the following exploration and discussion, students should be able to:

✴ demonstrate why triangles are a useful shape in structural design.

teacher note

You might wish to conduct the following exploration as a demonstration. It is designed to illustrate the importance of the triangle in building construction and to provoke student interest. It may be omitted without loss of mathematical content.

Exploration

In this exploration, students investigate the structural strength of various geometric shapes by creating lateral surfaces of various prisms.

a–d. Students use index cards to create lateral surfaces for triangular, rectangular, pentagonal, and hexagonal prisms.

e. Students apply pressure to the solids and record their observations. They should note that the triangular prism resists distortion under pressure, thus demonstrating the structural integrity of the triangular shape.

Introduction

Have you ever wondered how a carpenter selects the angle at which to cut a board? Or how builders know what measurements to make to ensure that a house has square corners and straight walls? Although they may not always realize it, they are applying the rules of a mathematical system.

Most jobs require at least some mathematics, but the design, construction, and decoration of a house involve geometry and trigonometry in nearly every step.

Like a home, a mathematical system is built on a foundation. Instead of bricks and mortar, however, this foundation is made of undefined terms, **definitions**, and accepted truths or **axioms**.

You already are familiar with many of the undefined terms, definitions, and axioms of plane geometry. For example, *point* and *line* are undefined terms. A triangle can be defined as a three-sided polygon. And Euclid's first axiom assumes that any two points can be joined by a straight line.

Unlike axioms, however, **theorems** must be proven before they can be accepted as facts. To prove a theorem true, you must construct a convincing argument supported only by definitions, axioms, or previously proven theorems.

The definitions, axioms, and theorems of a mathematical system serve as its rules and regulations. In this module, you examine—and prove—some useful theorems of plane geometry.

Exploration

Although other geometric figures play important roles in home construction, none outshines the simple triangle. In this exploration, you investigate some of the strengths of triangles.

a. Fold an index card exactly in half along its longer side. (The length of the crease should equal that of the shorter side.) Repeat this process for a second card. Cut each card along the crease.

b. 1. Draw dotted lines on one of the half-cards that divide it into thirds, as shown on the right in Figure **12-1**.

FIGURE 12-1
Half-card divided into thirds.

324

---

2. Fold the half-card along each line. As shown in Figure **12-2**, tape the outer edges together to form the lateral surfaces of a triangular prism.

FIGURE 12-2 Triangular prism.

c. Fold another half-card into fourths. Tape the edges to form the lateral surfaces of a rectangular prism, as shown in Figure **12-3**.

FIGURE 12-3 Rectangular prism.

d. 1. Fold one of the remaining half-cards into fifths. As shown in Figure **12-4**, tape the edges to form a pentagonal prism.

2. Fold the last card into sixths. Tape the edges to form the lateral surfaces of a hexagonal prism.

pentagonal   hexagonal
prism   prism

FIGURE 12-4 Pentagonal and hexagonal prisms.

e. 1. Hold a prism between your thumb and first two fingers. Try to roll the prism between your thumb and fingers by gently applying pressure to the lateral surfaces and edges. Record your observations.

2. Repeat Step **1** with each of the prisms you created.

Discussion

a. Describe what you noticed as you rolled each of the prisms back and forth between your thumb and fingers.

b. From the observations you made in Part **e** of the exploration, why do you think that triangular shapes are commonly used in architectural designs?

c. Describe some of the places where you have seen triangular shapes in architecture.

A support for a roof, bridge, or other elevated structure is a **truss.** Figure **12-5** shows a truss for a peaked roof.

FIGURE 12-5 **Roof truss.**

Notice that the basic shape of a truss is a triangle. Within the truss, several other triangles provide the strength needed to hold up a roof.

In a typical house, a series of identical trusses is nailed atop the walls at 2-ft intervals. In mathematics, two figures that are identical in size and shape are **congruent.**

mathematics note

Two polygons are **congruent** ($\cong$) if they can be made to coincide with each other. For this to be possible, the measures of *all* corresponding sides and *all* corresponding angles must be equal.

When describing congruent polygons, the corresponding vertices must be listed in the same order. In Figure **12-6,** for example, quadrilateral *PQRS* is congruent to quadrilateral *YZWX.* This can be written as *PQRS* $\cong$ *YZWX.*

326   Module 12 ■ *So You Want to Build a House*

Discussion

a. Sample response: All of the shapes, except the triangular prism, collapsed as they were rolled between the fingers.

b. Sample response: The shape of the triangle cannot be changed without destroying one of its sides. So it appears to be structurally stronger than any of the other geometric shapes we tested.

c. Sample response: Triangles appear in supports for bridges, roofs, floors, and tents.

ACTIVITY 1

Students determine the minimal number of measurements required to guarantee that two triangles are congruent. Students then develop the Side-Side-Side (SSS) and Side-Angle-Side (SAS) triangle congruencies.

teacher note

The designation of certain axioms and theorems in a geometric system often depends on the student's level of maturity. The SSS and SAS triangle congruencies are treated as axioms in this activity. Their acceptance as such relies on the observations made in the exploration.

It should be pointed out throughout this module that repeated observation is not considered a proof, but may be sufficient support to accept a statement as reasonable.

The Angle-Side-Angle (ASA) and Angle-Angle-Side (AAS) triangle congruencies are proved as theorems in Activity **3.**

Materials List

■ ruler (one per student)
■ protractor (one per student)

Technology

■ geometry utility

teacher note

Students who use a geometry utility will not require rulers or protractors.

Student Outcomes

After completing the following explorations and discussions, students should be able to:

✳ apply definitions, axioms, and theorems from a geometric system to a real-world context

✳ identify and use Side-Side-Side (SSS) and Side-Angle-Side (SAS) triangle congruencies

✳ identify included sides and angles

✳ write congruence statements

✳ write conditional statements in "if-then" form.

Exploration 1

a. Students construct two non-congruent triangles that have one congruent side.

b. Students construct two non-congruent triangles that have one congruent angle.

c. Students construct two non-congruent triangles that have two congruent sides.

Discussion 1

a. Sample response: No. In the exploration, it was possible to create two non-congruent triangles that have one congruent side.

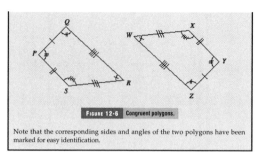

FIGURE 12-6 Congruent polygons.

Note that the corresponding sides and angles of the two polygons have been marked for easy identification.

When two triangles are congruent, each pair of corresponding sides and each pair of corresponding angles have equal measures. However, it is not necessary to measure every side and angle to guarantee congruence. Which measurements are necessary? In this activity, you examine two of the mathematical properties that allow carpenters to answer this question.

Exploration 1

One way to determine which measurements are necessary to guarantee congruence is to explore triangles that are *not* congruent.

a. 1. Construct a triangle. Measure one of its sides.

   2. Attempt to construct a triangle that is not congruent to the first, but which has a side congruent to the measured side. Record your observations.

b. 1. Construct a triangle. Measure one of its angles.

   2. Attempt to construct a triangle that is not congruent to the first, but which has an angle congruent to the measured angle. Record your observations.

c. 1. Construct a triangle. Measure two of its sides.

   2. Attempt to construct a triangle that is not congruent to the first, but which has sides congruent to the two measured sides. Record your observations.

Discussion 1

a. Can you guarantee that two triangles are congruent if they have one side congruent? Explain your response.

Module 12 ■ *So You Want to Build a House*   **327**

b. Can you guarantee that two triangles are congruent if they have one angle congruent?

c. Can you guarantee that two triangles are congruent if they have two sides congruent?

d. In Exploration **1**, you investigated pairs of triangles that had one set of congruent angles. From the Level 1 module "A New Angle on an Old Pyramid," you should recall the **Angle-Angle-Angle (AAA) property:** If the angles of one triangle are congruent to the corresponding angles of another triangle, then the triangles are similar.

The AAA property makes it unnecessary to investigate pairs of triangles that have two sets of congruent angles. Why is this true?

e. As mentioned in the previous mathematics note, the corresponding vertices of congruent polygons must be listed in the same order. Figure **12-7** shows four triangles. Using the markings given, which of these triangles, if any, are congruent?

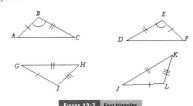

FIGURE 12-7 Four triangles.

Exploration 2

In this exploration, you attempt to create congruent triangles given specific information. You then write conjectures regarding the measurements required to guarantee congruent triangles.

a. Construct a triangle $\triangle ABC$. Record its angle measures and side lengths.

b. 1. Construct $\overline{DE}$ so that $\overline{DE} \cong \overline{AB}$.

2. Construct $\angle DEF$ so that $\angle DEF \cong \angle ABC$.

3. Construct $\overline{EF}$ so that $\overline{EF} \cong \overline{BC}$.

c. Record the angle measures and side lengths for $\triangle DEF$.

d. Compare $\triangle ABC$ and $\triangle DEF$. Record your observations.

e. Repeat Parts **a–d** for two different triangles.

b. Sample response: No. In the exploration it was possible, to create two non-congruent triangles that have one congruent angle.

c. Sample response: No. In the exploration it was possible to create two non-congruent triangles that have two congruent sides.

d. Sample response: If a triangle has two angles that are congruent, then the third angle also must be congruent. According to the AAA property, two triangles with all three angles congruent are similar. Similar triangles do not have to be congruent.

Note: Because the AAA property of similarity can be proved, it is commonly referred to as a theorem.

e. $\triangle ABC \cong \triangle FED$ and $\triangle GHI \cong \triangle JKL$

Exploration 2

In this exploration, students examine pairs of triangles to develop the SAS and SSS triangle congruencies. **Note:** Students will be asked to state their conjectures as conditional statements in the following discussion.

a–e. Students construct several pairs of triangles that have two congruent, corresponding sides and a congruent included angle. They should record the measures of the sides and angles of each pair.

f. Sample response: If two sides and the included angle of one triangle are congruent to two corresponding sides and the included angle of another triangle, then the two triangles are congruent.

g–k. Students construct several pairs of triangles that have three congruent, corresponding sides. They should record the measures of the sides and angles of each pair.

　l. Sample response: If three sides of one triangle are congruent to three corresponding sides of another triangle, then the two triangles are congruent.

Discussion 2

a. Sample response: A side is included between two angles if its endpoints are the vertices of the angles.

b. Sample response: If two sides and the included angle of one triangle are congruent to two corresponding sides and the included angle of another triangle, then the two triangles are congruent.

c. Sample response: Yes. In the exploration, it was not possible to create two non-congruent triangles that had two corresponding sides and the included angles congruent.

teacher note

Students should be cautioned throughout this module that repeated observation is not considered a proof and does not guarantee that a statement is always true.

d. 1. Sample response: If three sides of one triangle are congruent to three corresponding sides of another triangle, then the two triangles are congruent.

　2. Sample response: Yes. In the exploration it was not possible to create two non-congruent triangles that had three corresponding sides congruent.

e. Sample response: ASA for the Angle-Side-Angle congruency and SSS for the Side-Side-Side congruency.

f. Sample response: The minimum number is 45. The measurements could be of the three sides of each truss or they could be of two sides and the included angle. Either way it requires three measurements for each truss.

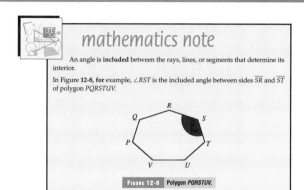

mathematics note

An angle is **included** between the rays, lines, or segments that determine its interior.

In Figure **12-8**, for example, $\angle RST$ is the included angle between sides $\overline{SR}$ and $\overline{ST}$ of polygon *PQRSTUV*.

Figure 12-8 Polygon *PQRSTUV*.

f. Considering your observations in Parts **a–e**, write a conjecture about the minimum measurements required to guarantee the congruence of two triangles. Use the terms *corresponding sides* and *included angle* in your conjecture.

g. Construct a triangle $\triangle LMN$. Record its angle measures and side lengths.

h. 1. Construct $\overline{PQ}$ so that $\overline{PQ} \cong \overline{LM}$.

　2. Construct a circle with its center at Q and a radius of MN.

　3. Construct another circle with its center at P and a radius of LN.

　4. Label the points where the two circles intersect R_1 and R_2.

i. Record the angle measures and side lengths for $\triangle PQR_1$ and $\triangle PQR_2$.

j. Compare $\triangle LMN$, $\triangle PQR_1$, and $\triangle PQR_2$. Record your observations.

k. Repeat Parts **g–j** for two different triangles.

l. Based on your observations in Parts **g–k**, write another conjecture about the minimum measurements required to guarantee the congruence of two triangles. Use the term *corresponding sides* in your conjecture.

Discussion 2

a. The previous mathematics note defined an **included angle**. How would you define an included side for a polygon?

---

mathematics note

A **conditional statement** is one that can be written in **if-then form**. A conditional consists of two parts: the **hypothesis** and the **conclusion**. The hypothesis is the "if" part of the conditional. The conclusion is the "then" part.

For example, consider the conditional statement, "If an animal is a German shepherd, then the animal is a dog." In this case, the hypothesis is "an animal is a German shepherd." The conclusion is "the animal is a dog."

b. Express your conjecture in Part **f** of Exploration **2** as a conditional statement.

c. If two triangles have two sets of corresponding sides and the included angles congruent, do you think that the two triangles are always congruent? Why or why not?

d. 1. Express your conjecture in Part **l** of Exploration **2** as a conditional statement.

　2. Do you think that this conjecture is true? Why or why not?

e. The name of the Angle-Angle-Angle property is often shortened to AAA. What abbreviations would you suggest for your conjectures in Exploration **2**?

f. Imagine that you are a carpenter. To support a roof, you must build 15 congruent triangles. What is the fewest number of measurements you must make to guarantee that all 15 triangles are congruent? What are these measurements?

g. In Figure **12-9** below, *N* is the midpoint of $\overline{IS}$ and $\overline{WG}$.

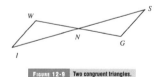

Figure 12-9 Two congruent triangles.

　1. How would you use mathematical symbols to describe the two congruent triangles?

　2. Which of your conjectures in Exploration **2** applies to this situation? Explain your response.

　3. Which of the following statements are true: $\overline{WI} \cong \overline{GS}$, $\overline{WN} \cong \overline{SN}$, and $\angle W \cong \angle G$? Justify your responses.

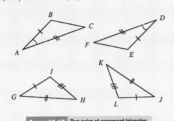

mathematics note

In plane geometry, if two sides and the included angle of one triangle are congruent to the corresponding sides and angle of another triangle, then the triangles are congruent. This is referred to as the **Side-Angle-Side (SAS) axiom.**

If all three sides of a triangle are congruent to the corresponding sides of another triangle, then the triangles also are congruent. This is referred to as the **Side-Side-Side (SSS) axiom.**

In Figure **12-10,** for example, △*ABC* ≅ △*DEF* by Side-Angle-Side (SAS), while △*GHI* ≅ △*JKL* by Side-Side-Side (SSS).

FIGURE 12-10 Two pairs of congruent triangles.

When two geometric figures are congruent, all their corresponding parts (such as sides, angles, or radii) also are congruent. In other words, corresponding parts of congruent figures are congruent.

In Figure **12-10,** for example, because △*ABC* ≅ △*DEF*, it is also true that ∠*B* ≅ ∠*E*, ∠*C* ≅ ∠*F*, and $\overline{BC} \cong \overline{EF}$.

Warm-Up

1. List the corresponding angles and sides for each pair of congruent triangles below.
   a. △*ABC* ≅ △*XYZ*
   b. △*ABC* ≅ △*ZXY*
   c.

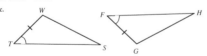

2. In each of Parts **a–c** below, identify the triangle that is congruent to △*ABC*. Justify your responses.
   a.

   b.

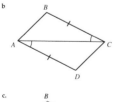

   c.

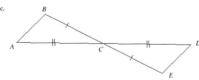

---

g. 1. △*WNI* ≅ △*GNS*

2. Sample response: These triangles are congruent by Side-Angle-Side (SAS). Because vertical angles are congruent, ∠*WNI* ≅ ∠*GNS*. These angles are included between the congruent sides formed by the midpoint: $\overline{WN} \cong \overline{NG}$; $\overline{IN} \cong \overline{SN}$.

3. Sample response: The statements $\overline{WI} \cong \overline{GS}$ and ∠*W* ≅ ∠*G* are true. The two triangles are congruent, so all of the corresponding parts of the two triangles also are congruent.

   The statement $\overline{WN} \cong \overline{SN}$ is false, because these are not corresponding sides of the congruent triangles.

Warm-Up

1. a. ∠*A* ≅ ∠*X*, ∠*B* ≅ ∠*Y*, ∠*C* ≅ ∠*Z*, $\overline{AB} \cong \overline{XY}$, $\overline{AC} \cong \overline{XZ}$, $\overline{BC} \cong \overline{YZ}$
   b. ∠*A* ≅ ∠*Z*, ∠*B* ≅ ∠*X*, ∠*C* ≅ ∠*Y*, $\overline{AB} \cong \overline{ZX}$, $\overline{AC} \cong \overline{ZY}$, $\overline{BC} \cong \overline{XY}$
   c. ∠*S* ≅ ∠*H*, ∠*T* ≅ ∠*F*, ∠*W* ≅ ∠*G*, $\overline{ST} \cong \overline{HF}$, $\overline{TW} \cong \overline{FG}$, $\overline{SW} \cong \overline{HG}$

2. a. Sample response: △*ABC* ≅ △*TSF* by SSS, because all three pairs of corresponding sides are congruent.
   b. Sample response: △*ABC* ≅ △*CDA* by SAS, because $\overline{AC}$ is congruent to itself and ∠*CAD* and ∠*BCA* are congruent, included angles between congruent sides.
   c. Sample response: △*ABC* ≅ △*DEC* by SAS, because ∠*BCA* and ∠*ECD* are vertical angles (and therefore congruent) between congruent sides.

Assignment

Problems suitable for use as assessment items are identified by an asterisk (*).

1.1 Sample response: Yes. Each board is a side of a triangle. So the three sides of each triangle are congruent to the corresponding three sides of every other triangle. By SSS, all the triangles are congruent.

1.2 Sample response: There are two triangles formed by the wall, the ground, and the braces. The wall represents a shared side, and the distance from the wall to each stake is the same. The angle formed by the ground and wall is 90° on both sides of the wall. So two sides and the included angle of one triangle are congruent to two corresponding sides and the included angle of the other triangle. This means that the triangles must be congruent by SAS, so the corresponding third sides also are congruent. So the carpenter could use the same length for both braces.

* 1.3 a. $\triangle FBA \cong \triangle HDE$ by SAS and $\triangle AGC \cong \triangle EGC$ by SSS.

  b. They are corresponding sides of congruent triangles.

Assignment

1.1 To build five congruent triangular supports, a carpenter cuts five sets of three boards each. In each set, the corresponding boards are the same length. She then gives one set to each of five different helpers and asks them to nail the boards into triangles. Will the triangles be congruent? Explain your response.

1.2 When builders raise a wall, they often must secure it with temporary supports or braces. The diagram below shows a wall supported by two braces.

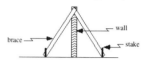

To create this support, a carpenter attached one end of the first brace to the wall, then made sure that the wall was perpendicular to the ground. After driving a stake into the ground, he attached the other end of the brace to the stake.

He measured the distance from that stake to the wall and placed a second stake the same distance from the other side of the wall. He then attached the second brace, which is the same length as the first one.

What mathematics did the carpenter use for this construction? Explain your response.

1.3 The following diagram shows the design for a truss. The boards on the top and bottom of the truss are chords. The interior boards are web members.

In this truss, $\angle A \cong \angle E$. Point C is the midpoint of the bottom chord, $\overline{AE}$; the lengths of the two top chords, $\overline{AG}$ and $\overline{EG}$, are equal.

The distance from A to B is the same as the distance from D to E, and the distance from A to F is the same as the distance from H to E.

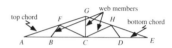

a. Which triangles in this truss are congruent? Explain your response.

b. How do you know that $\overline{BF} \cong \overline{DH}$?

Module 12 ■ *So You Want to Build a House* **333**

c. The following steps prove that $\overline{FC} \cong \overline{HC}$. Explain why each step is true.

1. $\overline{BF} \cong \overline{DH}$
2. $\angle FBA \cong \angle HDE$
3. $\angle FBC \cong \angle HDC$
4. $\overline{AC} \cong \overline{EC}$
5. $\overline{AB} \cong \overline{ED}$
6. $\overline{BC} \cong \overline{DC}$
7. $\triangle FBC \cong \triangle HDC$
8. $\overline{FC} \cong \overline{HC}$

d. Use a step-by-step process like that in Part **c** to explain how you know that $\overline{GC}$ is perpendicular to the bottom chord, $\overline{AE}$. (*Hint:* Two lines are perpendicular when they intersect to form congruent adjacent angles.)

* * * * *

1.4 A flight of stairs consists of stringers and treads, as shown below.

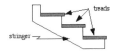

To create the stringers, a carpenter cuts congruent triangles from a rectangular board. The outline of each triangle can be drawn using a framing square. This tool consists of two legs that form a right angle. Each leg is marked in units like a ruler.

The following diagram shows how a framing square was used to draw three triangles on a board.

a. Explain how the carpenter can make sure that all three triangles are congruent to each other.

b. When making a stair stringer, why is it important that each triangle cut from the board be congruent?

1.5 In the diagram below, $\overline{AC}$ and $\overline{BC}$ are radii of circles with centers at A and B, respectively. Describe how you know that $\triangle ACB \cong \triangle ADB$.

c. 1. They are corresponding sides of congruent triangles.
   2. They are corresponding angles of congruent triangles.
   3. They are both supplementary angles to equal angles.
   4. Point C is a midpoint, so both halves are congruent.
   5. This was given in the problem.
   6. The same amount was subtracted from both lengths.
   7. SAS
   8. They are corresponding sides of congruent triangles.

d. 1. $\triangle AGC \cong \triangle EGC$ by SSS.
   2. $\angle GCA \cong \angle GCE$ because they are corresponding angles in congruent triangles.
   3. $\overline{GC} \perp \overline{AE}$ because the two adjacent angles are congruent.

* * * * *

1.4 a. Sample response: The carpenter must use the same marks on the square each time. This makes congruent triangles by SAS because the two sides of one triangle would be congruent to the two corresponding sides of the second triangle. The corresponding included angle is always congruent because the framing square is always at 90°.

b. Sample response: It would guarantee that all the stairs are the same size and same height. Also, if all the triangles are congruent and the first stair is level, then all the stairs would be level.

1.5 The distance from A to D is the same as the distance from A to C because they are radii of the same circle. The distance from B to D is also the same as the distance from B to C because they are radii of the same circle. The side $\overline{AB}$ is shared by both triangles. So the three sides of one triangle are congruent with the corresponding three sides of the second triangle—making the triangles congruent by SSS.

ACTIVITY 2

Students examine a proof of the Pythagorean theorem. They then make conjectures and write them as conditional statements. Students write and explain proofs concerning parallel lines and their related angles and various proofs of the Pythagorean theorem.

teacher note

A brief assessment of the mathematical content in Activities **1** and **2**, for use at your discretion, appears in the Teacher Resources for this module.

Materials List

- graph paper (several sheets per group)

Technology

- geometry utility
- symbolic manipulator

teacher note

Students who use a geometry utility will not require graph paper.

You might wish to allow students to use a symbolic manipulator for the binomial multiplication found in this activity and ask them to explain the results in terms of the distributive property of multiplication over addition. The focus of these operations is not to build manipulative skills, but to facilitate a proof of the Pythagorean theorem.

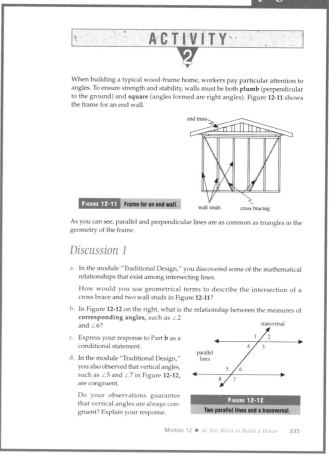

ACTIVITY 2

When building a typical wood-frame home, workers pay particular attention to angles. To ensure strength and stability, walls must be both **plumb** (perpendicular to the ground) and **square** (angles formed are right angles). Figure 12-11 shows the frame for an end wall.

FIGURE 12-11 Frame for an end wall.

As you can see, parallel and perpendicular lines are as common as triangles in the geometry of the frame.

Discussion 1

a. In the module "Traditional Design," you discovered some of the mathematical relationships that exist among intersecting lines.

How would you use geometrical terms to describe the intersection of a cross brace and two wall studs in Figure **12-11**?

b. In Figure **12-12** on the right, what is the relationship between the measures of **corresponding angles**, such as ∠2 and ∠6?

c. Express your response to Part **b** as a conditional statement.

d. In the module "Traditional Design," you also observed that vertical angles, such as ∠5 and ∠7 in Figure **12-12**, are congruent.

Do your observations guarantee that vertical angles are *always* congruent? Explain your response.

FIGURE 12-12
Two parallel lines and a transversal.

Module 12 ■ *So You Want to Build a House*   335

Student Outcomes

After completing the following discussions and exploration, students should be able to:

✳ apply definitions, axioms, and theorems from a geometric system to a real-world context

✳ write conditional statements in "if-then" form

✳ use direct proof as a method of establishing theorems in Euclidean geometry

✳ examine and write proofs (or explanations of proofs) of the Pythagorean theorem.

Discussion 1

a. Sample response: The studs represent parallel lines. The cross brace represents a transversal. So they would represent two parallel lines cut by a transversal.

b. They are congruent.

c. If two parallel lines are cut by a transversal, then the corresponding angles are congruent.

d. Sample response: No. It is possible that there is an example where vertical angles are not congruent. You have to examine *every* set of vertical angles before you can be sure.

mathematics note

Although diagrams, pictures, and multiple observations may be used to support a conjecture, they cannot prove it. To prove a statement, you must create a convincing argument based on logical reasoning. This process is referred to as **proof.**

If the conjecture is written as a conditional, it is necessary to show that the entire if-then statement is true. In other words, to prove that a conditional is always true, a proof must show that the conclusion is true for *every* case in which the hypothesis is true.

There are different methods of proofs. One method is the **direct proof.** A direct proof consists of a series of connected factual statements that are supported by definitions, axioms, or proven theorems. In a direct proof of a conditional, the statements should lead directly from the hypothesis to the conclusion.

For example, consider the conditional statement, "If two angles are supplementary to two congruent angles, then the two angles are congruent." In this case, the hypothesis is "two angles are supplementary to two congruent angles." The conclusion is "the two angles are congruent."

To prove that a conditional is true, you first assume that the hypothesis is true. The two pairs of angles shown in Figure **12-13** illustrate the hypothesis: $\angle b \cong \angle c$ with $\angle a$ supplementary to $\angle b$ and $\angle d$ supplementary to $\angle c$.

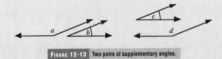

FIGURE 12-13 Two pairs of supplementary angles.

In the following direct proof, the variables a, b, c, and d allow for any possibility in which the hypothesis is true.

Because $\angle a$ is supplementary to $\angle b$ and $\angle d$ is supplementary to $\angle c$, $m\angle a + m\angle b = 180°$ and $m\angle d + m\angle c = 180°$.

Because both sums equal 180°, $m\angle a + m\angle b = m\angle d + m\angle c$.

Because $\angle b \cong \angle c$, $m\angle b = m\angle c$ and it is possible to substitute $m\angle b$ for $m\angle c$ in the previous equation. So $m\angle a + m\angle b = m\angle d + m\angle b$.

Subtracting $m\angle b$ from both sides of the equation results in $m\angle a = m\angle d$, which means that $\angle a \cong \angle d$.

Therefore, if two angles are supplementary to two congruent angles, then the two angles are congruent.

336　Module 12 ■ *So You Want to Build a House*

e. 1. Make a conditional statement about the relationship between the vertical angles formed by two intersecting lines.

   2. Using any pair of vertical angles in Figure **12-12**, try to prove your conditional statement.

     Note: Once a proof has been completed, the conditional statement becomes a theorem. It then can be used to support other proofs.

f. 1. Name a pair of the **alternate interior angles** shown in Figure **12-12**.

   2. Make a conditional statement about the relationship between the alternate interior angles formed by a transversal intersecting two parallel lines.

   3. Using any pair of alternate interior angles in Figure **12-12**, try to prove your conditional statement. (*Hint:* Use your theorem from Part **f** in the argument.)

Exploration

In the Level 1 module "A New Angle on an Old Pyramid," you learned how Egyptian builders might have used the relationship among the sides in a right triangle to help them construct the ancient pyramids. The **Pythagorean theorem** continues to be useful for modern builders.

mathematics note

The **Pythagorean theorem** states that, in a right triangle, the square of the length of the longest side (the hypotenuse) equals the sum of the squares of the lengths of the other sides (the legs).

In Figure **12-14**, for example, $\angle C$ is a right angle, $\overline{AB}$ is the hypotenuse, and $\overline{BC}$ and $\overline{AC}$ are the legs. Because $\triangle ABC$ is a right triangle, $a^2 + b^2 = c^2$, where a and b are the lengths of the legs and c is the length of the hypotenuse.

FIGURE 12-14 A right triangle.

teacher note

The mathematics note states that "to prove that a conditional is always true, a proof must show that the conclusion is true in *every* case in which the hypothesis is true." By the laws of logic, a conditional is false only when the hypothesis is true and the conclusion is false.

Students will be introduced to truth value and truth tables in the Level 3 module "Prove It."

e. 1. If two lines intersect, then the vertical angles are congruent.

   2. Sample response: Because they form a straight angle, $m\angle 1 + m\angle 2 = 180°$. Likewise, $m\angle 3 + m\angle 2 = 180°$ because they form a straight angle. So $m\angle 1 + m\angle 2 = m\angle 3 + m\angle 2$ because they both equal 180°. Subtracting $m\angle 2$ from both sides of the equation results in $m\angle 1 = m\angle 3$, so vertical angles $\angle 1$ and $\angle 3$ are congruent.

f. 1. Sample response: $\angle 3$ and $\angle 5$ are alternate interior angles.

   2. If two parallel lines are cut by a transversal, then the alternate interior angles are congruent.

   3. Sample response: Since the lines are parallel, $\angle 1 \cong \angle 5$ because corresponding angles are congruent. Also, $\angle 1 \cong \angle 3$ because they are vertical angles formed by two intersecting lines. Therefore the alternate interior angles $\angle 3$ and $\angle 5$ are congruent by substituting $\angle 3$ for $\angle 1$.

teacher note

The instructions below can be used to create the squares shown in Figure **12-15** and may be distributed to students. As an alternative, you may create this figure yourself and transfer the file to each student's computer or calculator.

Step 1. Use a geometry utility to create the larger square.
    a. Create one side of the larger square by constructing a segment.
    b. Create a second side by marking one end of the segment as the center and rotating the segment and other endpoint 90°.
    c. Create a segment joining the unconnected endpoints. Mark this segment as a mirror line.
    d. Reflect all the points and segments in the mirror line.

Step 2. Create the four right triangles within the larger square using the following steps.
    a. Draw the second diagonal of the larger square. (The first was the mirror line created in Step **1c**.)
    b. Create a point at the intersection of the two diagonals. This point is the center of the larger square.
    c. Locate a moveable point on one side of the square. This point will control the size of the triangles in the figure.
    d. Use the center of the square and the point on the side of the square to create a circle. The circle should have its center at the center of the square and pass through the point on the square.
    e. Construct a line passing through the center of the square and the point on the square. Place points where this line intersects the circle.
    f. Construct a line perpendicular to the line in Step **2e** and passing through the center of the square. Place points where this line intersects the circle.
    g. Connect the four points of intersection found in Steps **2e** and **2f** to form a smaller square.
    h. Hide (but do not delete) the circle, the center of the square, and all of the lines and segments except those forming the smaller square. This should result in a small square with four unattached points that were the corners of the larger square.
    i. Construct eight segments to reform the larger square by joining the eight points in the figure. The result should look like Figure **12-15**.

Step 3. Save the file.

Over the centuries, many different people have proven the Pythagorean theorem in many different ways. In this exploration, you examine one of these proofs.

a. Create two squares as shown in Figure 12-15 below. The four triangles are all congruent right triangles. The longest sides of the four right triangles create the smaller square.

FIGURE 12-15 Two squares.

b. Determine the area of each right triangle.

c. Determine the area of the larger square.

d. Determine the area of the smaller square.

e. Describe how to find the area of the smaller square using the areas of the right triangles and the area of the larger square.

f. Rewrite your formula from Part **e** using the lengths a, b, and c shown in Figure 12-15.

g. Compare your formula to those of other students. Determine if they are equivalent.

Discussion 2

a. How did you determine if your formula from Part **f** of the exploration was equivalent to those of your classmates?

b. A proof must show that a theorem is true for every case in which the hypothesis is true.

1. What is the hypothesis for the Pythagorean theorem?

2. Does your work in the exploration provide a proof of the Pythagorean theorem? Why or why not?

3. How many different examples would you have to work through to prove that the Pythagorean theorem is true?

Exploration

a. Students may copy the diagram onto graph paper or create it on a geometry utility. (See previous teacher note.)

   If using graph paper, students should make sure that all vertices are on lattice points (to eliminate the possibility of estimation error).

b. **Note:** The sample responses given for Parts **b–d** use $a = 4$, $b = 3$, and $c = 5$. Student answers will vary, depending on the size of the square they choose to create.

   Sample response: $A = 0.5(3)(4) = 6$ units^2.

c. Sample response: $A = (3 + 4)^2 = 49$ units^2.

d. Sample response: $A = (5)(5) = 25$ units^2.

e. Sample response: To find the area of the smaller square, find the area of the larger square and subtract the area of the four right triangles.

f. $c^2 = (a + b)^2 - (0.5)(a)(b) - (0.5)(a)(b) - (0.5)(a)(b) - (0.5)(a)(b)$

g. Students compare their responses to others and determine if they are equivalent.

Discussion 2

a. Sample response: I put the same numbers into my formula and their formulas. If the answers were the same, the formulas were the same.

b. 1. The hypothesis of the Pythagorean theorem is "a triangle is a right triangle."

   2. Sample response: No, because we only looked at few examples.

   3. Sample response: You would have to look at every possible right triangle, which would be impossible.

c. 1. Sample response: You would multiply $(a + b)(a + b)$. First, you would multiply a by the terms in the second set of parentheses. Then you would multiply b by the terms in the second set of parentheses. Finally, you would simplify the result by adding the terms that both contain ab.

2. Students simplify their formulas. The result should be $c^2 = a^2 + b^2$.

3. Sample response: Yes. Because the legs of the right triangles are labeled as a and b and the hypotenuse is labeled as c, $c^2 = a^2 + b^2$ represents the Pythagorean theorem.

teacher note

It is important for students to understand that $c^2 = a^2 + b^2$ represents the Pythagorean theorem only if the triangle is appropriately labeled with the legs as a and b and the hypotenuse as c.

d. 1. Sample response: The expression $(a + b)^2$ represents the area of the larger square. There are four right triangles with an area of $(\frac{1}{2}ab)$ each. By subtracting the area of the four triangles from the area of the larger square, you are left with the area of the smaller square which is c^2.

2. $c^2 = a^2 + b^2$

3. Sample response: Yes. Because the values of a, b, and c could be any values that make a right triangle, it proves that for any right triangle $c^2 = a^2 + b^2$, which is the Pythagorean theorem.

e. Sample response: No. Using the distributive property, $(a + b)^2 = a^2 + 2ab + b^2$ which is not the same as $a^2 + b^2$.

Warm-Up

1. a. Because angle a is a vertical angle with the 65° angle, they are congruent: $m\angle a = 65°$.

b. Since Because angles a and b form a straight angle, the sum of their measures must be 180°: $m\angle b = 115°$.

c. Because angles c and b are vertical angles, they are congruent: $m\angle c = 115°$.

d. Because angles a and d are alternate interior angles formed by two parallel lines, they are congruent: $m\angle d = 65°$.

e. Because angles b and e are corresponding angles formed by two parallel lines, they are congruent: $m\angle e = 115°$.

c. The **distributive property of multiplication over addition** can be illustrated by the equation $a(b + c) = ab + ac$. This property can be used to multiply mathematical expressions such as $(a + b)(c + d)$, a process often referred to as **binomial multiplication**. In this case, the distributive property is actually used two times:

$$(a + b)(c + d) = a(c + d) + b(c + d)$$
$$= ac + ad + bc + bd$$

1. Describe how the distributive property can be used to rewrite the expression $(a + b)^2$.

2. Simply your formula from Part f of the exploration using the distributive property.

3. Is your formula from Part f equivalent to the Pythagorean theorem? Explain your response.

d. 1. One formula for the area of the smaller square in Figure 12-15 is:

$$c^2 = (a + b)^2 - 4\left(\frac{1}{2}ab\right)$$

Explain why this formula is an appropriate response to Part f of the exploration.

2. Use the distributive property to help simplify this formula.

3. Does your result prove the Pythagorean theorem? Explain your response.

e. Are $(a + b)^2$ and $a^2 + b^2$ equivalent expressions? Justify your response.

Warm-Up

1. In the diagram below, lines l and m are parallel. Determine the measure of each named angle and justify your responses.

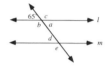

2. Determine the unknown length in each right triangle below.

2. a. $\sqrt{10^2 + 8^2} = \sqrt{164} \approx 12.8$ units

b. $\sqrt{13^2 - 5^2} = \sqrt{144} = 12$ units

c. $\sqrt{24^2 - 16^2} = \sqrt{320} \approx 17.9$ units

3. Multiply each of the following binomials.

   a. $(a + b)(x + y)$
   b. $(a + b)(a - b)$
   c. $(b - a)(a - b)$
   d. $(m + n)^2$
   e. $(a - b)^2$
   f. $(2x + 3y)(x - 7y)$

Assignment

2.1 In the wall frame shown below, the wall studs are parallel, equal in length, and evenly spaced.

   a. Identify all of the pairs of angles that are congruent. Justify your responses.
   b. What axiom or theorem guarantees that the cross braces are equal in length?
   c. Each wall stud is $1\frac{1}{2}$ in. thick and $92\frac{5}{8}$ in. long. The space between studs is $14\frac{1}{2}$ in. How long is each cross brace? Justify your response.

2.2 When two parallel lines are cut by a transversal, the same-side interior angles (such as ∠3 and ∠6 in the diagram below) appear to have a certain relationship.

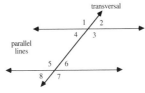

   a. Make a conjecture about this relationship by observing several sets of parallel lines that are intersected by a transversal.
   b. Write your conjecture as a conditional statement.
   c. Write a direct proof for your conjecture.

340　Module 12　■　*So You Want to Build a House*

---

3. **a.** $ax + ay + bx + by$
   b. $a^2 - ab + ab - b^2 = a^2 - b^2$
   c. $ba - b^2 - a^2 + ba = -b^2 + 2ba - a^2$
   d. $(m + n)(m + n) = m^2 + mn + mn + n^2 = m^2 + 2mn + n^2$
   e. $(a - b)(a - b) = a^2 - ab - ab + b^2 = a^2 - 2ab + b^2$
   f. $(2x + 3y)(x - 7y) = 2x^2 - 14xy + 3xy - 21y^2 = 2x^2 - 11xy - 21y^2$

Assignment

Problems suitable for use as assessment items are identified by an asterisk (*).

2.1 **a.** If parallel lines are cut by a transversal, then the alternate interior angles are congruent: $\angle a \cong \angle e$ and $\angle c \cong \angle d$.

   If two lines intersect, then the vertical angles are congruent: $\angle b \cong \angle d$.

   If parallel lines are cut by a transversal, then the corresponding angles are congruent: $\angle b \cong \angle c$ and $\angle f \cong \angle g$.

   b. Sample response: The Pythagorean theorem guarantees that the cross braces will be the same length. They are the hypotenuses of right triangles with congruent legs.

   c. Sample response:

$$\text{brace} = \sqrt{[3(14\tfrac{1}{2} + 1\tfrac{1}{2})]^2 + (92\tfrac{5}{8} + 1\tfrac{1}{2} + 1\tfrac{1}{2})^2} \approx 107 \text{ in.}$$

2.2 **a.** Sample response: The sum of the measures of the same-side interior angles appears to be 180°.

   b. Sample response: If two parallel lines are cut by a transversal, then the same-side interior angles are supplementary.

   c. Sample response: Because they form a straight angle, $m\angle 3 + m\angle 4 = 180°$. Because they are congruent alternate interior angles, $m\angle 4 = m\angle 6$. By substituting ∠6 for ∠4, $m\angle 3 + m\angle 6 = 180°$. Because their sum is 180°, ∠3 and ∠6 are supplementary.

2.3 a. The inner figure in square 2 is a square. All four sides have length c because all four triangles are congruent. As shown in the diagram below, the sum of the measures of the interior angles of the triangle (angles 1, 2, and 3) is 180°. The sum of the measures of angles 1, 4, and 5 is also 180° because they form a straight angle. Angle 3 is congruent to angle 5, so angle 4 must be congruent to angle 2. Therefore, angle 4 is a right angle. Similarly, all four angles of the inner quadrilateral are right angles.

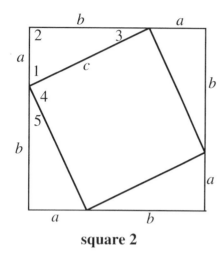

square 2

b. Because square 1 contains four congruent right triangles and two different squares, its area is:

$$4\left(\frac{1}{2}ab\right) + a^2 + b^2$$

or $2ab + a^2 + b^2$. Because square 2 contains four congruent right triangles and one square, its area is:

$$4\left(\frac{1}{2}ab\right) + c^2$$

or $2ab + c^2$. Because squares 1 and 2 are congruent:

$$2ab + a^2 + b^2 = 2ab + c^2$$
$$a^2 + b^2 = c^2$$

2.3 No evidence exists for the original proof of the Pythagorean theorem, but it is generally attributed to Pythagoras himself. According to legend, Pythagoras sacrificed an ox to celebrate the significance of this proof.

The "ox-killer proof" considered two squares, each with a side length of $a + b$. As shown below, square 1 is divided into six non-overlapping regions, while square 2 is divided into five such regions.

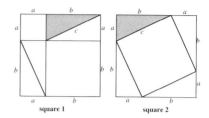

square 1   **square 2**

a. What type of quadrilateral is the inner figure in square 2? Justify your response.

b. Use the areas of squares 1 and 2 to prove the Pythagorean theorem. (*Hint:* Express each square's area as the sum of the areas of its regions.)

2.4 Five years before he became the 20th president of the United States, James A. Garfield discovered a creative proof of the Pythagorean theorem. In his proof, he calculated the area of a trapezoid in two ways: by using the area formula for a trapezoid, and by adding the areas of the three right triangles that compose the trapezoid, as shown below. Verify that his method produces the formula $a^2 + b^2 = c^2$.

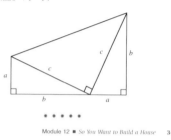

* * * * *

Module 12 ■ *So You Want to Build a House*   341

* 2.4 In general, the formula for the area of a trapezoid is:

$$\frac{1}{2}(b_1 + b_2)h$$

In this case, the formula yields the expression below:

$$\frac{1}{2}(a+b)(a+b) = \frac{1}{2}(a+b)^2 = \frac{1}{2}(a^2 + 2ab + b^2)$$

Adding the areas of the three right triangles yields the expression:

$$\frac{1}{2}ab + \frac{1}{2}ab + \frac{1}{2}c^2 = ab + c^2$$

Setting these two expressions equal to each other:

$$\frac{1}{2}(a^2 + 2ab + b^2) = ab + \frac{1}{2}c^2$$
$$a^2 + 2ab + b^2 = 2ab + c^2$$
$$a^2 + b^2 = c^2$$

✳ ✳ ✳ ✳ ✳

2.5 The diagram below shows the frame of an end wall and an end truss for a storage shed. Each wall stud in the frame is $1\frac{1}{2}$ in. thick and $92\frac{5}{8}$ in. high. The top and bottom boards on the wall are also $1\frac{1}{2}$ in. thick.

The end truss is 9 ft, $9\frac{1}{2}$ in. long. The top boards in the truss are each 5 ft, $1\frac{15}{16}$ in. long.

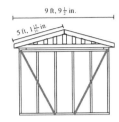

9 ft, $9\frac{1}{2}$ in.

5 ft, $1\frac{15}{16}$ in

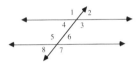

a. What is the highest point of the end wall and truss? Round your answer to the nearest 1/8 in. and describe any assumptions you made.

b. The architect wants to make the shed taller by changing only the roof trusses. This will make the roof steeper, but not wider. Neighborhood building codes restrict the height of any storage building to 12 ft. Considering this restriction, what is the maximum length of the top boards of the new trusses? Round your answer to the nearest 1/8 in. and describe any assumptions you made.

2.6 When two parallel lines are cut by a transversal, the alternate exterior angles (such as ∠2 and ∠8) appear to have a certain relationship.

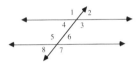

a. Make a conjecture about this relationship by observing several sets of parallel lines that are intersected by a transversal.

b. Write your conjecture as a conditional statement.

c. Write a direct proof for your conjecture.

2.5 **a.** Sample response: Assuming that the bottom of the truss is at the top of the wall, the wall portion of the total height is $92\frac{5}{8} + 3(1\frac{1}{2}) = 97\frac{1}{8}$ in. Half of the truss forms a right triangle. The bottom leg is equal to half the truss length or $58\frac{3}{4}$ in. The hypotenuse is the length of the top board of the truss or $61\frac{15}{16}$ in. Using the Pythagorean theorem, the truss portion of the total height is

$$\sqrt{(61\tfrac{15}{16})^2 - (58\tfrac{3}{4})^2} \approx 19\tfrac{5}{8} \text{ in.}$$

So the total height of the end wall and truss is approximately $116\frac{3}{4}$ in. or 9 ft, $8\frac{3}{4}$ in.

b. Sample response: Assuming that the bottom of the truss is at the top of the wall, the wall portion of the total height is $92\frac{5}{8} + 3(1\frac{1}{2}) = 97\frac{1}{8}$ in. This leaves $144 - 97\frac{1}{8} + 46\frac{7}{8}$ in. for the truss height. Half of the truss forms a right triangle. The bottom leg is equal to half the truss length or $58\frac{3}{4}$ in. The other leg is the height of the truss or $46\frac{7}{8}$ in. Using the Pythagorean theorem, the maximum length of the top board is

$$\sqrt{(58\tfrac{3}{4})^2 + (46\tfrac{7}{8})^2} \approx 75\tfrac{1}{8} \text{ in.}$$

2.6 **a.** The alternate exterior angles appear to be congruent.

b. If two parallel lines are cut by a transversal, then the alternate exterior angles are congruent.

c. Because they are corresponding angles formed by two parallel lines and a transversal, ∠2 ≅ ∠6. Because they are vertical angles formed by two intersecting lines, ∠6 ≅ ∠8. By substituting ∠8 for ∠6, ∠2 ≅ ∠8. So alternate exterior angles formed by two parallel lines cut by a transversal are congruent.

* 2.7 **a.** Sample response: In triangles *ACD* and *CBD*, angles *CAD* and *BCD* are complements of the same angle and thus are congruent. Similarly, angles *ACD* and *CBD* are complements of the same angle and are congruent. Thus, triangles *ACD* and *CBD* are similar.

In triangles *ACD* and *ABC*, angle *CAB* is a common angle and, as argued above, angles *ACD* and *CBD* are congruent. Thus, triangles *ACD* and *ABC* similar. In the same fashion, triangles *CBD* and *ABC* are similar.

b. Sample response: From the sets of similar triangles, the following proportions are true:

$$\frac{b}{c} = \frac{m}{b} \quad \text{and} \quad \frac{a}{c} = \frac{n}{a}$$

c. The proportions given in Part **b** yield the expressions $b^2 = cm$ and $a^2 = cn$. Adding these equations and simplifying results in the following:

$$a^2 + b^2 = cm + cn$$
$$a^2 + b^2 = c(m + n)$$
$$a^2 + b^2 = c(c)$$
$$a^2 + b^2 = c^2$$

2.8 **a.** Sample response: Step 1 begins with the squares on the legs of the right triangle. By holding one side of square *ABCD* fixed and shearing the square, you obtain parallelogram *AB′C′D*, as seen in the following drawing:

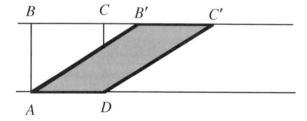

Square *ABCD* and its sheared image, parallelogram *AB′C′D*, have the same area because they have the same base (*AD*) and height (*CD*).

b. Sample response: To reach Step 2 from Step 1, two squares have been sheared to form parallelograms with a common side. To reach Step 3, this shape is translated down by a length of *c*. In Step 4, the triangle area is translated down by a length of *c*.

Note: Euclid's method of shearing demonstrates the Pythagorean theorem by showing that the sum of the areas of the squares on the legs is equal to the area of the square on the hypotenuse.

2.7 In his proof of the Pythagorean theorem, British mathematician John Wallis used similar right triangles, as shown in the diagram on the right.

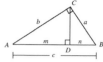

a. Prove that △*ACD* ~ △*CBD* ~ △*ABC*.

b. Use the measures *a*, *b*, *m*, *n*, and *c* to write two true proportions.

c. Use the proportions in Part **b** to prove the Pythagorean theorem.

2.8 Shearing is a transformation that can be used to create parallelograms of equal area by holding one side of a rectangle fixed and sliding the opposite side along the line containing this side. The diagram on the right shows one example of this process.

Euclid began one proof of the Pythagorean theorem with squares on the sides of a right triangle, as in Step **1**. He sheared the squares to obtain the two shaded parallelograms in Step **2**.

The shaded polygon in Step **2** was then transformed to reach Step **3**. Finally, another transformation of a part of the shaded polygon was performed to reach Step **4**.

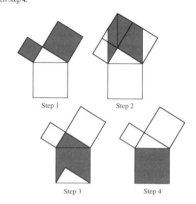

a. Use one of the shaded squares in Step **1** and its sheared image in Step **2** to demonstrate that the areas are equal.

b. Describe in detail the mathematics that occur at each step and explain how this process demonstrates the Pythagorean theorem.

Research Project

According to E. S. Loomis in *The Pythagorean Proposition*, more than 350 different methods have been used to prove the Pythagorean theorem. Use the Internet to search for "proof of Pythagorean theorem." Identify a method that has not already been examined in this activity. Make a presentation to your class in which you explain the selected proof.

In Activity **1**, you investigated the SAS and SSS relationships for triangles. In this activity, you develop two other conjectures about the measurements necessary to create congruent triangles. You then attempt to write a mathematical proof for each conjecture—in other words, to make your conjectures into theorems.

Exploration

a. Create a triangle *ABC*. Record its angle measures and side lengths.

b. 1. Create another triangle *DEF* so that △*DEF* ~ △*ABC*.

   2. Measure the angles and sides of △*DEF*.

   3. Recall that the **scale factor** of two similar figures is the ratio of their corresponding sides. Determine the scale factor for △*ABC* and △*DEF*.

c. Adjust △*DEF* until the ratio of corresponding sides is 1:1.

d. When the scale factor is 1, what is the relationship between the two triangles?

Discussion

a. When two similar triangles are congruent, what is the ratio of their corresponding sides? Explain your response.

b. Consider two triangles with two corresponding angles and a corresponding side congruent. Can you guarantee that the two triangles are congruent? Why or why not?

Research Project

Searching the Internet for "proof of Pythagorean theorem" will return many sites that contain various proofs of the theorem. Students should present one not found in this module and explain how the proof succeeds.

Students develop and prove the Angle-Side-Angle (ASA) and Angle-Angle-Side (AAS) triangle congruence theorems.

Materials List

■ ruler (one per student)

■ protractor (one per student)

Technology

■ geometry utility

---

teacher note

If students use a geometry utility, they will not require rulers and protractors.

The instructions below can be used to create the appropriate figures and may be distributed to students. As an alternative, you may create the figures yourself and transfer the file to each student's computer or calculator.

Step 1. Set the preferences so that angle and distance measurements have a unit precision and scalars have a precision of hundredths.
Create △*ABC* by joining three segments.

Step 2. Follow the instructions below to create a similar triangle using dilations.
   a. Create a point to be the center of dilation.
   b. Construct lines passing through the center of dilation and each of the vertices of △*ABC*.
   c. Create point *D* on the line passing through *A*.
   d. Construct a line through *D* and parallel to $\overline{AB}$.
   e. Construct a point at the intersection of this parallel line and the line passing through *B*. Label this point *E*.
   f. Construct a line through *D* and parallel to $\overline{AC}$.
   g. Construct a point at the intersection of this parallel line and the line passing through *C*. Label this point *F*.
   h. Construct the segments to create △*DEF*.
   i. Hide (but do not delete) all of the lines you created. Leave all the line segments visible.
   j. Save the file.
   k. To find the scale factor, select the sides for which you want the ratio. From the Measure menu, select Ratio.

Step 3. To adjust △*DEF*, move point *D*. To relocate or reshape the construction, move any other point.

Student Outcomes

After completing the following exploration and discussion, students should be able to:

✳ write conditional statements in "if-then" form

✳ use direct proof as a method of establishing theorems in Euclidean geometry.

Exploration

a–b. Students create two similar triangles and record their angle and side measures, along with the ratio of corresponding sides.

c. Students adjust the similar triangles until the scale factor is 1.

d. The triangles are congruent.

Discussion

a. The corresponding sides of congruent triangles are congruent, so the ratio of corresponding sides is 1:1.

b. Sample response: Yes. If two angles of a triangle are congruent to two corresponding angles in a second triangle, the third angles also are congruent. This guarantees that the two triangles are similar by AAA.

When two triangles are similar, the corresponding sides are proportional. If one pair of corresponding sides are congruent, the ratio is 1:1, which means that all corresponding sides are congruent. Therefore the two triangles are congruent.

c. 1. Sample response: If two angles and the included side of one triangle are congruent to two corresponding angles and the included side of another triangle, then the two triangles are congruent.

2. Sample response: ASA.

3. Sample response: If two angles of a triangle are congruent to two corresponding angles in a second triangle, then the third angles also are congruent. This guarantees that the two triangles are similar. When triangles are similar, the corresponding sides are proportional. If the included sides are congruent, the ratio is 1:1, which means that all corresponding sides are congruent. Therefore, the two triangles are congruent.

d. 1. Sample response: AAS congruence does not require the congruent corresponding sides to be included sides.

2. Sample response: The congruent corresponding sides would not be the included sides. Otherwise, the proof would be the same. **Note:** Students write this proof in Problem **3.1.**

e. $\triangle ABC \cong \triangle GIH$ by AAS; $\triangle DEF \cong \triangle JLK$ by ASA; $\triangle GHI \cong \triangle JKL$ by AAS

---

c. Consider two triangles with two corresponding angles and the included side congruent.

   1. Make a conjecture about these triangles in the form of a conditional statement.

   2. What abbreviation could you use to name your conjecture?

   3. Try to prove that your conjecture is always true.

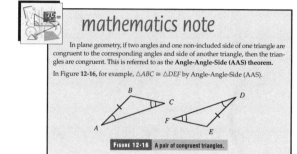

mathematics note

In plane geometry, if two angles and one non-included side of one triangle are congruent to the corresponding angles and side of another triangle, then the triangles are congruent. This is referred to as the **Angle-Angle-Side (AAS) theorem.**

In Figure **12-16**, for example, $\triangle ABC \cong \triangle DEF$ by Angle-Angle-Side (AAS).

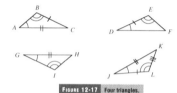

FIGURE 12-16 A pair of congruent triangles.

d. 1. How does the congruence described in the previous mathematics note differ from the theorem you proved in Part **c** of this discussion?

   2. Describe how you could modify your proof from Part **c** to prove AAS congruence.

e. Figure **12-17** below shows four triangles. Which, if any, of these triangles are congruent? Justify your responses.

FIGURE 12-17 Four triangles.

Warm-Up

1. Given the information below, determine which pairs of triangles are congruent. (*Hint:* Draw a picture of each pair.) Justify your responses.

   a. $\angle A \cong \angle P$, $\angle C \cong \angle Q$, $\overline{AB} \cong \overline{PR}$

   b. $\angle A \cong \angle Q$, $\angle B \cong \angle P$, $\overline{AB} \cong \overline{QP}$

   c. $\angle A \cong \angle R$, $\overline{AC} \cong \overline{RQ}$, $\overline{AB} \cong \overline{RP}$

2. Consider each pair of triangles below. Identify the pairs that can be proved congruent, and indicate how you would support your proof. If the marked sides and angles do not supply enough information for you to prove congruence, explain why this is so. (Arrows indicate parallel sides.)

   a.   b.

   c.   d.

   e. f.

Assignment

3.1 **a.** Steps **1–7** below outline a proof of the AAS theorem. However, some key words or symbols are missing, along with the justification for each step, except Step **3**. Fill in the blanks in the proof and provide justification for each of the remaining steps.

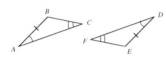

1. If $\angle A \cong \angle D$ and $\angle C \cong \angle F$, then $\angle B \cong \angle E$.

Warm-Up

1. **Note:** If a triangle can be proved congruent by AAS, then it also can be proved congruent by ASA. The converse also is true.
   a. $\triangle ABC \cong \triangle PRQ$ by AAS
   b. $\triangle ABC \cong \triangle QPR$ by ASA
   c. $\triangle ABC \cong \triangle RPQ$ by SAS
2. a. $\triangle ACD \cong \triangle BCD$ by AAS
   b. $\triangle ACD \cong \triangle BCD$ by SSS
   c. $\triangle ABC \cong \triangle CDA$ by SAS
   d. $\triangle ABC \cong \triangle EDC$ by AAS
   e. Sample response: It is not possible to prove congruence. The given information shows two sets of corresponding sides that are congruent, but the given angle is not the included angle. The only triangle congruency theorem with two sets of congruent corresponding sides is SAS, which requires the included angle.
   f. $\triangle ABC \cong \triangle EDC$ by ASA

Assignment

Problems suitable for use as assessment items are identified by an asterisk (*).

* **3.1 a.** Sample response:
   1. If $\angle A \cong \angle D$ and $\angle C \cong \angle F$, then $\angle B \cong \angle E$. If two angles of a triangle are congruent to two corresponding angles of another triangle, then the third angles of the triangles are congruent.

2. If $\angle A \cong \angle D$, $\angle C \cong \angle F$, and $\angle B \cong \angle E$, then $\triangle ABC$ and $\triangle DEF$ are similar triangles by the AAA property.

3. If $\overline{AB} \cong \overline{DE}$, then the scale factor of $\triangle ABC$ to $\triangle DEF$ is 1. The scale factor of similar geometric figures is defined as the ratio of corresponding sides.

4. If $\triangle ABC \sim \triangle DEF$, then:

$$\frac{AB}{DE} = \frac{AC}{DF} = \frac{BC}{EF} = \frac{1}{1}$$

If two geometric figures are similar, then corresponding lengths are proportional.

5. If

$$\frac{BC}{EF} = \frac{1}{1} \quad \text{and} \quad \frac{AC}{DF} = \frac{1}{1}$$

then $\overline{BC} \cong \overline{EF}$ and $\overline{AC} \cong \overline{DF}$. If two lengths have a ratio of 1:1, then they are equal in length or congruent.

6. Therefore, $\triangle ABC$ and $\triangle DEF$ are congruent triangles. If the sides and angles of one triangle are congruent to the corresponding sides and angles of another triangle, then the triangles are congruent.

7. So, if two angles and one non-included side of a triangle are congruent to the corresponding angles and side in a second triangle, then the two triangles are congruent.

b. Sample response: The following diagram shows two triangles with two congruent corresponding angles and a congruent, corresponding, non-included side.

Because $\angle A \cong \angle D$ and $\angle C \cong \angle F$, $\angle B \cong \angle E$.

Because $\angle B \cong \angle E$, $\angle C \cong \angle F$, and $\overline{BC} \cong \overline{EF}$, $\triangle ABC \cong \triangle DEF$ by ASA.

Therefore, if two angles and the non-included side of one triangle are congruent to the corresponding angles and non-included side of another triangle, then the triangles are congruent.

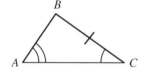
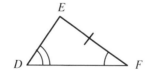

---

page 347

2. If $\angle A \cong \angle D$, $\angle C \cong \angle F$, and $\angle B \cong \angle E$, then $\triangle ABC$ and $\triangle DEF$ are _____ triangles.

3. If $\overline{AB} \cong \overline{DE}$, then the scale factor of $\triangle ABC$ to $\triangle DEF$ is _____. The scale factor of similar geometric figures is defined as the ratio of corresponding sides.

4. If $\triangle ABC \sim \triangle DEF$, then: $\frac{AB}{DE} = \frac{AC}{DF} = \frac{BC}{EF} = \frac{1}{1}$

5. If $\frac{BC}{EF} = \frac{1}{1}$ and $\frac{AC}{DF} = \frac{1}{1}$

then $\overline{BC}$ _____ $\overline{EF}$ and $\overline{AC}$ _____ $\overline{DF}$.

6. Therefore, $\triangle ABC$ and $\triangle DEF$ are _____ triangles.

7. So, if two angles and one non-included side of a triangle are congruent to the corresponding angles and side in a second triangle, then the two triangles are _____.

b. Write another direct proof for AAS that uses SSS, SAS, or ASA as part of the proof.

3.2 Is it possible to create two *non-congruent* triangles with two corresponding sides congruent and one corresponding angle congruent? Justify your response.

3.3 Some triangles are referred to as "special triangles" because of the easily remembered relationships among their sides. One of these—the 30-60-90 triangle—has angle measurements of 30°, 60°, and 90°.

In Parts **a–d** below, you investigate the side lengths of 30-60-90 triangles.

a. Construct an equilateral triangle of any size. From one vertex, construct a perpendicular to the opposite side. This segment divides the equilateral triangle into two triangles.

1. What is the measure of each angle of an equilateral triangle? Explain your response.

2. What is the measure of the angle formed by the intersection of the perpendicular and the opposite side? Explain your response.

3. Write a proof of this conditional statement: "If a perpendicular is drawn from the vertex of an equilateral triangle to the opposite side, then the two triangles formed are congruent."

b. What are the angle measures of the two congruent triangles in Part **a**? Explain your response.

Module 12 ■ *So You Want to Build a House*   347

3.2 Sample response: Yes. For example, the two sides and the non-included angle are given as $\overline{AB}$, $\overline{BC}$, and $\angle BAC$ in the figure below. In this example, there may be two different triangles possible. The circle illustrates that both segments labeled $\overline{BC}$ are congruent radii and shows the two possibilities for point C.

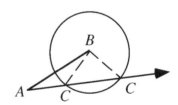

c. 1. Sketch one of the congruent triangles from Part a. Let the shortest side be 5 cm long. Measure and record the lengths of the remaining sides.

   2. Suppose you let the shortest side be x cm long. Express the lengths of the other sides in terms of x. (*Hint:* Use the Pythagorean theorem.)

d. Write a conditional statement expressing the relationship among the sides of a 30-60-90 triangle.

3.4 A furniture company makes tabletops in the shape of a regular hexagon. The edge of the table consists of six pieces like the one shown below. Each edge piece has one pair of parallel sides.

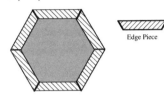

Edge Piece

a. Determine the measure of each interior angle in an edge piece. (*Hint:* Divide the tabletop into six congruent triangles.)

b. Identify the type of polygon represented by an edge piece. Is it a regular polygon? Explain your response.

c. If each edge piece is 8 cm wide, and the side that touches the tabletop is 45 cm long, what is the perimeter of the finished table?

3.5 For the background on a billboard, Britney must paint two intersecting stripes, each 10 cm wide, as shown in the following diagram. Each stripe must be the same length and each must create a 30° angle with the lower edge of the billboard.

3.3 **a. 1.** Sample response: Each angle is 60° because the sum of the three angles is 180° and all the angles of an equilateral triangle are congruent.

   2. Sample response: When two lines are perpendicular, the angles formed measure 90°.

   3. Sample response: All the angles of an equilateral triangle are congruent. The perpendicular forms two right triangles with a shared side within the equilateral triangle. The equal angles of the equilateral triangle and the 90° angle formed by the perpendicular, along with the shared side, proves the two right triangles congruent by AAS.

b. Sample response: Since the sum of the measures of the interior angles of a triangle is 180° and two of the angles measure 90° and 60°, so the remaining angle must be 30°.

c. 1. Sample response: The sides are 5 cm, 10 cm, and approximately 8.7 cm, as shown below.

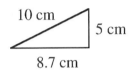

   2. If the shortest side is x cm, then the longest side (the hypotenuse) is $2x$ cm. Using the Pythagorean theorem, the third side is

$$\sqrt{(2x)^2 - x^2} = \sqrt{4x^2 - x^2} = \sqrt{3x^2} = x\sqrt{3} \text{ cm.}$$

d. If a triangle has angles of 30°, 60°, and 90°, then the sides are in the ratio of $1:2:\sqrt{3}$.

3.4 **a.** The angle measures are 60° and 120°.

b. Sample response: Each edge piece is an isosceles trapezoid. The pieces are not regular polygons. The sides have differing lengths and the angles have differing measures.

c. Sample response: Using the equilateral triangle with vertex at the center of the table, the distance from the center of the table to the start of the edge piece is $22.5\sqrt{3}$ cm. Half of the length of each side of the table can be found by solving the equation $x\sqrt{3} = 8 + 22.5\sqrt{3}$, because the distance from the center of the table to the outer edge is the longest leg of a 30-60-90 triangle and is 8 cm farther from the center than the start of the edge piece. Each outside edge length is therefore:

$$\frac{16\sqrt{3}}{3} + 45 \text{ cm}$$

The perimeter is 6 times this length or $270 + 32\sqrt{3}$ ≈ 325.4 cm.

3.5 a. Sample response: Britney should mark off a distance, say 30 cm, along the bottom of the billboard. Then she should place the framing square so that the mark for 15 cm on one of the legs is aligned with the 30-cm mark on the bottom of the billboard. She should then adjust the square so that the edge of the other leg passes through the bottom corner of the billboard. The framing square now forms a 30-60-90 triangle with the bottom of the billboard. A line drawn along the side of the square would be at 30° with the bottom of the billboard. The diagram below illustrates this solution.

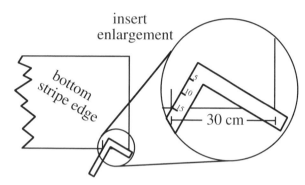

b. Sample response: From the diagram below, the height of the peak of the stripes is equal to $x + y$. Both can be found using the properties of 30-60-90 triangles.

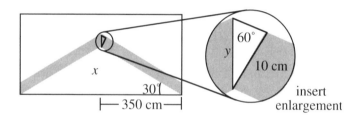

The value of x can be found as follows:

$$(2x)^2 = x^2 + 350^2 \quad \text{or} \quad x = \frac{350\sqrt{3}}{3} \approx 202.1 \text{ cm}$$

The value of y can be found as shown below:

$$y^2 = 10^2 + (0.5y)^2 \quad \text{or} \quad y = \frac{20\sqrt{3}}{3} \approx 11.5 \text{ cm}$$

Therefore, the height of the peak of the stripes is:

$$\frac{370\sqrt{3}}{3} \approx 213.6 \text{ cm}$$

＊＊＊＊＊

a. Britney's only measurement tool is a framing square. How can she use it to help mark the bottom edges of the stripes? (*Hint:* Use the properties of 30-60-90 triangles.)

b. The billboard is 7 m long. How far above the lower edge of the billboard will the tip of the stripes be located?

＊ ＊ ＊ ＊ ＊

3.6 An **isosceles triangle** has two congruent sides. The angle included between the two congruent sides is the **vertex angle**. The other two angles are **base angles**.

Write a proof of the conditional statement, "If a triangle is an isosceles triangle, then the two base angles are congruent." (*Hint:* Draw a line from the vertex of the triangle that bisects the base. Prove that the two triangles formed are congruent.)

3.7 The furniture company in Problem **3.4** plans to make tabletops in the shapes of other regular polygons.

a. Determine the measure of each interior angle in an edge piece for an octagonal table.

b. To automate production, the company would like to determine a formula for the interior angle of an edge piece for tabletops with any number of sides.

Write a formula for the interior angle of an edge piece for a table with n sides.

In previous activities, you wrote and proved conjectures about congruent triangles. In this activity, you examine some other geometric shapes, including rectangles, squares, and parallelograms.

Exploration

a. Create a parallelogram $ABCD$ whose interior angles are not right angles and whose consecutive sides are not congruent. Record the measures of the sides and angles.

3.6 Sample response: The diagram below shows an isosceles triangle ABC and a segment BD that bisects the base AC.

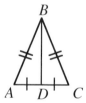

Because the triangle is isosceles, $\overline{AB} \cong \overline{BC}$. Because $\overline{BD}$ bisects $\overline{AC}$, $\overline{AD} \cong \overline{CD}$. Since $\overline{BD}$ is a shared side, $\triangle ABD \cong \triangle CBD$ by SSS.

Since they are corresponding angles in congruent triangles, $\angle A \cong \angle C$. Therefore, the base angles of an isosceles triangle are congruent.

3.7 **a.** The edge piece is an isosceles trapezoid. Its larger angles measure 112.5° and its smaller angles 67.5°.

b. Sample response, where a is the measure of each interior angle of a regular polygon with n sides:

$$a = \frac{1}{2}\left(180 - \frac{360}{n}\right)$$

ACTIVITY 4

In this activity, students investigate characteristics of quadrilaterals. They make conjectures about these characteristics and prove them using congruent triangles. They then apply these theorems to home construction.

Materials List

- ruler (one per student)
- protractor (one per student)
- graph paper (several sheets per student)

Technology

- geometry utility

teacher note

A brief assessment of the mathematical content in Activities **3** and **4,** for use at your discretion, appears in the Teacher Resources for this module.

teacher note

If students use a geometry utility, they will not require rulers, protractors, and graph paper.

The instructions below can be used to create an "adjustable" parallelogram and may be distributed to students. The first two segments control the lengths of the sides. Moving point A allows the user to change the vertex angles.

As an alternative, you may create the figures yourself and transfer the file to each student's computer or calculator.

Step 1. Use a geometry utility to create a parallelogram.
   a. Create $\overline{AB}$ to represent the length of side AB of the parallelogram.
   b. Create $\overline{BC}$ to represent the length of side BC of the parallelogram.
   c. Create a point *not* on either segment. Label this point B. This is vertex B of the parallelogram.
   d. Create a circle with center at vertex B and radius of length $\overline{AB}$. Create a point on the circle. Label this point A. This is vertex A of the parallelogram.
   e. Construct the segment joining vertex A and vertex B. This is side AB of the parallelogram.
   f. Create a circle with center at vertex B and radius of length $\overline{BC}$. Create a point on the circle. Label this point C. This is vertex C of the parallelogram.
   g. Construct the segment joining vertex C and vertex B. This is side BC of the parallelogram.
   h. Construct a line through vertex A and parallel to side BC.
   i. Construct a line through vertex C and parallel to side AB.
   j. Construct a point at the intersection of the two lines. This is vertex D of the parallelogram.
   k. Hide (but do not delete) the lines and circles, leaving the segments and points.
   l. Construct the segments to complete the sides of the parallelogram.
   m. Save the file.

Step 2. Construct the diagonals of the parallelogram. The diagonals should be separated into four segments for observation purposes.
   a. Create the diagonals of parallelogram $ABCD$ by constructing a segment joining the appropriate vertices.
   b. Construct a point of intersection where the two diagonals meet. Label this point E.
   c. Hide (but do not delete) the diagonals, leaving point E.
   d. Construct four segments by joining each vertex to point E.
   e. Save the file.

Student Outcomes

After completing the following exploration and discussion, students should be able to:

✳ apply definitions, axioms, and theorems from a geometric system to a real-world context

✳ make conjectures about some selected properties of quadrilaterals

✳ prove some properties of quadrilaterals.

Exploration

a–b. Students create, label, and measure a parallelogram and its diagonals.

c–e. Students modify the parallelogram to create a rectangle, square, and rhombus. They compare the lengths of the diagonals of the different quadrilaterals.

f. Students create another parallelogram, then repeat Parts **c–e**, focusing on the measures of the angles formed by the intersection of the diagonals and the angles formed by the diagonals and the sides.

teacher note

In the following discussion, students summarize their observations concerning the characteristics of quadrilaterals. You might wish to create a classroom chart of their responses.

Discussion

a. There are 10 diagonals not shown.

b. Sample response: The vertices V and U are adjacent. Diagonals join non-adjacent vertices.

c. 1. Sample response: A parallelogram is a quadrilateral with two pairs of parallel sides.
   2. Sample response: A rectangle is a parallelogram with one right angle.
   3. Sample response: A square is a rectangle with all sides congruent.
   4. Sample response: A rhombus is a parallelogram with all sides congruent.

d. 1. Sample response: The diagonals went from being different in length to being congruent.
   2. Sample response: The length of the diagonals changed, but they remained congruent.
   3. Sample response: The diagonals went from being congruent to being of different lengths.

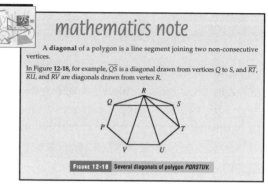

mathematics note

A **diagonal** of a polygon is a line segment joining two non-consecutive vertices.

In Figure **12-18**, for example, $\overline{QS}$ is a diagonal drawn from vertices Q to S, and $\overline{RT}$, $\overline{RU}$, and $\overline{RV}$ are diagonals drawn from vertex R.

FIGURE 12-18 Several diagonals of polygon *PQRSTUV*.

b. 1. Construct the diagonals of parallelogram *ABCD*.
   2. Record the names and lengths of the diagonals.

c. 1. Modify the parallelogram to create rectangle *ABCD*.
   2. Record the names and lengths of the diagonals of rectangle *ABCD*.
   3. What changes did you observe in the modification from parallelogram to rectangle?

d. 1. Modify rectangle *ABCD* to create square *ABCD*.
   2. Record the names and lengths of the diagonals of square *ABCD*.
   3. What changes did you observe in the modification from rectangle to square?

e. 1. Modify square *ABCD* to create rhombus *ABCD*. (Recall that a rhombus has all sides congruent, but may not have all angles congruent.)
   2. Record the names and lengths of the diagonals of rhombus *ABCD*.
   3. What changes did you observe in the modification from square to rhombus?

f. 1. Create another parallelogram *ABCD* and construct its diagonals.
   2. Record the measures of the angles formed at the intersection of the diagonals.
   3. Record the measure of the angles formed by the diagonals and the sides of *ABCD*.
   4. Repeat Parts **c–e**, recording and comparing angle measures instead of side lengths.

350   Module 12 ■ *So You Want to Build a House*

---

e. 1. Sample response: The measures of the angles formed by the diagonals change, but the adjacent angles remain non-congruent.
   2. Sample response: The angles formed by the diagonals become congruent. This means that the diagonals become perpendicular to each other.
   3. Sample response: The angles formed by the diagonals remain congruent, indicating that the diagonals are still perpendicular to each other.

f. 1. Sample response: The angles formed by the diagonals and the sides of the quadrilateral change, but adjacent angles remain different in measure.
   2. Sample response: The angles formed by the diagonals and the sides of the quadrilateral change so that they all become congruent. This means that the angles formed by the diagonals and the sides of a square all measure 45°. This also indicates that the diagonals of a square bisect each of the angles of the square.
   3. Sample response: The angles formed by the diagonals and the sides of the quadrilateral change so that the angles at opposite vertices of the rhombus are congruent with each other, but not with the angles formed at adjacent vertices. This indicates that the diagonals bisect each angle of the rhombus.

Discussion

a. Figure **12-18** shows four of the diagonals of polygon *PQRSTUV.* How many diagonals are *not* shown?

b. Explain why $\overline{VU}$ is not a diagonal of the polygon in Figure **12-18**.

c. Mathematical definitions must be precise. A definition for a triangle, for example, should allow you to distinguish it from other possible geometric shapes. Give a definition for each of the following:

   1. a parallelogram
   2. a rectangle
   3. a square
   4. a rhombus.

d. Describe the observations you made about the lengths of the diagonals as you changed quadrilateral *ABCD* in each of the following ways:

   1. from a parallelogram to a rectangle
   2. from a rectangle to a square
   3. from a square to a rhombus

e. Repeat Part **d** for the angles formed at the intersection of the diagonals.

f. Repeat Part **d** for the angles formed by the diagonals and the sides.

g. For each type of quadrilateral used in the exploration, make a conjecture about:

   1. the lengths of the diagonals
   2. the lengths of the segments formed by the intersecting diagonals
   3. the angles formed at the intersection of the diagonals
   4. the angles formed by the diagonals and the sides.

h. A **kite** is a quadrilateral with two distinct pairs of consecutive congruent sides. Explain your responses to each of the following questions.

   1. Is a parallelogram a kite?
   2. Is a rectangle a kite?
   3. Is a square a kite?
   4. Is a rhombus a kite?
   5. Is a kite a parallelogram, rectangle, square, or rhombus?

g. 1. Sample response: If a quadrilateral is a parallelogram but not a rectangle, then its diagonals are of different lengths.

   If a quadrilateral is a rectangle, then its diagonals are congruent.

   If a quadrilateral is a square, then its diagonals are congruent.

   If a quadrilateral is a rhombus but not a square, then its diagonals are of different lengths.

2. Sample response: If a quadrilateral is a parallelogram, then its diagonals bisect each other.

   If a quadrilateral is a rectangle, then its diagonals bisect each other.

   If a quadrilateral is a square, then its diagonals bisect each other.

   If a quadrilateral is a rhombus, then its diagonals bisect each other.

3. Sample response: If a quadrilateral is a parallelogram but not a rhombus or a square, then the angles formed by the intersection of the diagonals are not congruent.

   If a quadrilateral is a rectangle but not a square, then the angles formed by the intersection of the diagonals are not congruent.

   If a quadrilateral is a square, then its diagonals are perpendicular to each other.

   If a quadrilateral is a rhombus, then its diagonals are perpendicular to each other, thus the angles formed measure 90°.

4. Sample response: If a quadrilateral is a parallelogram but not a rhombus or a square, then the angles formed by the sides and the diagonals are not congruent.

   If a quadrilateral is a rectangle but not a square, then the angles formed by the sides and the diagonals are not congruent.

   If a quadrilateral is a square, then the angles formed by the sides and the diagonals are congruent and the diagonals bisect the interior angles of the square.

   If a quadrilateral is a rhombus, then the angles formed by the sides and the diagonals at opposite vertices are congruent and the diagonals bisect the interior angles of the rhombus.

h. 1. A parallelogram that is neither a rhombus nor a square is not a kite because its consecutive sides are not congruent.

   2. A rectangle that is not a square is not a kite because its consecutive sides are not congruent.

   3. A square is a kite because it has two distinct pairs of consecutive congruent sides.

   4. A rhombus is a kite because it has two distinct pairs of consecutive congruent sides.

   5. A kite does not fit the definition of a parallelogram because its opposite sides are not parallel.

   A kite does not fit the definition of a rectangle because its opposite sides are not parallel and it may not contain a right angle.

   A kite does not fit the definition of a square because all of its sides do not have to be equal and it may not contain a right angle.

   A kite does not fit the definition of a rhombus because all of its sides do not have to be equal.

i. **1.** If a quadrilateral is a parallelogram, then its opposite sides are parallel.

 2. If two parallel lines are cut by a transversal, then the alternate interior angles are congruent.

 3. This is a shared side and any segment is congruent with itself.

 4. ASA

 5. If two triangles are congruent, then the corresponding sides of the triangles are congruent.

j. **1.** If a quadrilateral is a parallelogram, then its opposite sides are parallel: $\overline{AB} \parallel \overline{CD}$.

 2. If two parallel lines are cut by a transversal, then the alternate interior angles are congruent:

$$\angle ABE \cong \angle CDE \text{ and } \angle BAE \cong \angle DCE.$$

 3. If a quadrilateral is a parallelogram, then its opposite sides are congruent: $\overline{AB} \cong \overline{CD}$.

 4. $\triangle ABE \cong \triangle CDE$ by ASA

 5. If two triangles are congruent, then the corresponding sides of the triangles are congruent:

$$\overline{AE} \cong \overline{CE} \text{ and } \overline{BE} \cong \overline{DE}.$$

 6. Therefore $\overline{AC}$ and $\overline{BD}$, the diagonals of $ABCD$, bisect each other.

Warm-Up

1. a. False. A quadrilateral with all sides congruent could be a rhombus without a right angle.

 b. False. A parallelogram that is a square or a rhombus also would be a kite.

 c. True. Even though it also could be a square, a square also is a rectangle.

 d. False. A parallelogram with a right angle is still a parallelogram, but it is also a rectangle.

i. Figure **12-19** shows parallelogram $ABCD$. Steps **1–5** below provide a proof of the conditional statement: "If a quadrilateral is a parallelogram, then its opposite sides are congruent." Describe how you know that each step is true.

FIGURE 12-19 Parallelogram *ABCD.*

 1. $\overline{AB} \parallel \overline{CD}$

 2. $\angle ADB \cong \angle CBD$ and $\angle ABD \cong \angle CDB$

 3. $\overline{BD} \cong \overline{BD}$

 4. $\triangle ADB \cong \triangle CBD$

 5. Therefore, $\overline{AD} \cong \overline{CB}$ and $\overline{AB} \cong \overline{CD}$.

j. Figure **12-20** shows parallelogram $ABCD$ and its diagonals. Using $ABCD$, how could you prove that the diagonals of a parallelogram bisect each other? (*Hint:* Use the theorem you proved in Part **i** above to show that two non-adjacent triangles, such as $\triangle AEB$ and $\triangle CED$, are congruent.)

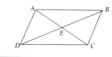

FIGURE 12-20 Parallelogram *ABCD* and its diagonals.

Warm-Up

 1. Indicate if the following statements are true or false. (Recall that a true statement must be true *in every case*.) Justify your answers.

 a. A quadrilateral with all sides congruent is a square.

 b. A parallelogram is not a kite.

 c. A parallelogram with congruent diagonals is a rectangle.

 d. A parallelogram is not a rectangle.

2. Sketch a copy of the parallelogram below. Mark all of the congruent angles and segments appropriately.

3. For each quadrilateral below, identify the axiom or theorem which guarantees that the indicated triangles are congruent. Mark the angles and segments that must be congruent before your selected axiom or theorem can be applied. (Arrows indicate parallel sides.)

   a. △ABC ≅ △DCB   **b.** △ABC ≅ △DBC   **c.** △ABC ≅ △DCB

Assignment

4.1 Recall that the converse of the conditional statement "If A, then B" is the conditional statement "If B, then A."

   a. Write the converse of the statement "If a parallelogram is a rectangle, then its diagonals are congruent."

   b. Sketch a parallelogram *ABCD* with congruent diagonals. Mark your sketch with any other information that you know to be true.

   c. Write a proof for the converse you gave in Part **a.** (*Hint:* For a parallelogram to be a rectangle, it must have a right angle. Show that △*ABD* ≅ △*BAC* and ∠*BAD* ≅ ∠*ABC*. You can then use parallel lines to show that ∠*BAD* and ∠*ABC* must be right angles.)

4.2 In Part **f** of the exploration, you might have observed that the diagonals of a square appear to be perpendicular.

   a. Write this conjecture as a conditional statement.

   b. Draw and label a figure that illustrates the hypothesis of your conditional statement. Mark your sketch with any other information that you know to be true.

   c. Write a proof for the conditional statement that you wrote in Part **a.**

---

2. Sample response:

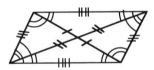

3. **a.** These triangles are congruent by AAS:

   b. These triangles are congruent by SSS:

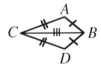

   c. These triangles are congruent by SAS:

Assignment

Problems suitable for use as assessment items are identified by an asterisk (*).

4.1 **a.** If the diagonals of a parallelogram are congruent, then it is a rectangle.

   b. Sample sketch:

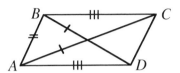

   c. As given in the problem, $\overline{AC} \cong \overline{BD}$. Because the quadrilateral is a parallelogram, then the opposite sides are congruent: $\overline{AD} \cong \overline{BC}$. Since $\overline{AB}$ is a shared side, △ABD ≅ △BAC by SSS.

   If two triangles are congruent, then the corresponding angles are congruent: ∠BAD ≅ ∠ABC.

   If two parallel lines are cut by a transversal, then the same-side interior angles are supplementary: ∠BAD + ∠ABC = 180°.

   If the sum of the measures of two congruent angles equals 180°, then each angle must measure 90°: ∠BAD = 90° and ∠ABC = 90°.

   Because ABCD has at least one right angle, it is a rectangle, by definition.

   Therefore, if a quadrilateral has congruent diagonals, then it is a rectangle.

4.2 **a.** If a quadrilateral is a square, then its diagonals are perpendicular to each other.

   b. Sample sketch:

   c. If a quadrilateral is a square, then all sides are congruent: $\overline{AB} \cong \overline{AD}$. If a quadrilateral is a square, then the diagonals bisect the opposite angles: ∠BAE ≅ ∠DAE. Since $\overline{AE}$ is a shared side, △BAE ≅ △DAE by SAS.

   If two triangles are congruent, then the corresponding angles are congruent: ∠BEA ≅ ∠DEA.

   If two lines intersect to form congruent adjacent angles, then the lines are perpendicular: $\overline{AC} \perp \overline{BD}$.

   Therefore, if a quadrilateral is a square, then the diagonals are perpendicular to each other.

4.3 a. 1. The triangles are isosceles. Because all sides of a square are congruent, the triangles will have two sides congruent.

2. The measures of the angles are 45°, 45°, and 90°. The 90° angle is an interior angle of the square. The two 45° angles are formed because the diagonals of a square bisect the interior angles.

b. Sample response: The sides are 5 cm, 5 cm, and approximately 7.1 cm as shown below.

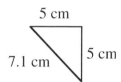

If the shortest side is x cm, then the other leg is also x cm, because the triangle is isosceles. Using the Pythagorean theorem, the third side is

$$\sqrt{x^2 + x^2} = \sqrt{2x^2} = x\sqrt{2} \text{ cm.}$$

c. If a triangle has angle measures of 45°, 45°, and 90°, then the ratio of the sides is $1:1:\sqrt{2}$.

4.4 a. Sample response: The frame has to be a parallelogram because the opposite sides are congruent. It could also be a rectangle, square, or rhombus because these are also parallelograms, but more information must be given to know for sure.

b. Sample response: The carpenters could measure the length of the diagonals to see if they are equal. This would guarantee that the parallelogram is a rectangle.

* * * * *

4.5 Sample response: The diagram below shows a kite and a diagonal that joins the vertices of the included angles of its congruent sides.

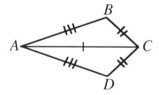

From the definition of a kite, $\overline{AB} \cong \overline{AD}$ and $\overline{CB} \cong \overline{CD}$. Because $\overline{AC}$ is a shared side, $\triangle ABC \cong \triangle ADC$ by SSS.

If two triangles are congruent, then the corresponding angles are congruent: $\angle BAC \cong \angle DAC$ and $\angle BCA \cong \angle DCA$.

Therefore, if a quadrilateral is a kite, then the diagonal that joins the vertices of the included angles of its congruent sides bisects the included angles.

4.3 In Problem **3.3**, you found that the sides of a 30-60-90 triangle have a special relationship. The longest side is twice as long as the shortest side, and the third side is $\sqrt{3}$ times as long as the shortest side.

A special relationship also exists among the sides of a 45-45-90 triangle.

a. Construct a square of any size. Create one of its diagonals. This divides the square into two triangles.

1. Are the triangles equilateral, isosceles, or scalene? Justify your response.

2. What are the measures of the angles of the triangles? How do you know?

b. Sketch one of the triangles. Let the shortest side be 5 cm. Measure all of the remaining sides.

Suppose you let the shortest side be x cm long. Express the lengths of the other sides in terms of x. (*Hint:* Use the Pythagorean theorem.)

c. Write a conditional statement expressing the relationship among the sides of a 45-45-90 triangle.

4.4 A team of carpenters must build a rectangular frame for the foundation of a house. They have cut the boards and nailed them together. After measuring each side of the frame, the carpenters know that opposite sides are equal.

a. Does this guarantee that the frame is a parallelogram, rectangle, square, rhombus, or none of these? Explain your response.

b. Without measuring any angles, what can the carpenters do to ensure that the frame is a rectangle? Justify your response.

* * * * *

4.5 As previously mentioned, a kite has two pairs of consecutive, congruent sides. Each congruent pair of sides forms an included angle. Write a proof to show that the diagonal which joins the vertices of these included angles bisects those angles.

4.6 At a construction site, you observe two workers carrying out the following actions.

After raising and bracing the frame of a vertical wall, one worker holds the end of a tape measure to a top corner of the frame. The other worker stretches the tape to the bottom corner farthest away from the first worker. They record this measurement on a clipboard.

The first worker now moves to the other end of the wall and holds the tape measure at the upper corner. The other worker again stretches the tape to the bottom corner farthest away from the first worker. They record another measurement.

4.6 Sample response: The workers are trying to make sure the wall forms a rectangle. The theorem they are applying states: "If the diagonals of a quadrilateral are congruent, then the quadrilateral is a rectangle."

After adjusting the bracing, they repeat their previous actions. In fact, the two workers continue to repeat the entire process until they get the same measurement twice in a row.

What are the workers trying to do? What mathematical theorem are they applying?

4.7 A farmer has asked an architect to design a barn. She wants one end of the barn to have two windows and a door on the lower level and a double door in the upper level, as shown below.

The farmer would like the height of the main floor to be $1\frac{1}{2}$ times that of the loft. The lower part of the roof should have a 45° slope from the horizontal, and the upper roof should have a 30° slope. The two parts of the roof should rise the same distance. The height of the peak will be 8.5 m.

a. Make a sketch of the outer frame of the barn (shown in bold in the diagram above). Use your sketch to determine the length of each of the seven pieces of lumber in the outer frame.

b. This end of the barn will be sheathed with plywood. If each sheet of plywood measures 125 cm by 250 cm, how many sheets should the farmer buy?

4.7 **a.** Sample sketch:

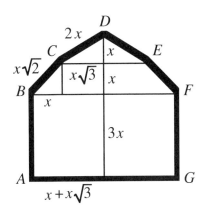

Because the total height of the barn is to be 8.5 m, $5x = 8.5$ and $x = 1.7$ m. So the lengths of the boards in each outer frame are 5.1 m for $\overline{AB}$ and $\overline{FG}$, $1.7\sqrt{2} \approx 2.4$ m for $\overline{BC}$ and $\overline{EF}$, 3.4 m for $\overline{CD}$ and $\overline{DE}$, and $2(1.7 + 1.7\sqrt{3}) \approx 9.3$ m for $\overline{AG}$.

b. Sample response: From the sketch above, the area for $\triangle CDE$ is:

$$\frac{1}{2}\left(2 \bullet 1.7 \bullet \sqrt{3}\right)(1.7) \approx 5 \text{ m}^2$$

The area of the trapezoid $BCEF$ is:

$$\frac{1}{2}(1.7)\left(2 \bullet 1.7 + 2 \bullet 1.7\sqrt{3}\right) \approx 7.9 \text{ m}^2$$

The area of the rectangle $ABFG$ is:

$$(3 \bullet 1.7)\left[2\left(1.7 + 1.7\sqrt{3}\right)\right] \approx 47.4 \text{ m}^2$$

This makes the total area for the face of the barn approximately 60.3 m². Each piece of plywood covers 31,250 cm² or 3.125 m². So it would take 20 sheets of plywood.

teacher note

An additional assessment, for use at your discretion, appears in the Teacher Resources for this module.

Summary Assessment

1. a. Sample response: No. The frame is a parallelogram because the opposite sides are congruent. If the angles are 90°, the parallelogram must be a rectangle. The diagonals of a rectangle are congruent. These diagonals are not, so the frame is not a rectangle and does not have all right angles.

   b. Sample response: The diagonals should both measure $\sqrt{12^2 + 10^2} \approx 15.62$ m. This is because each diagonal and the sides of a rectangle form a right triangle in which the diagonal is the hypotenuse.

2. Sample response: The original squares have a total area of $a^2 + b^2$. Moving the triangles does not change the total area. The area of the new square formed is c^2. Therefore $a^2 + b^2 = c^2$, where a and b are the legs of a right triangle and c is the hypotenuse. So this proves the Pythagorean theorem.

3. Sample response: The diagram below shows an isosceles triangle with a segment drawn from the vertex to the midpoint of the base.

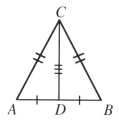

Because the triangle is isosceles, it has two congruent sides: $\overline{AC} \cong \overline{BC}$. Because D is the midpoint of $\overline{AB}$, $\overline{AD} \cong \overline{BD}$. Because $\overline{CD}$ is a shared side, $\triangle ACD \cong \triangle BCD$ by SSS.

  If two triangles are congruent, then the corresponding angles are congruent: $\angle ADC \cong \angle BDC$.

  If two intersecting lines meet to form congruent adjacent angles, then the lines are perpendicular: $\overline{CD} \perp \overline{AB}$.

  Therefore, if a segment drawn from the vertex of an isosceles triangle to the midpoint of the base, then the segment is perpendicular to the base.

Summary Assessment

1. Two carpenters built a frame for the floor of a house in the shape of a quadrilateral. The shorter sides of the frame measure 10 m. The longer sides measure 12 m. The two diagonals of the frame measure 16.4 m and 14.7 m. The frame must contain all right angles before the construction can continue.

   a. Does the frame have all right angles? Justify your response.

   b. If you answered "yes" to Part **a**, what are the measures of the angles formed by the intersecting diagonals?

   If you answered "no" to Part **a**, how long should the diagonals be to guarantee that the frame contains all right angles? Justify your response.

2. The figure below shows two squares. The larger square measures a units on a side. The smaller square measures b units on a side.

   Two segments have been drawn through the squares and each measures c units. They form two right triangles, as shown below.

   If the two triangles are rotated 90° as shown below, the following diagram results.

   Explain how this proves the Pythagorean theorem.

3. Write a proof of the conditional statement, "If a segment is drawn from the vertex of an isosceles triangle to the midpoint of the base, then the segment is perpendicular to the base." (*Hint:* If two adjacent angles formed by intersecting lines are congruent, then the lines are perpendicular.)

4. Many houses are designed to reduce the amount of materials needed to build them. One such design is called the A-frame. As the name implies, the structure uses a frame shaped like the letter A.

The diagram below shows the front of an A-frame house with a triangular window with four panes.

The A-frame forms an isosceles triangle. Its sides are 8.2 m long and the bottom is 4.9 m across. The window frame forms a triangle similar to that of the A-frame, with a scale factor of 2/3.

How much glass does the window require? Explain your response.

4. Sample response: Using the Pythagorean theorem, the height of the A-frame is $\sqrt{8.2^2 + 2.45^2} \approx 7.8$ m. So the area of the A-frame is approximately $1/2(4.9)(7.8) = 19.11$ m^2. The areas of similar figures are proportional to the square of the scale factor, therefore the area of the triangular window is $(2/3)^2(19.11) \approx 8.5$ m^2.

(7, 13)

Hurry! Hurry! Hurry! Step Right Up!

Overview

In this module, students use geometric models to explore experimental probabilities, theoretical probabilities, conditional probabilities, and expected values.

Activity 1:   Students use geometric models to determine experimental probabilities and use geometric formulas to compare theoretical and experimental probabilities.

Activity 2:   Students use expected values to determine costs and analyze the fairness of games.

Activity 3:   Students explore multistage and conditional probabilities.

Objectives

In this module, students will:

* compare experimental and theoretical probabilities (1, 2)

* determine theoretical probabilities using geometric models (1, 2, 3)

* find probabilities of complementary events (1)

* determine expected values (2, 3)

* identify events as independent or dependent (3)

* use tree diagrams to determine probabilities (3)

* determine conditional probabilities (3).

Prerequisites

For this module, students should know:

* how to determine the area of regular polygons and circles

* the definition of a fair game

* how to graph systems of linear inequalities on a coordinate plane

* the definition of complementary events

* how to create tree diagrams and use them to determine probabilities

* how to identify the sample space for an experiment

* how to determine theoretical and experimental probabilities

* how to calculate expected value.

 Flashbacks, for use at your discretion, appear in the Teacher Resources for this module. These brief problem sets provide a review of some prerequisite skills for each activity.

Planning Guide

Activity	Materials	Technology	Time Line
Introduction and Activity **1**	■ dimes ■ quarters ■ centimeter graph paper ■ cardboard ■ tape ■ rulers ■ pizza boxes (optional)	■ none	3 days
Activity **2**	■ dice	■ none	2 days
Activity **3**	■ poker chips ■ paper bags	■ random number generator	4 days
Assessment Activities	■ none	■ none	3 days **Total: 12 days**

Introduction

This module uses carnival games to introduce geometric models for determining probability.

Student Outcomes

After completing the following discussion, students should be able to:

✳ begin considering probability using geometric models

✳ recall the definition of a fair game.

Discussion

a. Sample response: The spinner has a better chance because it appears to win half the time. The dart looks like it has less than a 50% chance of winning.

b. Sample response: It is necessary to use the tip so that a single point determines the part of the board in which the spinner lands. If the entire head of the arrow is considered, the spinner could land in more than one part of the board.

c. 1. Students may mention tossing rings onto the necks of pop bottles, throwing a ball through an opening, shooting at a target with an air rifle, using a sledge-hammer to ring a bell, shooting a basketball through a hoop, throwing darts at balloons, knocking over bottles with a ball, playing a raffle, or catching metal disks with a magnet attached to a fishing pole.

   2. Some games, such as shooting baskets or throwing darts, involve at least some degree of skill. Others, such as raffles or bingo, are based on chance. Still others involve a mix of chance and skill.

d. Answers will vary. Students might prefer the dart game because at least some skill is involved. Others may choose the spinner game, arguing that the chances of winning seem better. **Note:** Students are not expected to calculate the probabilities of winning at this time. This situation is revisited in Problem **1.5**.

e. Because most carnival games are designed both for entertainment and profit-making, they usually are not fair games in the mathematical sense. Many carnival games allow few winners, or offer inexpensive prizes, to keep the expected value low. Some students may argue that foul play also makes some games unfair (for example, weighted bottles or bent rifle sights).

Introduction

A carnival barker beckons to you from the midway: "Step right up! You look like a winner!" The barker's booth is decorated with enticing prizes. He says that you can choose from one of two games. One requires you to throw a dart at a board while blindfolded, the other involves twirling a spinner on an identical board.

To win, either the dart or the arrow must land in the unshaded portion of the board. The two game boards are shown in Figure 13-1 below.

FIGURE 13-1 Two carnival game boards.

"Put your ticket down," says the barker, "choose a game, and take a chance." When you hesitate, the barker assures you that you can continue throwing darts until one hits the board and that the spinner is equally likely to stop at any point on its arc.

Discussion

a. Which has a better chance of landing in the unshaded portion of the board: a dart thrown while blindfolded, or the arrow on the spinner? Explain your response.

b. When determining whether or not the arrow landed in the unshaded portion, why should you consider only the tip of the arrow?

c. 1. What kinds of carnival games have you played or seen others play?

   2. Were those games based on skill or on chance? Explain your reasoning.

d. Which of the games shown in Figure **13-1** would you rather play? Why?

e. Do you think that carnival games are fair? Explain your response.

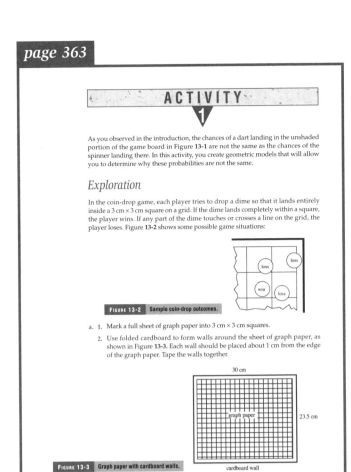

ACTIVITY 1

As you observed in the introduction, the chances of a dart landing in the unshaded portion of the game board in Figure **13-1** are not the same as the chances of the spinner landing there. In this activity, you create geometric models that will allow you to determine why these probabilities are not the same.

Exploration

In the coin-drop game, each player tries to drop a dime so that it lands entirely inside a 3 cm × 3 cm square on a grid. If the dime lands completely within a square, the player wins. If any part of the dime touches or crosses a line on the grid, the player loses. Figure **13-2** shows some possible game situations:

FIGURE 13-2 Sample coin-drop outcomes.

a. 1. Mark a full sheet of graph paper into 3 cm × 3 cm squares.

   2. Use folded cardboard to form walls around the sheet of graph paper, as shown in Figure **13-3**. Each wall should be placed about 1 cm from the edge of the graph paper. Tape the walls together.

FIGURE 13-3 Graph paper with cardboard walls.

Module 13 ■ *Hurry! Hurry! Hurry! Step Right Up!* 363

ACTIVITY 1

In this activity, students use geometric models to determine probability.

Materials List

- dimes (one per group)
- quarters (one per group; for Problem **1.1**)
- centimeter graph paper (one sheet per group)
- rulers (one per group)
- cardboard (four sheets per group)
- pizza boxes (optional)
- tape

---

teacher note

In the following exploration, students may use pizza boxes as an alternative to building cardboard enclosures. Students should mark the bottom of each box with a 3 cm × 3 cm grid, leaving a border of at least 1 cm on each side. They should then use the dimensions of the box and its corresponding grid to determine the probabilities of winning the game.

This exploration works well for groups of two students. After one student drops the coin onto the grid, the other can judge and record wins or losses. If any part of the dime touches or crosses a line on the grid, the player loses.

In Part **e**, students are asked to find the area of the region that represents a win. This area might be difficult for some students to visualize. You might wish to create a model using a square drawn on an overhead transparency to represent one square on the grid and a circle of paper to represent the dime. By punching a hole in the center of the "dime" and inserting a marker, you can trace the outline of the winning region as you move the dime inside the square.

Student Outcomes

After completing the following exploration and discussion, students should be able to:

✳ create geometric models to determine theoretical probabilities

✳ compare experimental and theoretical probabilities.

Exploration

Students play the coin-drop game and record the experimental outcomes.

a. Students create a game board with four walls around it.

b–c. **Note:** If dimes are dropped from too great a height, they might bounce over the walls. Placing a notebook under the grid can reduce bouncing.

d. Experimental probabilities will vary. The theoretical probability of winning is approximately 0.16 when the game is played on an 8.5 in. × 11 in. board.

e. 1. Answers may vary. Given a dime with a radius of 0.9 cm, the center of the dime must be at least 0.9 cm from each line on the grid.

2. Using the center of the dime as a reference point, the region that models all winning outcomes is a square within the 3 cm × 3 cm square. The following diagram shows eight possible positions for winning dimes, the centers of these dimes, and the square formed by the centers of all winning coins.

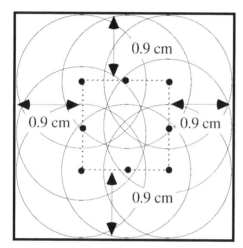

The area of the region that models winning outcomes is approximately $(3 - (2 \cdot 0.9))^2 = 1.44$ cm^2.

3. The theoretical probability can be determined by dividing the area of the inner square (representing all winning outcomes) by the area of the outer square (representing all possible outcomes):

$$\frac{\text{area of inner square}}{\text{area of outer square}} = \frac{1.44 \text{ cm}^2}{9 \text{ cm}^2} = \frac{4}{25} = 0.16$$

f. Answers will vary. For a large number of trials, the experimental probability is likely to approximate the theoretical probability.

Discussion

a. Sample response: If any other point is used, the orientation of the coin would have to be considered when determining the area that represents a win. This would make the problem very hard to solve.

b. Assuming that the walls are at least 0.9 cm from the grid, the probability of winning is the same for any number of squares (n):

$$\frac{n \cdot \text{area of inner square}}{n \cdot \text{area of outer square}} = \frac{1.44n}{9n} = \frac{1.44}{9} = \frac{4}{25} = 0.16$$

b. Drop a dime onto the grid from the height of a chair seat (about 45 cm). Record the result of the drop as a win or loss.

c. Repeat Part **b** nine more times.

d. 1. Compile the total number of wins and losses for the entire class.

2. Use the class data to determine the experimental probability of winning the game.

mathematics note

If each outcome in a sample space has the same chance of occurring, then the **theoretical probability** of an event E is determined using the following ratio:

$$P(E) = \frac{\text{number of outcomes in the event}}{\text{total number of outcomes in the sample space}}$$

When the outcomes in an event can be represented as points in a **geometric model**, the theoretical probability of the event may be found using the ratio below:

$$P(E) = \frac{\text{measure of geometric model representing outcomes in the event}}{\text{measure of geometric model representing all outcomes in the sample space}}$$

Some examples of geometric measures are lengths, angle measures, areas, and volumes.

For example, consider a carnival game that involves throwing a dart at balloons. There are 16 balloons with a mean diameter of 10 cm attached to a square board 60 cm on each side. To win a prize, players must break a balloon. As shown in Figure **13-4**, the balloons can be represented as circles, while the board can be represented as a square.

FIGURE 13-4   Balloons on a board.

Assuming that the dart is equally likely to hit any point on the board, the probability of breaking a balloon (and winning a prize) can be found as follows:

$$P(\text{win}) = \frac{\text{area of 16 circles}}{\text{area of board}} = \frac{16 \cdot (\pi \cdot 5^2)}{60 \cdot 60} \approx 0.35 = 35\%$$

e. Consider one 3 cm × 3 cm square on the grid. To determine the theoretical probability of winning using a geometric model, you first must identify the area that models all winning outcomes.

1. How close can a dime's center come to the side of a 3 cm × 3 cm square and still represent a win?

2. Using the center of the dime as a reference point, determine the area of the region that models all winning outcomes.

3. Use the area determined in Step **2** and the area representing all possible outcomes to find the theoretical probability of winning.

f. Compare the experimental probability of winning you determined in Part **d** with the theoretical probability from Part **e**.

Discussion

a. In a spinner game, the tip of the arrow serves as the reference point for determining the outcome of each spin. In the coin-drop game, you used the center of the dime. Why is this an appropriate reference point?

b. Does the number of 3 cm × 3 cm squares on the grid affect the probability of winning the coin-drop game? Explain your response

c. In Part **f** of the exploration, how did the experimental probability of winning the coin-drop game compare to its theoretical probability?

d. Describe how you could make the coin-drop game impossible to win.

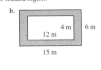
c. Answers will vary. These probabilities may or may not be approximately equal, depending on the class results. For a large number of trials, the experimental probability is likely to be close to the theoretical probability.

d. Sample response: The game could be made impossible to play by using a coin with a diameter that is greater than the dimensions of the squares, or by using squares with dimensions that are less than the diameter of the dime.

Warm-Up

1. **a.** $P(\text{shaded}) \approx 0.91$

   b. $P(\text{shaded}) \approx 0.47$

   c. $P(\text{shaded}) = 1$

   d. $P(\text{shaded}) = 0.67$

2. **a.** Sample graph:

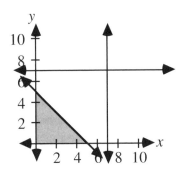

   b. $\dfrac{12.5}{49} \approx 0.26$

3. Sample response: Given any event E, the event that E does not occur is its complement. The sum of the probabilities of two complementary events is 1 because this represents the sum of the probabilities of all possible outcomes.

Assignment

Problems suitable for use as assessment items are identified by an asterisk (*).

1.1 **a.** The region that models all winning outcomes is the square formed by the centers of all winning quarters. Because the radius of a quarter is approximately 1.2 cm, the area of this region can be found as follows: $(3 - (2 \bullet 1.2))^2 = 0.36$ cm^2.

   b. The theoretical probability of winning the coin-drop game using a quarter is:

$$\frac{\text{area of inner square}}{\text{area of outer square}} = \frac{0.36 \text{ cm}^2}{9 \text{ cm}^2} = \frac{1}{25} = 0.04$$

* 1.2 **a.** The region that models all winning outcomes is the square formed by the centers of all winning dimes. Because the radius of a dime is approximately 0.9 cm, the area of this region can be found as follows: $(4 - (2 \bullet 0.9))^2 = 4.84$ cm^2.

   b. The theoretical probability of winning this version of the game is:

   $$\frac{\text{area of inner square}}{\text{area of outer square}} = \frac{4.84 \text{ cm}^2}{16 \text{ cm}^2} = \frac{121}{400} = 0.3025$$

1.3 **a.** Using a geometric model, the probability of landing in the yellow ring is the ratio of the area of the yellow ring to the area of the entire target:

   $$\frac{\pi(10)^2 - \pi(7)^2}{\pi(13)^2} = \frac{\pi(51)}{\pi(169)} = \frac{51}{169} \approx 0.30$$

   b. Sample response: No. It is not really a random event because players can aim the dart at a particular point.

* 1.4 **a.** As shown in the diagram below, students can consider all the positions of the ball's center that will knock down the pin:

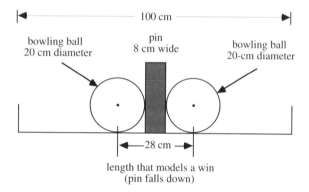

Using this geometric model, the width of all possible paths of the ball's center down the lane is $(100 - 2 \bullet 10)$, or 80 cm. The width of the paths that result in knocking down the pin is 28 cm. The probability of winning is $28/80 = 7/20 = 0.35$.

   b. As shown in the diagram below, if the pin is placed against one rail, the ball can pass on only one side of the pin. Because the center of the ball can pass no closer than 10 cm from the rail, the width of the paths that result in knocking down the pin is 8 cm. This reduces the probability of winning to $8/80 = 1/10 = 0.1$.

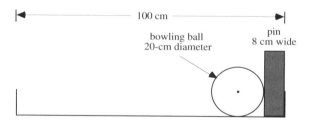

1.2 To attract more players, the carnival decides to allow players to drop dimes onto a grid of 4 cm × 4 cm squares.

   a. Describe the area within a 4 cm × 4 cm square that represents a win.

   b. Determine the theoretical probability of winning this version of the coin-drop game.

1.3 In another kind of carnival game, players throw darts at a circular board. As shown in the diagram below, the board is divided into four concentric regions, each painted a different color.

The radius of the red region in the center of the board is 4 cm. The width of each of the remaining regions is 3 cm.

   a. Assuming that a dart has an equal chance of landing at any point on the board, what is the theoretical probability that it lands in the yellow region? Explain your response.

   b. Is throwing a dart at a target typically a random event? Explain your response.

1.4 In Bowl-o-rama, a bowling pin with a diameter of 8 cm is placed somewhere near the center of a lane 100 cm wide. To keep the ball in play, the lane has rails on each side. To win the game, a blindfolded player must knock down the pin using a bowling ball 20 cm in diameter.

   a. Assuming that the pin will fall if it is touched by the ball, what is the probability of winning the game? Justify your response.

   b. Would placing the bowling pin against one of the rails affect the probability of winning the game? Explain your response.

1.5 Sample response: I would rather play the spinner game because the probability of winning is greater. Each of the four central angles where the spinner is located measure 90°, so the probability that the spinner lands in the unshaded portion of the board is:

$$\frac{90° + 90°}{360°} = 0.5$$

The probability of a dart landing in the unshaded portion of the board is the sum of areas of the two unshaded rectangles, divided by the total area of the board:

$$\frac{40 \bullet 70 + 40 \bullet 90}{130 \bullet 110} \approx 0.448$$

✳ ✳ ✳ ✳ ✳

1.5 In the introduction to this module, a carnival barker offered you a chance to play either a dart game or a spinner game. (See Figure 13-1.) To win, either the dart or the arrow must land in the unshaded portion of the board. The measurements of the game board are shown below.

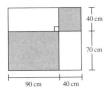

Based on the theoretical probabilities of winning, which game would you rather play? Explain your response.

* * * * *

1.6 Consider two real numbers, x and y, where $0 \le x \le 5$, and $0 \le y \le 5$.

    a. Graph all the possible ordered pairs (x,y) on a two-dimensional coordinate system.

    b. Determine the area of the region that represents all the possible ordered pairs (x,y).

    c. Graph all the possible ordered pairs (x,y) where $x + y \le 3$, $0 \le x \le 5$, and $0 \le y \le 5$.

    d. Given a point (x,y) selected at random from Part **a**, determine the probability that $x + y \le 3$. Justify your response.

    e. Given a point selected at random from Part **a**, determine the probability that $x + y \ge 6$. Justify your response.

1.7 After jumping from an airplane, a parachutist must land safely in a square parking lot 75 m on each side. The parking lot is free of hazards, except for at the corners. In each corner of the lot, there is a utility pole with a street light. If the parachutist lands within 10 m of a utility pole, the parachute's lines will get caught on the light.

    a. Draw a sketch of the parking lot and the utility poles. Shade the areas in which the parachutist should not land.

    b. Determine the area in which it is safe to land.

* 1.6 **a.** Sample graph:

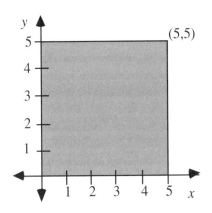

b. The area of all the possible outcomes is 25 units².

c. Sample graph:

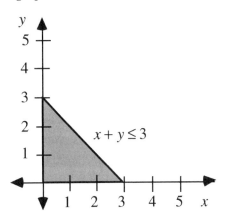

The area of the shaded region is $(1/2)(3)(3) = 4.5$ units².

d. Using a geometric model, the probability that $x + y \le 3$ is $4.5/25 = 0.18$.

e. The following sample graph shows the region bounded by $x + y \ge 6$, $0 \le x \le 5$, and $0 \le y \le 5$.

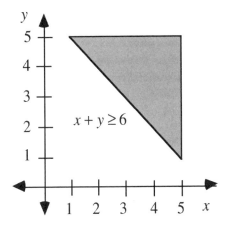

The area of the shaded region is $(1/2)(4)(4) = 8$ units². Using a geometric model, the probability that $x + y \ge 6$ is $8/25 = 0.32$.

* 1.7 **a.** Sample sketch:

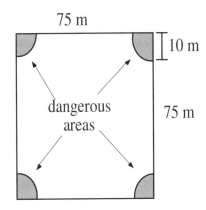

b. Sample response: The dangerous area is a circle with a radius of 10 m. Therefore, the area of the parking lot in which it is safe to land is:

$$75^2 - \pi 10^2 \approx 5300 \text{ m}^2.$$

c. 1. Using a geometric model, the probability that the parachutist lands safely can be found as follows:

$$\frac{\text{safe area}}{\text{parking lot area}} \approx \frac{5300}{5625} \approx 0.94$$

2. The probability that the parachute's lines get tangled in a security light is:

$$\frac{\text{unsafe area}}{\text{parking lot area}} \approx \frac{\pi 10^2}{75^2} \approx \frac{314}{5625} \approx 0.06$$

d. Sample response: The probabilities in Part **c** add to 1 because they are complementary events.

1.8 a. Sample graph:

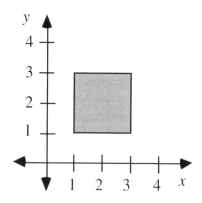

b. The area of the shaded region in the graph above is 4 units^2.

c. Sample graph:

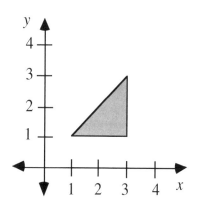

The area of the shaded region in the graph above is 2 units^2.

d. Using a geometric model, the probability is $2/4 = 0.5$.

e. Using a geometric model, the probability is $2/4 = 0.5$. **Note:** The events described in Parts **d** and **e** are not complementary, because the points on the line $y = x$ are included in both.

c. Assuming that the parachutist is equally likely to land anywhere in the parking lot, determine each of the following probabilities:

  1. the parachutist lands safely

  2. the parachute's lines get caught on a security light.

d. What is the relationship between the two probabilities in Part **c**?

1.8 Consider two real numbers, x and y, where $1 \le x \le 3$ and $1 \le y \le 3$.

  a. Graph all the possible ordered pairs (x,y) on a two-dimensional coordinate system.

  b. Determine the area of the region that represents all the possible ordered pairs (x,y).

  c. Graph all the possible ordered pairs (x,y) where $y/x \le 1$, $1 \le x \le 3$, and $1 \le y \le 3$.

  d. Given a point (x,y) selected at random from Part **a**, determine the probability that $y/x \le 1$. Justify your response.

  e. Given a point selected at random from Part **a**, determine the probability that $y/x \ge 1$. Justify your response.

ACTIVITY 2

In another carnival game, players roll a six-sided die. The game costs $1.00 to play. The values of the prizes that correspond with the six possible rolls are shown in Table **13-1** below.

TABLE 13-1 ■ Value of Prizes in Die Game

Roll of Die	Value of Prize
1	$1.50
2	$1.00
3	$0.50
4	$0.00
5	$0.00
6	$0.00

Judging from the values of the prizes, do you think this is a fair game? In the following exploration, you use mathematics to help answer this question.

ACTIVITY 2

In this activity, students calculate expected value and determine whether or not a game is mathematically fair.

 teacher note

A brief assessment of the mathematical content in Activities **1** and **2**, for use at your discretion, appears in the Teacher Resources for this module.

Materials List

■ dice (one die per group)

Exploration

a. Play the die game 10 times. Record the number of wins for each prize.

b. 1. Compile the data from Part **a** for the entire class.

   2. Use the class data to determine the experimental probability of winning each prize.

c. Determine the theoretical probability of winning each prize.

d. Compare the experimental probability of winning each prize to the theoretical probability.

mathematics note

The mean value of an experiment is the **expected value**. Expected value is determined by adding the products of the value of each event and its corresponding theoretical probability.

For example, suppose a carnival game uses the spinner shown in Figure **13-5**. The measures of the three central angles are 45°, 135°, and 180°, respectively. Using a geometric model, the probability of winning $25 is 45/360 = 1/8, the probability of winning $15 is 135/360 = 3/8, and the probability of winning $0 is 180/360 = 1/2.

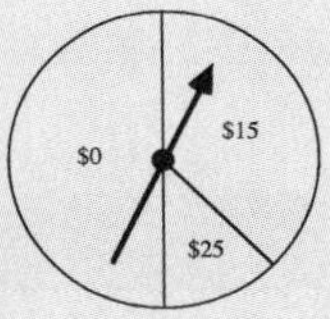

FIGURE 13-5 Spinner with three central angles.

The expected value for this game is the sum of the products of each prize value and its corresponding probability. This can be calculated as follows:

$$\frac{1}{8} \cdot \$25 + \frac{3}{8} \cdot \$15 + \frac{1}{2} \cdot \$0 = \$8.75$$

This indicates that, for a large number of plays, the mean amount won per play is likely to be close to $8.75.

Student Outcomes

After completing the following exploration and discussion, students should be able to:

✳ determine expected values

✳ identify fair games

✳ create fair games.

Exploration

a–b. Students should recognize that the chances of winning each prize are not equally likely.

c. The theoretical probability of each outcome is shown below.

Value of Prize	Roll of Die	Probability
$1.50	1	1/6
$1.00	2	1/6
$0.50	3	1/6
$0.00	4	1/6
$0.00	5	1/6
$0.00	6	1/6

Because three of the outcomes result in a prize of $0.00, its theoretical probability is:

$$1/6 + 1/6 + 1/6 = 3/6 = 1/2.$$

d. The experimental probabilities may or may not approximate the theoretical probabilities.

e. The expected value can be found as follows:

$$\frac{1}{6} \cdot \$1.50 + \frac{1}{6} \cdot \$1.00 + \frac{1}{6} \cdot \$0.50 + \frac{1}{2} \cdot 0 = \$0.50$$

Discussion

a. Sample response: No. You are not equally likely to win each prize. A non-winning roll of 4, 5, or 6 is three times more likely to occur than any single winning roll.

b. The cost to play ($1.00) and the expected value ($0.50) are not equal, so the game is not mathematically fair. To make the game fair, students may suggest reducing the cost to play, increasing the value of the prizes, or changing the probabilities of winning the prizes.

c. Answers will vary. To pay wages, travel costs, and other expenses, carnival operators must make a profit from their games. It would be unreasonable to expect a mathematically fair game under these circumstances.

Warm-Up

1. The expected value is 7.
2. The expected value is 20.
3. $1.50

e. Determine the expected value of the die game.

Discussion

a. When playing the die game, are you equally likely to win each prize? Explain your response.

b. A **fair game** is one in which the expected value equals the cost to play. Is the die game mathematically fair? If so, justify your response. If not, suggest at least one way to make it fair.

c. Is it reasonable to expect a carnival game to be mathematically fair? Explain your response.

Warm-Up

1. An experiment has three possible outcomes. The following table shows the value and probability of each one. Calculate the expected value for this experiment.

Outcome	Probability
12	1/6
9	1/3
4	1/2

2. Another experiment also has three possible outcomes. The following table shows the value and probability of each one. Calculate the expected value for this experiment.

Outcome	Probability
10	1/6
20	2/3
30	1/6

3. The following table shows the prize values for a game of chance, along with the probability of winning each one. Determine the cost to play that will make this a fair game.

Prize	Probability
$2.00	1/4
$1.00	1/2
$2.00	1/4

Assignment

2.1 In another version of the die game, prizes are awarded as shown in the following table.

Roll of Die	Value of Prize
1	$2.00
2	$0.00
3	$0.50
4	$0.00
5	$0.50
6	$0.00

Determine the cost to play that makes this a fair game.

2.2 In one version of the coin-drop game described in Activity **1**, the theoretical probability of winning is 4/25. The game costs $1.00 to play. Winning players receive a prize worth $5.00. Losing players receive no prize.

a. Determine the expected value for this game.

b. Given that the prize value remains $5.00, change the cost of playing to make this a fair game.

c. Given that the cost of playing remains $1.00, change the value of the prize to make this a fair game.

2.3 In another version of the coin-drop game, the theoretical probability of winning is 1/25. This game also costs $1.00 to play. However, winning players receive a prize worth $15.00.

a. Determine the expected value for this game.

b. Given that the prize value remains $15.00, change the cost of playing to make this a fair game.

c. Given that the cost of playing remains $1.00, change the value of the prize to make this a fair game.

2.4 Imagine that you are the manager of a carnival. One of the game operators has designed a new game. In this game, players pick 1 card from an ordinary deck of 52 cards. An ace wins $10.00, a face card (king, queen, or jack) wins $1.00, and all other cards win nothing. Determine the cost to play to make this a fair game.

* * * * *

Assignment

Problems suitable for use as assessment items are identified by an asterisk (*).

* **2.1** To make this a fair game, the cost to play must equal the expected value:

$$\frac{1}{2} \bullet \$0.00 + \frac{1}{3} \bullet \$0.50 + \frac{1}{6} \bullet \$2.00 = \$0.50$$

2.2 a. The expected value can be calculated as follows:

$$\frac{21}{25} \bullet \$0.00 + \frac{4}{25} \bullet \$5.00 = \$0.80$$

b. To make the game mathematically fair, the cost to play must be decreased to $0.80.

c. The value of the prize that makes the game mathematically fair can be calculated as follows:

$$\frac{21}{25} \bullet \$0.00 + \frac{4}{25} \bullet x = \$1.00$$

$$x = \$6.25$$

* **2.3 a.** The expected value can be calculated as follows:

$$\frac{24}{25} \bullet \$0.00 + \frac{1}{25} \bullet \$15.00 = \$0.60$$

b. To make the game mathematically fair, the cost to play must be decreased to $0.60.

c. The value of the prize that makes the game mathematically fair can be calculated as follows:

$$\frac{24}{25} \bullet \$0.00 + \frac{1}{25} \bullet x = \$1.00$$

$$x = \$25.00$$

2.4 To make this a fair game, the cost to play must equal the expected value:

$$\frac{1}{13} \bullet \$10 + \frac{3}{13} \bullet \$1 + \frac{9}{13} \bullet \$0 = \$1.00$$

✳ ✳ ✳ ✳ ✳

2.5 a. In the following sample graph, the shaded region represents all the possible pairs of numbers in the interval [0, 5] for which the sum is less than or equal to 3.

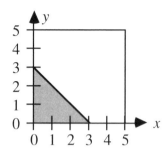

The probability of Juan winning is the area of the shaded region divided by the area of the square:

$$\frac{4.5}{25} = 0.18 = 18\%$$

b. Because Juan theoretically wins $0.50 in 18% of the games and loses $0.20 in 82% of the games, the expected value can be calculated as follows: $0.18 \cdot 0.50 + 0.82 \cdot -0.20 \approx -0.07$.

c. Sample response: Juan can expect to lose an average of approximately $0.07 each time he plays. Therefore, he should not play the game.

d. Answers will vary. Sample response: If Joan continues to pay Juan $0.50 each time he wins, then solving the following equation for x gives the amount that Juan should pay Joan to make the expected value the same for both players.

$$0.18 \cdot \$0.50 = 0.82x$$
$$\$0.11 \approx x$$

If Juan continues to pay Joan $0.20 each time she wins, then solving the following equation for x gives the amount that Joan should pay Juan to make the expected value the same for both players.

$$0.18x = 0.82 \cdot \$0.20$$
$$x \approx \$0.91$$

2.6 a. The shaded region in the sample sketch below is the region that results in a winning toss. It is a square that measures approximately 3.6 cm on a side.

b. The probability of winning is $P(w) = 3.6^2/6^2 = 0.36$.

c. The expected value is $0.36 \cdot (\$1) = \$0.36$.

2.5 Joan and Juan are playing a game that involves randomly selecting two real numbers in the interval [0, 5]. Joan offers to pay Juan $0.50 every time the sum of the two numbers is less than or equal to 3, if he will pay her $0.20 every time the sum is greater than 3.

   a. Before deciding whether to accept these rules, Juan wants to know his chances of winning. Use a geometric model to determine the probability that Juan will win.

   b. Determine the expected value of the game for Juan.

   c. Do you think Juan should accept Joan's rules? Explain your response.

   d. Modify the prize amounts so that the expected values for both players are equal.

2.6 In a coin-drop game, players try to land quarters inside a 6 cm × 6 cm square on a grid. The game costs $0.25 to play. If the quarter lands completely within a square, the player wins $1.00. If any part of the quarter touches or crosses a line on the square, the player loses. (The diameter of a quarter is approximately 2.4 cm.)

   a. Sketch a picture of a 6 cm × 6 cm square. Show the area in which the center of the quarter must land to win.

   b. What is the probability of winning the game?

   c. What is the expected value of this game?

   d. How would you change this game to make it fair?

Research Project

Design your own carnival game. Calculate the expected value and determine the cost to play required to make it a fair game. Exchange your game with a classmate. Check each other's designs to verify that the games are fair. Present your game to the class.

In the fishing derby, players hook three rings, one at a time, from a tank of swirling water. The tank contains 10 rings. Four of the rings are marked with a small red dot and six are marked with a small blue dot.

d. Sample response: If the cost of playing the game were raised to $0.36, the game would be a fair game. The game also could be made approximately fair by reducing the prize to $0.69.

Research Project

After students have presented their games to the class, you might wish to ask them to discuss modifications that might make the games profitable at a carnival.

In this activity, students examine multistage probabilities.

  teacher note

A brief assessment of the mathematical content in Activity **3**, for use at your discretion, appears in the Teacher Resources for this module.

Players receive 1 point for each blue ring and 2 points for each red ring. After each ring is caught, it is placed back in the tank before the player's next try. Table 13-2 below shows the total number of points required to win each prize.

TABLE 13-2 ■ Prizes in the Fishing Derby	
Prize	**Number of Points Needed**
rabbit's foot key chain	3
celebrity poster	4
black hat with a pink feather	5
large teddy bear	6

To win a particular prize, a player must have the exact number of points for that prize after hooking three rings. To win the celebrity poster, for example, a player must have exactly 4 points. Players with 5 or 6 points cannot win the poster, even though they might have had exactly 4 points at some time before hooking the last ring. Points earned in one game cannot be added to points earned in another game.

Exploration 1

a. To simulate the fishing derby, place 4 red chips and 6 blue chips in a container.

1. Without looking, draw one chip from the container. Record its color, then return it to the container.

2. Repeat Step 1 two more times, mixing the chips before each draw.

3. Determine the total number of points for the three draws. As in the actual fishing derby, each blue chip is worth 1 point and each red chip is worth 2 points.

b. 1. Play the game 10 times. Record the points earned in each game.

2. Compile the experimental results for the entire class.

3. Using the compiled results, determine the experimental probability of winning each prize.

c. Create a tree diagram to show the possible outcomes in the fishing derby after a player's first catch. Label each branch with a theoretical probability.

d. Create a tree diagram to show the possible outcomes after all three catches. Label each branch with a theoretical probability.

Materials List

■ poker chips (4 red and 6 blue per group)

■ paper bags or other opaque containers (one per group)

Technology

■ random number generator

Student Outcomes

After completing the following explorations and discussions, students should be able to:

✳ identify events as independent or dependent

✳ use tree diagrams to determine probabilities

✳ calculate conditional probabilities.

Exploration 1

Students simulate the fishing derby by drawing objects from a bag. **Note:** To ensure random draws, the objects should be indistinguishable by touch.

a–b. Students simulate the fishing derby 10 times, then combine their results with the class. Sample data for 100 trials:

Event	Points	Number of Occurrences	Experimental Probability
3 red	6	8	0.08
2 red, 1 blue	5	25	0.25
1 red, 2 blue	4	46	0.46
3 blue	3	21	0.21

c. Sample tree diagram:

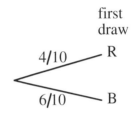

d. The eight possible outcomes are RRR, RRB, RBR, RBB, BRR, BRB, BBR, and BBB (where R represents red and B represents blue). Sample tree diagram:

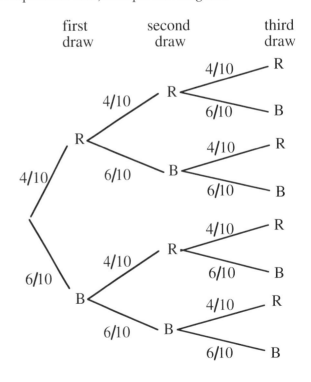

e. Students should calculate the following probabilities:

$P(RRR) = (4/10)^3 = 0.064,$

$P(RRB) = (4/10)^2 \bullet 6/10 = 0.096,$

$P(RBR) = (4/10)^2 \bullet 6/10 = 0.096,$

$P(RBB) = 4/10 \bullet (6/10)^2 = 0.144,$

$P(BRR) = (6/10) \bullet (4/10)^2 = 0.096,$

$P(BRB) = (6/10)^2 \bullet 4/10 = 0.144,$

$P(BBR) = (6/10)^2 \bullet 4/10 = 0.144,$ and

$P(BBB) = (6/10)^3 = 0.216.$

f. 1. The probabilities of winning each prize are as follows: $P(6) = 0.064$, $P(5) = 3 \bullet 0.096 = 0.288$, $P(4) = 3 \bullet 0.144 = 0.432$, and $P(3) = 0.216$.

2. For a large number of trials, the experimental probabilities are likely to be close to the theoretical probabilities.

Discussion 1

a. There are eight possible outcomes.

b. 1. There is one way to get 3 points: BBB.

2. Any combination of 2 blues and 1 red earns 4 points. There are three possibilities: BBR, BRB, and RBB.

3. Any combination of 2 reds and 1 blue earns 5 points. There are three possibilities: RRB, RBR, and BRR.

4. There is one way to earn 6 points: RRR.

5. There is no way to earn 7 points.

mathematics note

Two events A and B are **independent** if $P(A \text{ and } B) = P(A) \bullet P(B)$. Three events A, B, and C are independent if each pair of events is independent and $P(A \text{ and } B \text{ and } C) = P(A) \bullet P(B) \bullet P(C)$. This definition can be extended to any number of independent events.

Given two independent events, the occurrence of one has no effect on the likelihood of the occurrence of the other. Two events that are not independent are said to be **dependent**.

For example, consider tossing two coins—a penny and a nickel—one at a time. The outcome of tossing the penny does not affect the outcome of tossing the nickel, so the two tosses are independent events.

The probability of obtaining heads on either coin, or $P(H)$, is 1/2. The probability of obtaining heads on the penny and the nickel, or $P(H \text{ and } H)$, is:

$$P(H \text{ and } H) = P(H) \bullet P(H) = \frac{1}{2} \bullet \frac{1}{2} = \frac{1}{4}$$

e. In the fishing derby, hooking the first ring, hooking the second ring, and hooking the third ring are independent events. Use your tree diagram from Part **d** and the definition given in the mathematics note to determine the theoretical probability of each outcome.

f. 1. Determine the theoretical probability of winning each prize in the fishing derby.

2. Compare these probabilities with the experimental probabilities that you found in Part **b**.

Discussion 1

a. From your tree diagram in Part **d** of Exploration **1**, how many possible outcomes are there in the fishing derby?

b. Describe the different sets of three rings that result in each of following numbers of points:

1. 3

2. 4

3. 5

4. 6

5. 7

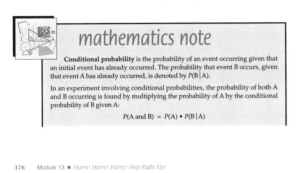

page 376

c. Why do you think the rings with red dots are worth more points than the ones with blue dots?

d. 1. Does hooking a red ring on the first try affect the probability of hooking a blue one on the second try? Explain your response.

   2. Does it affect the probability of hooking a red ring on the second try? Why or why not?

e. Which prize do you think is awarded most often? Why?

f. 1. Describe how you could use technology to model the fishing derby.

   2. Would you expect this simulation to produce the same results as the simulation in Exploration **1**? Explain your response.

g. Which information is likely to better represent the long-term results of playing the fishing derby: the data from 10 simulations, or the compiled class data? Explain your reasoning.

Exploration 2

In the next town on the carnival circuit, the operator of the fishing derby changes the rules of the game. The change requires players to keep each ring hooked instead of returning it to the tank. This new version of the derby is supposed to give players a better chance of winning a hat or a teddy bear. The rest of the game remains the same.

a. Predict how the rule change will affect the probability of winning each prize.

b. Create a tree diagram to show the possible outcomes in the new fishing derby. Label each branch with a theoretical probability.

mathematics note

Conditional probability is the probability of an event occurring given that an initial event has already occurred. The probability that event B occurs, given that event A has already occurred, is denoted by $P(B|A)$.

In an experiment involving conditional probabilities, the probability of both A and B occurring is found by multiplying the probability of A by the conditional probability of B given A:

$$P(A \text{ and } B) = P(A) \cdot P(B|A)$$

376   Module 13 ■ *Hurry! Hurry! Hurry! Step Right Up!*

c. Sample response: Because there are fewer rings with red dots than rings with blue dots, the probability of drawing a red ring is less than that of drawing a blue one.

d. 1. Sample response: No. Because the object is returned to the container and mixed in with the others, the second draw is from the same set of objects as the first.

   2. Sample response: No, for the same reasons mentioned above.

e. Some students may predict that the rabbit's foot is the prize most often won because it requires the fewest points. Considering theoretical probabilities, however, the celebrity poster should be the most frequently awarded prize.

f. 1. Answers may vary. Sample response: Generate random numbers from 1 to 10, inclusive. The numbers from 1 to 4 represent a red ring and earn 2 points. The numbers from 5 to 10 represent a blue ring and earn 1 point.

   2. Students may expect the simulations to produce the same results. Since each is repeated a relatively few number of times, however, the results are likely to vary. Over the long run, the simulations should produce similar results because they involve the same theoretical probabilities.

g. Sample response: Because it contains more trials, the class data should better represent the long-term results of the game. The experimental probability should be closer to the theoretical probability as the number of trials increases.

Exploration 2

In this exploration, students examine conditional probabilities by simulating a version of the fishing derby without replacement.

a. Responses will vary. Some students may observe that the probabilities of scoring 6 points (RRR) or 3 points (BBB) are decreased.

b. The possible outcomes are the same as those in the original version of the game: RRR, RRB, RBR, RBB, BRR, BRB, BBR, and BBB. Sample tree diagram:

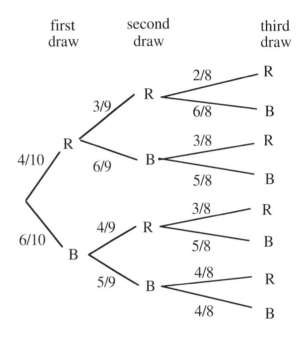

c. Students should determine the probabilities of each outcome as follows:

$P(\text{RRR}) = 4/10 \bullet 3/9 \bullet 2/8 = 1/30 \approx 0.03$,

$P(\text{RRB}) = 4/10 \bullet 3/9 \bullet 6/8 = 1/10 \approx 0.1$,

$P(\text{RBR}) = 4/10 \bullet 6/9 \bullet 3/8 = 1/10 = 0.1$,

$P(\text{RBB}) = 4/10 \bullet 6/9 \bullet 5/8 = 1/6 \approx 0.17$,

$P(\text{BRR}) = 6/10 \bullet 4/9 \bullet 3/8 = 1/10 \approx 0.1$,

$P(\text{BRB}) = 6/10 \bullet 4/9 \bullet 5/8 = 1/6 \approx 0.17$,

$P(\text{BBR}) = 6/10 \bullet 5/9 \bullet 4/8 = 1/6 \approx 0.17$, and

$P(\text{BBB}) = 6/10 \bullet 5/9 \bullet 4/8 = 1/6 \approx 0.17$.

Using these probabilities, the theoretical probabilities of obtaining each score are $P(6) = 1/30 \approx 0.03$, $P(5) = 3/10 = 0.3$, $P(4) = 3/6 = 0.5$, and $P(3) = 1/6 \approx 0.17$.

d. Students may design their own simulations using either a container of red and blue objects or a random number generator. Sample response: Generate random numbers from 1 to 10, inclusive. The numbers 1 to 4 represent the red rings and are worth 2 points. The numbers 5 to 10 represent the blue rings and are worth 1 point. During a single round of the simulation, any number that comes up more than once is ignored and another number is generated.

e. The following table shows some sample data for 100 trials. In this case, the experimental probabilities closely approximate the theoretical probabilities.

Event	Points	Number of Occurrences	Experimental Probability
3 red	6	3	0.03
2 red, 1 blue	5	31	0.31
1 red, 2 blue	4	45	0.45
3 blue	3	21	0.21

Discussion 2

a. Sample response: When using a random number generator, ignoring any number that comes up more than once in a single round models its removal from the tank.

b. In the new version of the game, the theoretical probability of getting 6 points decreases from 0.064 to approximately 0.03.

c. Sample response: Although the chances of winning a hat have improved slightly, the chances of winning a bear have decreased. Overall, the chances of winning one or the other has also decreased. In the original game, the chances of winning a hat or a bear are $0.288 + 0.064 = 0.352$. In the new version, the chances of winning a hat or a bear are approximately $0.3 + 0.033 = 0.333$.

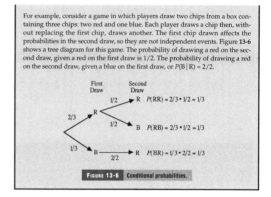

For example, consider a game in which players draw two chips from a box containing three chips: two red and one blue. Each player draws a chip then, without replacing the first chip, draws another. The first chip drawn affects the probabilities in the second draw, so they are not independent events. Figure 13-6 shows a tree diagram for this game. The probability of drawing a red on the second draw, given a red on the first draw is 1/2. The probability of drawing a red on the second draw, given a blue on the first draw, or $P(\text{B} \mid \text{R}) = 2/2$.

FIGURE 13-6 Conditional probabilities.

c. Use your tree diagram to determine the theoretical probability of winning each prize.

d. Create a simulation for this version of the game.

e. 1. Conduct your simulation a total of 10 times. Record the points earned and the prize won each time.

2. Compile the results from the entire class.

3. Using the compiled results, determine the experimental probability of winning each prize.

4. Compare these experimental probabilities with the theoretical probabilities that you determined in Part **c**.

Discussion 2

a. Which part of your simulation models the rule that each ring caught must be removed from the tank?

b. Are the chances of getting 6 points in the new fishing derby better or worse than in the original version of the game?

c. Does the rule change appear to have improved the chances of winning a hat or a teddy bear?

Module 13 ■ *Hurry! Hurry! Hurry! Step Right Up!* 377

d. 1. Sample response: The probabilities are different because the first chip drawn is not replaced in the box. Because the numbers and kinds of chips in the box have changed, the probabilities must be adjusted.

2. There is only one blue chip in the game, so the probability of drawing two blue chips is 0.

d. 1. In the game modeled in Figure 13-6, why are the probabilities of obtaining a red chip on the second draw different from the probability of obtaining a red chip on the first draw?

2. What is the probability of drawing two blue chips in this game?

Warm-Up

1. Explain the difference between dependent and independent events. Include examples in your response.

2. What is conditional probability?

3. A bag contains 10 red marbles, 8 green marbles, and 6 blue marbles. Consider an experiment in which marbles are drawn from the bag, one at a time, and replaced before another marble is drawn. Determine each of the following probabilities:

   a. $P(B)$
   b. $P(R)$
   c. $P(GB)$
   d. $P(BGR)$
   e. $P(RRR)$

Assignment

3.1 a. What is the theoretical probability of winning a prize in the original fishing derby? Explain your response.

   b. What is the theoretical probability of earning 7 points in the original fishing derby? Explain your response.

   c. What is the expected value, in points, of the original fishing derby?

3.2 a. What is the expected value, in points, of the new fishing derby?

   b. Which version of the fishing derby would you rather play? Explain your response.

3.3 Both versions of the fishing derby cost $1.00 to play. The values of the prizes are shown in the following table.

Prize	Value
rabbit's foot key chain	$0.25
celebrity poster	$0.60
black hat with pink feather	$0.80
large teddy bear	$2.00

Warm-Up

1. Sample response: Two events are independent if the occurrence of one event does not affect the probability of the other event occurring. Two tosses of a coin are independent events. The probability of a head on the first toss does not affect the probability of a head on the second toss.

   Two events are dependent if they are not independent. For example, drawing a card from a deck and not replacing it affects the probabilities for the second card drawn from the same deck. Because they are not independent, the two draws are dependent events.

2. Conditional probability is the probability of an event occurring given that an initial event has already occurred.

3. a. 1/4
   b. 5/12
   c. 1/12
   d. 5/144
   e. 125/1728

Assignment

Problems suitable for use as assessment items are identified by an asterisk (*).

* 3.1 a. Because all the outcomes result in a prize, and because the sum of their probabilities is 1, the probability of winning some prize in the fishing derby is 1.

   b. Because no combination of three rings adds up to 7 points, the probability of earning 7 points is 0.

   c. The expected value, in points, can be determined as follows:

$$\frac{8}{125} \bullet 6 + \frac{36}{125} \bullet 5 + \frac{54}{125} \bullet 4 + \frac{27}{125} \bullet 3 = 4.2$$

* 3.2 a. The expected value, in points, is:

$$\frac{1}{30} \bullet 6 + \frac{3}{10} \bullet 5 + \frac{1}{2} \bullet 4 + \frac{1}{6} \bullet 3 = 4.2$$

   b. Answers will vary. The probabilities of winning a poster or hat increased slightly in the new version, while the probabilities of winning a key chain or teddy bear decreased.

3.3 a. Sample response: For the game to be fair, the expected value must equal the cost to play. The expected value of the original fishing derby is:

$$\frac{8}{125} \bullet \$2.00 + \frac{36}{125} \bullet \$0.80 + \frac{54}{125} \bullet \$0.60 + \frac{27}{125} \bullet \$0.25 \approx \$0.67$$

   One way to make this a fair game would be to reduce the cost to play to $0.67.

   b. Sample response: For the game to be fair, the expected value must equal the cost to play. The expected value of the new version is:

$$\frac{1}{30} \bullet \$2.00 + \frac{3}{10} \bullet \$0.80 + \frac{1}{2} \bullet \$0.60 + \frac{1}{6} \bullet \$0.25 \approx \$0.65$$

   One way to make this a fair game would be to reduce the cost to play to $0.65.

* 3.4 a. There are four equally likely outcomes when tossing two coins: HH, HT, TH, and TT. Therefore, the probabilities of each result can be determined as follows: $P(1 \text{ step}) = P(HT) + P(TH) = 1/2 = 0.5$, $P(0 \text{ steps}) = P(TT) = 1/4 = 0.25$, and $P(-1 \text{ step}) = P(HH) = 1/4 = 0.25$.

   b. The expected value, in number of stairs, is:

$$\frac{1}{4} \bullet 0 + \frac{1}{2} \bullet 1 + \frac{1}{4} \bullet -1 = \frac{1}{4} = 0.25$$

   c. Sample response: Because 10 • 0.25 = 2.5, Guinn is likely to be 2 or 3 steps up from the starting point.

   d. If the game starts on the middle of the 25 stairs (or the 13th stair), a player must move up 12 stairs to win. On average, Guinn would need 48 turns (12/0.25 = 48) to get to the top step.

✳ ✳ ✳ ✳ ✳

* 3.5 **a.** Answers will vary, depending on student estimates of Laurie's body size. The probability of finding her on the first probe may be calculated by the following ratio:

$$\frac{\text{area of back of Laurie's body}}{\text{total area of avalanche}}$$

For example, if a student estimates that Laurie's area is 6800 cm², then the probability of finding her body on the first probe is:

$$\frac{6800 \text{ cm}^2}{10 \text{ m} \cdot 12 \text{ m}} = \frac{0.68 \text{ m}^2}{120 \text{ m}^2} \approx 0.006 = 0.6\%$$

b. It will take Jamal approximately 20 min to search the entire area:

$$\frac{120 \text{ m}^2}{6 \text{ m}^2/\text{min}} = 20 \text{ min}$$

c. Because Jamal can search the entire area in 20 min, the probability of finding her in the first 10 min is 0.5, as is the probability of finding her in the second 10 min.

From the tree diagram below, the probability that she is found in the first 10 min and survives is 0.5 • 0.8 = 0.4. The probability that she is found in the second 10 min and survives is 0.5 • 0.55 = 0.275. Her total probability of survival is 0.4 + 0.125 = 0.675.

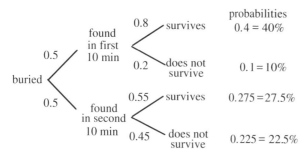

3.6 **a.** Sample tree diagram:

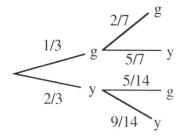

b. **1.** 2/21
   2. 10/21
   3. 3/7
c. The expected value is approximately $0.33.

a. Is the original fishing derby a fair game? If so, justify your response. If not, describe how you could modify the game to make it fair.

b. Is the new fishing derby a fair game? If so, justify your response. If not, describe how you could modify the game to make it fair.

3.4 Guinn and Ebdul are playing the stair-step game. This game starts on the middle step of a long staircase. Each player's turn consists of flipping two coins and moving up or down according to the following rules: if no heads appear on a player's two coins, the player does not move; if one head appears, the player moves up one stair; if two heads appear, the player moves down one stair.

The staircase has 25 steps. The game is over when one player wins by reaching the top step, or loses by reaching the bottom step.

a. If movement is described in terms of the number of stairs moved upwards, then each player's turn in the game has three possible results: 1 step, 0 steps, and –1 step.

What is the probability of each of these results?

b. What is the expected value, in number of stairs moved upwards, for each turn in the stair-step game?

c. Where on the staircase do you think Guinn will be after 10 turns?

d. How many turns do you think it will take for a player to reach the top step? Explain your response.

* * * * *

3.5 Jamal and Laurie are enjoying a cross-country ski trip in Yellowstone National Park. As they pass under a cornice of snow, a small avalanche occurs. Laurie is swept down the hill and buried.

Jamal rushes to search for his friend. The debris from the avalanche is spread over a rectangular region 12 m by 10 m. Laurie could be buried anywhere in this area. Jamal estimates that the snow is no more than 2 m deep. Using the cord from his hood, he lashes two ski poles together to form a pole about 2.5 m long. This enables him to probe the full depth of the snow.

a. Assume that Laurie is lying face down under the snow. Using your own estimate of Laurie's body size, determine the probability that Jamal will find Laurie on his first probe with the pole.

b. If Jamal can search an area of 6 m² every minute, how long will it take him to search the entire region of the avalanche?

c. Assume that if Jamal probes the location in which Laurie is buried, he will find her. If Jamal finds Laurie within the first 10 min of the search, there is an 80% chance that she will survive. If he finds her from 10 to 20 min after the avalanche, her chances of survival fall to about 55%. What is the probability that Laurie will survive her ordeal?

3.6 A carnival game involves drawing two chips from a container for a cost of $0.25. The container holds 15 chips. Of this total, 5 are green and 10 are yellow. Without looking, each player draws one chip from the container, keeps it, then draws another chip.

If the player draws two green chips, she wins $1.00. If she draws one green and one yellow, she wins $0.50. If any other combination is drawn, the player wins nothing.

a. Use a tree diagram to show the different outcomes for this game.

b. What is the probability of drawing each of the following?

   1. two green chips

   2. one green chip and one yellow chip

   3. two yellow chips

c. On average, how much should a player expect to win per game?

Summary Assessment

1. As part of its annual fundraiser, a local charity has designed a game called Auto Dart. Each player throws one dart at a computerized board. After the dart lands, the board lights up, displaying three red zones and one blue zone. The dimensions of the board, along with one possible arrangement of the zones, are shown in the diagram below.

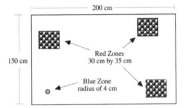

If the dart lands in the blue zone, the player wins a car worth $10,000. If the dart lands in any of the three red zones, the player wins a miniature replica of the car valued at $25. If the dart lands anywhere else on the board, the player wins nothing. After each throw, the computer randomly relocates the winning zones. These zones are always the same size and never overlap.

Imagine that you are the charity's financial advisor. Analyze the Auto Dart game and decide if the charity should use it in the fundraiser. Write a letter to the charity explaining your recommendation. Your letter should include the following:

a. the probability of winning each prize in Auto Dart

b. the expected value for the game

c. the lowest price, rounded to the nearest dollar, that the charity could charge for the game and still expect to make a profit

d. the number of miniature replicas and full-sized cars the charity can expect to award to the first 1000 players

e. the probability of two players in a row winning full-sized cars.

teacher note

An additional assessment, for use at your discretion, appears in the Teacher Resources for this module.

Summary Assessment

1. Student responses should take the form of a letter and should include the following information.
   a. The total area of the board is 30,000 cm². The area of the red zones is $3(30 \cdot 35) = 3150$ cm². Assuming that the dart is equally likely to land anywhere on the board, the probability of landing in a red zone is $3150/30,000 = 21/200 = 0.105$.

   The area of the blue zone is $\pi(4^2) \approx 50$ cm². The probability of landing in the blue zone is approximately $50/30,000 \approx 0.002$. The probability of not landing in either winning zone is $(30,000 - 3150 - 50.27)/30,000 \approx 0.893$. **Note:** This may also be calculated by $1 - P(\text{red zone}) - P(\text{blue zone})$.

   b. The expected value can be calculated as follows:
   $(0.893 \cdot \$0) + (0.105 \cdot \$25) + (0.002 \cdot \$10,000) \approx \$22.63$

   c. Assuming no other costs, the lowest price the charity could charge to play, and still hope to earn some profit, is $23.00.

d. For the first 1000 players, the charity should plan to award about $1000 \cdot 0.105 = 105$ miniature replicas, and $1000 \cdot 0.002 = 2$ full-sized cars.

e. Each game is an independent event, therefore the probability that two players in a row win full-sized cars is approximately $0.002^2 \approx 0.000004$, or about 4 in 1,000,000.

Student recommendations will vary. At a cost to play of $23.00, the charity could expect to earn an average of approximately $0.37 per player. Based on this small per-player profit, some students might recommend against using this game as a fund-raiser. They also might mention the possibility of having to award a full-sized car before earning enough money to pay for it, or suggest that the high cost of playing could discourage potential players.

2. Student responses again should take the form of a letter. To determine probabilities, some may construct a tree diagram like the one shown below:

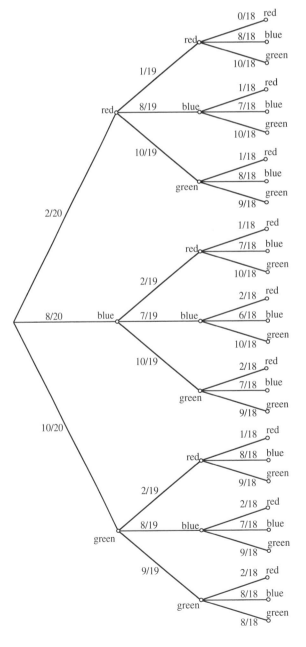

The probabilities and point values for each possible draw of three balls are shown in the following table.

Balls Drawn	Point Value	Probability
3 red	15	$0/6840 = 0.000$
2 red, 1 blue	12	$48/6840 \approx 0.007$
2 red, 1 green	11	$60/6840 \approx 0.009$
1 red, 2 blue	9	$336/6840 \approx 0.049$
1 red, 1 blue, 1 green	7	$960/6840 \approx 0.140$
1 red, 2 green	8	$540/6840 \approx 0.079$
3 blue	6	$336/6840 \approx 0.049$
2 blue, 1 green	5	$1680/6840 \approx 0.246$
1 blue, 2 green	4	$2160/6840 \approx 0.316$
3 green	3	$720/6840 \approx 0.105$

The probabilities for winning each prize can be calculated by adding the probabilities for the appropriate point values. The expected value for the game is shown in the table below.

Points	Prize Value	Probability	Product
[12, 15]	$3.00	$48/6840 \approx 0.007$	$0.02
[9, 11]	$1.75	$396/6840 \approx 0.058$	$0.10
[6, 8]	$0.40	$1836/6840 \approx 0.268$	$0.11
[3, 5]	$0.00	$4560/6840 \approx 0.667$	$0.00
		Expected Value	$0.23

Over the long term, the carnival can expect to earn an average profit of $0.77 per player. Based on this relatively large profit, students may recommend that the carnival add the game.

2. A carnival manager has created a new game called Blind Draw. In this game, players draw three small balls from a container. The container holds 20 balls: 10 green balls worth 1 point each, 8 yellow balls worth 2 points each, and 2 red balls worth 5 points each.

Players cannot see the contents of the container, and they remove each ball after it is drawn. The point total for three balls determines the prize won. A total of 6–8 points wins a pennant, 9–11 points wins a small stuffed animal, and 12 or more points wins a large stuffed animal. Points from one game cannot be carried over to another game.

The pennants cost the carnival $0.40 each, the small stuffed animals cost $1.75 each, and the large stuffed animals cost $3.00 each. The manager plans to charge $1.00 to play the game.

As the carnival's financial advisor, write a letter to the manager describing your recommendations on this game. Use mathematics to support your position.

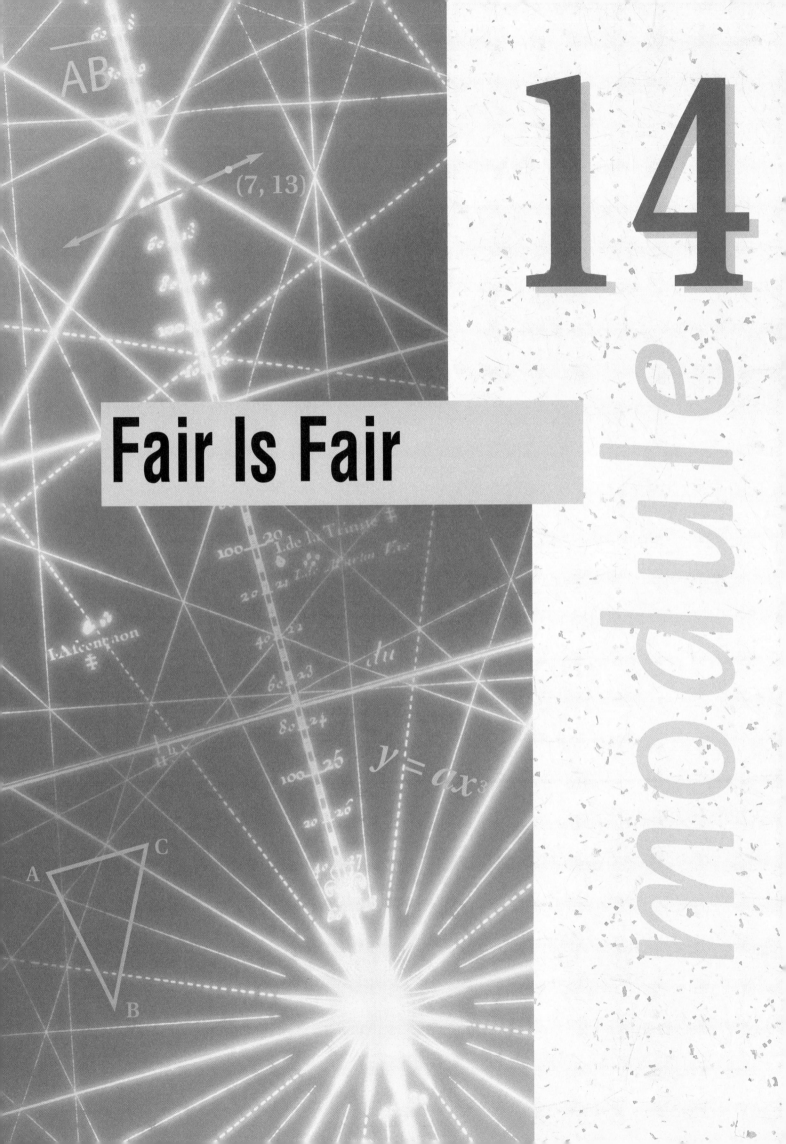

Fair Is Fair

14

module

Overview

This module introduces several practical methods to achieve a fair division of both continuous and discrete items.

Introduction:	Students explore their own definitions of fair and unfair division.
Activity 1:	Students identify continuous and discrete items and learn two algorithms for dividing continuous objects between two people.
Activity 2:	Students extend fair division of continuous objects to more than two people.
Activity 3:	Students investigate an algorithm for dividing a discrete object between two people.
Activity 4:	Students adapt the algorithm for dividing a discrete object to more than one object and more than two people.

Objectives

In this module, students will:

✳ identify the properties of fair division (Introduction, 1, 2, 3)

✳ investigate algorithms that result in fair divisions (Introduction, 1, 2, 3)

✳ identify items as continuous or discrete (1)

✳ make fair divisions of continuous items among two or more people (1, 2)

✳ make fair divisions of discrete items among two or more people (3, 4).

Prerequisites

For this module, students should know:

✳ how to find an arithmetic mean

✳ how to use a spreadsheet

✳ how to use a geometry utility.

 Flashbacks, for use at your discretion, appear in the Teacher Resources for this module. These brief problem sets provide a review of some prerequisite skills for each activity.

Planning Guide

Activity	Materials	Technology	Time Line
Introduction	■ none	■ none	1 day
Activity **1**	■ scissors ■ blank paper ■ rulers	■ geometry utility	2 days
Activity **2**	■ scissors ■ blank paper ■ rulers ■ doughnuts or candy bars ■ plastic knives	■ geometry utility ■ spreadsheet	2 days
Activity **3**	■ bid-and-divide template (optional)	■ spreadsheet	2 days
Activity **4**	■ bid-and-divide template (optional)	■ spreadsheet	2 days
Assessment Activities	■ none	■ spreadsheet	2 days **Total: 11 days**

 teacher note

A blackline master of the bid-and-divide template appears in the Teacher Resources for this module.

Introduction

A fair division is obtained when each individual involved is satisfied with the share received. What is fair depends upon the value each individual places on the item. It is relatively easy to divide a sum of money into equal parts. But equal does not necessarily mean fair. For example, dividing a plot of land into portions of equal area might leave one person with a slag heap and another with a gold mine. In this module, students explore various ways to achieve a fair division.

Student Outcomes

After completing the following discussion, students should be able to:

✴ describe their own notions of a fair division.

Discussion

a. Students are likely to use descriptions like "equal shares," "shares of the same size," and "equal parts." You might wish to point out that a fair division does not necessarily mean that all parties involved receive equal amounts. Fairness is based on the method used to divide the items and the value each individual places on them.

b. Answers will vary.
   1. Sample response: A fair division would give each person $8.33 and contribute the remaining penny to charity. An unfair division would give $6 to one person, $6 to the second, and $13 to the third.
   2. Sample response: A fair division would give each person $2\frac{2}{5}$ pieces. An unfair division would give 2 pieces to each of three people and 3 pieces to each of two people.
   3. Sample response: A fair division would involve selling both the ring and car and dividing the money equally. An unfair division would give one person both items. **Note:** Some students might suggest that giving one person the car and the other the ring is an unfair division. However, it is also possible for the two parties to consider this as fair, depending on how they value the items.
   4. Sample response: In a fair division, one person keeps the motorcycle and receives $25,333.33, while the other two receive $37,333.33, and the extra penny is given away. In an unfair division, one of the people would receive $80,000 in cash, one would receive $20,000, and the other would get the motorcycle.
   5. Sample response: Based on need for water, it would be fair if the large man received 1.25 L and the child received 0.75 L. It would be unfair for the man and child each to receive 1 L.

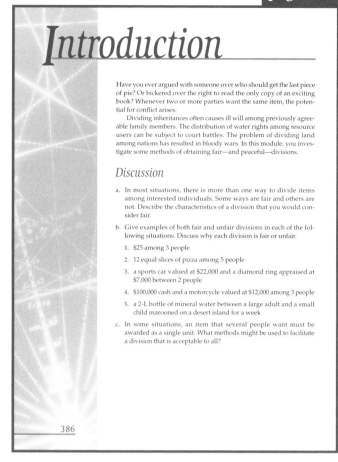

Introduction

Have you ever argued with someone over who should get the last piece of pie? Or bickered over the right to read the only copy of an exciting book? Whenever two or more parties want the same item, the potential for conflict arises.

Dividing inheritances often causes ill will among previously agreeable family members. The distribution of water rights among resource users can be subject to court battles. The problem of dividing land among nations has resulted in bloody wars. In this module, you investigate some methods of obtaining fair—and peaceful—divisions.

Discussion

a. In most situations, there is more than one way to divide items among interested individuals. Some ways are fair and others are not. Describe the characteristics of a division that you would consider fair.

b. Give examples of both fair and unfair divisions in each of the following situations. Discuss why each division is fair or unfair.
   1. $25 among 3 people
   2. 12 equal slices of pizza among 5 people
   3. a sports car valued at $22,000 and a diamond ring appraised at $7,000 between 2 people
   4. $100,000 cash and a motorcycle valued at $12,000 among 3 people
   5. a 2-L bottle of mineral water between a large adult and a small child marooned on a desert island for a week

c. In some situations, an item that several people want must be awarded as a single unit. What methods might be used to facilitate a division that is acceptable to all?

386

c. Sample response: Sell the item and divide the money equally, or award the item to one individual who then would compensate the others.

ACTIVITY 1

In practice, not all divisions are fair. Some people might use their authority to make divisions without concern for fairness. For example, a military officer assigning duties or a construction manager delegating tasks might consider efficiency or safety first, and fairness later. In a bankruptcy court, on the other hand, even a judge who tries to distribute assets fairly among all creditors might not seem completely fair to those involved.

mathematics note

A fair division problem exists when individuals must divide a set of items among themselves. A **fair division** occurs when all individuals, by their own assessment, consider the portions they are awarded as fair. "Fairness" depends on each individual's opinion. This opinion may not agree with the opinion of others involved.

An item is considered **continuous** if it may be awarded in parts in a fair division. For example, a cake is continuous, but the plate it is served on is not.

Exploration

a. One technique for dividing a continuous object between two persons is the **cut-and-choose method.** In this method, one person cuts the object into two shares. The other person then chooses the desired piece.

Create figures similar to those illustrated below. Use scissors and the cut-and-choose method to achieve a fair division in each case.

1.   2.

ACTIVITY 1

In this activity, students explore various methods of dividing continuous items between two people.

Materials List

- blank paper (two sheets per group)
- scissors (one pair per group)
- ruler (one per group)

Technology

- geometry utility (optional)

teacher note

In the following exploration, students may use shapes drawn with a geometry utility. Once choices have been made, students can use the utility to determine the areas of their chosen portions and see if their estimates of a fair division also result in an equal division. **Note:** Regardless of actual area, if both individuals believe the division was fair, then a fair division occurs.

Exploration

a. Students are likely to determine fairness by estimating area. They may use a coin toss to decide who cuts and who chooses.

b. Students can use a ruler to simulate a knife. As in Part **a,** they may use a coin toss to decide who controls the "knife."

Discussion

a. Since one person determined the size of the pieces and the other person received the first choice, both should be satisfied.

b. Sample response: It was hard to judge a fair portion of the irregularly shaped object. It also was difficult to decide who should cut and who should pick.

c. Sample response: Because each person has the opportunity to stop the knife, both should be satisfied with the results.

d. Some participants might feel that the process offers too little time to choose.

e. Sample response: The cut-and-choose and continuous-knife methods could be used on a candy bar, a pizza, a sandwich, or a plot of land.

f. Sample response: Neither of these methods would work with a car, a house, a pet, or a stereo. These items lose value if divided into parts. They also would be hard to use with a bowl of cherries or a compact disc collection.

Warm-Up

1. A fair division occurs when all individuals, by their own assessment, consider the portions they are awarded as fair.

2. **a.** An apple pie is continuous because it can be divided into parts in a fair division.

   b. A live fish is not continuous because it cannot be divided into parts in a fair division.

   c. Sample response: A rectangular plot of land may be considered continuous for a fair division, if the parties can agree on fair portions.

   d. Sample response: Three concert tickets could be considered as continuous in a fair division if there are three people involved. Otherwise, the tickets are not continuous.

b. A second technique for dividing a continuous object is the **continuous-knife method.** In this technique, a knife is held above the left edge of the object and moved slowly from left to right. Either person can stop the knife to cut off a piece that represents a fair share. The person who stops the knife receives the portion to the left. The second person receives the remaining portion. (The continuous-knife method also may be performed by moving the knife from top to bottom instead of left to right.)

Create a figure similar to the illustration below. Use a ruler to model the continuous-knife method to achieve a fair division. Draw a line where the "knife" is stopped. Use scissors to cut along the line.

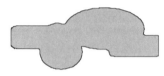

Discussion

a. Did the cut-and-choose method result in a fair division? Why or why not?

b. Describe any difficulties that arose when using the cut-and-choose method.

c. Why would you expect the continuous-knife method to result in a fair division?

d. What difficulties arose when using the continuous-knife method?

e. What kinds of objects can be divided by the methods described in the exploration?

f. What kinds of items should not be divided using either of these methods? Explain your response.

Warm-Up

1. Describe the conditions that are necessary for a fair division to occur.

2. Which of the following items could be considered continuous for a fair division? Justify your responses.

   a. an apple pie

   b. a live goldfish

   c. a rectangular plot of land

   d. three concert tickets

388   Module 14 ■ *Fair Is Fair*

Assignment

1.1 John and Leticia have some pizza to share. As shown in the diagram below, part of the pizza is cheese and part is pepperoni.

a. Describe how the two friends could divide the pizza fairly and explain how this method results in a fair division.

b. How might the friends change their method if John does not like pepperoni and Leticia does?

1.2 In this problem, you use a geometry utility to model the continuous-knife problem for two people.

a. Create an irregular polygon. Draw a line segment to act as the "knife," then move the segment across the polygon until it appears to be fairly divided into two portions.

b. Determine the areas of the resulting portions of the polygon.

c. Would this method result in a fair division? Explain your response.

1.3 Xang and Katelyn are willing to share the last submarine sandwich. Describe at least two different methods, other than cut-and-choose or continuous-knife, that might be used to accomplish a fair division. Rank your methods in order of preference and justify your decisions.

1.4 The figure below shows a plot of land with a large circular swimming pool. Describe how two people might divide this plot of land into two fair portions.

* * * * *

Assignment

Problems suitable for use as assessment items are identified by an asterisk (*).

1.1 **a.** Sample response: The friends could use the continuous-knife method to divide the part of the pizza that has only cheese on it, then repeat the process for the part that has pepperoni on it.

b. Sample response: The friends could divide the pizza so that Leticia receives all the pepperoni and some cheese while John receives all cheese.

1.2 **a–b.** Students may model the continuous-knife method from top to bottom and from left to right. The areas determined may or may not be equal. Sample response:

Area(A) = 9.8 square cm

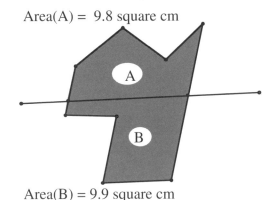

Area(B) = 9.9 square cm

c. Sample response: The division is fair if both participants are satisfied with their portions. **Note:** Student responses should reflect the idea that equal areas are not necessary for a fair division.

1.3 Answers will vary. Sample response: My three methods are listed below. The first one seems most likely to result in a fair division because both people participate in choosing the place to cut.

1. Each marks what he or she considers the middle of the sandwich. They then cut exactly between the two marks.

2. The two friends ask a third person to cut the sandwich into two parts and assign portions.

3. Each starts eating from opposite ends of the sandwich until the sandwich is gone.

* 1.4 Sample response: The two people could use the cut-and-choose method to divide the land. One person might think that the portion with the pool is more valuable than the land without the pool, so they might divide it as shown below. For example, if I were awarded the portion with the pool, I would be willing to take less land. If I did not receive the portion with the pool, I would accept more land as compensation.

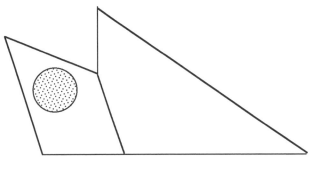

✳ ✳ ✳ ✳ ✳

1.5 a. Students may describe the cut-and-choose method, the continuous-knife method, or a method of their own.

b. Sample response: The material may have been neither the correct shape nor size on which to fit the pattern.

1.6 Answers will vary. Students may try either the cut-and-choose or continuous-knife method, but a fair division in this case probably would involve more than just the distribution of approximately equal areas of land. For example, both children might want access to the road and to the creek.

1.7 Sample response: Let *m* be any line through point *O* separating the parallelogram *ABCD* into two parts as shown.

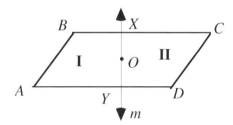

If Part I is rotated 180° about point *O*, it matches Part II exactly. **Note:** Point *A* matches *C* and point *B* matches *D* by the point symmetry of the figure. Point *X* matches *Y* because *O* is the midpoint of $\overline{XY}$. You might wish to ask students to discuss why this is true.

1.5 To complete a home economics project, Willis and Karissa each need enough cloth to sew a pair of shorts. The diagram below shows the piece of material they must divide between them.

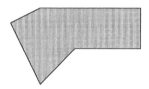

a. Describe how this piece of material could be divided fairly.

b. After the cloth was divided, Willis was able to finish his project, but Karissa ran into trouble. What problems might Karissa have encountered, even though she originally considered the division a fair one?

1.6 Mr. and Mrs. Summers would like to give the property shown in the map below to their two grown children.

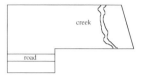

Both children would like to build homes on this land. Describe how the property could be divided fairly.

1.7 A figure has **point symmetry** if it can be rotated 180° about a point and each point in the image coincides with a point in the preimage. For example, the rectangle below has point symmetry about the point where its two diagonals intersect.

In the parallelogram below, point *O* is the point where the diagonals intersect. Explain why any line through point *O* divides the parallelogram into two regions with equal areas.

A C T I V I T Y
2

Not all fair division problems involve only two parties. When three or more individuals are involved, the situation can become much more complicated.

To obtain a fair division among several people, some additional assumptions must be made. First, all persons involved must be capable of determining a fair portion. The value that each individual places on a particular portion might depend on more than just its size. Each person should get a fair share based on his or her own assessment.

In the division of land, for example, one person might consider lake frontage more valuable than forests. In such a case, that person could accept a smaller piece of land with lake frontage as a fair share.

Exploration

One way to divide a continuous object among three or more people is the **reduction method.** Parts a–e below describe the steps that must be followed to divide an item among three people using the reduction method. Use these steps to simulate the division of a doughnut or candy bar.

a. The individuals determine the order in which each will participate in the division.

b. The first person "reduces" the item by cutting off a fair share.

c. The second person has a choice: either reduce the portion cut by the previous person or leave it intact. If the second person leaves the portion intact, then the third person has the same choice.

d. The last person to reduce the piece receives that portion and is now out of the process.

A C T I V I T Y
2

Students investigate another method for fairly dividing continuous items.

teacher note

A brief assessment of the mathematical content in Activities **1** and **2**, for use at your discretion, appears in the Teacher Resources for this module.

Materials List

■ blank paper (two sheets per group)

■ scissors (one pair per group)

■ doughnuts, cake, or candy bars (one per group)

Technology

■ geometry utility

---

teacher note

In the following exploration, students divide an object using the reduction method. As an alternative to using doughnuts, cake, or candy bars, you may ask students to create irregularly shaped objects out of paper.

Students might need some practice with the reduction algorithm before becoming comfortable with its use. They should gain a better appreciation of the algorithm's utility after completing the discussion.

Student Outcomes

After completing the following exploration and discussion, students should be able to:

✳ identify the properties of a fair division

✳ fairly divide an item considered continuous among three or more people.

Exploration

Students examine an algorithm for dividing a continuous object among three people. This algorithm can be extended to any number of people.

Discussion

a. Sample response: A person would reduce the share if it seemed to be too large.

b. If no one reduces a portion, the person who cut it receives it.

c. Sample response: The reduction method should result in a fair division because each of the participants has an opportunity to reduce an unfair portion.

d. Sample response: Yes. It is similar to the cut-and-choose method.

e. Sample response: Because each person considers the item as a whole before the division takes place, the sum of the fractional values must be 1. For example, if an item is divided into two parts, one person might assign a value of 1/2 to each part. Another person might consider the same parts as 1/3 and 2/3 of the item. In either case, the sum of the fractional values is 1.

f. As described in Activity **1,** the cut-and-choose method can be used only with two people. The other methods can be adjusted easily to allow an unlimited number of participants.

Warm-Up

1. The area of the region to the right of the division line is 8.24 cm^2; the area of the region to the left is 8.5 cm^2.

2. Sample response: The division is not equal, but it could be a fair division if the people receiving each region are satisfied with their respective portions.

e. The remaining two people divide the rest of the item by repeating the reduction method or by using any other method for fairly dividing an object between two people. Any pieces removed through reduction, but not yet awarded, are included in this division.

Discussion

a. In the reduction method, when would a person choose to reduce a share?

b. Who receives the first piece if no one reduces it?

c. Do you think that the reduction method will result in a fair division of a candy bar? Explain your response.

d. Would this method result in a fair division for two people? Why or why not?

e. In any division of a continuous item, the fractional value assigned to each portion may vary from person to person. The sum of these fractional values, however, is always 1. Why is this true?

f. Could the cut-and-choose method, the continuous-knife method, or the reduction method be used when more than three people are involved in the division of a continuous object? Explain your response.

Warm-Up

1. Does the division line in the figure below create two regions of equal area? Explain your response.

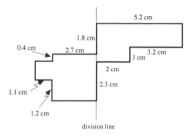

2. Is the division in Problem **1** fair? Explain your response.

Assignment

2.1 Imagine that you and two friends have decided to share a candy bar using the reduction method. One of your friends makes each of the first cuts shown in Parts **a** and **b** below. In each case, would you reduce the portion on the left or let this cut stand? Explain your responses.

1.

first cut

2.

first cut

2.2 **a.** Describe a method other than those previously mentioned in this module of dividing a continuous object fairly among three people.

b. Will your method work when five people are involved? If so, explain how. If not, modify your method so that it will work.

2.3 Create an irregularly shaped object out of paper. Describe a fair division of this object among three or more people.

2.4 Chadd, Rusty, and Kristi own a lawn-mowing service. They have been hired to mow a park that contains about 2 acres of grass. The park includes flat areas, hilly regions, and groves of trees—all of which must be mowed.

a. Why would the reduction method fail to provide a fair division in this case? Explain your response.

b. Describe how the park can be divided so that each of the three must mow a fair portion of the grass.

c. Both Chadd and Kristi use push mowers, while Rusty uses a riding mower. How does this fact affect your response to Part **b**?

* * * * *

2.5 Use a geometry utility to model the continuous-knife method of dividing an irregular polygon among four or more people. Describe how the method was altered to accommodate additional people.

Module 14 ■ *Fair Is Fair* 393

teacher note

Problem **2.1** should help students further understand the reduction method. Problem **2.4** asks students to adapt the reduction method to a new situation. Problems **2.6** and **2.7** allow students to determine their own algorithms for sharing a continuous object among three or more people.

Assignment

Problems suitable for use as assessment items are identified by an asterisk (*).

2.1 **a.** Sample response: I would not reduce this portion because it is already less than one-third of the candy bar.

b. Sample response: I would reduce this potion because it is more than one-third of the candy bar.

2.2 **a.** Sample response: The first person cuts the object into two equal portions. The second person chooses one of the portions. The first person and the second person then cut their portions into thirds. The third person picks one portion from each person. The first person and the second person keep their remaining portions.

b. Sample response: Yes, this method can be modified for five people. For example, consider five people designated by the initials A, B, C, D, and E. Assign A and B to act as a team and C and D to act as a team. Ask the two teams to divide the object into two portions. Next, ask each team to divide its portion into two more portions, for a total of four portions. Now have A, B, C, and D each divide one of the "fourths" into five portions. Let person E pick one piece from each of the other people, who keep their remaining portions.

* 2.3 Answers will vary. Sample response: Persons 1 and 2 divide the object into two fair portions. Each person then divides their portion into three additional pieces. Person 3 selects one piece from person 1 and another from person 2, who keep their remaining pieces.

2.4 **a.** Sample response: In this case, most people would want the smallest share, not the largest. The reduction method would allow the last person making a choice to reduce his area to almost nothing, and one person would end up mowing most of the grass.

b. Sample response: Because the hills and tree groves are harder to cut, it might not be fair simply to divide the park into thirds. A method similar to the reduction method may be used if it is based on expansion instead. Once the first person chooses, the second and third persons have an opportunity to expand the section. The person who makes the last expansion gets that section to mow. The remaining two divide the rest of the park in a similar manner.

c. Answers will vary. Sample response: Rusty should have to cut a greater amount of the park, but he will have to be restricted to the open regions because the riding mower might have problems maneuvering in the groves.

* * * * *

2.5 Sample response: After the first person to stop the knife receives a portion, the rest continue with what portion remains. The process continues until each person has received a share.

Module 14 ■ *Fair is Fair* 373

2.6 **a.** Sample response: This is unfair because there will be conflicts with sleep, school, and extracurricular activities.

b. Answers will vary. Some students might suggest adding up the total hours in each month and using the reduction method, but this does not solve the problem as to when each child gets to listen. Others might suggest splitting each week into eight shifts, then assigning rotating shifts, as shown in the chart at the bottom of the page.

c. Sample response: No. Each child still should have control over the CD player the same amount of time. It should be up to the individual whether or not siblings are allowed to listen during his or her time.

2.7 **a.** Sample response: Since the profit is $480,000, the amount to be shared among employees is $240,000. The total number of years of service is 60. I divided the money using each employee's fraction of the total years of service as a multiplier. According to this method, employee A gets $80,000, B gets $40,000, C gets $96,000, and D gets $24,000.

b. Sample response: It seems fair to reward employees based on their years of service. However, if any employee is not satisfied with the allotted share, this would not qualify as a fair division.

2.6 Mr. and Mrs. Estrada have purchased a new compact disc (CD) player for their four children: Gisela, Milo, Hank, and Rozella. Each of the four likes a different type of music, so they must find a way to divide the time with the CD player fairly.

   a. Explain why it might not be fair simply to assign each child 6 hr a day with the CD player.

   b. Devise a method that fairly divides access to the CD player during one month.

   c. If Rozella and Hank suddenly start listening to the same type of music, should that change the method you devised in Part **b**? Explain your response.

2.7 A business owner has sold her company. She decides to share half of the profit from the sale with her employees, based on years of service. The following table shows the years of service for each employee.

Employee	Years of Service
A	20
B	10
C	24
D	6

   a. The profit from the sale is $480,000. Calculate the amount each employee should receive and describe how you determined each share.

   b. Do you think this division is fair? Explain your response.

ACTIVITY 3

In the previous activities, you examined the fair division of continuous objects. Some objects, however, are difficult or impractical to divide into parts. For example, how would you divide a car or a boat?

In this activity, you investigate the fair division of **discrete** items. An item is considered discrete if it can be awarded only as an entire unit in a fair division. For example, houses, cars, and boats are all discrete items.

Shift	Week 1	Week 2	Week 3	Week 4
Monday	Gisele	Milo	Hank	Rozella
Tuesday	Milo	Hank	Rozella	Gisele
Wednesday	Hank	Rozella	Gisele	Milo
Thursday	Rozella	Gisele	Milo	Hank
Friday	Gisele	Milo	Hank	Rozella
Saturday until 5:00 P.M.	Milo	Hank	Rozella	Gisele
Saturday after 5:00 P.M.	Hank	Rozella	Gisele	Milo
Sunday	Rozella	Gisele	Milo	Hank

Exploration

a. Along with a partner, choose a discrete item that you both would like to own but must divide fairly.

b. Develop a process that could be used to decide who will get the item.

c. Determine how the student who does not get the item should be compensated to make the division fair.

d. Determine the value of this settlement for each person.

Discussion

a. How was the person who did not receive the item compensated?

b. Did your method result in a fair division? Explain why or why not.

c. Is it necessary for the values of the item and the compensation to be equal to have a fair division?

d. Could your method be adjusted to accommodate more people and more items?

mathematics note

Mathematicians have developed some approaches to fair division that include steps you might not have considered. The **bid-and-divide** method, for instance, involves assigning a cash value to an item through a bidding process. The secret bids represent the amounts that individuals would be willing to pay for the item and determine the value to be divided fairly. The item is awarded to the highest bidder. The individual who receives the item then compensates the others for a fair share.

For example, imagine that you and a friend share a calculator. Your friend is moving to another town. The calculator is a discrete item, so the two of you must determine who will keep it. Using the bid-and-divide method, you each submit a secret bid that reflects the value you place on the calculator. Suppose that you bid $60 and your friend bids $70. Because $70 is the higher bid, the value to be divided fairly is $70. This is referred to as the **value pool.**

Because there are two of you, your share of the bids is half the value that you placed on the calculator, and your friend's share is half the value that she placed on it. You bid $60, so your share is 0.5($60) or $30. Your friend's share is 0.5($70) or $35. The sum of these shares, $30 and $35, accounts for $65 of the $70 in the

Module 14 ■ *Fair Is Fair*   395

ACTIVITY

Students investigate an algorithm for fairly dividing a discrete object.

Materials List

■ bid-and-divide template (optional; four or five copies per student or group; a blackline master appears in the Teacher Resources for this module)

Technology

■ spreadsheet (optional)

teacher note

The bid-and-divide method of dividing a discrete item between two people involves several steps. You may wish to lead students through the example described in the mathematics note.

The bid-and-divide template (included in the Teacher Resources for this module) consists of an expanded version of the chart in Figure **14-1.**

Student Outcomes

After completing the following exploration and discussion, students should be able to:

✴ make fair divisions of discrete items between two people.

Exploration

a. Each pair of students may pick any discrete item to divide. Sample response: A motorcycle.

b. Sample response: The two individuals flip a coin to decide who will receive the motorcycle.

c. Sample response: The individuals have the motorcycle appraised. The one who receives the motorcycle pays the other person half the appraised value.

d. Sample response: Because the person receiving the motorcycle pays the other person half the appraised value, the value of the settlement for both is the same.

Discussion

a. Sample response: The person who did not receive the item was paid cash as compensation.

b. Methods devised by students might or might not result in a fair division. Sample response: Yes, it is fair, because the pair agreed on a method and used an appraised value to assign equal shares.

c. Sample response: No. The fairness of a division is based on each person's perception of a fair share, not on equal values.

d. Some student methods may not be easily altered to accommodate more than two people and one item.

   Note: Students modify the bid-and-divide method outlined in this activity to accommodate more people and more items in Activity **4.**

e. Sample response: Using the high bid guarantees that all will get at least what they consider fair shares.

f. The high bid is always more than the sum of one-half the high bid and one-half the low bid (the shares of bids). As a result, there is always a positive value-pool balance to contribute to the total fair share.

g. The value pool sets the total value available. The settlements represent how the value pool is divided.

h. Compensation for the person who does not receive the item equals the cash required to create that person's fair share. That amount is paid by the person who receives the item. The sum of the two is 0.

Warm-Up

1. a. 65
   b. 8500
   c. 0.65

2. a. The value pool is the highest bid, or the value to be divided fairly.

   b. The value-pool balance is the difference between the value pool and the sum of the shares of the bids.

   c. The total fair share is the sum of a share of a person's bid and an equal share of the value-pool balance.

   d. The final settlement value is the sum of each person's compensation and the value of the item awarded, if any.

---

remainder of the value pool, $5, is the **value-pool balance**. Each person is awarded half this balance, or $2.50.

Because your friend's bid is higher than yours, she is awarded the calculator. Once the item is awarded, each person's compensation must be calculated. A chart similar to the one illustrated in Figure **14-1** may help you keep track of the calculations in the bid-and-divide method.

As shown in Figure **14-1**, your **total fair share** is the sum of a share of your bid and an equal share of the value-pool balance. In this example, your total fair share is $32.50 and your friend's is $37.50.

Compensation for each individual is determined by calculating the difference between the total fair share and the value of the item received. Your compensation, $32.50, equals the difference between your total fair share and the value of the item awarded—in this case, $0. Your friend's compensation is –$32.50, the difference between her total fair share and the value of the calculator.

	You	Friend	Value Pool	
Bids	60.00	70.00	Total of High Bid(s)	70.00
			–Total of Shares of Bid(s)	65.00
Sum of Bid(s)	60.00	70.00	Value-pool Balance	5.00
Share of Bid(s)	30.00	35.00		
Share of Value-pool Balance	2.50	2.50		
Total Fair Share	32.50	37.50		
(Item Awarded)	(none)	(calculator)		
Total Value Awarded	0.00	70.00		
Compensation	+32.50	–32.50		
Final Settlement Value	32.50	37.50		

FIGURE 14-1 Fair division using bid-and-divide method.

In a fair division of the calculator by this method, your friend keeps the calculator and compensates you $32.50 for your fair share. The **final settlement value** is the sum of each person's compensation and the value of the item awarded, if any. When a fair division has been administered properly, each person's final settlement value equals that person's total fair share. The sum of the final settlement values equals the total of bids in the value pool. The sum of the compensations equals 0.

Assignment

Problems suitable for use as assessment items are identified by an asterisk (*).

3.1 Sample chart:

	Yoshi	Shiho	Value Pool	
Bids	900.00	1050.00	Total of High Bids	1050.00
			– Total of Shares of Bids	975.00
Sum of Bids	900.00	1050.00	Value-pool balance	75.00
Share of Bids	450.00	525.00		
+ Equal Share of Value-pool balance	37.50	37.50		
Total Fair Share	487.50	562.50		
(Item Awarded)	(none)	(sword)		
Total Value Awarded	0.00	1050.00		
Compensation	+487.50	–487.50		
Final Settlement Value	487.50	562.50		

e. In the bid-and-divide method, why do you think the high bid is used to determine the value pool?

f. In the final settlement, why does each person always receive more than a fair share of that person's original bid?

g. Why must the sum of the final settlement values equal the value pool?

h. Why must the sum of the compensations equal 0?

Warm-Up

1. Determine the arithmetic mean of each of the following pairs of numbers.

   a. 40, 90   b. 1000, 16,000   c. 0.6, 0.7

2. Describe the significance of each of the following in the bid-and-divide process.

   a. value pool   b. value-pool balance

   c. total fair share   d. final settlement value

Assignment

3.1 Yoshi and Shiho have inherited an ancient Japanese sword. They decide to use the bid-and-divide method to determine who should keep the sword. Yoshi bids $900. Shiho bids $1050.

Complete the table below to determine a fair division in this situation.

	Yoshi	Shiho	Value Pool	
Bids	900	1050	Total of High Bid(s)	
			– Total of Shares of Bid(s)	
Sum of Bid(s)			Value-pool balance	
Share of Bid(s)				
+ Equal Share of Value-pool balance				
Total Fair Share				
(Item Awarded)				
Total Value Awarded				
Compensation				
Final Settlement Value				

3.2 **a.** Dena must pay Milo $14,000 in compensation.

b. Milo receives $14,000 in cash. Dena receives the car less $14,000 or $18,000 of value.

* 3.3 See the sample chart below.

	Leif	Neva	Value Pool	
Bids	120.00	130.00	Total of High Bids	130.00
			– Total of Shares of Bids	125.00
Sum of Bids	120.00	130.00	Value-pool balance	5.00
Share of Bids	60.00	65.00		
+ Equal Share of Value-pool balance	2.50	2.50		
Total Fair Share	62.50	67.50		
(Item Awarded)	(none)	(bike)		
Total Value Awarded	0.00	130.00		
Compensation	+62.50	–62.50		
Final Settlement Value	62.50	67.50		

3.4 Students may use a spreadsheet to explore different combinations of bids. Sample response: If Neva wants the bike, she should bid $175. Then, even if she doesn't get it, she will receive the largest possible fair share.

＊ ＊ ＊ ＊ ＊

3.5 See the sample table at the bottom of the page.

3.6 **a.** Sample response: If the expenses paid for the trip do not have to be considered a discrete item, each could receive half and pay the balance themselves. If it can be given to only one person, the one receiving the prize could reimburse the other half the value.

b. If Miranda and Willis both agree on a way for determining who is the recipient, then the chosen process is fair.

3.2 Milo and Dena have inherited an antique car from their grandfather. To determine a fair division, they decide to use the bid-and-divide method. Milo bids $24,000 for the car and Dena bids $32,000.

   a. Determine the amount of cash that Dena must pay Milo.

   b. What is each person's final settlement value?

3.3 Leif and Neva are the co-winners of an essay contest. The first prize is a bicycle. They decide to use the bid-and-divide method to determine who will keep the bike. Leif bids $120 and Neva bids $130. Determine the value of the final settlements.

3.4 Suppose Neva knows that Leif thinks the bike in Problem **3.3** is worth at least $150. However, she does not think that it is worth more than $175. Neva wants the bike. However, even if she doesn't get the bike, she would like to receive as much compensation as possible. What should she bid? Explain your response.

＊ ＊ ＊ ＊ ＊

3.5 Alexi and Norjar share first place in an academic challenge. Later, they realize that the real challenge is how to share the first prize—a new computer—and still remain friends.

They decide to use the bid-and-divide method to find a settlement that allocates possession of the computer to one of them, fair compensation to the other, and lasting friendship to both. If Alexi bids $800 and Norjar bids $900, determine the values of the final settlement.

3.6 By working together, Miranda and Willis have won first place in an essay contest. The prize is an all-expenses paid trip to Europe for one person. Both students contributed equally to the final draft of the essay. Now they must determine a fair method for dividing the prize.

The total dollar value of the trip is $1995. This amount includes travel ($1150), housing ($500), and food ($345).

   a. Determine a procedure for dividing the prize.

   b. Do you think that your method is fair? Explain your response.

	Alexi	Norjar	Value Pool	
Bids	800.00	900.00	Total of High Bids	900.00
			− Total of Shares of Bids	850.00
Sum of Bids	800.00	900.00	Value-pool balance	50.00
Share of Bids	400.00	450.00		
+ Equal Share of Value-pool balance	25.00	25.00		
Total Fair Share	425.00	475.00		
(Item Awarded)	(none)	(computer)		
Total Value Awarded	0.00	900.00		
Compensation	+425.00	−425.00		
Final Settlement Value	425.00	475.00		

ACTIVITY 4

The division of a family estate can involve several survivors and many items. In this activity, you adapt the bid-and-divide method to handle such a situation.

Exploration

a. Design a chart or spreadsheet similar to the one in Figure 14-1 to track the division of an estate that involves several items and several survivors. Your chart should be flexible enough for use in several different cases.

b. Write complete descriptions of each of the following situations, including the names of the people involved, the items that must be divided, and the bids made by each person for each item.

   1. Two people must divide three discrete items between them.

   2. Three or more people must divide one discrete item among them.

c. Determine a fair solution to each problem in Part **b.**

d. Explain to another group how they might use your chart or spreadsheet to accomplish a fair division.

Discussion

a. How is the value pool determined in your chart?

b. How are the shares of the bids in each column determined?

c. Could your chart be used to determine a fair division for two people who must divide a single object?

Warm-Up

1. Which of the following items should be considered discrete for a fair division? Justify your responses.

   a. a portable music player

   b. a lobster dinner

   c. a roundtrip airline ticket

ACTIVITY 4

Students modify the bid-and-divide method described in Activity **3** to fairly divide several items among three or more people.

teacher note

A brief assessment of the mathematical content in Activities **3** and **4,** for use at your discretion, appears in the Teacher Resources for this module.

Materials List

■ bid-and-divide template (optional; four or five copies per student or group; a blackline master appears in the Teacher Resources for this module)

Technology

■ spreadsheet

teacher note

The following exploration is designed for work in small groups. If you supply students with copies of the bid-and-divide template, they should begin with Part **b.**

Students might not be able to produce a spreadsheet that would complete all of the necessary calculations simply by entering the bid values. The sample spreadsheet given in Part **a** shows some possible formulas in the appropriate cells.

Student Outcomes

After completing the following exploration and discussion, students should be able to:

✳ fairly divide a set of discrete items among three or more people.

Exploration

a. Student responses will vary. The sample spreadsheet at the bottom of the page shows space for four items to be bid upon by four bidders. In this sample, the names of the bidders (and their bids) should be listed in columns C–F. The three narrow blank columns (D–F) should contain the same relative formulas as the column below the heading "Names."

b–c. Students write two problems and use their chart or spreadsheet to determine the solutions. One problem consists of dividing three discrete items among two people. The other involves dividing one discrete item among three or more people.

d. Students should include descriptions of the necessary formulas or calculations in their explanations.

Discussion

a. The value pool should equal the sum of the highest bids on all items.

b. An individual's share of the bids should be calculated by dividing the sum of all bids made by that individual by the number of people involved in the division.

c. Student responses will vary. The sample spreadsheet shown in Part **a** of the exploration may be adjusted to fairly divide any number of objects among any number of people.

Warm-Up

1. **a.** A portable music player should be considered discrete because it can be awarded only as an entire unit.

   b. Sample response: The dinner should be considered discrete if there are more than two people who wish to divide it.

   c. An airline ticket should be considered discrete because it can be awarded only as an entire unit.

	A	B	C	D	E	F	G	H
1	No. of People		Names					
2	item						value pool	
3	1	bid					high bid	=MAX(C3:F3)
4	2	bid					high bid	=MAX(C4:F4)
5	3	bid					high bid	=MAX(C5:F5)
6	4	bid					high bid	=MAX(C6:F6)
7	sum of bids		=SUM(C3:C6)					
8							total of high bids	=SUM(H1:H5)
9	share of bids		=C7/$B$1				total shares of bids	=SUM(C9:F9)
10	share of value-pool balance		=IF(C9=0,0,$H$10/$B$1)				value-pool balance	=H7–H8
11	total fair share		=C9+C10					
12								
13	value awarded	1	=IF(C3=MAX($C3:$F3),C3,0)					
14	value awarded	2	=IF(C4=MAX($C4:$F4),C4,0)					
15	value awarded	3	=IF(C5=MAX($C5:$F5),C5,0)					
16	value awarded	4	=IF(C6=MAX($C6:$F6),C6,0)					
17								
18	total value awarded		=SUM(C13:C16)					
19	compensation		=C11–C18					
20	final settlement value		=C18+C19					

2. Calculate the arithmetic mean of each of the following:

   a. 11, 19, 56, 4, 23

   b. $306.25, $412.00, $299.99, $343.43

Assignment

4.1 Dena and Milo must use the bid-and-divide method to distribute an antique car, a coin collection, and the family house. Dena bids $32,000 for the car, $6000 for the coins, and $126,000 for the house. Milo bids $24,000 for the car, $5000 for the coins, and $151,000 for the house.

   a. Determine a fair division of the three items.

   b. Who must pay cash as a compensation? How much will be paid?

   c. Does anyone receive more than a fair share?

   d. Explain the significance of the value-pool balance.

   e. If Dena changes her bid on the coin collection to $12,000, how will the final settlement values change?

   f. If Milo does not want the car, would it be a good strategy for him to bid $0? Explain your response.

   g. What is the best bidding strategy for someone who does not wish to receive an item but wants the final settlement value to be as large as possible?

4.2 Imagine that a charitable estate has donated a computer, a valuable painting, and a four-year college scholarship to two rival high schools, including your own school.

   a. Use appropriate technology to determine a fair division of the gift.

   b. Use a chart or spreadsheet to show a fair division in which your school receives the computer and the scholarship.

   c. Use a chart or spreadsheet to show a fair division in which your rival school receives the painting and the scholarship.

4.3 The four Hersey children all want the family grandfather clock. They cannot decide who will keep it, so they visit a lawyer. The lawyer asks each of the four to submit a secret bid. All four bids are shown in the table below.

Sibling	Jon	Kris	Anne	Dean
Bid	$950	$1000	$1250	$1300

Determine the value of the final settlement for each sibling.

2. **a.** 22.6

   b. $340.42

Assignment

Problems suitable for use as assessment items are identified by an asterisk (*).

4.1 **a.** Dena is awarded the car, the coins, and $52,500. Milo is awarded the house less $52,500. See the sample chart below.

Item		Dena	Milo	Value Pool	
1. car	**Bid**	32000	24000	high bid	32000
2. coins	**Bid**	6000	5000	high bid	6000
3. house	**Bid**	126000	151000	high bid	151000
sum of bids		164000	180000		
				total high bids	189000
share of bids		82000	90000	total shares of bids	172000
share of value-pool balance		8500	8500		
total fair share		90500	98500	value-pool balance	17000
value awarded	1	32000	0		
value awarded	2	6000	0		
value awarded	3	0	151000		
total value awarded		38000	151000		
compensation		52500	−52500		
final settlement value		90500	98500		

b. Milo pays a compensation of $52,500.

c. Both receive $8500 more than their share of bids.

d. The value-pool balance is the difference between the sum of the high bids and the sum of the shares of bids. It is divided equally among all the individuals involved. This guarantees that all receive more than what they expected as a fair share.

e. The items still would be awarded as in Part **a,** but Dena's compensation would be $51,000 instead of $52,500.

f. Sample response: No. If Milo places a bid of $0, his fair share will drop to $92,500 from $98,500 and the compensation he must pay will increase to $58,500 from $52,500.

g. Sample response: The best strategy for someone who does not want an item is to bid as closely as possible to the highest bid without going over. This increases the individual's share of bids and the final settlement.

4.2 a. Answers will vary. Students may use a spreadsheet to complete this problem.

b. See the sample response below.

c. See the sample response at the bottom of the next page.

Item		School	Rival	Value Pool	
1. computer	**Bid**	2000	1500	high bid	2000
2. painting	**Bid**	1500	2000	high bid	2000
3. scholarship	**Bid**	45000	40000	high bid	45000
sum of bids		48500	43500		
				total high bids	49000
share of bids		24250	21750	total shares of bids	46000
share of value-pool balance		1500	1500		
total fair share		25750	23250	value-pool balance	3000
value awarded	1	2000	0		
value awarded	2	0	2000		
value awarded	3	45000	0		
total value awarded		47000	2000		
compensation		–21250	21250		
final settlement value		25750	23250		

4.4 The Hersey children from Problem **4.3** also inherited a home stereo, a color television, and a sports car. Determine how these three items would be divided fairly if each sibling submitted the bids shown in the following table.

Items	Bids			
	Jon	Kris	Anne	Dean
stereo	$1500	$1750	$1000	$1200
television	$900	$600	$750	$500
car	$10,000	$12,000	$9500	$11,500

* * * * *

4.5 In your own home, identify a minimum of four objects of some value which you might want to divide fairly. Ask at least three people (parents, siblings, or friends) to submit bids on these objects, then determine a fair division.

4.3 Jon, Kris, and Anne receive $281.25, $293.75, and $356.25 in cash, respectively. Dean is awarded the clock and must pay compensation to the other three for a total of $931.25. His final settlement is $368.75.

4.4 Anne and Dean receive $3275 and $3762.50 in cash, respectively. Jon is awarded the television and $2662.50 in cash. Kris is awarded the stereo and the car. She pays compensation to the other three for a total of $9700.

* * * * *

4.5 Answers will vary but should follow the process described in this activity. You might wish to require students to explain the fair division process to parents or other adults.

Item		School	Rival	Value Pool	
1. computer	**Bid**	2000	1500	high bid	2000
2. painting	**Bid**	1500	2000	high bid	2000
3. scholarship	**Bid**	20000	25000	high bid	25000
sum of bids		23500	28500		
				total high bids	29000
share of bids		11750	14250	total shares of bids	26000
share of value-pool balance		1500	1500		
total fair share		13250	15750	value-pool balance	3000
value awarded	1	2000	0		
value awarded	2	0	2000		
value awarded	3	0	25000		
total value awarded		2000	27000		
compensation		11250	–11250		
final settlement value		13250	15750		

Research Project

This research project allows students to explore the relationship between methods of apportionment and the course of U.S. history. In the past, interest groups and political parties have often used the mathematics of apportionment to manipulate the assignment of representatives. In the presidential election of 1876, for example, Samuel L. Tilden (who won the popular vote) was defeated in the electoral college 185 to 184 by Rutherford B. Hayes. Hayes' one-vote margin of victory may be traced to the assignment of nine seats by political expediency rather than the Hamilton method.

Depending on the projects they select, students may encounter a variety of mathematical topics, including rounding, standard divisors and quotas, complex fractions, the geometric mean, and the method of equal proportions.

 teacher note

An additional assessment, for use at your discretion, appears in the Teacher Resources for this module.

Research Project

In this module, you examined the fair division of pizzas, televisions, and other objects. But the issue of fairness also applies to the allocation of less tangible items—such as political representation.

Since the establishment of the U.S. Constitution, the United States has had two chambers of Congress: the Senate and the House of Representatives. Each state receives two senators, regardless of land area or population. In 1941, the size of the House of Representatives was fixed at 435, divided according to population.

The distribution of representatives is referred to as **apportionment**. To learn more about the history of apportionment in the United States, complete either Part **a** or Part **b** below.

a. The method of apportionment for the U.S. House of Representatives has been the subject of frequent debate. The following table shows the apportionment methods used from 1790 to 2000. Select one of the entries in the table and write a report describing its mathematical and historical circumstances.

Census Years	Apportionment Method Used
1790–1830	Jefferson
1840	Webster
1850	Hamilton
1860–1870	Hamilton (modified)
1880–1890	Hamilton
1900–1910	Webster
1920	No new apportionment
1930	Webster
1940–2000	Huntington

b. Identify an event in U.S. history that was affected by apportionment. Describe the event and explain how apportionment affected its occurrence or outcome.

Summary Assessment

1. a. Sample response: If Maria divides the object into two equal parts, Gisele could divide each half in the following manner:

$$\frac{1}{2} = \frac{12}{50} + \frac{12}{50} + \frac{1}{50}$$

Therefore, the pieces in order of size would be:

$$\frac{12}{50}, \frac{12}{50}, \frac{12}{50}, \frac{12}{50}, \frac{1}{50}, \frac{1}{50}$$

Since Gisele gets to choose two of the first four pieces selected, she can gain an unfair advantage.

   b. Sample response: Maria divides the object into two parts. Gisele selects one of the two pieces and divides it into three parts. Micah does the same for the remaining part.

   Maria then picks one piece from Gisele and one from Micah. Gisele picks one piece from Micah and Micah picks one piece from Gisele.

   Now Gisele and Micah have a piece selected from each other and their remaining piece.

2. Sample response: Yes. Tawnya would receive what she thought was her fair share of the strudel. Vasu also would be content with half, because that is more than his opinion of a fair share.

Summary Assessment

1. Maria, Gisele, and Micah want to divide a continuous object into three parts. They follow the process described below.
   ■ Maria divides the object into two parts.
   ■ Gisele divides each of the two parts into three pieces.
   ■ Micah selects one piece of the object.
   ■ Maria selects one piece.
   ■ Gisele selects two pieces.
   ■ Maria selects one piece.
   ■ Micah is awarded the remaining piece.

   a. Explain why this procedure may not result in a fair division.

   b. Modify this process to ensure that a fair division occurs.

2. Tawnya and Vasu have received an apple strudel as a gift. Vasu would be content to have 3/8 of the strudel. Tawnya thinks her fair share is 1/2 of the strudel. Would a procedure that awarded 1/2 of the strudel to each of them be a fair division? Explain your response.

3. Miguel, Rolf, and Tristan are graduating from college. In their four years as roommates, they have made several purchases together, including a stereo, a calculator, and a compact disc collection. Now that each will be moving to a different town, they must divide these possessions. Devise a method that the roommates can use to achieve a fair division.

4. The three roommates in Problem **3** also own an old car that they used for grocery shopping and trips to the beach. They decide to use the bid-and-divide method to see who will keep the car. Miguel bids $400, Rolf bids $600, and Tristan bids $375.

   a. Determine the value of the final settlement for each person.

   b. If Tristan knows the amount of the other two bids and is not interested in keeping the car, how can he maximize the value of his final settlement?

3. Answers will vary. Sample response: The roommates could have the three items appraised, then draw straws to see who gets which item. The person with the most expensive item then could pay compensation to the other two. **Note:** Some students may consider the CD collection as a "continuous" item and divide it separately.

4. a. See the sample response at the bottom of the page.
   b. Tristan should make his bid as close as possible to the highest bid.

Item		Miguel	Rolf	Tristan	Value Pool	
1. car	**Bid**	400.00	600.00	375.00	high bid	600.00
sum of bids		400.00	600.00	375.00	total high bids	600.00
share of bids		133.33	200.00	125.00	total shares of bids	458.33
share of value-pool balance		47.22	47.22	47.22	value-pool balance	141.67
total fair share		180.55	247.22	172.22		
value awarded	1	0	600.00	0		
total value awarded		0	600.00	0		
compensation		180.55	–352.78	172.22		
final settlement value		180.55	247.22	172.22		

What's Your Orbit?

Overview

In this module, students explore methods of determining mathematical models for sets of data. Students use residuals and contextual clues to evaluate the goodness of fit and appropriateness of mathematical models, including linear, quadratic, cubic, exponential, and power functions.

Activity 1: Students review properties of exponents and explore graphs of equations of the form $y = ax^b$. They model various data sets with power equations and use residuals to evaluate how well those models fit the data.

Activity 2: Students use the sum of the squares of the residuals and residual plots to evaluate the goodness of fit for various models. They also examine the appropriateness of a model for the given context.

Objectives

In this module, students will:

✴ review properties of exponents (1)

✴ investigate how changes to a and b in an equation of the form $y = ax^b$ affects its graph (1)

✴ model data sets using regression equations, including linear, quadratic, cubic, exponential, and power functions (1, 2)

✴ use the sum of the squares of the residuals to determine quality of fit (1, 2)

✴ use residual plots to analyze regression models (2)

✴ use the context of the data to analyze regression models (2)

✴ evaluate the validity of predictions made using mathematical models (2).

Prerequisites

For this module, students should know:

✴ how to interpret negative and rational exponents

✴ the general forms of linear, quadratic, cubic, and exponential functions

✴ the general shapes of the graphs of linear, exponential, quadratic, and cubic functions

✴ how to determine the volume of a sphere

✴ how to find linear, quadratic, and exponential regression equations

✴ how to make calculations involving scientific notation

✴ how to find residuals.

 Flashbacks, for use at your discretion, appear in the Teacher Resources for this module. These brief problem sets provide a review of some prerequisite skills for each activity.

Planning Guide

Activity	Materials	Technology	Time Line
Activity **1**	▪ spherical balloons ▪ tape measure	▪ spreadsheet ▪ graphing utility	3 days
Activity **2**	▪ none	▪ spreadsheet ▪ graphing utility	3 days
Assessment Activities	▪ stopwatch ▪ meterstick ▪ string ▪ weighted objects	▪ spreadsheet ▪ graphing utility	3 days **Total: 9 days**

Introduction

In this module, students investigate mathematical modeling using some characteristics of the planets in our solar system. Students are encouraged to develop initial models using their knowledge of the graphs of functions, then to use technology as a tool for verifying or refining models.

Students examine the graphs of power equations of the form $y = ax^b$, then investigate the relationship between the circumference and volume of a balloon. Using a spreadsheet, students fit curves to scatterplots and evaluate models using the sum of the squares of the residuals.

Materials List

- large spherical balloons (one per group)
- metric tape measure (one per group)

Technology

- graphing utility
- spreadsheet

teacher note

Some graphing utilities restrict the domain of $y = ax^b$ to $x \geq 0$ for any non-integer value of b.

Student Outcomes

After completing the following explorations and discussions, students should be able to:

✳ predict the shape of a graph of a power equation of the form $y = x^b$ for $b > 1$, $0 < b < 1$, and $b < 1$

✳ rewrite power equations using only positive exponents

✳ express power equations with fractional powers in radical form

✳ distinguish between power equations and polynomial equations

✳ describe the effects of changes in the value of a on graphs of equations of the form $y = ax^b$

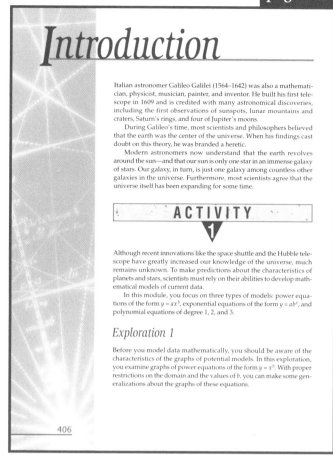

Introduction

Italian astronomer Galileo Galilei (1564–1642) was also a mathematician, physicist, musician, painter, and inventor. He built his first telescope in 1609 and is credited with many astronomical discoveries, including the first observations of sunspots, lunar mountains and craters, Saturn's rings, and four of Jupiter's moons.

During Galileo's time, most scientists and philosophers believed that the earth was the center of the universe. When his findings cast doubt on this theory, he was branded a heretic.

Modern astronomers now understand that the earth revolves around the sun—and that our sun is only one star in an immense galaxy of stars. Our galaxy, in turn, is just one galaxy among countless other galaxies in the universe. Furthermore, most scientists agree that the universe itself has been expanding for some time.

ACTIVITY 1

Although recent innovations like the space shuttle and the Hubble telescope have greatly increased our knowledge of the universe, much remains unknown. To make predictions about the characteristics of planets and stars, scientists must rely on their abilities to develop mathematical models of current data.

In this module, you focus on three types of models: power equations of the form $y = ax^b$, exponential equations of the form $y = ab^x$, and polynomial equations of degree 1, 2, and 3.

Exploration 1

Before you model data mathematically, you should be aware of the characteristics of the graphs of potential models. In this exploration, you examine graphs of power equations of the form $y = x^b$. With proper restrictions on the domain and the values of b, you can make some generalizations about the graphs of these equations.

406

✳ model data sets with power equations of the form $y = ax^b$

✳ calculate the residuals and the sum of the squares of the residuals for a mathematical model

✳ relate the sum of the squares of the residuals to the appropriateness of a mathematical model.

a. Choose a non-integer, rational value for b greater than 1.

  1. Express the value of b as a fraction m/n in lowest terms.

  2. Determine a decimal approximation of b.

b. 1. Using the fractional representation of b in Part **a**, graph the power equation $y = x^b$ over the domain $[-10, 10]$.

  2. On a separate coordinate system but using the same domain, graph the power equation $y = x^b$ using the decimal approximation of b.

  3. Compare the two graphs created in Steps **1** and **2**.

c. Repeat Parts **a** and **b** for another value of b greater than 1.

d. Repeat Parts **a** and **b** for two rational values of b between 0 and 1.

e. Repeat Parts **a** and **b** for two rational values of b less than 0.

Discussion 1

a. Judging from your investigations in Exploration **1,** how does the graph of a power equation using a fractional representation of b compare with the graph of the power equation using the corresponding decimal approximation?

b. Describe some possible values of b for each of the following graphs of equations of the form $y = x^b$.

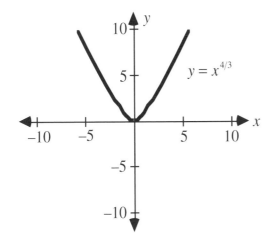

c. In the Level 2 module "Atomic Clocks Are Ticking," you examined the following properties of exponents.

  ■ If d is a real number greater than 0, m and n are positive integers, and m/n is in lowest terms,

  $$d^{m/n} = (d^{1/n})^m = (\sqrt[n]{d})^m = \sqrt[n]{d^m}$$

  ■ If d is a nonzero real number and n is an integer,

  $$d^{-n} = \frac{1}{d^n}$$

  ■ If d is a real number greater than 0,

  $$(d^m)^n = d^{m \cdot n} \quad \text{and} \quad \frac{d^m}{d^n} = d^{m-n}$$

Module 15 ■ *What's Your Orbit?*   **407**

Exploration 1

a. Students should be encouraged to select different values from others in the classroom. This allows them to encounter a wider variety of graphs from which to make observations.

  1. Sample response: $b = 4/3$.

  2. Sample response: $b \approx 1.333$.

b. The following graphs correspond with the sample responses given in Part **a** above.

  1. Sample graph:

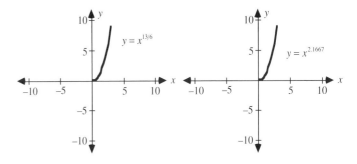

2. Sample graph:

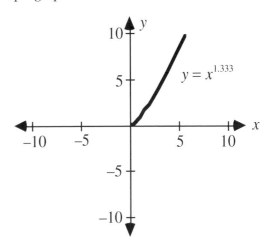

3. Answers will vary. Students should observe that the two graphs look virtually identical in the first quadrant. Depending on the value of b, the remainder of the graph may look very different.

c. Students repeat Parts **a** and **b** for another value of b greater than 1. The following sample response shows graphs of $y = x^{13/6}$ and $y = x^{2.1667}$.

d. Students repeat Parts **a** and **b** for two values of b between 0 and 1. The following sample response shows graphs of $y = x^{1/3}$ and $y = x^{0.333}$.

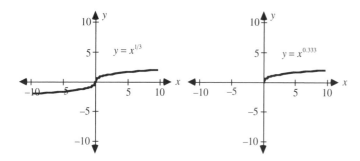

The sample response below shows graphs of $y = x^{3/8}$ and $y = x^{0.375}$.

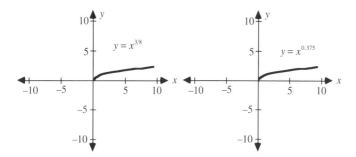

e. Students repeat Parts **a** and **b** for two values of b less than 0. The following sample response shows graphs of $y = x^{-3/2}$ and $y = x^{-1.5}$.

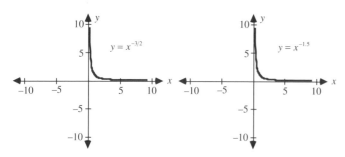

The sample response below shows graphs of $y = x^{-2/5}$ and $y = x^{-0.4}$.

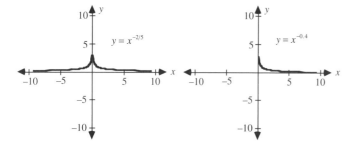

Discussion 1

a. In the first quadrant, the graphs of the power equations with decimal exponents are virtually identical to those with the exponents expressed as fractions. However, this is not always true in the other quadrants.

b. 1. Students should suggest values of b less than 0.
   2. Students should suggest values of b greater than 1.
   3. Students should suggest values of b between 0 and 1.

c. 1. $\dfrac{1}{x^{1/3}}$

   2. $\dfrac{1}{\sqrt[3]{x}}$

   3. $(\sqrt[10]{x})^3 = \sqrt[10]{x^3}$

d. 1. Sample response: The equation $y = x^{1/2}$ can also be expressed as $y = \sqrt{x}$. The square root of a negative number is undefined, so there are no values of y that correspond with negative values of x.

   2. Sample response: When expressed as a fraction, a decimal value of b always has a multiple of 10 in the denominator. Any equation with a rational exponent in which the denominator is even will not have a graph for $x < 0$. This occurs because even roots of negative numbers are undefined.

e. The expression is undefined at $x = 0$ for any negative value of b, because:

$$0^b = \frac{1}{0^{-b}} = \frac{1}{0}$$

f. Sample response: Increasing or decreasing the value of a will stretch or shrink the graph. Changing the sign of a will produce a reflection of the graph in the x-axis.

g. Sample response: A power equation of the form $y = ax^b$, where $a \neq 0$, is also a polynomial for integer values of b greater than or equal to 0. For example, the power equation $y = ax^2$ is a second-degree polynomial.

1. How could you express the equation $y = x^{-1/3}$ without using a negative exponent?
2. How could you express the equation $y = x^{-1/3}$ using a radical sign?
3. How could you express the equation $y = x^{0.3}$ using a radical sign?

d. 1. Why does a graph of $y = x^{1/2}$ show values only in the first quadrant?
   2. Why would you expect the graph of $y = x^b$, where b is the decimal approximation of a rational number, to show values only in the first quadrant?

e. Why is the expression x^b, when $b < 0$, undefined for $x = 0$?

f. In the Level 2 module "Drafting and Polynomials," you examined the effect of various values of a on polynomial equations of the form $y = ax^n$. How do you think the value of a will affect graphs of equations of the form $y = ax^b$?

g. For what values of b are power equations of the form $y = ax^b$ also polynomial equations?

Exploration 2

In this exploration, you investigate the relationship between the volume and circumference of a balloon. One way to measure the volume of a balloon is to count the number of "breaths" it contains. Before beginning this experiment, practice taking several even breaths.

a. Inflate your balloon one breath at a time. After each breath, measure the balloon's circumference. Record a minimum of six data points.

b. Create a scatterplot of your data.

c. One possible model for the data is a power equation. Suggest appropriate values for a and b in a model of the form $y = ax^b$.

d. Graph your suggested model on the same coordinate system as the scatterplot in Part b.

e. Create a spreadsheet with headings like those in Table 15-1 below.

TABLE 15-1 ■ Balloon Spreadsheet		
No. of Breaths (x)	Circumference (y)	y = ax^b

1. Enter your experimental data in the appropriate columns.

Exploration 2

a. Students should take small, even breaths and produce at least six data points. Sample data:

No. of Breaths	Circumference (cm)
1	31
2	42
3	53
4	58
5	65
6	70

b. Sample graph:

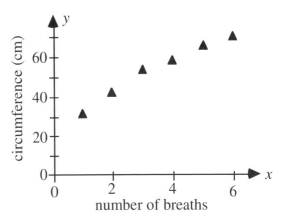

c. Sample response: For the first breath, $x = 1$ and $y = 31$. Substituting these values in the equation $y = ax^b$, yields $31 = a$. Therefore, an appropriate value for a is the circumference for the first breath. Judging from the shape of the graph, the value of b should be between 0 and 1, perhaps 0.5. Therefore, one possible model is $y = 31x^{0.5}$.

   Note: Considering the cubic relationship between length and volume in a sphere, some students may suggest a value of $1/3$ for b.

e–f. Students use a spreadsheet to determine the sum of the squares of the residuals, then use this sum to select a model that closely approximates the data. The following sample spreadsheet shows this sum for the equation $y = 31x^{0.46}$.

No. of Breaths	Circumference (cm)	y = ax^b	Square of Residual
1	31	31.00	0.00
2	42	42.64	0.41
3	53	51.39	2.59
4	58	58.66	0.44
5	65	65.00	0.00
6	70	70.68	0.46
		Sum	3.90

Discussion 2

a. Sample response: Substituting the data for one breath into the equation $y = ax^b$ results in $31 = a1^b$. Because $1^b = 1$ for any value of b, $31 = a$.

b. 1. Students might conclude that it is not possible to find the least sum using the spreadsheet method.

2. Sample response: According to the principle of least squares, the equation that results in the least sum of the squares of the residuals would represent the equation of this type that most closely fits the data.

c. Sample response: Information about the situation in which the data was collected can help you anticipate an appropriate model. For example, you could expect to model data collected for a freely falling object with a parabola, because the relationship between distance and time in this setting is quadratic.

Note: You might wish to remind students that, in situations where they know little about the setting, there can be great risk in making predictions outside the data set.

Warm-Up

1. Some sample graphs are shown below.

a.

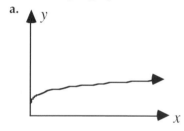

b.

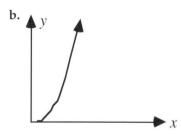

c.

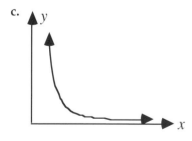

2. In the right-hand column, enter a spreadsheet formula that will calculate the approximate circumference given the number of breaths using an equation of the form $y = ax^b$. **Note:** Make sure to use this formula in each cell of the column.

f. Recall that a **residual** is the difference between an observed value and the corresponding value predicted by a model, and that the sum of the squares of the residuals can be used to evaluate how well a model fits a data set.

1. Use the spreadsheet to calculate the sum of the squares of the residuals for your model.

2. Adjust the values of a and b in your model to identify a power equation that closely approximates the data.

3. Record the corresponding sum of the squares of the residuals.

Discussion 2

a. Describe how you determined an appropriate value for a in Part **c** of Exploration **2**.

b. 1. Do you think that anyone in the class found the power equation with the least possible sum of the squares of the residuals for their data set? Explain your response.

2. If the power equation that produces the least possible sum of the squares of residuals could be found, how well do you think it would fit the data?

c. What types of information might help you evaluate the appropriateness of mathematical models?

Warm-Up

1. For each value of b below, sketch the graph of a power equation of the form $y = x^b$ over the domain (0, 10].

   a. 5/6   **b.** 7/4

   c. −10/3   **d.** 0.6667

   e. 2

2. Evaluate each function below, if possible, for the following values of x: −3, 0.25, and 7.

   a. $f(x) = 3.7x - 4.1$ **b.** $g(x) = 21.8x^{1.5}$

   c. $h(x) = \dfrac{4}{\sqrt{x}}$ **d.** $d(x) = -4.6x^2 + 20x + 6$

   e. $y(x) = 5.8x^3 + 2x^2 - 7$

d.

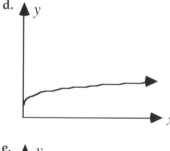

e.

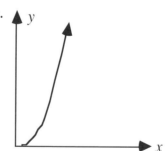

2. **a.** $f(-3) = -15.2$; $f(0.25) = -3.175$; $f(7) = 21.8$

   b. $g(-3) = -113.276$; $g(0.25) = 2.725$; $g(7) = 403.742$

   c. $h(-3)$ is not a real number; $h(0.25) = 8$; $h(7) \approx 1.51$

   d. $d(-3) = -12.6$; $d(0.25) = 10.7125$; $d(7) = -79.4$

   e. $y(-3) = -181.6$; $y(0.25) \approx -6.78$; $y(7) = 2080.4$

Assignment

1.1 The table below contains information about the planets in our solar system. The mean distance represents the average distance of a planet from the sun during its orbit. The period represents the time, measured in earth days, required for a planet to complete one orbit around the sun.

Planet	Mean Distance from Sun (millions of km)	Period (earth days)
Mercury	57.9	87.97
Venus	108.2	224.70
Earth	149.6	365.26
Mars	227.9	686.98
Jupiter	778.3	4331.87
Saturn	1427.0	10,760.27
Uranus	2869.6	30,684.65
Neptune	4496.6	60,189.55
Pluto	5899.9	90,468.77

a. Create a scatterplot of this data.

b. Determine an equation of the form $y = ax^b$ that models the data.

c. Is the model you selected a good one? Explain your response.

1.2 Imagine that it is the year 2039. Earth's inhabitants have colonized the moon. There are five lunar colonies, each housed in a pressurized hemispherical dome. The table below shows the diameter and volume of each dome.

Colony	Diameter (km)	Volume (km³)
Alpha	5.0	32.73
Beta	6.4	68.63
Gamma	5.6	45.98
Delta	8.2	144.35
Epsilon	7.6	114.92

a. Considering the relationship between the diameter and volume of a sphere, would a linear, exponential, or power equation provide the best model for this data?

b. Find an equation of the type identified in Part a to model the data.

Assignment

Problems suitable for use as assessment items are identified by an asterisk (*).

* 1.1 a. Sample scatterplot:

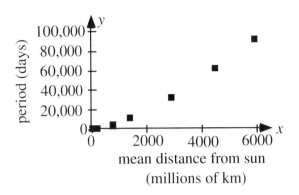

b. Sample response: Based on the shape of the scatterplot, the values of a and b should be greater than 0. One possible power equation is $y \approx 0.2x^{1.5}$.

c. Sample response: Visually, the model fits the data points extremely well. The sum of the squares of the residuals is about 270, which is relatively small compared to the data values.

1.2 a. Because the relationship of length to volume is cubic, students should predict that a cubic equation will provide the best model.

b. Answers may vary. One equation that models the data is $y \approx 2.1x^3$ where x = radius.

c. Using the sample equation given above, the volume of a dome with a diameter of 7.0 km should be about 90.0 km³.

1.3 a. See sample graph given in Parts **c** and **d** below.

b. Sample response: Based on the shape of the scatterplot, an exponential equation might provide a good model.

c–d. The following sample graph shows a graph of the equation $y = 833.3(1.2)^x$, along with a scatterplot of the data.

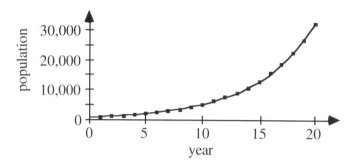

e. Sample response: From the table in Problem **1.2**, the volume of Beta colony's dome is 68.63 km³. This corresponds with a maximum population of 68,630. Judging from a graph of the model, Beta colony will reach its population limit in the 24th year.

1.4 a. Answers will vary. Sample data:

Object	Diameter (cm)	Circumference (cm)
A	5	16
B	6	19
C	8	25
D	10	31
E	35	110

b–c. The circumference of a circle equals $\pi \cdot d$, where d is the diameter. Therefore, a linear model of the form $y = \pi x$ should fit the data. The linear regression for the sample data is $y = 3.14x - 0.002$. This is a good approximation of $y = \pi x$.

d. Using the sample equation, the circumference of a disk with a radius of 1 m should be about 6.3 m.

✳ ✳ ✳ ✳ ✳

c. Use the equation determined in Part **b** to predict the volume of a hemispherical dome with a diameter of 7.0 km.

1.3 The table below shows the population of Beta colony during its first 20 years.

Year	Population	Year	Population
1	1000	11	6192
2	1200	12	7430
3	1440	13	8916
4	1728	14	10,699
5	2074	15	12,839
6	2488	16	15,407
7	2986	17	18,488
8	3583	18	22,186
9	4300	19	26,623
10	5160	20	31,948

a. Make a scatterplot of this data.

b. What type of equation do you think would provide a good model for the population growth of Beta colony?

c. Find an equation that describes the trend in the data.

d. Graph your equation on the same coordinate system as the scatterplot from Part **a**.

e. The population of Beta colony cannot exceed 1000 people per km³. Use your model, along with the dimensions of Beta colony's dome from Problem **1.2**, to determine how long it will take the population to reach this limit.

1.4 Find at least five round, flat objects of different sizes.

a. Measure and record their diameters and circumferences.

b. Based on the relationship between the diameter and circumference of a circle, what type of model would you expect to closely approximate the data collected in Part **a**?

c. Create a mathematical model of this data.

d. Use your model to predict the circumference of a disk with a radius of 1 m.

✳ ✳ ✳ ✳ ✳

1.5 A chemistry class at Centerville High School conducted an experiment to determine how much potassium nitrate would dissolve in 100 mL of water at various temperatures. The results of their experiment are shown below.

Temperature (°C)	Amount of Potassium Nitrate Dissolved (g)
5	27
20	54
40	77
60	94
80	109

a. Determine a power equation that closely models the data.

b. How much potassium nitrate do you think will dissolve in 100 mL of water at 70°C? Explain your response.

c. Do you think that it is reasonable to use your model to predict the amount of potassium nitrate that will dissolve in 100 mL of water at 110°C? Explain your response.

1.6 The table below shows the atomic radii and melting points for a family of elements known as the alkali metals. Because atoms are so small, their radii are often measured in angstroms, where 1 angstrom equals $1 \cdot 10^{-10}$ m. Melting point refers to the temperature at which a solid turns into a liquid.

Alkali Metals	Atomic Radius (angstroms)	Melting Point (°C)
Lithium	1.52	180
Sodium	1.86	98
Rubidium	2.44	39
Cesium	2.62	29

a. Create a scatterplot of melting point versus atomic radius.

b. Does there appear to be a positive or a negative association between atomic radius and melting point? Explain your response.

c. Find an equation that closely models this data and explain why you chose this type of model.

d. Potassium is also an alkali metal. Its atomic radius is approximately 2.31 angstroms. Use your model from Part c to predict the melting point of potassium.

412   Module 15 ■ *What's Your Orbit?*

1.5 **a.** Answers may vary. A sample scatterplot is shown below.

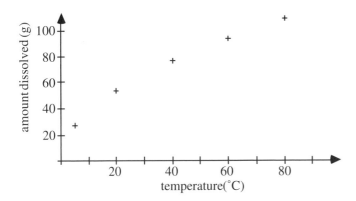

One power equation that fits the data is $y = 12.2x^{0.50}$. Using this model, the sum of the squares of the residuals is approximately 0.6827.

b. Using the sample equation given above, about 102 g of potassium nitrate should dissolve in 100 mL of water at 70°C.

c. Sample response: By substituting 110 into the power equation, you would expect 128 g of potassium nitrate to dissolve. However, since 110°C is outside the interval of the observed data (and higher than the boiling point of water at standard pressure), this prediction should be made with caution. Eventually, the amount of potassium nitrate that will dissolve in a fixed amount of water will reach a limit.

1.6 **a.** Sample scatterplot:

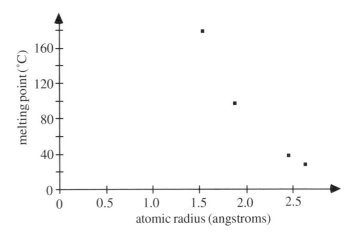

b. As the atomic radii increase, the melting points of the metals decrease. There is a negative association.

c. Answers may vary. Based on the shape of the scatterplot, some students might choose an exponential model. One exponential equation that approximates the data is $y = 2157.7(0.19)^x$. Using this model, the sum of the squares of the residuals is approximately 55.

Other students might suggest that melting point is related to the strength of atomic bonds. Because force varies inversely as the square of the distance, they may choose a power equation. One power equation that approximates the data is $y = 749x^{-3.34}$. Using this model, the sum of the squares of the residuals is approximately 41.

d. Using the power equation given in Part **b**, potassium has a predicted melting point of approximately 45.7°C.

e. Answers will vary. Sample response: The prediction is not a very accurate estimate of the actual melting point. Even though the atomic radius of potassium falls within the range of the data, the model fails. This might be because factors other than atomic radius also influence melting point.

ACTIVITY 2

Students use technology to determine regression equations for data sets, then compare the appropriateness of different models using residual plots.

teacher note

A brief assessment of the mathematical content in Activities **1** and **2**, for use at your discretion, appears in the Teacher Resources for this module.

Materials List

- none

Technology

- graphing utility
- spreadsheet

teacher note

Using most graphing utilities, the linear regression determines a model that gives the minimum sum of the squares of the residuals. On many calculators, however, the polynomial, power, and exponential regressions do not. Because these tools sometimes linearize the data first, they only approximate the minimum sum of the squares of the residuals.

---

e. The actual melting point of potassium is approximately 64°C. Compare this value with your prediction in Part **c** and suggest a possible explanation for any difference that occurs.

ACTIVITY 2

In the Level 1 module "Graphing the Distance," you used technology to find linear and quadratic regression equations to model data. In this activity, you examine power and exponential regressions and investigate another method for evaluating the appropriateness of models.

Exploration 1

Table **15-2** below shows data collected during a balloon experiment like the one described in Activity **1**.

TABLE 15-2 ■ Balloon Experiment Data	
No. of Breaths	Circumference (cm)
1	31
2	42
3	53
4	58
5	65
6	70

a. Use technology to find a power regression equation for the data in Table **15-2**.

b. Determine the sum of the squares of the residuals for this regression equation.

c. Describe how well the graph of the regression equation fits a scatterplot of circumference versus number of breaths.

d. Repeat Parts **a–c** using an exponential regression.

Discussion 1

a. Which regression equation—power or exponential—appears to provide a better model for the data? Explain your response.

Module 15 ■ *What's Your Orbit?*   413

Student Outcomes

After completing the following explorations and discussions, students should be able to:

✳ use technology to find power and exponential regressions

✳ use the sum of the squares of the residuals to evaluate the goodness of fit for a mathematical model

✳ use the context of the data to evaluate the appropriateness of a mathematical model

✳ examine the limitations of a mathematical model

✳ construct and analyze residual plots

✳ evaluate the goodness of fit of a model based on the residual plot

✳ choose an appropriate model for a given data set and context.

Exploration 1

a. For the given data, the power regression equation is $y = 31.03x^{0.458}$.

b. Using $y = 31.03x^{0.458}$, the sum of the squares of the residuals is 3.78.

b. Would you use this model to predict the circumference of a balloon after 50 breaths? Explain your response.

c. If asked to make a prediction based on a given data set, what steps would you take to find an appropriate model?

d. What other criteria might help you select the most appropriate model from several possibilities?

Exploration 2

In this exploration, you examine another tool for evaluating mathematical models: the **residual plot**.

a. Most of the asteroids in our solar system lie between the orbits of Mars and Jupiter. Table **15-3** shows the orbital period and mean distance from the sun for nine of these asteroids, listed in order of discovery. Use this data to make a scatterplot of period versus mean distance from the sun.

TABLE 15-3 ■ Orbital Period of Nine Asteroids		
Name	**Mean Distance from Sun (millions of km)**	**Period (earth years)**
Ceres	411.20	4.60
Pallas	411.84	4.61
Juno	396.48	4.36
Vesta	350.88	3.63
Astraea	382.88	4.14
Hebe	360.32	3.78
Iris	354.24	3.68
Flora	327.04	3.27
Metis	354.72	3.69

b. Select three of the following five types of equations: linear, quadratic, cubic, exponential, and power. For each type you select, determine a corresponding regression equation to model the data in Table **15-3**.

c. Create a graph of each regression equation on the same coordinate system as the scatterplot from Part **a**. To simplify comparison, use the same scales on the axes of all graphs.

c. The graph of the regression equation given above appears to fit all of the points in the sample data except one.

d. For the given data, the exponential regression $y = 29.68(1.17)^x$ results in a sum of the squares of the residuals of 88.83. Visually, the graph does not model the data as well as the power equation.

Discussion 1

a. Sample response: For the given data, the power equation appears to provide the better fit. This makes sense because you would not expect the relationship between length and volume to be exponential.

b. Sample response: No. The balloons probably would burst long before they held 50 breaths.

c. Sample response: First, you should plot the data points to see the general shape of the graph. Then you can decide what type of equation might give a graph with that shape, and use technology to find the corresponding regression equation. Before using the model to make predictions, you should try to determine if the relationship described by the model is appropriate for the context in which the data was collected.

d. Sample response: After considering the setting from which the data was gathered, you could examine both the sum of the squares of the residuals and how closely the shape of the model corresponds with the shape of the scatterplot.

teacher note

In the following exploration, students select three possible models for the data on mean distance from the sun and orbital period. The sample responses round values in regression equations to three significant digits. This rounding can have a substantial effect on the corresponding sum of the squares of the residuals.

Students are introduced to Kepler's third law of planetary motion in Part **d** of Discussion **2**. They learn that planetary orbits are elliptical, with the sun located at one focus, in the Level 4 module "It's Napped Time."

Exploration 2

The data in Table **15-4** can be fit with a variety of models. By examining the sums of the squares of the residuals along with graphs of the regression equations and residual plots, students should recognize the difficulty of assessing the appropriateness of models by fit alone.

a. Sample scatterplot:

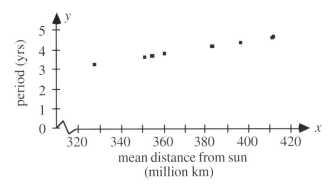

b. Students may select any three of the suggested models. Sample response: The linear regression is $y = 0.0159x - 1.96$, where y represents period in years and x represents mean distance from the sun in millions of kilometers. The sum of the squares of the residuals for this model is approximately $2.7 \cdot 10^{-3}$.

The quadratic regression is $y = 9.75 \cdot 10^{-6}x^2 + 8.64 \cdot 10^{-3}x - 0.601$, with a sum of the squares of the residuals of approximately $4.3 \cdot 10^{-5}$.

The exponential regression is $y = 0.889(1.004)^x$, with a sum of the squares of the residuals of approximately $5.9 \cdot 10^{-3}$.

c. The following three sample graphs show a scatterplot of the data along with each regression equation in Part **b**.

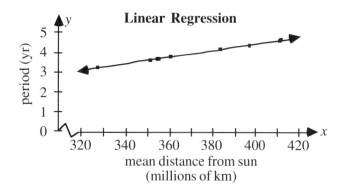

Linear Regression

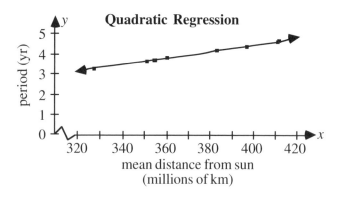

Quadratic Regression

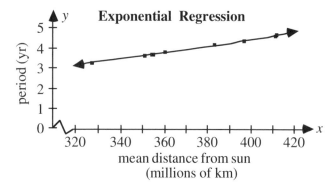

Exponential Regression

d. The following three sample graphs show a residual plot for each regression equation in Part **b**.

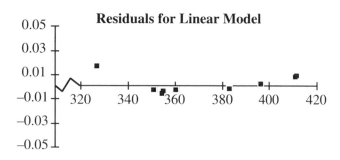

Residuals for Linear Model

mathematics note

A **residual plot** is a scatterplot created using the ordered pairs (x-value of the data, residual). If the sum of the squares of the residuals is relatively small, a residual plot in which the points are randomly scattered above and below the x-axis typically indicates that a reasonable model has been selected.

For example, Table **15-4** shows the x- and y-coordinates of a set of data points, the corresponding y-values predicted by the linear regression model $y = 0.75x + 1.14$, and the value of the residual for each data point.

TABLE 15-4 ■ Data Points, Predicted y-values, and Residuals

x-value	y-value	Predicted y-value	Residual
1	2	1.89	0.11
2	2	2.64	−0.64
3	4	3.39	0.61
4	5	4.14	0.86
5	4	4.89	−0.89
6	5	5.64	−0.64
7	7	6.39	0.61

Figure **15-1** shows the corresponding residual plot. Because no pattern appears to exist, this regression equation may be a reasonable model for the data.

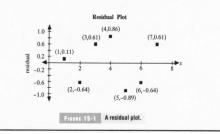

Residual Plot

FIGURE 15-1 A residual plot.

d. Create a residual plot for each model selected in Part **b**.

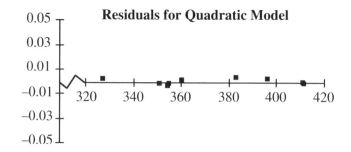

Residuals for Quadratic Model

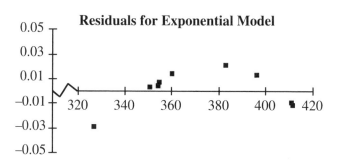

Residuals for Exponential Model

Discussion 2

a. Of the three regression equations you determined in Exploration **2**, which one appears to provide the best model of the data? Defend your choice.

b. Suppose that a new asteroid is discovered with a mean distance from the sun of $3.50 \cdot 10^8$ km.

   1. Describe how you would use your model to predict the asteroid's orbital period.

   2. How confident would you feel about the accuracy of this prediction? Explain your response.

c. Another known asteroid orbits the sun at a mean distance of $5.90 \cdot 10^9$ km.

   1. Using the model you selected in Part **a** of Discussion **2**, predict the asteroid's orbital period.

   2. How confident do you feel about the accuracy of your prediction?

d. German astronomer Johannes Kepler (1571–1630), who lived during the same time as Galileo, also studied the motion of planets. He developed a mathematical description of planetary motion that included three basic laws.

Kepler's third law stated that the ratio of the cube of the mean distance (*r*) from the sun to the square of the period (*p*) is a constant for every planet in the solar system. This can be represented algebraically as follows:

$$\frac{r^3}{p^2} = k$$

How does this information affect your choice of an appropriate model for the data in Table **15-3**?

Discussion 2

a. Sample response: All the equations appear to model the data well, although the quadratic regression has a smaller sum of the squares of the residuals than do the other two models. The residual plot of the quadratic regression appears to be the most randomly spread about the x-axis.

b. 1. Sample response: To estimate the asteroid's period in earth years, you can substitute 350 for x in the regression equation and find y.

   2. Sample response: Because the new asteroid's mean distance from the sun lies within the values in the data set, the prediction should be fairly accurate.

c. 1. Sample response: Using the quadratic regression model, the asteroid's orbital period should be approximately 390 years.

   2. Students should not feel confident about their predictions, because the mean distance is far outside the data interval used to create the model.

d. Based on Kepler's law, the most appropriate model should be a power regression, because solving the equation for p yields the following:

$$p^2 = \frac{r^3}{k}$$

$$p = \left(\frac{r^3}{k}\right)^{1/2}$$

$$= \frac{r^{3/2}}{k^{1/2}}$$

This can be thought of as a power equation of the form $p = ar^{3/2}$, where $a = 1/k^{1/2}$.

e. 1. The points of this residual plot appear to have a linear pattern. Therefore, another linear model might provide a better fit for the data.

   2. The points of this residual plot form a curved pattern. In this case, a linear model probably is not appropriate. **Note:** Some students might recognize the shape of the residual plot as a parabola and therefore suggest a quadratic model.

   3. The points of this residual plot appear to have no definite pattern and are distributed fairly evenly above and below the *x*-axis.

   4. The points of this residual plot appear to form an exponential curve. This suggests that an exponential model might be more appropriate.

Warm-Up

1. Sample response: As shown in the residual plot below, the residuals appear to form a pattern. This could indicate that a line is not an appropriate model for the data. It is possible that a polynomial of degree 3 (or higher) might provide a better model.

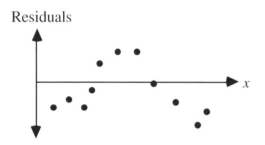

Residuals

2. **a.** $1.053 \cdot 10^{14}$
   b. 225.3666
   c. 27.8704
   d. $\dfrac{2a}{a\sqrt{2a}} = \dfrac{2}{\sqrt{2a}} = \dfrac{2}{\sqrt{2}}\, a^{-0.5}$

---

e. Each of the four graphs below is a residual plot for a linear model of a different data set. Which plots indicate that the linear model is appropriate for the data? Justify your responses.

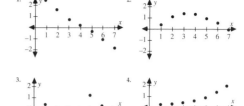

1.   2.

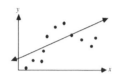

3.   4.

Warm-Up

1. Given the scatterplot and regression line below, sketch a residual plot. Discuss what the residual plot indicates about how well the line models the data.

2. Simplify each of the following expressions.

   a. $1.3 \cdot 10^{6}(8.1 \cdot 10^{7})$
   b. $\dfrac{4.62 \cdot 10^{5}}{2.05 \cdot 10^{3}}$
   c. $\dfrac{3.01 \cdot 10^{-6}}{1.08 \cdot 10^{-7}}$
   d. $\dfrac{2a}{a\sqrt{2a}}$

Assignment

2.1 A meteorite is a chunk of space debris that falls to the earth's surface. The force of impact sometimes forms a crater. The table below shows the depth and diameter of seven meteorite craters on earth.

Name of Crater	Diameter (m)	Depth (m)
Barringer	1240	210
Herault	230	50
Odessa 1	160	40
Odessa 2	21	5
Explosion 1	120	27
Explosion 2	47	14
Explosion 3	32	6

a. Create a scatterplot of crater depth versus diameter.

b. Select a regression equation to model the data. Use the sum of the squares of the residuals and a residual plot to support your choice.

c. Graph your equation on the same coordinate system as the scatterplot in Part a.

d. How closely does your model approximate the data? Explain your response.

e. 1. How confident would you be in predicting the depth of a crater with a diameter of 600 m? Explain your response.

2. How confident would you be in predicting the depth of a crater with a diameter of 5000 m? Explain your response.

f. The Wolf Creek crater has a diameter of approximately 820 m and a depth of approximately 30 m.

1. What depth would your model predict for a crater with a diameter of 820 m?

2. Compare this prediction with the actual depth of the Wolf Creek crater and suggest some possible explanations for any difference that occurs.

2.2 The distances involved when considering objects in the solar system are immense. For example, the mean distance from the sun to the earth is approximately $1.496 \cdot 10^8$ km. Even though light travels at an incredible speed, it still takes several minutes for light from the sun to reach earth.

Assignment

Problems suitable for use as assessment items are identified by an asterisk (*).

2.1 **a.** See sample graph given in Part **c** below.

b. Given the shape of the scatterplot, students may select a linear model. For the linear regression $y = 0.165x + 6.56$, the sum of the squares of the residuals is approximately 140.

A residual plot for the linear regression is shown below. The points appear to be randomly scattered about the *x*-axis, indicating that a reasonable model has been selected.

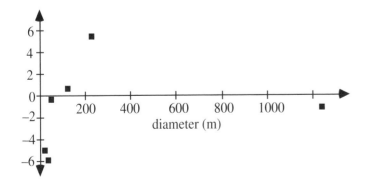

c. Sample graph:

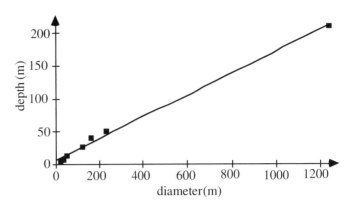

d. Sample response: The model seems to fit the data reasonably well. The lack of a pattern in the residual plot lends further support for a linear model. This relationship makes sense if all the craters have approximately the same shape.

e. 1. Sample response: I would be fairly confident, because the model fits the data well and a diameter of 600 m falls within the interval of the diameters in the data.

2. Sample response: Because 5000 m is far outside the data set, caution must be taken in making this prediction.

f. 1. Using the linear model given above, the predicted depth of the Wolf Creek crater is approximately 142 m.

2. Sample response: The ground at Wolf Creek might be considerably harder than at the places where the other meteorites hit, causing its crater to be much shallower. The mass of the meteorite in relation to its size also might have been less than that of the others.

* 2.2 **a.** Sample response: Because light travels at a constant speed, the time it takes for light to reach its destination should increase at a constant rate as the distance increases. Considering this fact, along with the shape of the scatterplot, a line through the origin should be an appropriate model.

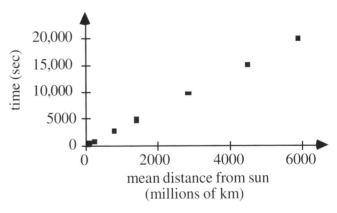

b. Sample response: The graph of the linear regression $y = 3.33x + 1.76$ is very close to all the data points. The sum of the squares of the residuals is approximately 81. The residual plot for this regression equation, shown below, also supports its use as a reasonable model.

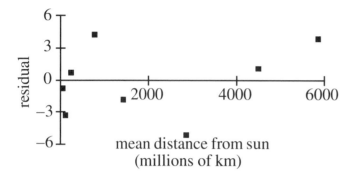

c. Using the model, it should take about 500 sec for light from the sun to reach earth.

d. Considering the speed of light, the time required to reach earth is:

$$\frac{1.496 \bullet 10^{11} \text{ m}}{3 \bullet 10^8 \text{ m/sec}} \approx 499 \text{ sec}$$

This is very close to the value predicted by the linear regression.

2.3 Sample response: A scatterplot of the data suggests that a power regression would provide an appropriate model.

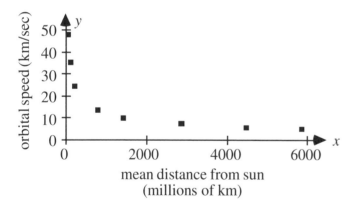

Using the power regression $y = 366x^{-0.501}$, the sum of the squares of the residuals is 0.02. The lack of a pattern in the residual plot supports the use of the power regression.

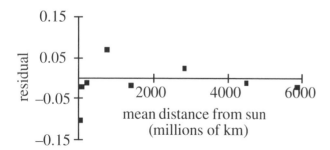

The following table shows the approximate time required for light from the sun to reach each of the other planets in our solar system, along with each planet's mean distance from the sun.

Planet	Mean Distance from Sun (millions of km)	Time for Light to Reach Planet (sec)
Mercury	57.9	195
Venus	108.2	360
Mars	227.9	763
Jupiter	778.3	2601
Saturn	1427.0	4757
Uranus	2869.6	9562
Neptune	4496.6	14,991
Pluto	5899.9	19,670

a. Find a regression equation that fits this data. Defend your selection.

b. Describe how well the equation models the data.

c. Use your model to determine the approximate time required for light from the sun to reach earth.

d. Light travels at a speed of approximately $3 \bullet 10^8$ m/sec. Given this information, did your model provide a reasonable prediction of the time required for light from the sun to reach earth?

2.3 Planets travel along their orbital paths at high speeds. The following table shows the mean distance from the sun and the orbital speed of eight planets in our solar system. Use this data to estimate earth's orbital speed, given that its mean distance from the sun is approximately $1.496 \bullet 10^8$ km. Defend your prediction.

Planet	Mean Distance from Sun (millions of km)	Orbital Speed (km/sec)
Mercury	57.9	47.8
Venus	108.2	35.0
Mars	227.9	24.1
Jupiter	778.3	13.1
Saturn	1427.0	9.6
Uranus	2869.6	6.8
Neptune	4496.6	5.4
Pluto	5899.9	4.7

Module 15 ■ *What's Your Orbit?*　419

Substituting earth's mean distance from the sun into this equation predicts an orbital speed of about 29.8 km/sec. This should be a reasonable prediction because earth's mean distance lies within the known data. (The actual value for earth's orbital speed is approximately 30.6 km/sec.)

Note: You might wish to demonstrate the following algebraic support for use of a power regression model:

The approximate length of the orbital path, where r represents the mean distance from the sun is $2\pi r$. The orbital speed v, therefore, is $v = 2\pi r/p$, where p represents the period.

From Kepler's third law (described in Part **d** of Discussion **2**), $p^2 = kr^3$, so $p = r\sqrt{kr}$. Substituting this value for p in the formula for orbital speed results in the following relationship:

$$v = \frac{2\pi r}{r\sqrt{rk}} = \frac{2\pi}{\sqrt{r} \bullet \sqrt{k}} = \left(\frac{2\pi}{\sqrt{k}}\right)\frac{1}{\sqrt{r}} = \left(\frac{2\pi}{\sqrt{k}}\right)r^{-0.5}$$

2.4 The farther a planet is from the sun, the colder its surface temperature is likely to be. The surface temperatures of planets, and other extreme temperatures, usually are measured in degrees Kelvin.

Note: The Kelvin temperature scale was invented by Sir William Thomson (1824–1927), also known as Lord Kelvin. The relationship between the Kelvin and Celsius scales is approximately $K = °C + 2.73$.

The table below shows the mean surface temperature for seven planets, along with their mean distances from the sun.

Planet	Mean Distance from Sun (millions of km)	Mean Surface Temperature (Kelvin)
Mercury	57.9	373
Mars	227.9	250
Jupiter	778.3	123
Saturn	1427.0	93
Uranus	2869.6	63
Neptune	4496.6	53
Pluto	5899.9	43

a. Use the information in the table to determine a model for predicting a planet's surface temperature given its mean distance from the sun. Defend your choice of models.

b. Because of their many similarities, Earth and Venus are often referred to as "sister" planets.

  1. Use your model to predict the surface temperature of the two planets, given that Earth's mean distance from the sun is approximately $1.496 • 10^8$ km, while Venus' is approximately $1.082 • 10^8$ km.

  2. Do you think that your predictions are reasonable? Explain your response.

c. Earth's actual mean surface temperature is approximately 295 K and Venus' is approximately 753 K. This difference can be attributed to several factors other than the mean distance from the sun, including the composition of each planet's atmosphere.

Given these facts, discuss the dangers of making predictions about complex phenomena using models that only describe the relationship between two quantities.

* * * * *

2.5 A weak solution of hydrogen peroxide is a common household antiseptic. When heated, hydrogen peroxide decomposes to form water and oxygen gas.

2.4 **a.** Sample response: The shape of a scatterplot of the data suggests that a power equation might be a good model. As shown below, the power regression $y = 2905x^{-0.478}$ appears to fit the data well. The sum of the squares of the residuals is about 3100.

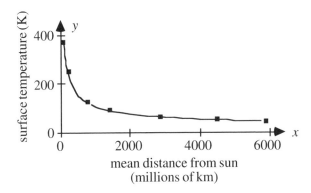

The lack of a pattern in the residual plot also supports the model.

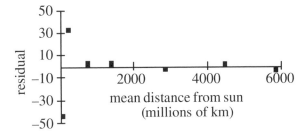

b. 1. Using the sample model, the predicted surface temperatures for Earth and Venus are approximately 265 K and 310 K, respectively.

  2. Sample response: Because the mean distances from the sun for the two planets fall well within the data set, it seems appropriate to assume that these predictions are reasonable.

c. Sample response: The prediction for Earth's temperature was reasonably close, but the one for Venus was not. Even though a model might appear to fit the data well, there could be many other factors that are not considered in the model. These factors could drastically affect the relationship between the quantities being compared. If little is known about the actual situation under study, care should be taken in making predictions based on a model.

*****

2.5 a. Sample response: The shape of the scatterplot suggests that an exponential regression might be appropriate. As shown below, the exponential regression $y = (1.00)(0.951)^x$ appears to fit the data well. The sum of the squares of the residuals is approximately $8 \cdot 10^{-5}$.

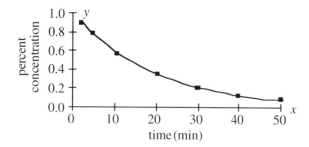

The lack of a pattern in the residual plot also supports the model.

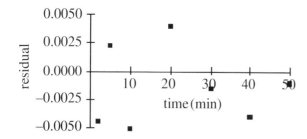

b. Using the sample model, the predicted amount of hydrogen peroxide remaining is 0.0024%.

c. Sample response: The predicted concentration is close to 0. This seems reasonable given the situation. However, it is important to be careful when making predictions far outside the range of the data.

  Note: You might wish to point out that the concentration of hydrogen peroxide eventually should reach 0. Using an exponential model, predicted values would approach 0, but not reach it.

2.6 a. Sample response: The shape of a scatterplot of the data suggests the use of a power regression. As shown below, the power regression $y = 5000x^{-1}$ appears to fit the data well. The sum of the squares of the residuals is approximately 0.5.

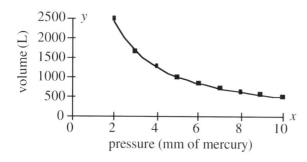

The table below shows the change in concentration over time for a heated solution of 1% hydrogen peroxide.

Time (min)	Percent Concentration
2	0.90
5	0.78
10	0.60
20	0.37
30	0.22
40	0.13
50	0.08

a. Find a regression equation that models this data. Justify your choice.

b. Use your model to predict the percentage of hydrogen peroxide that remains after 2 hr.

c. How confident are you in the prediction you made in Part **b**?

2.6 The pressure on a fixed amount of gas can be measured using a column of mercury. At a pressure of 500 mm of mercury, a certain amount of gas occupies 10 L. The information in the following table shows how the volume of the gas decreases as the pressure increases.

Volume (L)	Pressure (mm of mercury)
10	500
9	556
8	625
7	714
6	833
5	1000
4	1250
3	1667
2	2500

a. Find a regression equation that models this data. Justify your choice.

b. Use your model to predict the pressure on the gas when its volume is 7.33 L.

c. Do you think that your model will provide good predictions for the volumes of gas at very high pressures? Explain your response.

The lack of a pattern in the residual plot also supports the model.

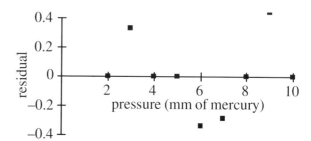

Note: Some students might observe that, according to Boyle's law, the volume of a dry gas at constant temperature varies inversely with the pressure on it. Algebraically, this implies that $V = k/P$, where V represents volume, P represents pressure, and k is a constant. This relationship can be expressed as $V = kP^{-1}$.

b. Using the power equation given above, the pressure on the gas should be approximately 682 mm of mercury.

c. Answers will vary. Some students may recognize that, at very high pressures, gases become liquids and Boyle's law no longer applies.

Research Project

Through taxes and user fees, the U.S. government collects money to pay for national defense, health care, road construction, and numerous other goods and services. These programs often cost more than the government's annual revenue. To make up the difference, the government must borrow money. The total amount owed is known as the national debt.

Conduct some research on the size of the national debt over the past 20 years. (Make sure to record the source of the data you collect.) Determine a reasonable model for this data.

Use your model to predict the size of the national debt 20 years from now. Describe some of the consequences that may occur if the debt continues to follow the trend described in your model. Finally, discuss why it might be risky to make long-term predictions based on your model.

422   Module 15 ■ *What's Your Orbit?*

Research Project

The national debt grew rapidly in the 1980s, leveled off slightly in the 1990s, then grew rapidly again. As shown in the table below, it reached approximately $7.4 trillion in 2004 (17 years after 1987).

Years after 1987	Debt (billions of $)	Years after 1987	Debt (billions of $)
0	2350	9	5225
1	2602	10	5413
2	2857	11	5526
3	3233	12	5656
4	3665	13	5674
5	4065	14	5807
6	4411	15	6228
7	4693	16	6783
8	4974	17	7379

Source: U.S. Department of the Treasury, 2005.

The linear regression equation $y = 265.8x + 2549$ appears to be a reasonable model for this data, as shown by the graph below. The sum of the squares of the residuals for this model is approximately 1,075,000.

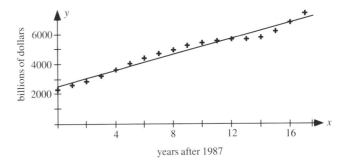

years after 1987

A residual plot appears to reveal a periodic pattern, although students are not expected to suggest periodic functions as models.

Student results will depend on the data sets they choose. In general, the national debt has been increasing for at least the past 50 years. However, students should use caution even when making short-term predictions, because the size of the annual deficit is affected by many political and economic considerations.

teacher note

An additional assessment, for use at your discretion, appears in the Teacher Resources for this module.

Summary Assessment

In this assessment, students investigate the relationship between the period of a pendulum and the length of its string.

Materials List

- string (as thin as possible; monofilament fishing line works well)
- weighted objects to simulate pendulums (one per group)
- stopwatch (one per group)
- metersticks (one per group)

Technology

- graphing utility
- spreadsheet (optional)

teacher note

You might wish to model the construction and observation of a pendulum before administering this assessment. Although taping the string to a desk will work, a ring stand might provide a better fixed point. For best results, students should be encouraged to keep the amplitude of the swing small. To calculate the period, students should measure the time required for 5 to 10 swings, then calculate the average time per swing.

Summary Assessment

Galileo's inventions and observations helped other astronomers make sense of the motion of the planets and stars. He also made important contributions to the study of other types of motion, including balls rolling on inclined planes, freely falling objects, and swinging pendulums.

While at the chapel of the University of Pisa, Galileo noticed that one of the chandeliers was swinging. Using his own heartbeat as a timer, he measured the time required for the chandelier to complete one swing. Upon returning to his room, he performed a series of experiments that resulted in "the law of the pendulum."

As shown in the diagram below, use a length of string to suspend an object from a fixed location.

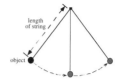

1. A pendulum completes one swing when it returns to the same side as its initial release. The time required for a pendulum to complete one swing is its **period**.

   a. Determine a method for measuring one period of your pendulum.

   b. Record the length of the string to the nearest 0.01 m and the period of the pendulum to the nearest 0.1 sec.

   c. Change the length of the string significantly. Record the new string length and the period for this pendulum.

   d. Repeat Part c for six different lengths of string.

2. a. Find a regression equation that fits the data and explain why you chose this type of model.

   b. What does the equation you chose in Part a reveal about the motion of pendulums?

   c. Describe some of the limitations of your equation for modeling the motion of pendulums.

3. In general, the relationship between the period p of a pendulum and the length l of its string can be described by $p = 2\pi\sqrt{l/g}$, where g is the acceleration due to gravity (about 9.8 m/sec²). How does the relationship expressed by your model compare to this one?

Module 15 ■ *What's Your Orbit?* 423

1. a. Students should collect data for 5–10 swings and obtain a mean value for the period.

   b–d. Sample data:

Length of string (m)	Period (sec)
2.82	3.4
2.49	3.2
2.18	3.2
1.49	2.5
0.94	1.9
0.64	1.5

2. a. Answers will vary. As shown in the following graph, the power regression $y = 1.96x^{0.562}$ models the sample data well. The sum of the squares of the residuals for this model is approximately 0.05.

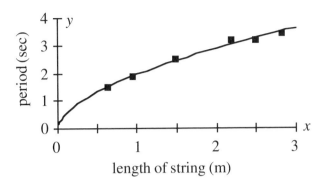

The lack of a pattern in the residual plot below also supports the choice of a power regression.

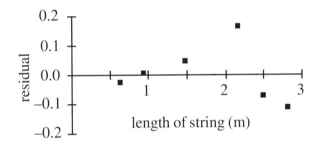

Note: Both the cubic and quadratic regressions also give reasonable models based on sum of the squares of the residuals and the residual plot.

b. Sample response: The equation that fits the data indicates that there is a positive correlation between string length and period. Because the exponent is close to 0.5, the equation also suggests that there might be a square-root relationship between string length and period.

c. Sample response: Predicting inside this range of data using the equation should be fairly accurate. Predicting outside the range of data, however, might not be accurate. This is because of the small number of data points and the likelihood of experimental error.

3. Sample response: The exponent in the power regression equation that fits the data is close to an exponent of 0.5 (the square root). The value of a in the model (1.96) also is close to its value in the given relationship:

$$\frac{2\pi}{\sqrt{9.8}} \approx 2.01$$

Glossary

allele—one of a pair of genes.

alternate exterior angles—congruent angles formed when two parallel lines are cut by a transversal; see diagram under *transversal.*

alternate interior angles—congruent angles formed when two parallel lines are cut by a transversal; see diagram under *transversal.*

Angle-Angle-Angle (AAA)—if the angles of one triangle are congruent to the corresponding angles of another triangle, then the triangles are similar.

Angle-Angle-Side (AAS)—if two angles and one non-included side of one triangle are congruent to the corresponding angles and side of another triangle, then the triangles are congruent.

Angle-Side-Angle (ASA)—if two angles and the included side of one triangle are congruent to the corresponding angles and included side of another triangle, then the triangles are congruent.

arc (of a circle)—part of a circle whose endpoints are the intersections, with the circle, of the sides of a central angle; the measure of an arc is the measure of its central angle; the length of an arc is the distance on the circle between the arc's endpoints.

arithmetic sequence—a sequence in which every term after the first is found by adding a constant value (the constant difference) to the preceding term.

arithmetic series—the sum of the terms of an arithmetic sequence.

axiom—an accepted truth.

axis of symmetry (of a parabola)—the line of symmetry of a parabola.

base angle (of an isosceles triangle)—either of the two angles that are not included between the two congruent sides.

bias—a factor that prevents a sample from representing the entire population.

bid-and-divide method—used to fairly divide discrete items among two or more people; the technique involves assigning a cash value to each item through a bidding process; each item is awarded to the highest bidder and the individual who receives the item, then compensates the others for a fair share.

census—the collection of data about an entire population.

central angle (of a circle)—angle formed by two rays drawn from the center of a circle.

central angle (of a regular polygon)—angle formed by rays drawn from the center of a circumscribed circle to two consecutive vertices of the polygon, dividing the polygon into congruent isosceles triangles; the measure of a central angle of a regular polygon with n sides is: $360°/n$.

chord—a line segment joining any two points on a circle; the perpendicular bisector of a chord passes through the center of the circle.

chromosome—part of a gene.

coefficient—a number multiplied by a product of variables or powers of variables in a term; the coefficients of x in the expression $ax^2 + bx + c$ are a, b, and c.

coefficient matrix—the matrix that represents the coefficients of the variables when a system of linear equations is written as a matrix equation; in the equation below, **M** is the coefficient matrix.

$$M \bullet X = C$$

$$\begin{bmatrix} a & b \\ c & d \end{bmatrix} \bullet \begin{bmatrix} x \\ y \end{bmatrix} = \begin{bmatrix} e \\ f \end{bmatrix}$$

cofactor (of an element)—the product of the corresponding element and –1 raised to a power that is the sum of the element's row and column position numbers in a large square matrix; used to calculate the determinant of the large matrix.

combination—a collection of symbols or objects in which order is not important; the number of combinations of n different symbols or objects taken r at a time, denoted by $C(n,r)$ or $_nC_r$, is given by the following formula:

$$C(n,r) = \frac{P(n,r)}{P(r,r)} = \frac{P(n,r)}{r!} = \frac{1}{r!} \bullet \frac{n!}{(n-r)!} = \frac{n!}{r!(n-r)!}$$

common difference—the constant value added to each term in an arithmetic sequence to form the next term.

common ratio—the constant ratio between any two consecutive terms in a geometric sequence.

complement (of an event E)—the event that E does not occur; represented by the symbol E' (read "E prime" or "E complement"); the sum of the probabilities of two complementary events is 1.

complementary angles—two angles are complementary when the sum of their measures is 90°.

complete requirement graph—a requirement graph that has simple components at the end of each branch.

composition of transformations—the result of two or more transformations performed on a figure.

conclusion—the "then" part of a conditional statement.

conditional probability—the probability of an event occurring given that an initial event already has occurred; the probability that event B occurs, given that event A already has occurred, is denoted by $P(B|A)$.

conditional statement—a statement that can be written in if-then form; consists of two parts: the hypothesis and the conclusion.

confidence statement—declares that a population parameter lies within a specific range of values.

congruent—exactly equal in size and shape; the symbol for congruence is $\cong$.

conjunction—combines two mathematical statements with the word *and*; can be represented as the intersection of two sets.

constant matrix—the matrix that represents the constants when a system of linear equations is written as a matrix equation; in the equation below, **C** is the constant matrix.

$$M \bullet X = C$$

$$\begin{bmatrix} a & b \\ c & d \end{bmatrix} \bullet \begin{bmatrix} x \\ y \end{bmatrix} = \begin{bmatrix} e \\ f \end{bmatrix}$$

constraint—condition that limits the number of possible solutions to a problem.

continuous item—can be awarded in parts in a fair division.

continuous-knife method—a technique for dividing a continuous object between two people; a knife is held above the left edge of the object and moved slowly from left to right; either person can stop the knife to cut off a piece that represents a fair share; the person who stops the knife receives the portion to the left; the second person receives the remaining portion.

converse—the converse of a statement in the form "If A, then B" is the statement "If B, then A"; the converse of a true if-then statement may or may not be true.

corner point—an intersection of two or more boundary lines of a feasible region; also called a vertex.

corner principle—the maximum and minimum values of an objective function occur at the corner points of the feasible region.

corresponding angles—congruent angles formed when two parallel lines are cut by a transversal; see diagram under *transversal*.

cosine (of an angle)— in a right triangle, the ratio of the length of the leg adjacent to the angle to the length of the hypotenuse.

cross—the act of combining genes from two parents.

cut-and-choose method—a technique for dividing a continuous object between two people; one person cuts the object in two shares; the other person then chooses the desired piece.

degree (of a polynomial)—equals the greatest exponent of the variable in a polynomial expression.

dependent events—events that are not independent.

determinant (of a 2×2 matrix **M**)—the difference of the two diagonals of the matrix; denoted by $\det \mathbf{M}$ or $|\mathbf{M}|$; for a matrix **M** in the form given below, $\det \mathbf{M} = ad - bc$.

$$\mathbf{M} = \begin{bmatrix} a & b \\ c & d \end{bmatrix}$$

determinant (of a square matrix larger than 2×2)—the sum of the products of minors and cofactors for each element in a single row or column.

diagonal (of a polygon)—a line segment joining two non-consecutive vertices.

dilation—a transformation that pairs a point P, the center, with itself and any other point X with a point X' on ray PX so that $PX'/PX = r$, where r is the scale factor; a dilation with center C and scale factor r is denoted as $\mathbf{D}_{C,r}$.

dilation (with center at the origin)—a transformation such that every point Q with coordinates (x,y) has an image Q' with coordinates (rx,ry), where r is the scale factor, and $r \neq 0$; denoted as $\mathbf{D}_{O,r}$.

direct proof—consists of a series of connected factual statements that are supported by definitions, axioms, or proven theorems.

discrete item—can be awarded as a unit in a fair division.

distance formula—the distance d between two points (x_1,y_1) and (x_2,y_2) on the coordinate plane is $d = \sqrt{(x_2 - x_1)^2 + (y_2 - y_1)^2}$.

distributive property (of multiplication over addition)—$a(b + c) = ab + ac$ or $(b + c)a = ba + ca$.

domain (of a relation)—the set of first elements in ordered pairs of the form (x,y).

dominant trait—the trait that appears when the alleles in a pair are different.

element—an item in a matrix.

end behavior (of a function)—the corresponding changes in the y-values of a function as the x-values increase (or decrease) without bound.

equal matrices—matrices with the same dimensions for which corresponding elements are equal.

event—a subset of a sample space.

expected value—the mean value of an experiment; determined by adding the products of the value of each event and its corresponding theoretical probability.

experimental probability (of an event)—the ratio of the number of times an event occurs to the total number of trials.

explicit formula—a rule for finding for calculating any specific term in a sequence.

exponential decay—a decrease in a population that can be described by an exponential function of the form $f(x) = a(1 + r)^x$ where r is negative and represents the decay rate.

exponential function—a function of the form $y = a \bullet b^x$, where $a > 0$ and either $0 < b < 1$ or $b > 1$.

exponential growth—an increase in a population that can be described by an exponential function of the form $f(x) = a(1 + r)^x$ where r is positive and represents the growth rate.

factor (of a polynomial)—in general, $(x - c)$ is a factor of $f(x)$ if $f(c) = 0$.

factored form (of a polynomial function)—$f(x) = a(x - c_1)(x - c_2)(x - c_3) \cdots (x - c_n)$, where c_i is a zero or root.

factorial—a product of the positive integers from 1 to n; if n is a positive integer, then n factorial (denoted by $n!$) can be expressed as $n! = n \bullet (n - 1) \bullet (n - 2) \bullet \cdots \bullet 3 \bullet 2 \bullet 1$; zero factorial, or $0!$, is defined as 1.

factoring—the process of using the distributive property to represent a mathematical expression as a product.

fair division—occurs when all individuals, by their own assessment, consider the portions they are awarded as fair.

fair game—a game in which the expected value equals the cost to play.

feasible region—all the points that satisfy the limitations, or constraints, of a linear-programming problem.

finite sequence—a sequence that has a specific number of terms.

finite series—the sum of the terms of a finite sequence.

frequency (of a data item)—number of observed occurrences of that item.

frequency table—table consisting of two columns; one displays data items, the other displays the number of observed occurrences of each item.

function—a relation in which each element of the domain is paired with an element of the range and each element of the domain occurs in only one ordered pair.

fundamental counting principle—if an event that can occur in m ways is followed by an event that can occur in n ways, then the total number of ways that the two events can occur is $m \bullet n$.

gene—biological structure that controls the heredity of traits.

genetics—the study of heredity.

genotype—the pair of alleles that determines the presence or absence of a particular characteristic; all of an individual's inherited traits.

geometric model (of an event)—a model that uses geometric measures, such as lengths, angle measures, areas, or volumes, to determine the theoretical probability of the event.

geometric sequence—a sequence in which every term after the first is found by multiplying the preceding term by a constant value (the common ratio).

geometric series—the sum of the terms of a geometric sequence.

greatest integer function—assigns every real number x in the domain to the greatest integer less than or equal to x; can be written as $y = [x]$.

height (of a cylinder or prism)—the perpendicular distance between the two bases.

heredity—the process by which characteristics are passed from one generation to the next.

histogram—graph that displays information using rectangles or bars of uniform width and scales with uniform intervals.

homogeneous form (of a point)—when represented as a column matrix, the homogeneous form of a point (x,y) is:

$$\begin{bmatrix} x \\ y \\ 1 \end{bmatrix}$$

hypotenuse—the longest side in a right triangle; the side opposite the right angle.

hypothesis—the "if" part of a conditional statement.

identity matrix—the matrix that, when multiplied on the left, produces the identity transformation; for example, the 3×3 identity matrix is:

$$\mathbf{I} = \begin{bmatrix} 1 & 0 & 0 \\ 0 & 1 & 0 \\ 0 & 0 & 1 \end{bmatrix}$$

identity transformation—preserves the size, shape, and position of a figure.

image—any subset of points that results from a transformation; if point A is the preimage, then the image of a point A can be represented as A' (read "A prime").

included angle—the angle between the rays, lines, or segments that determine its interior.

inconsistent (system of equations)—a system of equations that has no solution.

independent events—events for which the probability of any one event occurring is unaffected by the occurrence or non-occurrence of any of the other events; for two independent events A and B, P(A and B) = P(A) • P(B); this definition can be extended to any number of independent events.

independent variable—a variable for which values do not depend on the outcome of another variable.

inequality—a mathematical sentence using one or more of the symbols <, >, ≤, or ≥; one way to describe a real-number interval.

infinite interval—a set of real numbers greater than or less than a given value; so called because it increases or decreases without bound.

infinite sequence—a sequence in which every term has a successor.

inscribed polygon—a polygon for which every vertex lies on the same circle.

interval (of real numbers)—set of all real numbers between two fixed endpoints; each endpoint may or may not be included in the interval.

interval notation—in interval notation, a square bracket,] or [, indicates that the endpoint is included in the interval; a parenthesis,) or (, indicates that the endpoint is not included in the interval.

isometry—a transformation for which the preimage is congruent to its image.

isosceles triangle—a triangle with two congruent sides; the angle included between the two congruent sides is the vertex angle; the other two angles are base angles.

kite—a quadrilateral with two distinct pairs of congruent sides.

leg (of a right triangle)—one of the two shorter sides in a right triangle; a side opposite an acute angle.

limit (of a sequence)—for a sequence $k_1, k_2, k_3, \ldots, k_n, \ldots$, the limit is a number L if for any prescribed accuracy, there is a term k_m such that all terms after k_m are within this given accuracy of L.

line of reflection—the perpendicular bisector of each segment connecting a preimage point to its corresponding image point under a reflection; every point on the line of reflection is its own image.

line of symmetry—the line passing through a figure, for which, under a reflection in that line, each point in the image coincides with a point in the preimage.

line symmetry—an object has line symmetry if the object is its own image in a reflection in a line.

linear programming—a method used to maximize or minimize an objective (such as profit), subject to linear constraints.

linear regression—the linear model that results in the least sum of the squares of the residuals; also called the least-squares line.

major arc—an arc with a measure greater than 180°.

margin of error—a common way of describing the interval within which a parameter is likely to fall.

matrix (plural **matrices** or **matrixes**)—a rectangular arrangement of rows and columns used to organize information; a matrix of i rows and j columns has dimensions $i \times j$ (read "i by j"); named using a bold, uppercase letter or descriptive word.

matrix addition—can be performed on two matrices with the same dimensions by adding the corresponding elements of each matrix; matrix subtraction can be performed in a similar manner.

matrix multiplication—is defined only when a matrix with dimensions $k \times m$ is multiplied with a matrix with dimensions $m \times q$; the dimensions of the product matrix are $k \times q$; each row of the first matrix is "multiplied" with each column of the second matrix, as shown below.

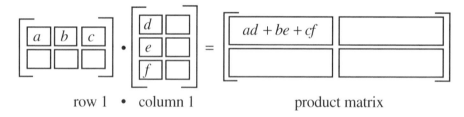

row 1 • column 1   product matrix

maximum standard deviation (of all possible sample proportions)—occurs when the population proportion $p = 0.5$; the value of 2 maximum standard deviations for all possible sample proportions equals:

$$2 \bullet \sigma = 2 \bullet \sqrt{\frac{0.5(1 - 0.5)}{n}} = \frac{2 \bullet 0.5}{\sqrt{n}} = \frac{1}{\sqrt{n}}$$

mean (of all possible sample proportions)—equals the population proportion p for any given sample size n.

minor arc—an arc with a measure less than 180°.

minor determinant (or **minor**)—the determinant of a smaller square matrix within a large square matrix.

multiplicative inverse (of a matrix **M**)— is written $\mathbf{M}^{-1}$ and has the property that $\mathbf{M} \bullet \mathbf{M}^{-1} = \mathbf{M}^{-1} \bullet \mathbf{M} = \mathbf{I}$, where **I** is the identity matrix for matrix multiplication.

mutually exclusive events—two events that cannot occur at the same time in a single trial; for two mutually exclusive events A and B, $P(A \text{ and } B) = 0$.

n **factorial**—denoted by $n!$; if n is a positive integer, then $n! = n \bullet (n - 1) \bullet (n - 2) \bullet \cdots \bullet 3 \bullet 2 \bullet 1$.

negative exponent—an exponent that is a negative number; can be represented as follows, when a is a nonzero real number and n is an integer: $a^{-n} = 1/a^n$.

nth root (of a non-negative number a)—a number s such that $s^n = a$; the non-negative nth root of a is denoted as $\sqrt[n]{a}$.

objective function—the function that describes the objective to be minimized or maximized in a linear-programming problem.

one-to-one correspondence—a function between two sets that pairs each element in the domain with exactly one element in the range, and each element in the range with exactly one element in the domain.

parabola—the graph of a second-degree polynomial.

parameter—a quantity that describes a population.

Pascal's triangle—an arithmetic number pattern named in honor of the French philosopher Blaise Pascal; see diagram below.

```
            1
          1   1
        1   2   1
      1   3   3   1
    1   4   6   4   1
```

permutation—an ordered arrangement of symbols or objects; the number of permutations of n different symbols or objects taken r at a time, denoted by $P(n,r)$ or $_nP_r$, is given by the following formula:

$$P(n,r) = n(n-1)(n-2)\cdots(n-r+1) = \frac{n!}{(n-r)!}$$

perpendicular distance—the distance from a point to a line or a plane; equal to the length of the segment, perpendicular to the line or plane, that connects the point to that line or plane.

phenotype—the trait that appears for a given pair of alleles; all of an individual's observable traits.

point of tangency—the intersection of a circle and the tangent line, segment, or ray.

polygon—a union of coplanar segments intersecting only at endpoints; at most two segments intersect at any one endpoint and each segment intersects exactly two other segments. See *side*; *vertex*.

polynomial (in one variable)—an algebraic expression of the general form $a_n x^n + a_{n-1} x^{n-1} + a_{n-2} x^{n-2} + \cdots + a_1 x^1 + a_0$ where n is a whole number and the coefficients a_i are real numbers for $i = 0, 1, 2, \ldots, n$.

polynomial function—a function f for which $f(x)$ is defined as a polynomial in x.

population—the group of all objects, individuals, or observations about which information is to be gathered.

population proportion—percentage of a population with a given characteristic.

power equation—an equation of the form $y = ax^b$.

preimage—any subset of points in the domain of a transformation.

prism—a three-dimensional solid determined by two congruent polygons in parallel planes whose corresponding vertices are connected by segments; the two congruent and parallel faces are the prism's bases; the parallelograms formed by joining the corresponding vertices of the bases are the prism's lateral faces; prisms are named by the polygonal shape of the bases.

product matrix—the result of multiplying two matrices; when a matrix with dimensions $k \times m$ is multiplied with a matrix with dimensions $m \times q$, the dimensions of the product matrix are $k \times q$.

proof—a convincing argument based on logical reasoning that shows that the conclusion is true for *every* case in which the hypothesis is true.

Punnett square—a chart used to identify the possible combinations from a genetic cross.

Pythagorean theorem—in a right triangle, the square of the length of the longest side (the hypotenuse) equals the sum of the squares of the lengths of the other sides (the legs).

quadratic function—a function f in which $f(x)$ is equal to a quadratic expression in x; also called a second-degree function; can be written in the general form $f(x) = ax^2 + bx + c$, where $a \neq 0$.

radioactive decay—the spontaneous disintegration of a radioactive substance; the process by which the number of radioactive atoms decreases.

radius (of a regular polygon)—the radius of the circle in which the polygon can be inscribed.

range (of a relation)—the set of second elements in ordered pairs of the form (x,y).

rational exponent—an exponent in the form m/n; can be represented as follows, when $a \geq 0$ and m/n is in lowest terms: $a^{m/n} = (a^{1/n})^m = (\sqrt[n]{a})^m = \sqrt[n]{a^m}$.

recessive trait—the trait that does not appear when the alleles in a pair are different.

recursion—the process of using a recursive formula.

recursive formula—a rule for calculating any term in a sequence by using the preceding term(s).

reduction method—a technique for dividing a continuous object among three or more people.

reflection (in a line)—a transformation that pairs each point on the line with itself and each point in the preimage with a corresponding point in the image so that the line of reflection is the perpendicular bisector of the segment connecting each point in the preimage with its image; a reflection in line m is denoted as r_m.

regression equation—a function of a particular form that fits a set of paired data as closely as possible.

regular polygon—a polygon in which all sides are congruent and all interior angles are congruent.

relation (between two variables)—a set of ordered pairs of the form (x,y).

rep tile—a shape that can be partitioned into congruent shapes, each one similar to the original.

requirement graph—a tree diagram that shows each product's components at each level of its assembly.

residual—the difference between the y-coordinate of a data point and the corresponding y-value of a linear model.

residual plot—a scatterplot created using the ordered pairs (x-value of the data, residual); if the sum of the squares of the residuals is relatively small, a residual plot in which the points are randomly scattered above and below the x-axis typically indicates that a reasonable model has been selected.

rhombus—a parallelogram with two consecutive congruent sides.

root (of a number)—can be represented using exponents of the form $1/n$, where n is a natural number. If the nth root of a exists, it can be represented as follows: $\sqrt[n]{a} = a^{1/n}$.

root (of a polynomial)—a solution to an equation of the form $f(x) = 0$; also called a zero.

rotation—a transformation that pairs one point C, the center, with itself and every other point P with a point P' that lies on a circle with center C such that $m\angle PCP'$ is the magnitude of the rotation; counterclockwise rotations about a point are denoted by positive degree measures; clockwise rotations are represented by negative degree measures.

rotational symmetry—an object has rotational symmetry about a point if, when rotated through an angle about that point, each point in the image coincides with a point in the preimage.

sample—a subset of the population.

sample proportion—percentage of a sample with a given characteristic.

sample space—the set of all possible outcomes for an experiment.

scalar—a real number, or a quantity that can be measured using a single real number.

scalar multiplication—the multiplication of each element of a matrix by a constant, or scalar; the multiplication of a matrix **M** by a scalar k is denoted by $k \bullet \mathbf{M}$.

scale factor—the ratio of corresponding sides for two similar figures.

secant (of a circle)—a line that intersects the circle in two points.

sector (of a circle)—a region bounded by the sides of a central angle and an arc of the circle.

semicircle—an arc with a measure of exactly 180°.

sequence—an ordered list; each item in the list is a term of the sequence.

side—segment of a polygon.

Side-Angle-Side (SAS)—if two sides and the included angle of one triangle are congruent to the corresponding sides and angle of another triangle, then the triangles are congruent.

Side-Side-Side (SSS)—if all three sides of a triangle are congruent to the corresponding sides of another triangle, then the triangles also are congruent.

similar—two objects are similar if they have the same shape and the ratios of corresponding lengths are proportional; the ratio of corresponding sides is the scale factor; the symbol for similarity is ∼.

simple random sample—selected so that each member of the population has the same chance of being included in the sample.

sine (of an angle)—in a right triangle, the ratio of the length of the leg opposite the angle to the length of the hypotenuse.

slope (of a line)—ratio of the change in vertical distance to the change in horizontal distance between any two points on a line; a vertical line has no slope.

slope-intercept form (of the equation of a line)—an equation of the form $y = mx + b$, where m is the slope and b is the y-intercept.

sphere—the set of all points in space that are the same distance from a given point, the center of the sphere; the common distance is the radius of the sphere.

square of a residual—the square of the distance from a data point to the model; in general, the smaller the sum of the squares of the residuals, the more closely a model approximates the data.

standard deviation—a measure of spread often represented by the Greek letter σ (sigma) and determined by the following formula, where μ represents the mean and n is the number of items in the set:

$$\sigma = \sqrt{\left((x_1 - \mu)^2 + (x_2 - \mu)^2 + \cdots + (x_n - \mu)^2 \right) / n}$$

standard deviation (of all possible sample proportions)—can be calculated using the following formula, where p is the population proportion and n is the sample size:

$$\sigma = \sqrt{\frac{p(1-p)}{n}}$$

statistic—a quantity that describes a sample.

step function—a function that has different constant values of the range over adjacent intervals of the domain.

stratified sampling—requires that a population be divided into parts; each part is a stratum (plural, strata); to produce a stratified sample, simple random samples are taken from each stratum; these samples do not necessarily have to be the same size.

substitution method—can be used to solve a system of linear equations; begins by solving an equation for one variable; the resulting expression is then substituted for that variable in another equation in the system; this process is repeated until a solution can be identified.

surface area (of a sphere)—equals $4\pi r^2$, where r is the radius.

system of linear equations—a set of two or more equations whose graphs are lines; a solution to a system of linear equations is a point where all the lines intersect.

systematic sampling—accomplished by collecting data from every nth unit of a population after randomly choosing a starting point.

tangent (of a circle)—a line, segment, or ray in the plane of the circle that intersects the circle in exactly one point and is perpendicular to a radius at that point

tangent (of an angle)—in a right triangle, the ratio of the length of the leg opposite the angle to the length of the leg adjacent to the angle.

term (of a sequence)—an item in an ordered list; may be represented by a subscripted variable of the form p_1 (read "p sub one"); the general or nth term may be represented by p_n.

theorem—a conjecture proven to be true for all cases.

theoretical probability (of an event)—the ratio of the number of outcomes in an event to the total number of outcomes in the sample space, where each outcome in the sample space has the same chance of occurring; can be written as $P(E)$.

total requirement matrix—matrix in which each item sold is represented in a column heading, while each simple component or composite product is represented in a row heading; each element indicates the number of that simple component or composite product required to produce the corresponding item sold.

transformation (in a plane)—a one-to-one correspondence of the plane onto itself; the points of the plane are the domain of the transformation, and every point on the plane is affected.

translation—a transformation that pairs every point $P(x,y)$ with an image point $P'(x + h, y + k)$; denoted as $T_{P,P'}$.

translation vector—vector that describes a translation from $P(x,y)$ to $P'(x + h, y + k)$; can be denoted by the ordered pair $\langle h,k \rangle$, a bold, lowercase letter, or with an arrow.

transpose—the matrix formed by turning all the rows of a given matrix into columns and vice versa; the transpose of matrix $\mathbf{A}$ is denoted by $\mathbf{A}^T$ or $\mathbf{A}'$.

transversal—a line that cuts across a set of lines or the sides of plane figure; the following diagram shows a transversal and two parallel lines; in this diagram, $\angle 2$ and $\angle 6$ are corresponding angles, $\angle 4$ and $\angle 6$ are alternate interior angles, and $\angle 2$ and $\angle 8$ are alternate exterior angles.

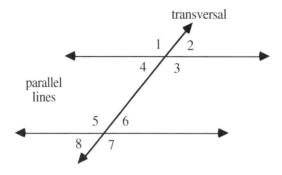

tree diagram—a mathematical model that shows all the possible outcomes for a series of events or decisions; each line segment in a tree diagram is a branch.

trigonometric ratios—ratios of the lengths of sides in right triangles.

variable matrix—the matrix that represents the variables when a system of linear equations is written as a matrix equation; in the equation below, **X** is the variable matrix.

$$M \cdot X = C$$

$$\begin{bmatrix} a & b \\ c & d \end{bmatrix} \cdot \begin{bmatrix} x \\ y \end{bmatrix} = \begin{bmatrix} e \\ f \end{bmatrix}$$

vertex (of a feasible region)— an intersection of two or more boundary lines; also called a corner point.

vertex (of a parabola)—the intersection of a parabola and its axis of symmetry.

vertex (of a polygon)—intersection of two sides of a polygon; plural *vertices*.

vertex angle (of an isosceles triangle)—the angle included between the two congruent sides.

vertex form (of a quadratic function)—a function of the form $f(x) = a(x - c)^2 + d$, where a, c, and d are real numbers and $a \neq 0$; the coordinates of the vertex are (c,d).

vertical angles—two non-straight, non-adjacent angles formed by two intersecting lines; vertical angles are congruent.

vertical line test—given a graph on a coordinate plane with the domain represented on the horizontal axis and the range on the vertical axis, if a vertical line can be drawn that intersects the graph in more than one point, then the graph does not represent a function.

volume (of a cylinder or prism)—equals the product of the area of a base and the height.

volume (of a pyramid or a cone)—equals one-third of the product of the area of the base and the height.

volume (of a sphere)—equals $(4/3)\pi r^2$, where r is the radius.

x-intercept—x-coordinate of the point where a line or curve intersects the x-axis.

y-intercept—y-coordinate of the point where a line or curve intersects the y-axis.

zero factorial (or **0!**)—defined as 1.

zero—for a function f, c is a zero if $f(c) = 0$; also called a root.

Selected References

Acker, A., and C. Jaschek. *Astronomical Methods and Calculations*. Chichester, UK: John Wiley & Sons, 1986.

Barasch, M. *Theories of Art: From Plato to Winkelman*. New York: New York University Press, 1985.

Bennett, Jr., A. B. "Visualizing the Geometric Series." *Mathematics Teacher* 82 (February 1989): 130–36.

Bennett, S., D. DeTemple, M. Dirks, B. Newell, J. M. Robertson, and B. Tyus. *Fair Divisions: Getting Your Fair Share*. High School Mathematics and Its Applications (HiMAP) Project. Module 9. Arlington, MA: COMAP, 1987.

Better Homes and Gardens. *American Patchwork and Quilting*. Des Moines, IA: Meredith Corporation, 1985.

Blackman, W. *Geometry in Architecture*. Berkeley, CA: Key Curriculum Press, 1984.

Brodlie, K. W. *Mathematical Methods in Computer Graphics and Design*. London: Academic Press, 1980.

Brualdi, R. A. *Introductory Combinatorics*. New York: Elsevier North-Holland, 1977.

Buchanan, O. L. *Limits: A Transition to Calculus*. Boston: Houghton Mifflin, 1985.

Consortium for Mathematics and Its Applications (COMAP). *For All Practical Purposes: Introduction to Contemporary Mathematics*. New York: W. H. Freeman and Co., 1988.

Dahlke, R., and R. Fakler. "Geometrical Probability—A Source of Interesting and Significant Applications of High School Mathematics." In *Readings for Enrichment in Secondary School Mathematics*, ed. by Max A. Sobel. Reston, VA: National Council of Teachers of Mathematics (NCTM), 1988.

DeLange, J. *Matrices*. Utrecht, The Netherlands: Research Group on Mathematics Education, 1990.

Draiver, H. E. *Indians of North America*. Chicago: University of Chicago Press, 1961.

Gallup, G. *The Sophisticated Poll Watcher's Guide*. Ephrata, PA: Princeton Opinion Press, 1972.

Gardan, Y. *Mathematics and CAD. Volume 1: Numerical Methods for CAD*. Cambridge, MA: The MIT Press, 1986.

Garland, T. H. *Fascinating Fibonaccis: Mystery and Magic in Numbers*. Palo Alto: Dale Seymour Publications, 1987.

Gates, T. "How Do Planets Stay in Orbit?" Lecture presented at the National Council of Teachers of Mathematics (NCTM) Convention in Seattle, WA. 31 March–3 April, 1993.

Gilfillan, S. C. *Inventing the Ship*. Chicago: Follett Publishing Co., 1935.

Goodspeed, J. K. "But My Parents Both Have *Brown* Eyes." *Science and Children* 22 (January 1985): 9–12.

Hall, S. *The Fourth World: The Heritage of the Arctic*. New York: Alfred A. Knopf, Inc., 1987.

Harshbarger, R. J., and J. J. Reynolds. *Mathematical Applications for Management, Life, and Social Sciences*. Lexington, MA: D.C. Heath, 1992.

Heintz, R. E. "It's in the Bag." *Mathematics Teacher* 70 (February 1977): 132–36.

Hulse, C. *The Rule of Art: Literature and Painting in the Renaissance*. Chicago: University of Chicago Press, 1990.

Huntley, H. E. *The Divine Proportion: A Study in Mathematical Beauty*. New York: Dover Publications, 1970.

Ince, S. *Genetic Counseling*. White Plains, NY: March of Dimes Birth Defects Foundation, 1987.

Krause, M. C. *Multicultural Mathematics Materials*. Reston, VA: National Council of Teachers of Mathematics, 1983.

Lafarge, O. *A Pictorial History of the American Indian*. New York: Crown Publishers, 1956.

Landwehr, J. M., J. Swift, and A. E. Watkins. *Exploring Surveys and Information from Samples*. Palo Alto, CA: Dale Seymour Publications, 1988.

Laubin, R., and G. Laubin. *The Indian Tipi: Its History, Construction, and Use*. New York: Ballantine Books, 1985.

Lewell, John. *A–Z Guide to Computer Graphics*. New York: McGraw-Hill, 1985.

Libby, W. F. *Radiocarbon Dating*. Chicago, IL: University of Chicago Press, 1952.

Lindgren, B. W., G. W. McElrath, and D. A. Berry. *Introduction to Probability and Statistics*. New York: Macmillan Publishing Co., 1978.

Littmann, M. *Planets Beyond: Discovering the Outer Solar System*. New York: John Wiley & Sons, 1990.

Loomis, E. S. *The Pythagorean Proposition*. Classics in Mathematics Education I. Reston, VA: NCTM, 1968.

Lott, J. W., and A. W. Wilson. "Applications of the Step Function." *The Illinois Mathematics Teacher* 30 (January 1979): 2–7.

Maletsky, E. M. "Visualization, Estimation, Computation." *Mathematics Teacher* 75 (December 1982): 759–64.

Malkevitch, J., G. Froelich, and D. Froelich. "Codes Galore." The History of Mathematics and Its Applications (HistoMAP) Project. Module 18. Arlington, MA: COMAP, 1991.

Mange, A. P., and E. J. Mange. *Genetics: Human Aspects*. Sunderland, MA: Sinauer Associates, 1990.

Mathematical Association of America (MAA) and National Council of Teachers of Mathematics (NCTM). *A Sourcebook of Applications of School Mathematics*. Reston, VA: NCTM, 1980.

McArdle, W. D., F. I. Katch, and V. L. Katch. *Exercise Physiology*. Philadelphia: Lea & Febiger, 1991.

Mizrahi, A., and M. Sullivan. *Finite Mathematics with Applications for Business and Social Sciences*. New York: John Wiley & Sons, 1973.

Moore, D. S. *Statistics: Concepts and Controversies*. New York: W. H. Freeman and Co., 1991.

Moore, P., and G. Hunt. *Atlas of the Solar System*. Chicago, IL: Rand McNally & Co., 1983.

Nabokov, P., and R. Easton. *Native American Architecture*. New York: Oxford University Press, 1989.

National Council of Teachers of Mathematics. *Historical Topics for the Mathematics Classroom*. Reston, VA: NCTM, 1989.

Nielsen, L. and M. de Villiers. *Is Democracy Fair? The Mathematics of Voting and Apportionment*. Berkeley, CA: Key Curriculum Press, 1997.

Nelsen, R. B. *Proofs Without Words*. Washington, DC: The Mathematical Association of America, 1993.

Nord, G., Malm, E., and J. Nord. "Counting Pizzas: A Discovery Lesson Using Combinatorics." *The Mathematics Teacher* 95 (January 2002): 8–14.

North Carolina School of Science and Mathematics, Department of Mathematics and Computer Science. *Geometric Probability*. Reston, VA: National Council of Teachers of Mathematics, 1988.

North Carolina School of Science and Mathematics, Department of Mathematics and Computer Science. *Contemporary Precalculus through Applications*. Dedham, MA: Janson Publications, 1992.

Papy, G. *Modern Mathematics*. London: Collier-Macmillan, 1968.

Peitgen, H.-O., H. Jürgens, D. Saupe, E. Maletsky, T. Perciante, and L. Yunker. *Fractals for the Classroom*. New York: Springer-Verlag, 1991.

Pokorny, C. K., and C. F. Gerald. *Computer Graphics: The Principles Behind the Art and Science.* Irvine, CA: Franklin, Beedle & Associates, 1989.

Reimer, W., and L. Reimer. *Historical Connections in Mathematics: Resources for Using History of Mathematics in the Classroom.* Fresno, CA: AIMS Educational Foundation, 1992.

Rosenberg, N. S. "Genetic Counseling." Undergraduate Mathematics and Its Applications (UMAP) Project. Module 456. Arlington, MA: COMAP, 1987.

Sharron, S., ed. *Applications in School Mathematics.* 1979 Yearbook. Reston, VA: NCTM, 1979.

Sincich, T. *Statistics by Example.* San Francisco, CA: Dellen Publishing Company, 1982.

Steinhaus, H. *Mathematical Snapshots.* New York: Oxford University Press, 1960.

Sutherland, D. C. "Error-Detecting Identifications Codes for Algebra Students." *School Science and Mathematics* 90(April 1990): 283–290.

Tan, S. T. *Applied Finite Mathematics.* Boston, MA: PWS Publishing, 1994.

Taylor, R. E. *Radiocarbon Dating: An Archaeological Perspective.* Orlando, FL: Academic Press, 1987.

U.S. Bureau of the Census. *Statistical Abstract of the United States: 2005.* Washington, DC: U.S. Government Printing Office, 2005.

U.S. Department of Health and Human Services. "Your Social Security Number." Social Security Administration Publication 05-10002. Washington, DC: U.S. Government Printing Office, 1993.

Usiskin, Z. "The Greatest Integer Symbol—An Applications Approach." *The Mathematics Teacher* 70 (December 1977): 739–743.

Vazsonyi, A. *Finite Mathematics, Quantitative Analysis for Management.* Santa Barbara, CA: Wiley/Hamilton, 1977.

Wheeler, J. A. *A Journey into Gravity and Spacetime.* Scientific American Library. New York: W. H. Freeman and Co., 1990.

Zuwaylif, F. H. *General Applied Sciences.* Reading, MA: Addison-Wesley, 1970.